AQA

GCSE Mathematics Modular

Sue Chandler Ewart Smith

Higher

Module 5

www.heinemann.co.uk
✓ Free online support
✓ Useful weblinks
✓ 24 hour online ordering

01865 888058

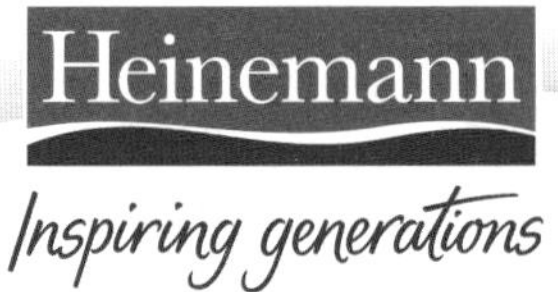

Heinemann is an imprint of Harcourt Education Limited, a company incorporated in England and Wales, having its registered office: Halley Court, Jordan Hill, Oxford OX2 8EJ. Registered company number: 3099304

www.harcourt.co.uk

Heinemann is the registered trademark of Harcourt Education Limited

First published 2007

12 11 10 09 08 07
10 9 8 7 6 5 4 3 2 1

British Library Cataloguing in Publication Data is available from the British Library on request.

ISBN 978 0 435807 24 5

Typeset by Tech-Set Ltd
Original illustrations © Harcourt Education Limited, 2007
Illustrated by Phil Garner
Cover design by mccdesign ltd
Cover photo: Digital Vision ©
Printed in the United Kingdom by Scotprint

Acknowledgements
Harcourt would like to thank those schools who gave invaluable help in the development and trialling of this course.

The author and publisher would like to thank the following individuals and organisations for permission to reproduce photographs:

Photos.com p**10** top; Dreamstime / Andreas Rodgriguez p**10** bottom; Dreamstime / Photomafia p **34**; Harcourt Ltd / Debbie Rowe p**35**; Corbis / Zefa / Mika p**37**; Harcourt Ltd p**54**; Getty Images / Photodisc pp**75**, **101**, **113**; Corbis / Randy Faris p**88**; Corbis / Brand X Photos p**89**; Alamy / Edward Parker p**112**; Corbis / The Art Archive p**118**; Corbis pp**142**, **201**, **219**; Dreamstime / Patrick Hermann p**203**

Every effort has been made to contact copyright holders of material reproduced in this book. Any omissions will be rectified in subsequent printings if notice is given to the publishers.

There are links to relevant websites in this book. In order to ensure that the links are up-to-date, that the links work, and that the sites are not inadvertently linked to sites that could be considered offensive, we have made the links available on the Heinemann website at www.heinemann.co.uk/hotlinks. When you access the site, the express code is 7245P.

How to use this book

This book is designed to give you the best possible preparation for your AQA GCSE Module 5 Examination. The authors are experienced writers of successful school mathematics textbooks and each book has been exactly tailored to your GCSE maths specification.

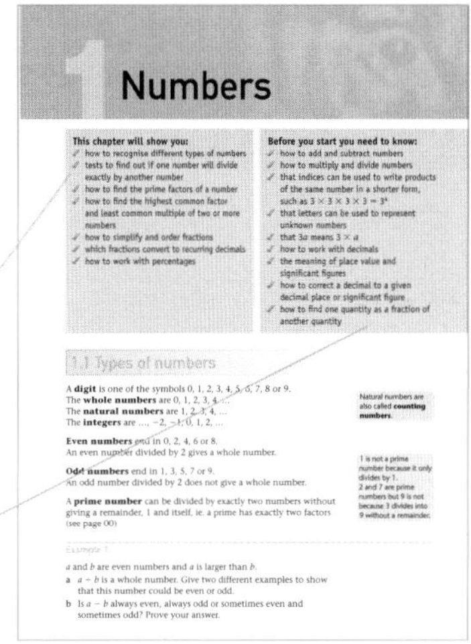

1 Numbers

This chapter will show you:
- ✓ how to recognise different types of numbers
- ✓ tests to find out if one number will divide exactly by another number
- ✓ how to find the prime factors of a number
- ✓ how to find the highest common factor and least common multiple of two or more numbers
- ✓ how to simplify and order fractions
- ✓ which fractions convert to recurring decimals
- ✓ how to work with percentages

Before you start you need to know:
- ✓ how to add and subtract numbers
- ✓ how to multiply and divide numbers
- ✓ that indices can be used to write products of the same number in a shorter form, such as $3 \times 3 \times 3 \times 3 = 3^4$
- ✓ that letters can be used to represent unknown numbers
- ✓ that $3a$ means $3 \times a$
- ✓ how to work with decimals
- ✓ the meaning of place value and significant figures
- ✓ how to correct a decimal to a given decimal place or significant figure
- ✓ how to find one quantity as a fraction of another quantity

1.1 Types of numbers

A **digit** is one of the symbols 0, 1, 2, 3, 4, 5, 6, 7, 8 or 9.
The **whole numbers** are 0, 1, 2, 3, 4, ...
The **natural numbers** are 1, 2, 3, 4, ...
The **integers** are ..., −2, −1, 0, 1, 2, ...

Natural numbers are also called **counting numbers**.

Even numbers end in 0, 2, 4, 6 or 8.
An even number divided by 2 gives a whole number.

Odd numbers end in 1, 3, 5, 7 or 9.
An odd number divided by 2 does not give a whole number.

A **prime number** can be divided by exactly two numbers without giving a remainder, 1 and itself, ie. a prime has exactly two factors (see page 00)

1 is not a prime number because it only divides by 1.
2 and 7 are prime numbers but 9 is not because 3 divides into 9 without a remainder.

Example 1

a and b are even numbers and a is larger than b.

a $a - b$ is a whole number. Give two different examples to show that this number could be even or odd.

b Is $a - b$ always even, always odd or sometimes even and sometimes odd? Prove your answer.

Finding your way around

To help you find your way around when you are studying and revising use the

- **contents list** – this gives a detailed breakdown of the topics covered in each chapter
- **list of objectives** at the start of each chapter – this tells you what you will learn in the chapter
- **list of prerequisite knowledge** at the start of each chapter – this tells you what you need to know before starting the chapter
- **index** – on page 296 – you can use this to find any topic covered in this book.

Remembering key facts

At the end of each chapter you will find

- **a summary of key points** – this lists the key facts and techniques covered in the chapter
- **grade descriptions** – these tell you which techniques and skills most students need to be able to use to achieve each exam grade
- **a glossary** – this gives the definitions of the mathematical words used in the chapter.

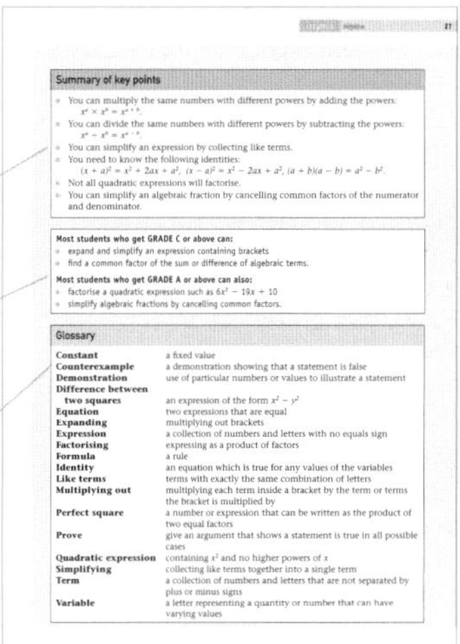

Algebra 27

Summary of key points
- You can multiply the same numbers with different powers by adding the powers: $x^a \times x^b = x^{a+b}$.
- You can divide the same numbers with different powers by subtracting the powers: $x^a \div x^b = x^{a-b}$.
- You can simplify an expression by collecting like terms.
- You need to know the following identities: $(x + a)^2 = x^2 + 2ax + a^2$, $(x - a)^2 = x^2 - 2ax + a^2$, $(a + b)(a - b) = a^2 - b^2$.
- Not all quadratic expressions will factorise.
- You can simplify an algebraic fraction by cancelling common factors of the numerator and denominator.

Most students who get GRADE C or above can:
- expand and simplify an expression containing brackets
- find a common factor of the sum or difference of algebraic terms.

Most students who get GRADE A or above can also:
- factorise a quadratic expression such as $6x^2 - 19x + 10$
- simplify algebraic fractions by cancelling common factors.

Glossary

Constant	a fixed value
Counterexample	a demonstration showing that a statement is false
Demonstration	use of particular numbers or values to illustrate a statement
Difference between two squares	an expression of the form $x^2 - y^2$
Equation	two expressions that are equal
Expanding	multiplying out brackets
Expression	a collection of numbers and letters with no equals sign
Factorising	expressing as a product of factors
Formula	a rule
Identity	an equation which is true for any values of the variables
Like terms	terms with exactly the same combination of letters
Multiplying out	multiplying each term inside a bracket by the term or terms the bracket is multiplied by
Perfect square	a number or expression that can be written as the product of two equal factors
Prove	give an argument that shows a statement is true in all possible cases
Quadratic expression	containing x^2 and no higher powers of x
Simplifying	collecting like terms together into a single term
Term	a collection of numbers and letters that are not separated by plus or minus signs
Variable	a letter representing a quantity or number that can have varying values

Exercises and practice papers

- **Worked examples** show you exactly how to answer exam questions.
- **Tips and hints** highlight key techniques and explain the reasons behind the answers.
- **Exam practice** questions work from the basics up to exam level. Hints and tips help you achieve your highest possible grade.
- The icon UAM against a question is Using and Applying mathematics.
- **An examination practice paper** on page 267 helps you prepare for your written examination.
- **Answers** for all the questions are included at the end of the book.

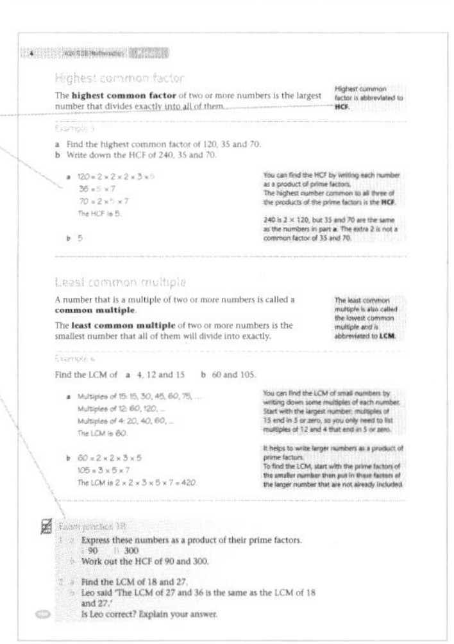

4

Highest common factor

The **highest common factor** of two or more numbers is the largest number that divides exactly into all of them.

Highest common factor is abbreviated to **HCF**.

Example 3

a Find the highest common factor of 120, 35 and 70.
b Write down the HCF of 240, 35 and 70.

a $120 = 2 \times 2 \times 2 \times 3 \times 5$
$35 = 5 \times 7$
$70 = 2 \times 5 \times 7$
The HCF is 5.

b 5

You can find the HCF by writing each number as a product of prime factors.
The highest number common to all three of the products of the prime factors is the **HCF**.

240 is 2 × 120, but 35 and 70 are the same as the numbers in part **a**. The extra 2 is not a common factor of 35 and 70.

Least common multiple

A number that is a multiple of two or more numbers is called a **common multiple**.

The **least common multiple** of two or more numbers is the smallest number that all of them will divide into exactly.

The least common multiple is also called the lowest common multiple and is abbreviated to **LCM**.

Example 4

Find the LCM of a 4, 12 and 15 b 60 and 105.

a Multiples of 15: 15, 30, 45, 60, 75, ...
Multiples of 12: 60, 120, ...
Multiples of 4: 20, 40, 60, ...
The LCM is 60.

You can find the LCM of small numbers by writing down some multiples of each number. Start with the largest number: multiples of 15 end in 5 or zero, so you only need to list multiples of 12 and 4 that end in 5 or zero.

b $60 = 2 \times 2 \times 3 \times 5$
$105 = 3 \times 5 \times 7$
The LCM is $2 \times 2 \times 3 \times 5 \times 7 = 420$

It helps to write larger numbers as a product of prime factors.
To find the LCM, start with the prime factors of the smaller number then put in those factors of the larger number that are not already included.

Exam practice 1B

1 a Express these numbers as a product of their prime factors.
i 90 ii 300
b Work out the HCF of 90 and 300.

2 a Find the LCM of 18 and 27.
b Leo said 'The LCM of 27 and 36 is the same as the LCM of 18 and 27.'
Is Leo correct? Explain your answer.

Coursework, communication and technology

- **Mini coursework tasks** throughout the book will help you practice the skills needed for your GCSE coursework tasks.
- **ICT tasks** will highlight opportunities to use computer programs and the Internet to help your understanding of mathematical topics.
- **Class discussion** sections allow you to talk about problems and what techniques you might use to solve them.

Contents

MODULE 5 Higher tier

10 Straight-line graphs

11 Inequalities

12 Congruence and constructions

13 Transformations

14 Enlargement

15 Circle geometry

1 Numbers

This chapter will show you:

- ✓ how to recognise different types of numbers
- ✓ tests to find out if one number will divide exactly by another number
- ✓ how to find the prime factors of a number
- ✓ how to find the highest common factor and least common multiple of two or more numbers
- ✓ how to simplify and order fractions
- ✓ which fractions convert to recurring decimals
- ✓ how to work with percentages

Before you start you need to know:

- ✓ how to add and subtract numbers
- ✓ how to multiply and divide numbers
- ✓ that indices can be used to write products of the same number in a shorter form, such as $3 \times 3 \times 3 \times 3 = 3^4$
- ✓ that letters can be used to represent unknown numbers
- ✓ that $3a$ means $3 \times a$
- ✓ how to work with decimals
- ✓ the meaning of place value and significant figures
- ✓ how to correct a decimal to a given decimal place or significant figure
- ✓ how to find one quantity as a fraction of another quantity

1.1 Types of numbers

A **digit** is one of the symbols 0, 1, 2, 3, 4, 5, 6, 7, 8 or 9.
The **whole numbers** are 0, 1, 2, 3, 4, …
The **natural numbers** are 1, 2, 3, 4, …
The **integers** are …, −2, −1, 0, 1, 2, …

Natural numbers are also called **counting numbers**.

Even numbers end in 0, 2, 4, 6 or 8.
An even number divided by 2 gives a whole number.

Odd numbers end in 1, 3, 5, 7 or 9.
An odd number divided by 2 does not give a whole number.

A **prime number** can be divided by exactly two numbers without giving a remainder, 1 and itself, i.e. a prime has exactly two factors (see page 3).

1 is not a prime number because it only divides by 1.
2 and 7 are prime numbers but 9 is not because 3 divides into 9 without a remainder.

Example 1

a and b are even numbers and a is larger than b.

a Suppose that $a \div b$ is a whole number. Give two different examples to show that this number could be even or odd.

b Is $a - b$ always even, always odd or sometimes even and sometimes odd? Prove your answer.

a $8 \div 2 = 4$ which is an even number
and $6 \div 2 = 3$ which is an odd number.

b $a - b$ is always an even number.
a can be written as $2n$ where n is a whole number,
b can be written as $2m$ where m is a whole number,
so $a - b = 2n - 2m = 2(n - m)$.
n and m are whole numbers so $n - m$ is a whole number.
$a - b$ is twice a whole number so it is even.

An even number can always be written as twice another whole number.

Exam practice 1A

1 Write down the difference between the largest and smallest prime number between 10 and 40.

2 Write true or false for each of these statements.
If the statement is false give an example to show this.
- a The sum of any two even numbers is always even.
- b The sum of any two odd numbers is always odd.
- c The sum of any even number and any odd number is always odd.

3 Write true or false. Give reasons for your answers.
- a The sum of two prime numbers is always a prime number.
- b The sum of two prime numbers may be a prime number.

4 p is a whole number.
For each statement write 'always true', 'always false' or 'could be true or false'.
- a $p + 7$ is an odd number.
- b $p + 2$ is a prime number.
- c $2p + 3$ is an odd number.
- d $p - 7$ is an integer.
- e $2p$ is an odd number.

5 David said 'The product of an even number and an odd number is always odd.' Give an example to show that David is wrong.

6 a and b are any two numbers.
Amjad said that $a - b$ is always a whole number.
Give an example to show that Amjad is wrong.

7 q is an even number.
For each statement write 'always true', 'always false' or 'could be true or false'. Give reasons for your answers.
- a $\frac{1}{2}q + 1$ is an odd number.
- b $q + 1$ is an even number.
- c $q \div 3$ is a whole number.

8 p and q are any two whole numbers and p is larger than q.
Write true or false.
a $p - q$ is a whole number.
b $q - p$ is a whole number.
c $2q - p$ in an integer.

9 Prove that the product of two even numbers is always even.

To prove this statement you need to show that it is true for *any* two even numbers.

1.2 Factors and multiples

A **factor** is a whole number that can divide into another whole number without a remainder. The factors of a number include 1 and the number itself.
When a factor is a prime number it is called a **prime factor**.

2 is a factor of 8 because $8 \div 2 = 4$.
2 is not a factor of 9 because $9 \div 2$ is not a whole number.

When a number is multiplied by a natural number the result is a **multiple** of the first number.

4, 8, 12 are multiples of 4.
36 and 1600 are also multiples of 4.

Writing a number as the product of prime factors

These tests are useful when you are looking for factors.

- An even number divides exactly by 2.
- A number divides exactly by 3 when its digits add up to a number that divides exactly by 3.
- A number ending in 5 or 0 divides exactly by 5.
- A number divides exactly by 9 when its digits add up to a number that divides exactly by 9.

So 171 will divide by 3 as $1 + 7 + 1 = 9$ and $9 \div 3 = 3$.

So 230 and 155 can be divided by 5.

So 261 can be divided by 9 as $2 + 6 + 1 = 9$ and $9 \div 9 = 1$.

Example 2

Express these numbers as a product of their prime factors.
a 36 **b** 180

a $36 = 4 \times 9$
$= 2 \times 2 \times 3 \times 3$
$= 2^2 \times 3^2$.

Start by writing 36 as the product of any two factors: $36 = 4 \times 9$.
Then each factor that is not prime can be written as the product of two factors. You can repeat this until all the factors are prime numbers.

b $180 \div 2 = 90$
$90 \div 2 = 45$
$45 \div 3 = 15$
$15 \div 3 = 5$
$5 \div 5 = 1$
So $180 = 2 \times 2 \times 3 \times 3 \times 5$
$= 2^2 \times 3^2 \times 5$.

Start by dividing by 2 as many times as possible.
Then divide by 3 as many times as possible.
Then divide by each prime number in turn until you are left with 1.

Two or more numbers can have the same factor. This is called a **common factor**.

Highest common factor

The **highest common factor** of two or more numbers is the largest number that divides exactly into all of them.

Highest common factor is abbreviated to **HCF**.

Example 3

a Find the highest common factor of 120, 35 and 70.
b Write down the HCF of 240, 35 and 70.

a $120 = 2 \times 2 \times 2 \times 3 \times 5$
$35 = 5 \times 7$
$70 = 2 \times 5 \times 7$
The HCF is 5.

You can find the HCF by writing each number as a product of prime factors.
The product of the primes common to all three numbers is the **HCF**.

b 5

240 is 2×120, but 35 and 70 are the same as the numbers in part **a**. The extra 2 is not a common factor of 35 and 70.

Least common multiple

A number that is a multiple of two or more numbers is called a **common multiple**.

The **least common multiple** of two or more numbers is the smallest number that all of them will divide into exactly.

The least common multiple is also called the lowest common multiple and is abbreviated to **LCM**.

Example 4

Find the LCM of **a** 4, 12 and 15 **b** 60 and 105.

a Multiples of 15: 15, 30, 45, **60**, 75, …
Multiples of 12: **60**, 120, ...
Multiples of 4: 20, 40, **60**, ...
The LCM is 60.

You can find the LCM of small numbers by writing down some multiples of each number. Start with the largest number: multiples of 15 end in 5 or zero, so you only need to list multiples of 12 and 4 that end in 5 or zero.

b $60 = 2 \times 2 \times 3 \times 5$
$105 = 3 \times 5 \times 7$
The LCM is $2 \times 2 \times 3 \times 5 \times 7 = 420$.

It helps to write larger numbers as a product of prime factors.
To find the LCM, start with the prime factors of the smaller number then put in those factors of the larger number that are not already included.

Exam practice 1B

1 a Express these numbers as a product of their prime factors.
i 90 ii 300
b Work out the HCF of 90 and 300.

2 a Find the LCM of 18 and 27.
b Leo said 'The LCM of 27 and 36 is the same as the LCM of 18 and 27.'

Is Leo correct? Explain your answer.

3 a Express these numbers as a product of their prime factors.
i 42 ii 126
b Find the HCF of 42 and 126.
c Write down the HCF of:
i 84 and 126 ii 84 and 252.

4 a Write down the LCM of 3, 5 and 6.
UAM b Explain how you can use your answer to part a to write down the LCM of:
i 3, 10 and 6 ii 3, 5 and 12.

5 a Write down the HCF of 6, 8 and 12.
UAM b Explain how you can use your answer to part a to write down the HCF of:
i 6, 16 and 12 ii 6, 24 and 36.

1.3 Fractions

A **fraction** is part of a unit or quantity.

The fraction 'two-thirds' is written $\frac{2}{3}$.

This is called the **numerator**.

This is the **denominator**.

The fractions $\frac{1}{2}$ and $\frac{5}{10}$ are the same size.

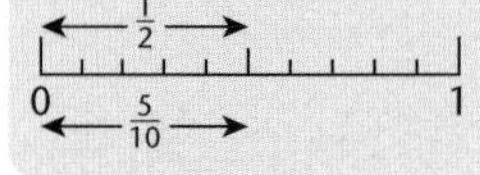

They are called **equivalent fractions**.

You can find equivalent fractions by multiplying or dividing the numerator and denominator by the same number.

$\frac{3}{5}$ and $\frac{12}{20}$ are equivalent fractions:

$$\frac{3}{5} \overset{\times 4}{=} \frac{12}{20}$$

Dividing the numerator and denominator by the same number gives an equivalent fraction with a smaller numerator and denominator. This is called **simplifying** the fraction or **cancelling**.
When a fraction has been simplified to give the smallest possible numerator and denominator, it is in its **simplest form** or its **lowest possible terms**.

Divide by a number that is a common factor of the numerator and denominator.

To compare fractions with different denominators change them into equivalent fractions with the same denominator.

Example 5

a Write $\frac{2}{5}$ as an equivalent fraction with denominator 15.

b Write $\frac{12}{42}$ in its simplest form.

c Which of the fractions $\frac{2}{5}$ and $\frac{12}{42}$ is nearer to $\frac{5}{14}$?

a $\frac{2}{5} = \frac{6}{15}$

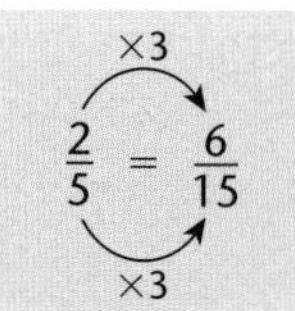

b $\frac{\cancel{12}^{2}}{\cancel{42}_{7}} = \frac{2}{7}$

12 and 42 have 6 as a common factor so divide both by 6.

c $\frac{12}{42} = \frac{2}{7} = \frac{20}{70}$

$\frac{2}{5} = \frac{28}{70}$

$\frac{5}{14} = \frac{25}{70}$

$\frac{28}{70}$ is nearer than $\frac{20}{70}$ to $\frac{25}{70}$

so $\frac{2}{5}$ is nearer than $\frac{12}{42}$ to $\frac{5}{14}$.

To compare the sizes of the three fractions, convert them into equivalent fractions with the same denominator.
This common denominator must be a multiple of 5, 7 and 14.
To keep the numbers as small as possible choose the LCM.

You may be able to do this comparison in your head. However, it is important in an examination to show your working or to explain how you get your answer.

Exam practice 1C

1 a Express these fractions as sixteenths:
i $\frac{1}{4}$ ii $\frac{3}{8}$ iii $\frac{3}{4}$

b Which of the fractions in part a is closest to $\frac{5}{32}$?

2 Write each of these fractions as equivalent fractions with denominator 30.

a $\frac{4}{15}$ b $\frac{5}{6}$ c $\frac{14}{15}$ d $\frac{4}{5}$

3 Write each fraction in its simplest form.

a $\frac{15}{60}$ b $\frac{75}{100}$ c $\frac{33}{72}$ d $\frac{72}{270}$ e $\frac{32}{128}$

4 a Which is the larger: $\frac{3}{7}$ or $\frac{2}{3}$?

b Which is the smaller: $\frac{4}{9}$ of a loaf or $\frac{3}{8}$ of it?

c Which is the smallest: $\frac{4}{5}$, $\frac{2}{3}$, or $\frac{5}{7}$?

5 a Write the fractions $\frac{2}{3}$, $\frac{2}{9}$ and $\frac{5}{12}$ in order of size, smallest first.

b Write the fractions $\frac{5}{8}$, $\frac{7}{16}$ and $\frac{9}{32}$ in order of size, largest first.

6 Which of the fractions $\frac{3}{4}$, $\frac{5}{9}$, $\frac{4}{9}$, $\frac{7}{12}$ is

a closest in value to $\frac{1}{2}$?

b closest in value to $\frac{2}{3}$?

c between $\frac{1}{2}$ and $\frac{2}{3}$?

7 Using the figures 1, 2, 3, 4 and 5 make a fraction with two digits on the top and two digits on the bottom that is

a less than $\frac{1}{2}$

b exactly $\frac{1}{2}$

c as close to $\frac{1}{2}$ as possible but not equal to $\frac{1}{2}$.

You can use each digit more than once.

1.4 Fractions and decimals

Decimal numbers are written with a decimal point after the units. The first digit after the decimal point represents tenths, the second represents hundredths, the third represents thousandths, and so on.

You can compare the size of two or more decimals by looking at the digits in each place value.

4.632 has more digits than 4.67 but that does not mean it is larger than 4.67.

Example 6

Which is the larger, 12.57 or 12.499?

12.57 is larger than 12.499.

The tens and the units are the same, but 5 tenths is larger than 4 tenths.

You can convert a decimal to a fraction by writing it as a number of tenths, hundredths, thousandths, and so on.

$0.15 = \frac{15}{100} = \frac{3}{20}$

To write a fraction as a decimal, divide the numerator by the denominator.

$\frac{3}{8}$ means $3 \div 8$

$8\overline{)3.000}$ gives 0.375 so $\frac{3}{8} = 0.375$

If you try to write $\frac{2}{3}$ as a decimal, you get 0.666... and so on for ever.
0.666... is called a **recurring decimal**. It is written $0.\dot{6}$.

The digit 6 recurs.

A dot over a digit means that it recurs. So $0.\dot{5}$ means 0.555 555 5...

Any decimal with a recurring digit or pattern of digits is called a recurring decimal.

$\frac{1}{13} = 0.076\,923\,076\,923\,076...$ where 076923 recurs. You write this as $0.\dot{0}76\,92\dot{3}$. The dots show the pattern of digits that repeat.

When you convert a fraction to a decimal you will either get an exact decimal or a recurring decimal.
You can tell whether a fraction will convert to an exact decimal by simplifying it and looking at the prime factors of its denominator.
Any combination of only 2s and 5s gives an exact decimal.

An exact decimal is sometimes called a **terminating decimal**.

Any exact decimal or recurring decimal can be written as a fraction.
You cannot write a decimal that has been rounded as an exact fraction because you do not know if the decimal is exact or recurring or neither.

$0.46 = \frac{4}{10} + \frac{6}{100} = \frac{46}{100} = \frac{23}{50}$
$0.075 = \frac{7}{100} + \frac{5}{1000} = \frac{75}{1000} = \frac{3}{40}$

Decimals that are not exact or recurring are irrational numbers.

Example 7

Which of the following fractions convert to a terminating decimal?

a $\frac{15}{24}$ **b** $\frac{7}{15}$

a $\frac{15}{24} = \frac{5}{8}$ and $\frac{5}{8} = \frac{5}{2 \times 2 \times 2}$ so $\frac{5}{8}$ gives an exact decimal.

b $\frac{7}{15} = \frac{7}{5 \times 3}$ gives a recurring decimal.

Make sure you simplify the fraction first.

b gives a recurring decimal as the denominator has a prime factor other than 2 and 5.

Example 8

Which of $\frac{4}{7}$ or 0.782 is nearer in value to $\frac{2}{3}$?

You can find which of the numbers is nearer $\frac{2}{3}$ by finding the difference between $\frac{2}{3}$ and each number.

$\frac{2}{3} - \frac{4}{7} = 0.095\ldots$

Press 2 ÷ 3 − 4 ÷ 7 =

$0.782 - \frac{2}{3} = 0.115\ldots$

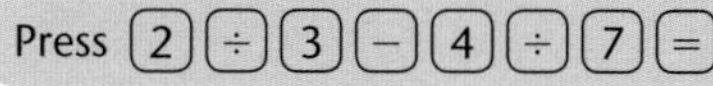

0.095... is smaller than 0.115... so $\frac{4}{7}$ is closer to $\frac{2}{3}$.

Exam practice 1D

1 a Convert $\frac{3}{4}$ to a decimal.
b Hence write $\frac{3}{40}$ as a decimal.

Use the fact that $\frac{3}{40}$ is one tenth of $\frac{3}{4}$.

2 a Convert $\frac{7}{8}$ to a decimal.
b Hence write $\frac{21}{800}$ as a decimal.

3 Express each fraction as an terminating decimal.
a $\frac{7}{25}$ b $\frac{3}{8}$ c $\frac{9}{50}$ d $\frac{7}{80}$ e $\frac{7}{400}$

Divide the top by the bottom and continue the division until it stops.

4 Which of the following fractions convert to a recurring decimal?
a $\frac{3}{10}$ b $\frac{1}{3}$ c $\frac{7}{12}$ d $\frac{18}{25}$ e $\frac{9}{15}$ f $\frac{4}{22}$

5 Write each fraction as a recurring decimal.
a $\frac{1}{3}$ b $\frac{6}{9}$ c $\frac{7}{9}$ d $\frac{5}{6}$

6 a Which is the larger, $\frac{9}{20}$ or 0.047?
b Which is the smaller, $\frac{19}{8}$ or 2.695?

7 Taj wrote $\frac{4}{3} = 1.3$. Explain why Taj is wrong.

8 a Arrange these numbers in order of size, the largest first.
0.05, $\frac{3}{16}$, 0.105, $\frac{2}{13}$, $\frac{6}{25}$
b Which of the numbers in part a is closest to $\frac{3}{10}$?

1.5 Converting percentages, fractions and decimals

The words **per cent** means 'out of 100'.
A percentage is a fraction with denominator 100.

You can convert a percentage to a fraction or a decimal by writing it as a fraction with denominator 100 and removing the percentage sign.

You can express a fraction or a decimal as a percentage by multiplying it by 100 and adding a percentage sign.

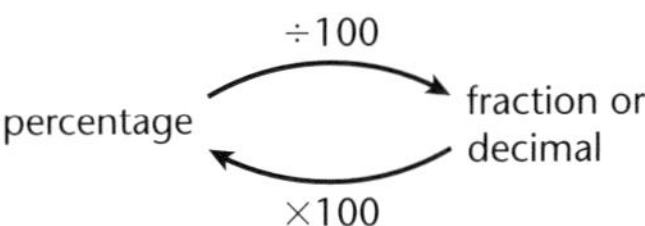

Example 9

Convert $10\frac{1}{2}\%$ to **a** a decimal **b** a fraction.

a $10\frac{1}{2}\% = 10.5\% = 10.5 \div 100$
$= 0.105$

To convert $10\frac{1}{2}\%$ to a decimal start by writing it as 10.5%.

b $10\frac{1}{2}\% = \frac{10.5}{100} = \frac{21}{200}$

Multiply top and bottom by 2 to give an equivalent fraction with a whole number numerator.

Example 10

Convert to percentages: **a** 1.27 **b** $\frac{3}{5}$

a $1.27 = 1.27 \times 100\% = 127\%$

b $\frac{3}{5} = \frac{3}{5} \times 100\%$
$= 3 \times 20\%$
$= 60\%$

To find $\frac{3}{5}$ of 100, divide 100 by 5 then multiply the answer by 3.

Alternatively, $\frac{3}{5} = 0.6$ and $0.6 = 60\%$.

Exam practice 1E

1 Convert to decimals:
a 75% b 12.5% c 160% d 5.18%

You should be able to do question 1 in your head. Just write down the answers.

2 Convert to fractions in their simplest form:
a 15% b 90% c 87.5% d $66\frac{2}{3}\%$

3 Convert to percentages:
a 0.86 b 0.02 c 1.57 d 0.265 e 0.005
f $\frac{1}{4}$ g $\frac{4}{5}$ h $\frac{3}{10}$ i $\frac{1}{8}$ j $4\frac{1}{2}$

$4\frac{1}{2}$ means $4 + \frac{1}{2}$.

4 In an exam Jenny got 32 questions correct out of 40.
What percentage did Jenny get correct?

5 Which is larger, 47% or $\frac{5}{9}$? Give a reason for your answer.

6 Arrange these in order of size, smallest first.

a 1.72, $1\frac{3}{4}$, 155%

b $\frac{2}{5}$, 35%, 0.5, $\frac{1}{3}$

1.6 Using percentages

You can find a percentage of a quantity by first dividing the quantity by 100 to find 1%.

You can sometimes use these facts as a short cut:

$10\% = \frac{1}{10}, \quad 100\% = 1, \quad 25\% = \frac{1}{4}, \quad 50\% = \frac{1}{2}$

Example 11

a Find 4% of £350.
b Write down 40% of £3500.

a 1% of £350 = £350 ÷ 100 = £3.50.
4% of £350 = 4 × £3.50 = £14.

4% of £350 = 4 × 1% of £350.

b 40% of £3500 = £1400.

40% = 10 × 4% and £3500 = 10 × £350 so 40% of £3500 = 100 × 4% of £350.

You can find one quantity as a percentage of another by first finding it as a fraction, then converting the fraction to a percentage.

Example 12

The cost of first class post for a large but light letter has risen from 32p to 44p.
a Find 44p as a percentage of 32p.
b Write down the percentage increase in the cost.

a $\frac{44}{32} = \frac{11}{8}$

Find 44p as a fraction of 32p and simplify the fraction.

$\frac{11}{8} \times 100\% = 1.375 \times 100\% = 137.5\%$

$\frac{1}{8} = 12.5\%$ so $\frac{11}{8} = 11 \times 12.5\% = 137.5\%$

b 37.5%

A percentage increase or decrease is always a percentage of the original amount.
The cost has increased to 137.5% of 32p so the increase is 37.5% of 32p.

Exam practice 1F

1 Write down:
- a 10% of £500
- b 20% of 60p
- c 70% of £10
- d 5% of £4000
- e 300% of £5
- f 25% of 120 kg

2 Andy buys a printer on-line for £150.
The delivery charge is 5% of this price.
- a Find the delivery charge.
- b How much does Andy pay in total?

3 5000 people were treated in the accident and emergency department at a hospital in June.
30% more people were treated in September.
How many people were treated in September?

Read the question carefully. Make sure you know what you are asked to find.

Class discussion

Dwain found $2\frac{1}{2}\%$ of 50.
This is his working:

$10\% = 5$
$5\% = 2.5$
$2\frac{1}{2}\% = 1.25$

a How did Dwain get his answer?
b How can you find $7\frac{1}{2}\%$ of 450?
c What is the easiest way of finding $17\frac{1}{2}\%$ of £1200 without using a calculator?
d Finding $17\frac{1}{2}\%$ of a sum of money is a common calculation in business. Why is this?

4 The area of this shape is 120 square centimetres.
70% of the area is orange.
Find the area, in square centimetres, that is purple.

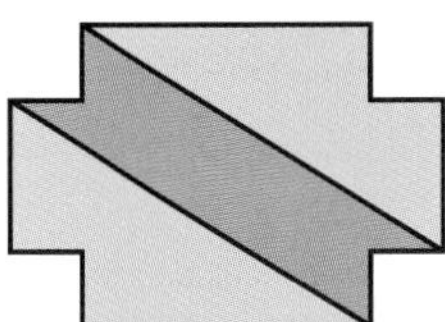

5 29.5% of £5500 = £1622.50
Write down the value of
- a 129.5% of £5500
- b 295% of £55
- c 2.95% of £55 000.

6 There were 20 000 ticket applications for a football match.
Only 5700 tickets were available.
Work out the percentage of the applications that were successful.

7 Cheryl paid £850 for some shares.
She sold the shares for £1500.
Find Cheryl's percentage profit.

The percentage profit is the profit as a percentage of the buying price.

8 a Work out £45 as a percentage of £320.
b Write down
- i £4.50 as a percentage of £32
- ii 45p as a percentage of £3.20.

Summary of key points

- The factors of a number include 1 and the number itself.
- You can find the highest common factor of two or more numbers by finding the highest number common to all of the products of prime factors.
- The multiples of a number include the number itself.
- You can find the lowest common multiple of two or more numbers by starting with the prime factors of the smallest number then multiplying them by the factors of the other numbers that are not already included.
- You can find equivalent fractions by multiplying or dividing the top and bottom of a fraction by the same number.
- You can convert a fraction to a decimal by dividing the numerator by the denominator. The decimal will be either exact or recurring.
- A fraction where the factors of the denominator are any combination of 2 and 5 will convert to an exact decimal. All other fractions convert to recurring decimals.
- You can convert a decimal to a fraction by writing it as a number of tenths, hundredths, thousandths, ... : $0.215 = \frac{215}{1000}$.
- You can convert percentages to fractions or decimals by dividing the percentage by 100 and removing the % sign. You do the opposite to convert a fraction or a decimal to a percentage:

percentage —(÷100)→ fraction or decimal
fraction or decimal —(×100)→ percentage

- You can find a percentage of a quantity by first dividing it by 100 to find 1%.

Most candidates who get GRADE C or above can:
- express a number as a product of prime factors in index form.

Most candidates who get GRADE A can also:
- express a fraction as a recurring decimal.

Glossary

Cancelling	dividing the numerator and denominator by the same number
Common factor	a number that divides exactly into two or more numbers
Common multiple	a number which two or more numbers will divide into exactly
Counting number	one of the numbers 1, 2, 3, 4, ...
Denominator	the bottom number in a fraction
Digit	one of the symbols 0, 1, 2, 3, 4, 5, 6, 7, 8 or 9
Equivalent fraction	a fraction that is the same size but with different numerator and denominator

Glossary (continued)

Even number	a number that divides exactly by 2
Factor	a number that divides exactly into a given number
Fraction	part of a unit or quantity
Highest common factor (HCF)	the largest number that divides into two or more numbers without a remainder
Improper fraction	a fraction whose numerator is greater than the denominator
Integer	one of the numbers ..., −2, −1, 0, 1, 2, ...
Least common multiple (LCM)	the smallest number that two or more numbers will divide into exactly
Lowest possible terms	a fraction whose numerator and denominator are as small as possible
Mixed number	the sum of a whole number and a proper fraction, e.g. $1\frac{1}{2}$
Multiple	any natural number multiplied by the given number
Natural numbers	the numbers 1, 2, 3, 4, ...
Numerator	the top number in a fraction
Odd number	a number that does not divide exactly by 2
Per cent	out of 100
Prime number	a number that only has two factors, 1 and itself
Prime factor	a factor that is a prime number
Proper fraction	a fraction whose numerator is less than the denominator
Recurring decimal	a decimal where the digits after the decimal point have a repeating pattern
Simplest form	a fraction whose numerator and denominator are as small as possible
Simplifying	find an equivalent fraction with smaller numerator and denominator
Terminating decimal	a decimal with a fixed number of digits after the decimal point
Whole numbers	the numbers 0, 1, 2, 3, 4, ...

2 Algebra

This chapter will show you:
- ✓ how to use letters in algebra
- ✓ how to manipulate expressions
- ✓ how to multiply out algebraic expressions containing brackets
- ✓ how to factorise algebraic expressions

Before you start you need to know:
- ✓ the meaning of indices
- ✓ the rules of arithmetic
- ✓ how to add and subtract fractions
- ✓ how to work with negative numbers

2.1 Formulae, expressions and equations

Algebra is a part of mathematics in which letters are used to represent unknown numbers or quantities, or numbers that can vary.

A **formula** is a rule connecting quantities.
The rule for finding the area of a square is a formula.
Using A for the area and l for the length of a side, the formula can be written using algebra as $A = l \times l$.
The area and length can vary. The letters A and l are called **variables**.

Area of a square = length of a side squared.

An **expression** is any collection of letters and numbers without an equals sign.

$l \times b$ is an expression.

An **equation** always has an equals sign. Usually two expressions are equal for only some values of the letters. When the two expressions are equal for any values of the letters, it is called an **identity**.

5 is the only value of x for which $x + 3 = 8$. It is not an identity. Two numbers can be multiplied in any order. So $a \times b = b \times a$ is an identity. It is true for any two numbers.

Simplifying expressions

Simplifying an expression means writing it in as short a form as possible.

When you multiply letters you can leave out the multiplication sign.

$2a$ means $2 \times a$, $3pq$ means $3 \times p \times q$, $5x^2$ means $5 \times x \times x$.

You can also use indices when a letter is multiplied by itself.
So $q \times q \times q$ can be written as q^3.

Convention says that you put numbers before letters, e.g. $2a$ rather than $a2$.

Laws of indices

In algebra letters represent numbers so the ordinary rules of arithmetic apply. You can use the laws of indices to simplify expressions.

You can multiply the *same* number with different powers by adding the powers.

$x^3 \times x^5 = x^{3+5} = x^8$

You can divide the *same* number with different powers by subtracting the powers.

$a^5 \div a^3 = a^{5-3} = a^2$

Remember that $a^0 = 1$, $a^{-b} = \frac{1}{a^b}$, $a^{\frac{1}{n}} = \sqrt[n]{a}$, $(x^a)^b = x^{ab}$

Example 1

Simplify: **a** $3x \times 4y$ **b** $2xy^2 \times 5x^4y^3$ **c** $(3x^2y^4)^3$

a $3x \times 4y = 3 \times x \times 4 \times y$
$= 3 \times 4 \times x \times y$
$= 12 \times xy$
$= 12xy$

The ordinary rules of arithmetic apply so you can change the order of the multiplication.

b $2xy^2 \times 5x^4y^3 = 2 \times x \times y^2 \times 5 \times x^4 \times y^3$
$= 2 \times 5 \times x \times x^4 \times y^2 \times y^3$
$= 10x^{1+4}\,y^{2+3}$
$= 10x^5y^5$

There is no need to write down all this working. If you are confident, go straight to the simplified form.

c $(3x^2y^4)^3 = 3^3(x^2)^3(y^4)^3 = 27x^6y^{12}$

A **term** in an expression is any collection of numbers and letters that are not separated by plus or minus signs.
So the terms in the expression $y^2 - 6y + 7$ are y^2, $6y$ and 7.

A term that is just a number, such as 7, is called a **constant**.

Like terms contain exactly the same combination of letters.
So x and $6x$ are like terms but x and x^2 are not.

Like terms can have different numbers in them but they must have exactly the same combination of letters.

Like terms can be added or subtracted to give a single term.
So $2x + 3x$ can be **simplified** to $5x$.
This is called **collecting like terms**.

$2x$ mean $x + x$ and $3x$ means $x + x + x$. Adding them gives 5 lots of x, or $5x$.

Example 2

Simplify: **a** $6ab - 4ba$ **b** $x^2 - 6x + 5 - 3x$

a $6ab - 4ba = 2ab$

The order in which you multiply does not matter, so $4ba = 4ab$. $6ab$ and $4ba$ and are like terms.

b $x^2 - 6x + 5 - 3x = x^2 - 6x - 3x + 5$
$= x^2 - 9x + 5$

The ordinary rules of arithmetic apply. You can rearrange the expression so that the like terms are together.

Example 3

Simplify: $\frac{x}{3} - \frac{2x}{5} + \frac{5x}{10}$

$\frac{x}{3} - \frac{2x}{5} + \frac{5x}{10} = \frac{10x}{30} - \frac{12x}{30} + \frac{15x}{30}$

$= \frac{13x}{30}$

These are like terms so you can simplify them. Remember that to add or subtract fractions you need to express them as equivalent fractions with the same denominator. Choose the LCM of 3, 5 and 10.

Exam practice 2A

1 Simplify:

a $3x \times 2x$ b $6p \times p$ c $2a \times 5b$
d $2y \times 4$ e $5 \times 4x$ f $3x^2 \times 3x$
g $3a^2 \times 4a \times a$ h $(-2p) \times (-2)$ i $(-2x) \times 2x$
j $(-2x) \times (-3y)$ k $5 \times (-5b) \times (-b)$ l $3x \times 2 \times (-2y)$
m $(4x)^2$ n $2 \times (-3y)^2$ p $5 \times (-2b)^2$

> Remember that the product of two negative numbers is positive. The product of a negative number and a positive number is negative.

2 Simplify:

a $4a^2b \times 3b^2a$ b $5ab \times 3b$ c $2p^2q \times 3q^2$
d $4x^2y \times 2xy^2$ e $2st \times 5s^2$ f $xy \times 4x^2y^5$
g $4xz \times 2x^3y$ h $2pq^2 \times 8pq^3 \times p$ i $7x^3y \times x^4y \times 2x$
j $4x^3 \times x^4$ k $(2ab^3)^3$ l $(4x^5y^2)^3$

3 Simplify:

a $3x + x + 2x$ b $3x - x + 2x$
c $-4x + 10x + 4x$ d $5 + 2y - 4y$
e $8x + 3x + 14 - 8$ f $5x - y + 2x + y$
g $9p - 6 + 3p + 6$ h $4a - 2b - 4a - 2b$
i $-2y + 8 - 3y - 5$

4 Simplify:

a $2x^2 + 6x + 4x$ b $a^2 + 5a + a - 5$
c $2x^2 + 6x - 3x - 9$ d $3x^2 - xy + 2xy - 1$
e $p^2 - 2p + 6 + 2p$ f $7 - 3y - y^2 + 2y$
g $7x^2 - 7x + 2x - 2$ h $a^2 - 2a + 2a + 4$
i $4x^2 - 3x + 8 + 3x$

5 Barry wrote

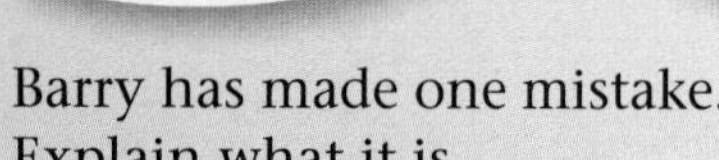

Barry has made one mistake.
UAM Explain what it is.

6 Simplify:

a $\frac{a}{2} - \frac{a}{3}$ b $\frac{2x}{5} - \frac{x}{3}$ c $\frac{3y}{4} + \frac{2y}{5}$
d $\frac{3a}{5} + \frac{2a}{10} - \frac{a}{2}$ e $\frac{5y}{6} - \frac{7y}{9} + \frac{3y}{18}$ f $\frac{b}{3} - \frac{4b}{7} + \frac{11b}{14}$

2.2 Multiplying out brackets

The expression $5(3x - 4)$ means 5 multiplied by each term inside the bracket. So $5(3x - 4) = 5 \times 3x - 5 \times 4 = 15x - 20$.
This process is called **multiplying out** the bracket.

> Multiplying out a bracket is sometimes called **expanding** the bracket.

Example 4

Multiply out and simplify $4(x + 3) - x(3x - 2)$.

$$4(x + 3) - x(3x - 2) = 4x + 12 - 3x^2 + 2x$$
$$= 6x + 12 - 3x^2$$

Expand each bracket.
Remember that $-x \times -2 = +2x$
Collect like terms.

The expression $(2x - 5)(x + 4)$ means each term in the second bracket is multiplied by each term in the first bracket.
So $(2x - 5)(x + 4) = 2x(x + 4) - 5(x + 4)$
$= 2x^2 + 8x - 5x - 20$
$= 2x^2 + 3x - 20$

You can use a grid like this:

	x	4
$2x$	$2x^2$	$8x$
-5	$-5x$	-20

Example 5

Multiply out and simplify $(2x - 5)(2x - 3)$.

$$(2x - 5)(2x - 3) = 2x(2x - 3) - 5(2x - 3)$$
$$= 4x^2 - 6x - 10x + 15$$
$$= 4x^2 - 16x + 15$$

If you are confident you can leave out the middle steps.

Exam practice 2B

1 Multiply out and simplify:
a $5(5 - 2x)$ b $3y(2 - 3y)$ c $2xy(3x - 4y)$
d $2x^2(3x - 5)$ e $x^2y(x - 2xy)$ f $2pq^2(p^2 - q^2)$
g $3ab^2(ab - bc)$ h $4xy(x^2 - 2y^2)$ i $5xyz(x - yz)$

2 Multiply out and simplify:
a $9x^2 - 4x(x - 3)$ b $2x + 3(7 - x)$
c $5x^2 + 3x(4 - x)$ d $2(2 - a) - a(7 - 2a)$
e $4b(b - 3) - 2(5 - b)$ f $3(x - 6y) + 2(x + y)$
g $x(x + y) + 3y(x - 3y)$ h $2(x - 5y) - (x + y)$
i $x(2 - 5x) - (2 - 3x)$

$-(x + y)$ means the same as $-1(x + y)$

3 Multiply out and simplify:
a $(x + 1)(x + 2)$ b $(x + 5)(x + 3)$ c $(a + 7)(a + 1)$
d $(2x + 1)(x + 1)$ e $(3x + 4)(x + 2)$ f $(2x + 8)(x + 9)$
g $(3x + 2)(2x + 1)$ h $(5x + 2)(2x + 3)$ i $(7x + 2)(6x + 5)$

4 Multiply out and simplify:
a $(x - 2)(x - 3)$ b $(x - 4)(x - 1)$ c $(x - 3)(x - 5)$
d $(3x - 2)(x - 4)$ e $(x - 5)(4x - 3)$ f $(5a - 1)(a - 4)$
g $(2x - 3)(3x - 2)$ h $(5b - 1)(2b - 3)$ i $(3s - 5)(4s - 7)$

5 Multiply out and simplify:
a $(x - 5)(x + 2)$ b $(x - 3)(x + 2)$ c $(x + 3)(x - 2)$
d $(2x + 3)(x - 2)$ e $(x - 3)(x + 4)$ f $(x - 2)(x + 6)$
g $(3x - 1)(2x + 1)$ h $(5x + 3)(2x - 1)$ i $(2a + 5)(3a - 2)$

6 Multiply out and simplify:

a $(x + 2)^2$
b $(x + 6)^2$
c $(x + 5)^2$
d $(x + 1)^2$
e $(3x + 5)^2$
f $(x + y)^2$
g $(x - 2)^2$
h $(x - 3)^2$
i $(x - 10)^2$
j $(3x - 1)^2$
k $(x - y)^2$
l $(5x - 2)^2$
m $(x - 3)(x + 3)$
n $(2x + 1)(2x - 1)$
p $(a - b)(a + b)$
q $(3x - 2)(3x + 2)$
r $(4x + 3)(4x - 3)$
s $(5y + 2)(5y - 2)$

7 Multiply out and simplify:

a $(2x - 3)(3x + 2)$
b $(7x + 2)(x + 3)$
c $(2x + 7)(3x - 4)$
d $(2a - b)(2a + b)$
e $(3s - 4t)^2$
f $(x^2 + 1)(x^2 + 3)$
g $(xy - 4)(xy + 4)$
h $(xy + z)(xy + 2z)$
i $(y^2 - 3)(y^2 + 2)$
j $x(x - 3)(x - 5)$
k $x^2(x + 6)(3x + 5)$
l $(x^2 - 2)(3x - 4)$

Multiply out the brackets first, then multiply the result by x.

8 George wrote $(4x - 3)^2 = 16x^2 - 9$.
UAM Explain why George is wrong.

2.3 Common factors

A factor of an algebraic expression is a number, letter or expression that divides into it exactly.
$2x = 2 \times x$ so 2 and x are factors of $2x$.

Two terms can have the same factor. This is called a common factor.

You can see the factors when you put the multiplication signs in.

Example 6

Find the common factors of **a** $4x$ and x^2 **b** $6x$ and $9x^2$.

a $4x = 2 \times 2 \times x$
$x^2 = x \times x$
x is a common factor.

Write numbers as the product of their prime factors.

A common factor is a number or letter that is in both products.

b $6x = 2 \times 3 \times x$
$9x^2 = 3 \times 3 \times x \times x$
3, x and $3x$ are common factors.

$3x$ is the HCF

Factorising an expression means writing it as the product of its factors.
When an expression has two or more terms, you need to find the common factor of all the terms.

Example 7

Factorise: **a** $x^2 - 3x$ **b** $6ab + 10b^2$

a $x^2 - 3x = (x \times x) - (3 \times x)$
$= x(x - 3)$

Write each term as a product of factors. You can leave this step out if you are confident. The common factors are written outside the bracket with the remaining factors inside.

Check: $x(x - 3) = x^2 - 3x$ ✓

You can check by multiplying out the bracket.

b $6ab + 10b^2 = (2 \times 3 \times a \times b) + (2 \times 5 \times b \times b)$
$= 2b(3a + 5b)$

Check: $2b(3a + 5b) = 6ab + 10b^2$ ✓

Exam practice 2C

1 Write down the highest common factor of:

a 2 and $4x$ b $6a$ and 3 c x^2 and $2x$
d x^2 and x^3 e xy and y^2 f $2st$ and $4t^2$
g $2x^2$ and $4x$ h x^2y and xy^2 i $4ab$ and $8ab^3$

2 Factorise:

a $3x + 6$ b $3x - 12$ c $8x + 4$
d $2x + 6$ e $5x + 5$ f $x^2 + 3x$
g $a^2 - 2a$ h $t^2 - 6t$ i $v^2 + 2v$
j $2x - x^2$ k $2a^2 + 5a$ l $6x - 2x^2$
m $2x + 2y$ n $x^2 - xy$ p $5a + 10b$
q $ab + ac$ r $2x^2 + xy$ s $xy + y^2$
t $2x^2 + 4y^2$ u $x^3 - 2x$

$5 = 5 \times 1$

3 Factorise:

a $y^3 - y^2$ b $x^3 - 3x^2$ c $2ab - 6b^2$
d $x^2y + xy^2$ e $5x^2 - 10xy$ f $4y^2 + 2xy$
g $3pq - 9p^2q^2$ h $12ab + 4a^2b$ i $6x^4 + 2x^2$
j $3a^2b - 6a^3b^2$ k $12x^3y + 9xy^2$ l $16pq^3 - 20p^2q$

4 Factorise:

a $2x + 2y + 4$ b $2a + 4b - 2c$ c $4a^2 + 2a - 8b$
d $3xy + 6x + 12$ e $3x + 6x^2 + 9$ f $ab + ac + ad$
g $x^2y - 2xy^2 + 4xy$ h $8pq + 2p^2 - 4pq^2$ i $3xy + 6x^2y + 9xy^3$

You need a common factor of all three terms.

2.4 Factorising perfect squares and the difference between two squares

A **quadratic expression** has the form $ax^2 + bx + c$ where a, b and c are constants and a is not zero. You get a quadratic expression when you multiply out two brackets with an x term in each bracket.

$(x - 4)(2x + 1) = 2x^2 - 7x - 4$

A **perfect square** is a number or expression that can be written as the product of two equal factors.

$(x + 3y)^2$ is a perfect square.

You need to be able to recognise quadratic expressions that can be written as perfect squares.

$(x + a)^2 = x^2 + 2ax + a^2$
$(x - a)^2 = x^2 - 2ax + a^2$

- the first and last terms are the squares of the two terms in the bracket,
- the middle term is twice the product of the two terms in the bracket,
- the sign of the middle term is the same as the sign in the bracket.

You can use these facts to recognise a quadratic expression that is a perfect square and then factorise it.

Example 8

a Factorise $4x^2 - 12x + 9$.
b Malik said that $9x^2 + 4x + 1$ is a perfect square. Explain why he is wrong.

a $4x^2 - 12x + 9 = (2x - 3)^2$

Check: $2 \times (2x) \times (-3) = -12x$ ✓

The first term is $(2x)^2$ and the last term is 3^2. Twice the product of $2x$ and 3 is $2 \times 6x = 12x$ so the answer is a perfect square. The middle term is $-12x$ so the sign in the bracket is '−'.

b $9x^2 + 4x + 1$
$9x^2 = (3x)^2$ and $1 = 1^2$
but $2 \times 3x \times 1 = 6x$, not $4x$

The **difference between two squares** is the difference between two expressions, each of which is a square.

Both $16 - x^2$ and $4a^2 - 9b^2$ are 'the difference between two squares'.

You get a difference between two squares when you multiply out two brackets of the form $(a + b)$ and $(a - b)$:

$$(a + b)(a - b) = a^2 - b^2$$

You can use this to factorise the difference between two squares: one factor is the sum of the square roots and the other is the difference of the square roots.

The middle terms cancel each other out: $a^2 + ab - ab - b^2$.

Example 9

Factorise: **a** $9x^2 - 25$ **b** $1 - 4y^2$

a $9x^2 - 25 = (3x)^2 - 5^2$
$= (3x + 5)(3x - 5)$

b $1 - 4y^2 = (1)^2 - (2y)^2$
$= (1 + 2y)(1 - 2y)$

Exam practice 2D

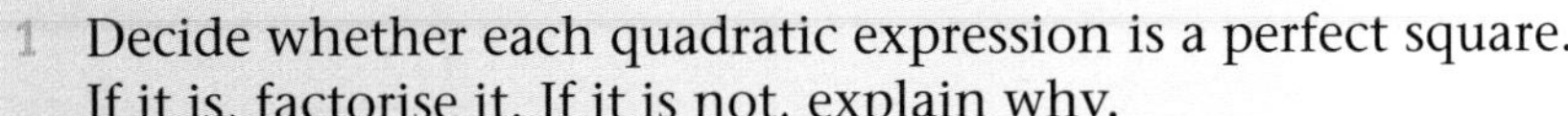

UAM 1 Decide whether each quadratic expression is a perfect square. If it is, factorise it. If it is not, explain why.

a $x^2 + 6x + 9$ b $x^2 + 18x + 9$
c $x^2 + 10x + 25$ d $x^2 + 8x + 16$
e $x^2 - 4x + 4$ f $x^2 - 2x + 1$
g $x^2 + 5x + 25$ h $4x^2 + 20x + 25$
i $9x^2 + 6x - 1$ j $9x^2 - 6x + 1$
k $36x^2 + 48x + 16$ l $x^2 + 4x - 4$
m $a^2 - 6ab + 9b^2$ n $4x^2 - 28x + 49$
p $4x^2 + 4xy + y^2$

2 Factorise:

a $x^2 - 4$ b $x^2 - 36$
c $x^2 - 81$ d $x^2 - y^2$
e $4x^2 - 9$ f $25a^2 - 9$
g $9a^2 - 16$ h $1 - s^2$
i $4 - 25x^2$ j $4x^2 - 25y^2$
k $36a^2 - 49b^2$ l $x^2y^2 - 1$

3 Peter wrote $a^2 - b^2 = (a - b)^2$.
UAM Explain why Peter is wrong.

4 By multiplying out the bracket prove that $(a + b)(a - b) = a^2 - b^2$.

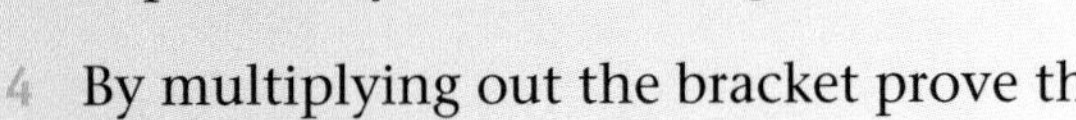

2.5 Factorising quadratic expressions

When the product of two brackets such as $(3x - 2)(x + 4)$ is multiplied out, the result is a quadratic expression. To factorise a quadratic expression you have to find the brackets that are its factors. You can do this by recognising the patterns when brackets are multiplied out.

$(3x - 2)(x + 4) = 3x^2 + 10x - 8$

$$(ax + b)(cx + d) = acx^2 + (adx + bcx) + bd$$

This is the product of the first term in each bracket.

This comes from collecting the product of the outside terms in each bracket and the product of the inside terms in each bracket.

This is the product of the last term in each bracket.

When a and c are positive then

- When b and d are both positive, the signs in the quadratic are all positive:
  $(x + 4)(x + 2) = x^2 + 6x + 8$.
- When b and d are both negative, the middle term in the quadratic is negative and the last term is positive:
  $(x - 4)(x - 2) = x^2 - 6x + 8$.
- When just one of b and d is negative, the last term is negative and the middle term may be either positive or negative:
  $(x + 4)(x - 2) = x^2 + 2x - 8$ and $(x + 3)(x - 5) = x^2 - 2x - 15$.

You can use these facts to help you find the factors of a quadratic expression.

Example 10

Factorise: **a** $x^2 - 5x + 6$ **b** $2x^2 + 11x + 5$ **c** $x^2 + 2x - 8$

a $x^2 - 5x + 6 = (x - 2)(x - 3)$

Check: $(x - 2)(x - 3)$
$= x^2 - 5x + 6$ ✓

The signs in the quadratic tell you that the signs in the brackets are both negative.
$x^2 = x \times x$, so the first term in each bracket is x.
$6 = 6 \times 1$ or 2×3 so the last terms in the brackets are either 6 and 1, or 2 and 3.
$(x - 6)(x - 1)$ gives a middle term of $(-6x - x) = -7x$ ✗
$(x - 2)(x - 3)$ gives a middle term of $(-2x - 3x) = -5x$ ✓

b $2x^2 + 11x + 5 = (2x + 1)(x + 5)$

Check: $(2x + 1)(x + 5)$
$= 2x^2 + 11x + 5$ ✓

The signs are all positive so the signs in the brackets are both positive.
The first term comes from $2x \times x$.
The last term comes from 5×1.
So there are two possible brackets
$(2x + 5)(x + 1) \Rightarrow$ middle term $2x + 5x = 7x$ ✗
$(2x + 1)(x + 5) \Rightarrow$ middle term $10x + x = 11x$ ✓

c $x^2 + 2x - 8 = (x + 4)(x - 2)$

Check: $(x + 4)(x - 2)$
$= x^2 + 2x - 8$ ✓

The constant is negative so the signs in the brackets are different.
$x^2 = x \times x$ so the first terms are both x and $8 = 8 \times 1$ or 4×2 so the last terms are ± 8 and ± 1, or ± 4 and ± 2.

You do not need to try every possible combination of letters and numbers. You will find with practice that you can spot combinations that do not work.

Example 11

Factorise: **a** $4x^2 - 25x + 6$ **b** $8x^2 + 4x - 12$ **c** $6x - 5 - x^2$

a $4x^2 - 25x + 6 = (4x - 1)(x - 6)$

Check: $(4x - 1)(x - 6) = 4x^2 - 25x + 6$ ✓

Possible first terms are $4x$ and x, or $2x$ and $2x$.
Possible last terms are 6 and 1, or 2 and 3.
The middle term is quite large, so try combinations of $4x$, x and 6, 1 first:
$(4x - 6)(x - 1) \Rightarrow$ middle term $-10x$ ✗
$(4x - 1)(x - 6) \Rightarrow$ middle term $-25x$ ✓

b $8x^2 + 4x - 12 = 4(2x^2 + x - 3)$
$= 4(2x + 3)(x - 1)$

Check: $4(2x + 3)(x - 1) = 4(2x^2 + x - 3)$
$= 8x^2 + 4x - 12$ ✓

4 is a common factor; take this out first then factorise the other quadratic factor.
Try $(2x + 1)(x - 3) \Rightarrow$ middle term $-5x$ ✗
$(2x + 3)(x - 1) \Rightarrow$ middle term x ✓

c $6x - 5 - x^2 = -1(-6x + 5 + x^2)$
$= -1\,(x^2 - 6x + 5)$
$= -1(x - 5)(x - 1)$ or $(5 - x)(x - 1)$

Check: $(5 - x)(x - 1) = -x^2 + 6x - 5$ ✓

Take -1 out as a factor so that the x^2 term is positive.
Then rearrange the terms in the bracket.

Example 12

a Factorise $a^2 - 2a - 8$.
b Hence, or otherwise, factorise $b^4 - 2b^2 - 8$.

a $a^2 - 2a - 8 = (a - 4)(a + 2)$

b $b^4 - 2b^2 - 8 = (b^2 - 4)(b^2 + 2)$
$= (b - 2)(b + 2)(b^2 + 2)$

When a is replaced by b^2, $a^2 - 2a - 8$ becomes $b^4 - 2b^2 - 8$ so you can replace a by b^2 in the factors. $b^2 - 4$ is the difference between two squares so it can be factorised; $b^2 + 2$ will not factorise.

Exam practice 2E

1 Factorise:
a $x^2 + 5x + 4$ b $x^2 + 7x + 12$ c $x^2 + 13x + 12$
d $x^2 + 11x + 18$ e $x^2 + 5x + 6$ f $x^2 + 7x + 10$
g $2x^2 + 7x + 6$ h $2x^2 + 5x + 3$ i $3x^2 + 5x + 2$
j $4x^2 + 20x + 9$ k $6x^2 + 19x + 15$ l $6x^2 + 17x + 12$

Check your answers by multiplying out the brackets.

2 Factorise:
a $x^2 - 8x + 12$ b $x^2 + 6x - 16$ c $x^2 - 2x - 15$
d $x^2 - 7x + 6$ e $x^2 - 5x + 4$ f $x^2 - 8x + 12$
g $3x^2 - 4x + 1$ h $3x^2 - 13x + 12$ i $6x^2 - 13x + 6$
j $6x^2 - 19xy + 10y^2$ k $3x^2 - 7x + 4$ l $4x^2 - 11x + 6$

3 Factorise:
a $x^2 + x - 12$ b $x^2 - 3x - 4$ c $x^2 + 4x - 12$
d $x^2 - 2x - 8$ e $x^2 + x - 6$ f $x^2 + 8x - 9$
g $6x^2 - x - 1$ h $8x^2 + 2x - 1$ i $5x^2 - 2x - 3$
j $4x^2 - 4x - 15$ k $7x^2 - 4x - 3$ l $9a^2 + 5ab - 4b^2$

4 a Factorise $x^2 - 8x - 9$.
b Hence, or otherwise, factorise $y^4 - 8y^2 - 9$.

5 Factorise:
a $2x^2 + 12x + 18$ b $45x^2 - 5$ c $7 + 3x - 4x^2$
d $x^2 + 3x - 4$ e $8x^2 - 18$ f $3x^2 - 3x - 6$
g $9 + 8x - x^2$ h $2x^2 - x + 3$ i $4x^2 + 16x + 16$
j $\frac{x^2}{4} - \frac{1}{9}$ k $2s^2 + 17s + 8$ l $2a^2 + 7ab + 3b^2$
m $5x^2 + 8x - 4$ n $(x - 2)^2 - y^2$ p $4 - 4x + x^2$
q $6 - x - x^2$ r $x^2 - 10x + 9$ s $(a - b)^2 - c^2$
t $x^4 - 2x^2 - 8$ u $4y^4 - 5y^2 + 1$ v $a^4 - 16b^4$

Always look for common factors first; then try to spot perfect squares or the difference between two squares.

Part u has four factors.

UAM
6 Explain why these expressions will not factorise.
a $2x^2 - 7x - 3$ b $x^2 + 12x + 9$ c $15x^2 - 39x - 14$

2.6 Simplifying algebraic fractions

You can simplify an algebraic fraction in the same way you simplify a numeric fraction: divide the numerator and the denominator by a factor that is common to both.

Example 13

Simplify: **a** $\frac{6x^2}{4x}$ **b** $\frac{(x-2)}{x^2-5x+6}$

a $\frac{6x^2}{4x} = \frac{3x \times \cancel{2x}}{2 \times \cancel{2x}} = \frac{3x}{2}$

2*x* is a common factor of $6x^2$ and 4*x*.

b $\frac{x-2}{x^2-5x+6} = \frac{\cancel{(x-2)}}{\cancel{(x-2)}(x-3)} = \frac{1}{(x-3)}$

Factorise the quadratic expression in the denominator. Then you can see that $(x - 2)$ is a common factor, so you can cancel it.

Exam practice 2F

1 Simplify:

a $\frac{2x}{4y}$ b $\frac{3x}{6}$ c $\frac{x^2}{xy}$ d $\frac{ab}{b^2}$

e $\frac{5}{15x}$ f $\frac{4xy}{6x}$ g $\frac{st}{5t}$ h $\frac{\pi r^2}{2r}$

i $\frac{6x^2}{12x}$ j $\frac{ab^2}{2a}$ k $\frac{9x^2}{6xy}$ l $\frac{ab^2}{abc}$

m $\frac{4xy}{x^3y}$ n $\frac{3x^3}{4x^2y}$ p $\frac{2\pi r}{4\pi r^4}$ q $\frac{x^3y^2}{3x^2y^5}$

2 Simplify:

Factorise the numerator and/or the denominator before trying to cancel.

a $\frac{2x-2y}{4x}$ b $\frac{6a}{3a-9b}$ c $\frac{xy-x^2}{3x}$

d $\frac{(x-2)}{(x-3)(x-2)}$ e $\frac{2x-4y}{5x-10y}$ f $\frac{2x^2+6x}{4x}$

g $\frac{3a-ab}{a^2}$ h $\frac{6xy}{3x^2-x}$ i $\frac{s^2-st}{7st}$

j $\frac{x+y}{x^2+xy}$ k $\frac{3a^2}{a^2-5a}$ l $\frac{2s-6t}{4t^2+2s}$

3 Graham wrote $\frac{2a-ab}{4ab} = \frac{2a-1}{4}$.

UAM Explain why Graham is wrong.

4 Simplify:

Use brackets to help you see common factors.

a $\frac{x-2}{x^2-3x+2}$ b $\frac{p-3}{p^2-6p+9}$ c $\frac{x^2+4x+3}{x+3}$

d $\frac{2x+3}{2x^2+5x+3}$ e $\frac{x^2-3x-10}{x+2}$ f $\frac{3x^2+x-2}{x+1}$

g $\frac{2a-4}{a^2-5a+6}$ h $\frac{2t+6}{t^2-t-12}$ i $\frac{x^2+5x+6}{2x^2-8}$

j $\frac{2x-8}{4x^2-4x-48}$ k $\frac{a+b}{a^2-b^2}$ l $\frac{2x^2-8}{3x+6}$

m $\frac{2x}{2x^2-2x-4}$ n $\frac{x^2-4}{x^2+2x}$ p $\frac{x^2+5x}{2x^2+9x-5}$

q $\frac{x^2+6x+8}{x^2-4}$ r $\frac{x^2-2x-3}{x^2+6x+5}$ s $\frac{2x^2-11x+15}{6x^2-13x-5}$

t $\frac{a^2-2a}{a^2-4}$ u $\frac{2x^2+13x+15}{4x^2-9}$ v $\frac{4x^2-25}{2x^2-x-15}$

2.7 Proof

You can show that a statement is **not** true by finding an example that contradicts it. This is called a **counterexample**.

You cannot use an example to prove that a statement is true. An example is a **demonstration** that the statement is true for that example. It may not be true for other examples.

To **prove** a statement you need to show that it is true for all possible examples. Variables are useful for proofs because they can stand for any possible number.

It is easy to make assumptions when deciding if a statement is true or false. Read the statement carefully. Remember that an integer can be positive or negative, and that a number can be a fraction or a number such as $\sqrt{2}$ or π.

Example 14

Decide if each statement is true or false.
If it is true, prove it. If it is false, find a counterexample.

a The sum of any three odd numbers is odd.

b The sum of any two consecutive integers is even.

These facts are useful when you are trying to prove that a statement is true.
If n is any natural number, you can use:

- $2n$ to represent any even number
- $2n + 1$ to represent any odd number
- $n - 1, n, n + 1,...$ to represent any consecutive whole numbers.

a True.
If a, b and c are any three whole numbers, $2a + 1$, $2b + 1$ and $2c + 1$ are any three odd numbers.
$(2a + 1) + (2b + 1) + (2c + 1) = 2a + 2b + 2c + 3$.
2 is not a factor of $2a + 2b + 2c + 3$ so it is an odd number.

b False.
2 and 3 are consecutive integers and $2 + 3 = 5$ which is odd.

Class discussion

Each of the following statements is wrong, but some people think they are correct. What assumptions have they made to lead them to think they are correct?

a When you halve a number, the answer is smaller than the number you start with.

b When you multiply two integers together, the answer is larger than either of those integers.

c 1 is a prime number.

d $a - b < a$ where a and b are any two integers and $a > b$.

e When you square any number less than 1, the answer is smaller than the number you start with.

Exam practice 2G

Decide if each statement is true or false.
If it is true, prove it. If it is false, find a counterexample.

1 The sum of any four consecutive natural numbers is a multiple of 4.

2 The sum of any four consecutive whole numbers is a multiple of 4.

3 The product of two even numbers is a multiple of 4.

4 The square of an even number is an even number.

5 The sum of any two fractions is less than 1.

6 The sum of any two prime numbers is an odd number.

7 When you reverse the digits of any two digit whole number, the difference between the number you start with and the new number is a multiple of 9.

8 The product of any three consecutive natural numbers is a multiple of 6.

Did you know

that Goldbach's conjecture is one of the oldest problems in mathematics?
It has not been proved or disproved.
It states: Every even integer greater than 2 can be written as the sum of two primes.

If the two digits are a and b, the numbers are $10a + b$ and $10b + a$.

Enrichment task

You can make two 2-figure numbers from two different digits. For example, the digits 2 and 5 make 25 and 52.

The difference between the squares of such numbers $= 99 \times$ (sum of the digits) $\times$ (difference between the digits).

a Show that this is true when one of the digits is zero.
b Prove that it is true for any two different digits.
c Does your proof work if the two digits are the same?
d Investigate what happens when you start with a 3-digit number.

Using the digits 2 and 5:

$52^2 - 25^2 = 2704 - 625$
$= 2079$

$99 \times (5 + 2) \times (5 - 2) = 99 \times 7 \times 3$
$= 2079.$

To prove this works for any two digits a and b, you need to show that

$(10a + b)^2 - (10b + a)^2 = 99(a + b)(a - b).$

Summary of key points

- You can multiply the same numbers with different powers by adding the powers: $x^a \times x^b = x^{a+b}$.
- You can divide the same numbers with different powers by subtracting the powers: $x^a \div x^b = x^{a-b}$.
- You can simplify an expression by collecting like terms.
- You need to know the following identities: $(x + a)^2 = x^2 + 2ax + a^2$, $(x - a)^2 = x^2 - 2ax + a^2$, $(a + b)(a - b) = a^2 - b^2$.
- Not all quadratic expressions will factorise.
- You can simplify an algebraic fraction by cancelling common factors of the numerator and denominator.

Most candidates who get GRADE C or above can:
- expand and simplify an expression containing brackets
- find a common factor of the sum or difference of algebraic terms.

Most candidates who get GRADE A or above can also:
- factorise a quadratic expression such as $6x^2 - 19x + 10$
- simplify algebraic fractions by cancelling common factors.

Glossary

Constant a fixed value
Counterexample a demonstration showing that a statement is false
Demonstration use of particular numbers or values to illustrate a statement
Difference between two squares an expression of the form $x^2 - y^2$
Equation two expressions that are equal
Expanding multiplying out brackets
Expression a collection of numbers and letters with no equals sign
Factorising expressing as a product of factors
Formula a rule
Identity an equation which is true for any values of the variables
Like terms terms with exactly the same combination of letters
Multiplying out multiplying each term inside a bracket by the term or terms the bracket is multiplied by
Perfect square a number or expression that can be written as the product of two equal factors
Prove give an argument that shows a statement is true in all possible cases
Quadratic expression containing x^2 and no higher powers of x
Simplifying collecting like terms together into a single term
Term a collection of numbers and letters that are not separated by plus or minus signs
Variable a letter representing a quantity or number that can have varying values

3 Equations and formulae

This chapter will show you:

✓ what an equation is
✓ how to solve linear equations algebraically
✓ how to form equations
✓ what a formula is
✓ how to use a formula
✓ how to make a formula using letters
✓ how to change the subject of a formula

Before you start you need to know:

✓ how to multiply and divide numbers
✓ how to work with positive and negative numbers
✓ how to simplify an expression
✓ how to multiply out brackets
✓ how to work with numerical fractions

3.1 Linear equations

A **linear equation** does not contain any power of the variable other than one.

$3x - 5 = 7x$ and $2x - 3(5x + 1) = 4x$ are linear equations. $x^2 = 16$ is not a linear equation.

An **equation** always has an equals sign between two expressions. Usually the two expressions are equal when the letter stands for some numbers but not all numbers. **Solving** the equation means finding those numbers.

There are two ways of solving an equation.

Think of $x + 3 = 5$ as a balance:

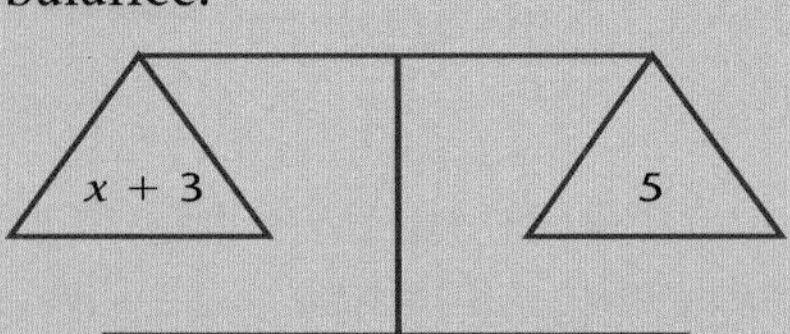

To keep the balance, do the same to both sides.
To get x on its own you need to subtract 3 from both sides:

$$x + 3 - 3 = 5 - 3$$
$$x = 2.$$

Think of $x + 3 = 5$ as a number machine:

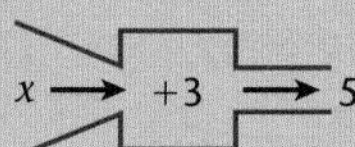

To find what goes in, reverse the number machine. The inverse operation to +3 is −3.

x ← −3 ← 5

$5 - 3 = 2$, so $x = 2$.

The solution can be a positive or negative number. It can also be a fraction or a mixed number.

Example 1

Solve these equations:

a $2x - 6 = 16$

b $7 - 3x = 8$

a $2x - 6 = 16$

$2x = 16 + 6$

$2x = 22$

$x = 11$

Using number machines:

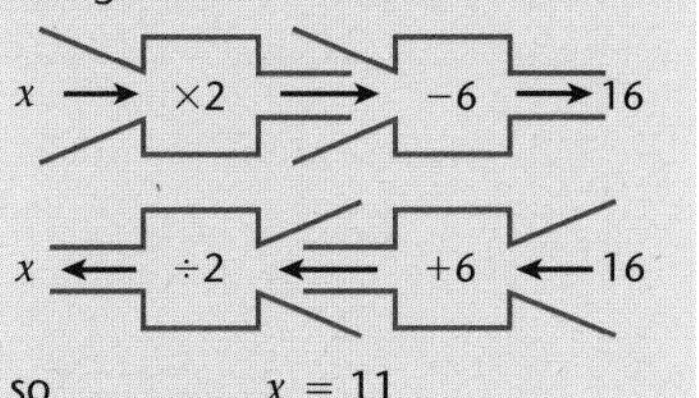

so $x = 11$

Check: $22 - 6 = 16$ ✓

b $7 - 3x = 8$

$7 = 8 + 3x$

$7 - 8 = 3x$

$-1 = 3x$

$-1 \div 3 = x$ so $x = -\frac{1}{3}$

Or

x → × −3 → +7 → 8

x ← ÷ −3 ← −7 ← 8

so $x = -\frac{1}{3}$

Check: $7 - 3(-\frac{1}{3}) = 7 + 1 = 8$ ✓

You need to be able to solve equations with the unknown on both sides.

Example 2

Solve these equations:

a $2x - 3 = x + 4$

b $3 + 5x = 17 - 2x$

a $2x - 3 = x + 4$

$x - 3 = 4$

$x = 4 + 3$

$x = 7$

Check: $2 \times 7 - 3 = 11$, $7 + 4 = 11$ ✓

Start by subtracting x from both sides: $2x - 3 - x = x - 3$ and $x + 4 - x = 4$.

b $3 + 5x = 17 - 2x$

$3 + 5x + 2x = 17 - 2x + 2x$

$3 + 7x = 17$

$7x = 17 - 3$

$7x = 14$

$x = 14 \div 7$

$x = 2$

Check: $3 + 5 \times 2 = 13$, $17 - 2 \times 2 = 13$ ✓

Add $2x$ to both sides.
Then collect like terms.

The equation may contain brackets.

Example 3

Solve these equations: **a** $3(2x - 4) = 18$
b $5(x - 2) - 2(2x - 4) = 16$

a $3(2x - 4) = 18$
$6x - 12 = 18$
$6x = 18 + 12$
$6x = 30$
$x = 30 \div 6 = 5$

Start by multiplying out the bracket.

b $5(x - 2) - 2(2x - 4) = 16$
$5x - 10 - 4x + 8 = 16$
$x - 2 = 16$
$x = 16 + 2 = 18$

Multiply out the brackets.
Remember $-2 \times (-4) = 8$.
Then collect like terms.

Exam practice 3A

1 Solve these equations:

a $x + 5 = 12$	b $x - 6 = 17$	c $a + 7 = 6$
d $t + 15 = 6$	e $3 + t = 15$	f $7 = x + 5$
g $10 - x = 8$	h $25 - x = 14$	i $12 - t = 5$
j $3 + x = 2$	k $13 = y + 15$	l $12 = 9 - y$

2 Solve these equations:

a $2x + 5 = 9$	b $3x + 2 = 5$	c $2x - 1 = 5$
d $5y - 4 = 6$	e $4a - 2 = 7$	f $5b - 9 = 6$
g $4s + 3 = 19$	h $8t - 2 = 7$	i $10x - 3 = 2$
j $4 = 3p - 5$	k $6x + 9 = 3$	l $2x + 7 = 3$
m $2 = 3x - 2$	n $15 = 4 + 11x$	p $5 = 6s + 4$
q $7x + 6 = 5$	r $14 = 2 + 5x$	s $4x + 11 = 2$

Give your answer to part f as a mixed number.

3 Solve these equations:

a $x + 3x = 40$	b $3x + 4x = 14$
c $5x - 2x = 7$	d $3x + 2x + x = 180$
e $4x + x + 4x = 90$	f $7x - 3x + x = 360$

4 Jodie wrote:

$2x - 4 = 6$
$2x = 2$
$x = 1$

UAM

Jodie's solution is wrong.
Explain her mistake.

5 Solve these equations:

a $2x + 1 = x + 5$	b $2x + 3 = x + 1$	c $2x + 3 = x + 9$
d $3x + 4 = 2x - 1$	e $2x - 4 = x + 7$	f $5x - 2 = 2x + 7$
g $5x + 2 = 4 + x$	h $3 - 5x = 2x + 4$	i $6x + 4 = 2x + 7$
j $2x - 3 = x - 7$	k $4 + 3x = 9 - 2x$	l $2 - x = 8 - 7x$

If two expressions are equal, it does not matter which one you write first. You can write the equation in part h as $2x + 4 = 3 - 5x$.

6 Solve these equations:

a $4(3x - 1) = 20$ b $2(5x + 1) = 7$ c $7(x - 2) = 5$
d $3(5x + 1) = 33$ e $6(2 - x) = 12$ f $2(3 - 2x) = 16$
g $7 = 2(x - 1)$ h $4 = 2(2x - 1)$ i $15 = 3(3x + 2)$

7 Solve these equations:

a $3x + 9 = 2(x + 7)$ b $4(x - 2) = 3x + 1$
c $7x + 3 = 3(x - 5)$ d $5x + 17 = 3(x + 6)$
e $3 - 2(x + 5) = 4$ f $6 + 3(x - 2) = 5$
g $1 + x - 2(3x - 1) = 5$ h $2(x + 1) = x + 6$
i $3(x - 2) = 2(x + 8)$ j $2(x - 1) - 4(2 - 2x) = 3$
k $3(2x + 4) = 5x - 1$ l $4x - 2 = 5(x - 3)$
m $3 - 2x = 1 - 3(1 - 3x)$ n $1 - 2(x + 4) = 5 + 3(2x - 1)$

Class discussion

Try to solve the equation $2 + 4x = 2(2x + 1)$.
What happens and why?

3.2 Equations containing fractions

You can get rid of fractions from an equation by multiplying both sides by a common multiple of the denominators.

Example 4

Solve: **a** $\frac{x}{3} - 5 = 2$ **b** $\frac{2x - 4}{3} = 3$ **c** $\frac{x - 1}{4} - \frac{2x + 1}{5} = 3$

a $\frac{x}{3} - 5 = 2$

$\frac{x}{3} = 7$ Add 5 to both sides.

$x = 7 \times 3 = 21$ Check: $\frac{21}{3} - 5 = 7 - 5 = 2$ ✓

b $\frac{(2x - 4)}{3} = 3$ Put brackets round any numerators and denominators containing more than one term.

$\frac{3 \times (2x - 4)}{3} = 3 \times 3$ Multiply both sides by 3.

$2x - 4 = 9$

$2x = 13$

$x = 13 \div 2 = 6\frac{1}{2}$ Check: $\frac{2 \times 6\frac{1}{2} - 4}{3} = \frac{13 - 4}{3} = \frac{9}{3} = 3$ ✓

c $\frac{(x - 1)}{4} - \frac{(2x + 1)}{5} = 3$ 20 is the LCM of 4 and 5. Multiply both sides by 20.

$20 \times \left(\frac{(x - 1)}{4} - \frac{(2x + 1)}{5}\right) = 20 \times 3$

$\frac{\cancel{20}^{5} \times (x - 1)}{\cancel{4}_{1}} - \frac{\cancel{20}^{4} \times (2x + 1)}{\cancel{5}_{1}} = 60$ Multiply out the brackets and collect like terms.

$5(x - 1) - 4(2x + 1) = 60$

$5x - 5 - 8x - 4 = 60$

$-3x - 9 = 60$

$-3x = 69$

$x = -23$ Check: $\frac{-23 - 1}{4} - \frac{-46 + 1}{5} = \frac{-24}{4} - \frac{-45}{5}$
$= -6 + 9 = 3$ ✓

Exam practice 3B

1 Solve these equations:

a $\frac{x}{2} = 5$ b $\frac{x}{5} = 4$ c $5 = \frac{x}{8}$

d $4 = \frac{x}{7}$ e $6 = \frac{5k}{4}$ f $4 = \frac{2b}{15}$

g $\frac{x}{2} = 2\frac{1}{2}$ h $\frac{2x}{3} = \frac{3}{5}$ i $\frac{x}{5} + 2 = 4$

j $\frac{p}{6} - 3 = 2$ k $2 + \frac{y}{5} = 3$ l $\frac{s}{7} - 2 = 1$

m $2 = 1 + \frac{x}{3}$ n $\frac{7x}{2} + 5 = 2$ p $\frac{2t}{3} + 7 = 2$

q $3 - \frac{5x}{2} = 2$

2 Solve these equations:

a $\frac{(x - 1)}{3} = 1$ b $\frac{(2x + 1)}{3} = 5$ c $\frac{(1 - x)}{2} = 3$

d $6 = \frac{(2 - 5x)}{2}$ e $\frac{2x - 1}{4} = 6$ f $\frac{4 - 3x}{2} = 1$

g $\frac{2a - 9}{7} = 5$ h $12 = \frac{3 - 5x}{3}$ i $\frac{x}{4} - \frac{1}{2} = \frac{1}{4}$

j $\frac{4}{5} = \frac{x}{15} - \frac{2}{3}$ k $\frac{x}{2} - \frac{3}{8} = \frac{3}{4}$ l $\frac{2}{5} + \frac{x}{4} = \frac{1}{2} + \frac{x}{20}$

3 Solve these equations:

a $\frac{x + 1}{5} = \frac{1}{2}$ b $\frac{3x - 2}{4} = \frac{2}{3}$

c $\frac{3}{4} = \frac{x + 1}{2}$ d $\frac{2x + 1}{5} = 3 - x$

e $\frac{x - 2}{4} = \frac{x + 3}{2}$ f $\frac{5x + 2}{3} = 2x$

g $\frac{x - 2}{4} = x + 3$ h $\frac{2x + 3}{5} = \frac{x - 1}{3}$

i $\frac{4x - 3}{6} = \frac{2 - x}{2}$ j $\frac{3 - 5y}{4} = \frac{2 - y}{6}$

k $\frac{x + 1}{2} + \frac{x + 3}{4} = 5$ l $\frac{x}{5} + \frac{x + 2}{4} = \frac{7}{20}$

m $\frac{x - 3}{4} - \frac{x - 4}{5} = \frac{3}{20}$ n $\frac{2x + 1}{5} - \frac{x - 2}{3} = 1$

p $\frac{2}{3} - \frac{x + 1}{4} = \frac{3}{4} - \frac{x + 5}{3}$

3.3 Writing expressions

You can write word problems using letters and numbers.

You need to use the clues in the words to decide how the letters and numbers are connected.

Example 5

Envelopes cost n pence each. Write down an expression for the cost of 20 envelopes.

Remember that an expression is a collection of letters, numbers and $+$, $-$, $\times$, and $\div$ signs. There is no equals sign.

$20 \times n$ pence
or $20n$ pence

20 envelopes cost 20 times the price of 1 envelope.

You are not always told which letters to use.
You can choose any letter to stand for the unknown number.

Example 6

John thinks of a number. He doubles the number and then adds three.
Write down an expression for John's answer.

Let x be the number that John thinks of.
Double the number is $2x$.
John's answer is $2x + 3$.

Write down what your letter stands for.

Double means multiply by 2. So the expression is $2x$.

Now add 3.

Exam practice 3C

1 a Soap costs c pence a bar.
Write an expression for the cost of 5 bars of soap.
b Apples cost 30 pence each.
Write an expression for the cost of n apples.
c A stick was x cm long. A piece 3 cm long is cut off the stick.
Write an expression for the length of the stick now.

2 a An internet order for groceries costs £C. The delivery charge is £5.
Write an expression for the total cost.
b Freya buys 2 books online costing £p each. There is a charge of £4 for postage. Find an expression for the total cost.
c One orange costs a pence. One apple costs b pence.
Write an expression for the total cost of 5 oranges and 4 apples.

3 a Write an expression for the distance round the sides of this rectangle.

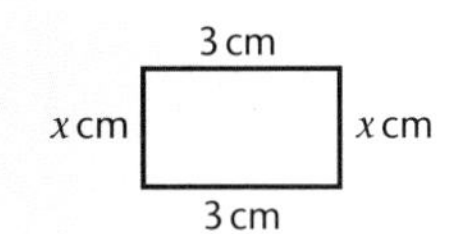

Simplify your answer.

b Write an expression for the distance round the sides of this shape.

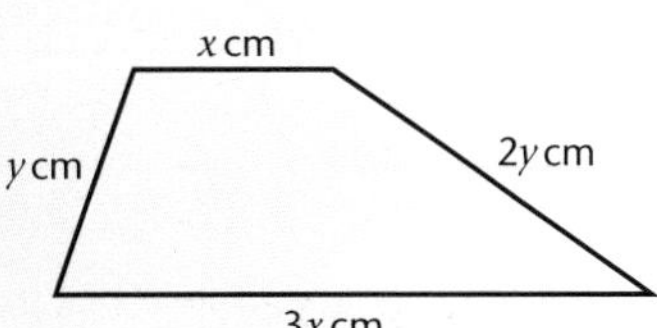

4 Each of these two boxes contains x beads.

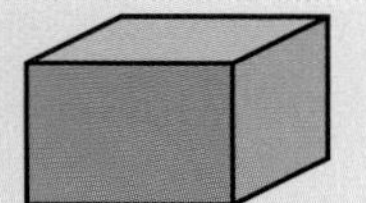 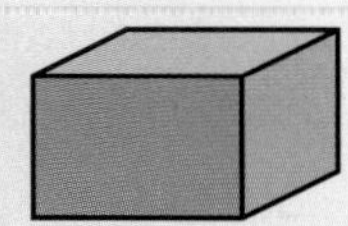

Marco takes 10 beads out of one of the boxes.
Show that the total number of beads left in the two boxes is $2(x - 5)$.

5 Show that the perimeter of this triangle is $(x + 1)^2$ cm.

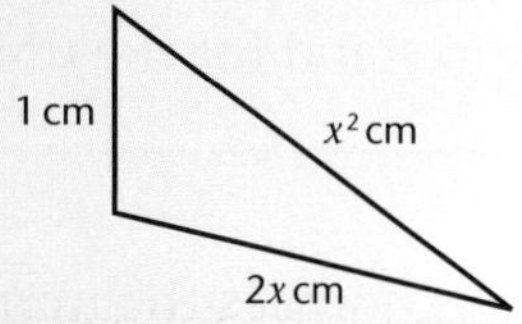

6 A chocolate muffin costs 5 pence more than a plain muffin. Write an expression for the cost of 1 chocolate muffin and 1 plain muffin.

You are not told the cost of either type of muffin, so choose a letter to stand for the cost of one of them.

3.4 Forming equations

You can form an equation by putting an equals sign between two expressions.

Example 7

In this triangle:
the length of BC is 3 cm less than the length of AC,
the length of AB is twice the length of BC,
the perimeter of the triangle is 27 cm.
Find the length of the shortest side.

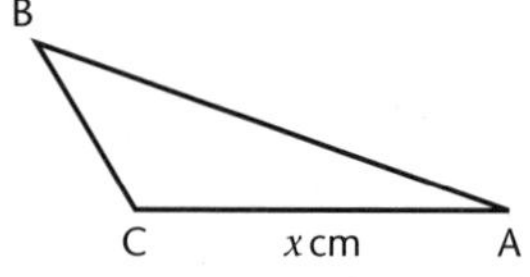

BC = $(x - 3)$ cm so AB = $2(x - 3)$ cm. — First find expressions for the length of BC and AB.

$x + (x - 3) + 2(x - 3) = x + x - 3 + 2x - 6$

$= 4x - 9$ — Then find an expression for the perimeter and simplify it.

$4x - 9 = 27$ — You know the perimeter is 27 cm so you can equate $4x - 9$ and 27. Solve the equation to find the value of x.

$4x = 36$

$x = 9$

The shortest side is $(9 - 3)$ cm = 6 cm. — Now answer the question.

Exam practice 3D

1 Two pieces of rope are joined together.

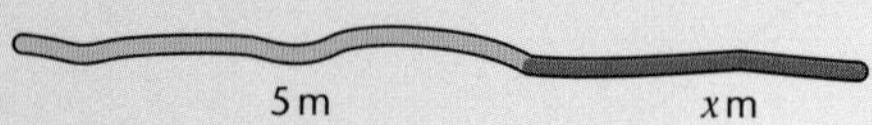

The total length is 8.5 m.
Write an equation and solve it to find the value of x.

2 Jason buys 3 batteries priced at c pence each.
He pays with a £2 coin.

Convert £2 to pence.

a Find an expression for the change Jason gets.
b He gets 80p change.
Write an equation and solve it to find the value of c.
c How much did each battery cost?

UAM

3 The distance round this shape is 58 cm.
Find the length of the shortest side.

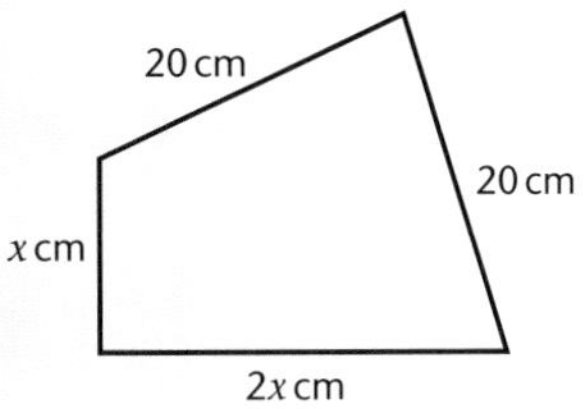

4 Find the number in each of the following:
a Rob thinks of a number. He doubles it and then subtracts 10. The answer is 16.
b Carol thinks of a number. She halves it and then adds 4. The answer is 8.
c Kingston thinks of a number. He subtracts 3 times his number from 25. His answer is 7.
d Nazreen thinks of a number. She adds six times the number to 30. Her answer is 42.

5 The sizes of three angles are $x°$, $(x + 10)°$ and $(x + 20)°$. They add up to 180°.
Find the size of the smallest angle.

UAM

6

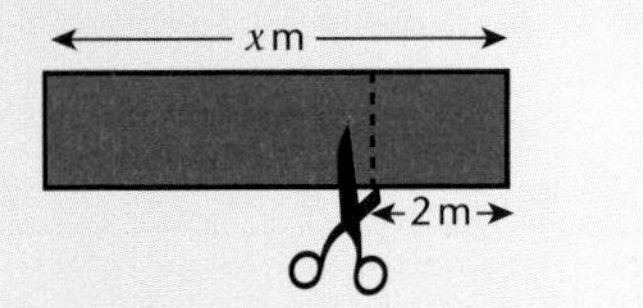

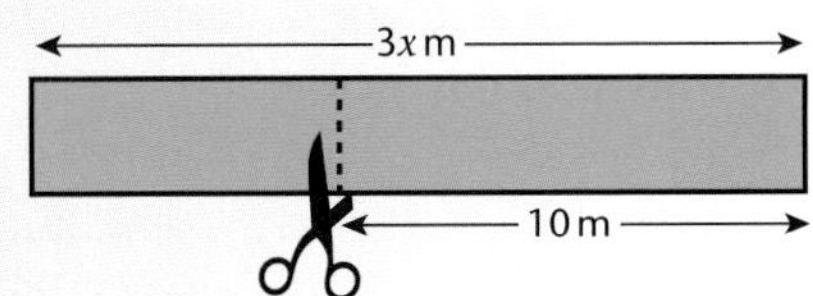

A piece is cut off each of these lengths of carpet.
a The two pieces of carpet left are the same length.
Form an equation and solve it to find the value of x.
b How long was the green carpet before the piece was cut off ?

UAM

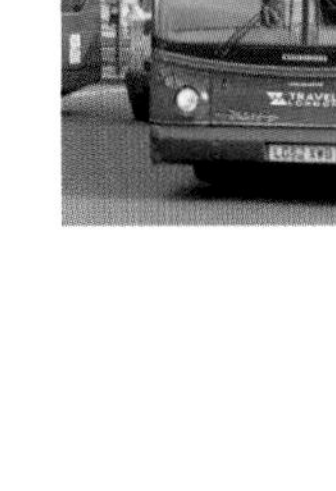

7 The bus fare for an adult is x pence.
The fare for a child is 50p less than this.
The cost of three child fares is 210p.
What is an adult fare?

UAM

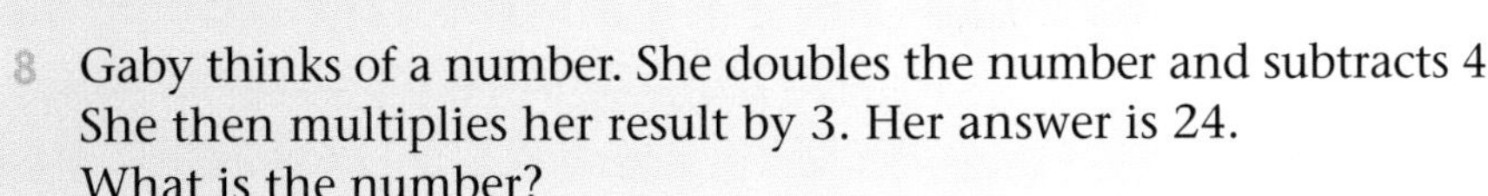

8 Gaby thinks of a number. She doubles the number and subtracts 4.
She then multiplies her result by 3. Her answer is 24.
What is the number?

UAM

9 Tom writes:

$$4 - 2(x - 3) = 1$$
$$4 - 2x - 6 = 1$$
$$2 - 2x = 1$$
$$2 = 1 + 2x$$
$$1 = 2x \text{ so } x = \frac{1}{2}$$

He has made two mistakes. Describe these mistakes.

UAM

Enrichment task

Kate uses this trick to find out someone's age without asking them.

She says: 'Multiply your age by 5, add 4 then subtract your age from the answer.
Now divide your answer by 4.
What did you get?'

Kate subtracts 1 from the answer she is given. The result is the person's age.

a Try this on some members of your family or class.
b Explain why it works using algebra.
c Create your own trick to find out someone's age.

3.5 Formulae

A **formula** is a rule connecting quantities.
The rule for finding the area of a rectangle is a formula.

Area of a rectangle = length × breadth.

You can make a formula using words or letters in the same way as you make an equation.

The plural of formula is formulae.

You can use a formula to find one quantity when you know the size of the other quantities by **substituting** their values into the formula. This gives an equation that you can solve.

Substitute means replace one quantity by another.

Example 8

The capacity of an engine is equal to the capacity of one cylinder multiplied by the number of cylinders.

a Using C for the capacity of the engine, c for the capacity of one cylinder and n for the number of cylinders, write a formula for C in terms of c and n,

b A car engine has a capacity of 1000 cubic centimetres and four cylinders.
Find the capacity of one cylinder.

This means you need to write C equal to an expression containing c and n.

a $C = cn$

First find an expression for the capacity of the engine in terms of c and n. Then equate your expression to C.

b $1000 = c \times 4 = 4c$

$c = 1000 \div 4 = 250$

The capacity of one cylinder = 250 cubic centimetres.

The engine has a capacity of 1000 cc, so replace C by 1000. The number of cylinders is 4 so replace n by 4. This gives an equation which you can solve.

When a formula contains a square involving the letter you want, isolate that term on one side of the equals sign.

Example 9

Use the formula $y = \frac{x^2}{r} + k$ to find x when $y = 10$, $r = 3$ and $k = \frac{14}{3}$.

$$y = \frac{x^2}{r} + k$$

$$10 = \frac{x^2}{3} + \frac{14}{3} = \frac{x^2 + 14}{3}$$

$$30 = 3 \times \frac{(x^2 + 14)}{3}$$

Multiply both sides by 3.

$$30 = x^2 + 14$$

$$x^2 = 16$$

$$x = \pm 4$$

Find the square root of both sides.
Remember that there are two square roots of a number, one positive and one negative. The symbol $\pm$ means 'plus or minus'.

Exam practice 3E

1 The perimeter of a rectangle is twice its length plus twice its width.
   a Using P for the perimeter, l for the length and w for the width, write a formula for P in terms of l and w.
   b i Find the perimeter of a rectangle 20 cm long and 15 cm wide.
      ii Find the width of a rectangle whose perimeter is 40 cm and whose length is 15 cm.

2 A computer repair shop charges £30 an hour plus the cost of new parts.
   a Write a formula for the total charge, £T, in terms of the number of hours, n, and the cost for new parts, £c.
   b The bill for a repair was £85. The cost of new parts was £10. How many hours did the shop charge for?

3 This metal machine part has two long rectangular faces and two shorter rectangular faces.
The total surface area (inside and outside) of this metal part is A.
   a Find a formula for A in terms of a, b and c.
   b Find the value of a when $A = 60\text{ mm}^2$, $b = 4\text{ mm}$ and $c = 2\text{ mm}$.

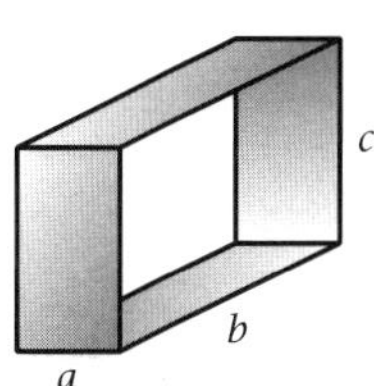

4 The formula for the area of a trapezium is $A = \frac{1}{2}h(a + b)$.
Find the area when $a = 15\text{ mm}$, $b = 4\text{ cm}$ and $h = 2.4\text{ cm}$.

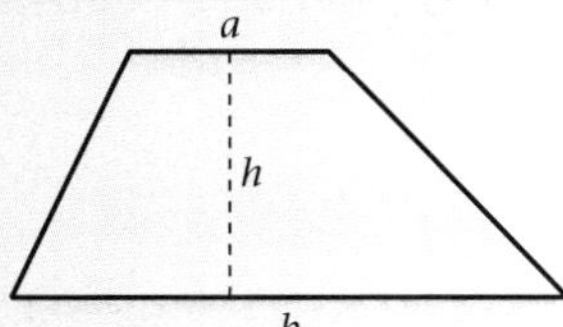

When you substitute values, make sure they are measured in the same unit. Two of the lengths are in cm and one is in mm, so convert 15 mm to cm.

5 Use the formula $s = ut - 5t^2$ to work out:
   a s when $u = 6$ and $t = 1$,
   b u when $s = 20$ and $t = -4$.

6 Use the formula $A = \frac{PRT}{100}$ to find:
   a A when $P = 100$, $R = 5$ and $T = 2$,
   b P when $A = 300$, $R = 4$ and $T = 3$.

7 Use the formula $p = \frac{1}{2}(q + r)$ to work out:
a p when $q = 3$ and $r = 5$,
b p when $q = 8$ and $r = -6$,
c q when $p = 6$ and $r = -8$.

8 Use the formula $R = a^2 + b^2$ to find:
a R when $a = 4$ and $b = 6$,
b R when $a = 2$ and $b = -5$.
c Will said that R is the same for $a = 2$ and $b = 3$ as for $a = -2$ and $b = -3$.
UAM Is Will correct? Explain your answer.

9 Use the formula $V = \pi r^2 h$ to find:
a V in terms of π when $r = 2$ and $h = 6$,
b h in terms of π when $V = 36$ and $r = 2$.

'In terms of π' means do not substitute a value for π but leave π in your answer.

10 Use the formula $r = a^2 + b^2$ to find the value of a when $r = 11$ and $b = -3$. Give an exact answer.

11 Given that $\frac{x^2}{4} + \frac{y^2}{9} = 1$, find the value of y when $x = 1$.

3.6 Changing the subject of a formula

When a letter is on its own on one side of the equals sign and is not on the other side, it is called the **subject** of the formula.

t is the subject of $t = u + v$.
A is not the subject of $A = 2t - \frac{1}{A}$ because A is on both sides.

Changing the subject of a formula means rearranging the formula so that another letter is the subject.

You can change the subject of a formula by thinking of it as an equation and solving it for the letter you want as the subject.

- Get rid of any fractions.
- Multiply out any brackets.
- Collect all terms containing the new subject on one side of the equals sign and all other terms on the other side.
- Factorise if necessary.
- Take the square root of both sides if necessary.

Remember that there are two square roots, one positive and one negative.

Example 10

Make l the subject of the formula $P = 2l + 2w$.

You need to 'solve' the formula for l.

$$P = 2l + 2w$$

$$P - 2w = 2l$$

Subtract $2w$ from both sides.

$$\frac{P - 2w}{2} = l \text{ or } l = \frac{P - 2w}{2}$$

Divide both sides by 2.

Example 11

Make x the subject of the formula $y = x + \frac{a}{10}(x + b)$.

This solution shows one step at a time. You can do some of these steps in your head but only if you are very confident that you will not make mistakes.

$y = x + \frac{a}{10}(x + b)$

$10y = 10 \times \left(x + \frac{a}{10}(x + b)\right)$

Multiply both sides by 10 to get rid of the fraction.

$10y = 10 \times x + \cancel{10} \times \frac{a}{\cancel{10}}(x + b)$

$10y = 10x + a(x + b)$

Multiply out the bracket.

$10y = 10x + ax + ab$

$10y - ab = 10x + ax$

$10y - ab = x(10 + a)$

Subtract ab from both sides to leave only the terms containing x one side of the equals sign. Then factorise.

$\frac{(10y - ab)}{(10 + a)} = x$ or $x = \frac{(10y - ab)}{(10 + a)}$

Divide both sides by $(10 + a)$.

Exam practice 3F

1 Make the letter in brackets the subject of the formula.

a $T = n + 6$ (n)
b $N = b - 3$ (b)
c $d = 2r$ (r)
d $A = lb$ (b)
e $C = \pi d$ (d)
f $d = st$ (s)
g $x = \frac{y}{2}$ (y)
h $y = 3x + 2$ (x)
i $t = 5p - 40$ (p)
j $c = x + 2y$ (y)
k $y = mx + c$ (x)
l $V = \frac{1}{3}Ah$ (A)
m $a = 2(b - 4)$ (b)
n $w = 3(a - 2b)$ (a)
p $G = \frac{h}{t} - s$ (h)
q $w = \frac{1}{2}y(x + b)$ (x)

2 This formula can be used to find the area, A, of a trapezium.

$2A = h(b + c)$

a Make b the subject of this formula.
b Find b when $A = 20$, $h = 4$ and $c = 4$.

3 Make the letter in brackets the subject of the formula.

Isolate the squared letter then put brackets round the other side of the equation before you take the square root. Remember, when $x^2 = a$, $x = \pm\sqrt{a}$.

a $P = ar + ah$ (h)
b $x = y - yc$ (y)
c $y = x^2 + k$ (x)
d $V = \pi r^2 h$ (r)
e $A = \frac{1}{2}bc + \frac{1}{2}ac$ (c)
f $T = 2\pi\sqrt{\frac{l}{g}}$ (l)
g $\frac{x}{a} + \frac{y}{b} = 2$ (x)
h $A = P + \frac{PRT}{100}$ (P)
i $x(y - 2) = 2y$ (y)
j $\frac{x + c}{2} = \frac{x - k}{3}$ (x)
k $k = \frac{x}{k + x}$ (x)
l $A = \frac{1}{2}(a + b) + \frac{1}{2}(a + c)$ (a)
m $r^2 = (x - 2)(y - 3)$ (x)
n $a(b - 4) = b(a + 6)$ (b)
p $A = \frac{h}{2}(a + b) - \frac{ah}{3}$ (a)
q $S = \frac{1}{2}n(a + k) + \frac{1}{2}n(a + l)$ (a)
r $V = \frac{4}{3}\pi r^3$ (r)
s $A = x^2 + y^2$ (y)

4 David tried to make a the subject of the formula $b^2 = a^2 - x^2$.
This is his working.

UAM

Is David correct?
Give reasons for your answer.

$$b^2 + x^2 = a^2$$
$$a = \pm\sqrt{b^2 + x^2}$$
$$a = \pm(b + x)$$

Summary of key points

- You can solve an equation by doing the same thing to both sides of the equation or by using inverse operations.
- When an equation contains brackets, start by multiplying out the brackets.
- When an equation contains fractions, multiply both sides by the LCM of the denominator to get rid of the fractions.
- You can use a formula to find one quantity when you know the values of the other quantities.
- To change the subject of a formula, rearrange it so that the new subject is in terms of the other quantities:
  - get rid of fractions and multiply out any brackets
  - collect all terms containing the new subject on one side of the equals sign and all other terms on the other side
  - factorise if necessary and take the square root of both sides if necessary.

Most students who get GRADE C or above can:

- solve equations containing brackets
- change the subject of a formula that contains the new subject in only one term.

Most students who get GRADE A or above can also:

- change the subject of a formula when the new subject appears twice.

Glossary

Equation two expressions connected by an equals sign
Formula a rule connecting quantities
Linear equation an equation that does not contain any power other than one
Solving finding values that make an equation true
Subject a quantity on its own on one side of the equals sign and not on the other side
Substitute replace one quantity by another

4 Simultaneous and quadratic equations

This chapter will show you:
- ✓ how to solve simultaneous linear equations
- ✓ different methods for solving quadratic equations
- ✓ how to solve one linear and one quadratic equation simultaneously
- ✓ how to use trial and improvement to solve equations

Before you start you need to know:
- ✓ how to solve a linear equation in one unknown
- ✓ how to form an equation
- ✓ how to factorise quadratic expressions
- ✓ how to find the areas of squares and rectangles
- ✓ the meanings of decimal places and significant figures
- ✓ how to simplify expressions containing surds

4.1 Simultaneous equations

Solving an equation means finding the value or values of the letters that make both sides of the equation equal.

There is often one solution that satisfies two linear equations.

When two equations have solutions in common, they are called **simultaneous equations**.

There are two algebraic methods you can use to solve a pair of linear simultaneous equations.

Elimination

One of the unknown letters is eliminated by adding or subtracting a pair of equations to give a linear equation in one unknown.
This is the easier method to use for a pair of linear equations.

Substitution

One equation is rearranged to make one unknown the subject.
This expression for the unknown is substituted into the other equation. This gives an equation in one unknown.

The solution of the equation $x + 4 = 6$ is $x = 2$.
The equation $y = 3x - 2$ has two unknowns.
It has many solutions: $x = 1$ and $y = 1$ is just one of them.

Simultaneous means occurring at the same time.

You can also solve simultaneous equations by drawing graphs. This is covered in Module 3.

Example 1

Solve the simultaneous equations: $x + y = 6$
$2x - y = 3$

$x + y = 6$ ①
$2x - y = 3$ ②

Number the equations to help you keep track of your work.

①+②: $(x + y) + (2x - y) = 6 + 3$
$3x = 9$
$x = 3$

Add the left-hand sides and add the right-hand sides of ① and ②. You can go straight to $3x = 9$ if you are confident that you will not make mistakes.

$x = 3$ in ①: $3 + y = 6$
$y = 3$

Substitute the value of x into either ① or ② to find y.

Check: $2(3) - 3 = 6 - 3 = 3$ ✓

You can check your answer by substituting the values of x and y into the other equation.

To eliminate one of the unknowns you may need to use a multiple of one or both equations.

Remember:
- add the equations when the signs of the terms are different
- subtract the equations when the signs are the same.

Example 2

Solve the simultaneous equations: $2x - 3y = 10$
$3x - 4y = 16$

$2x - 3y = 10$ ①
$3x - 4y = 16$ ②

Multiplying ① by 3 and ② by 2 gives $6x$ in both equations.

① ×3: $6x - 9y = 30$ ③
② ×2: $6x - 8y = 32$ ④

Renumber the equations and subtract because the signs of the x terms are the same.

④ − ③: $(6x - 8y) - (6x - 9y) = 32 - 30$
$6x - 8y - 6x + 9y = 2$

You can leave these steps out if you are confident you will not make mistakes with signs.

$y = 2$

$y = 2$ in ①: $2x - 6 = 10$
$2x = 16$
$x = 8$

$x = 8$ and $y = 2$

Check: in ②: $3 \times 8 - 4 \times 2 = 24 - 8 = 16$ ✓

You may need to rearrange the equations before you use elimination.

Example 3

Solve the simultaneous equations: $x = y + 5$
$2x + 3y = 5$

$x = y + 5$ ①
$2x + 3y = 5$ ②

Rearrange ① so that x and y are on the same side of the equals sign.

$x - y = 5$ ③
$2x + 3y = 5$ ②
③ ×3: $3x - 3y = 15$ ④
② + ④: $(2x + 3y) + (3x - 3y) = 5 + 15$
$5x = 20$
$x = 4$

Multiply ③ to give the same y term as in ②. Then add as the signs of the y terms are different.

$x = 4$ in ①: $4 = y + 5$
$4 - 5 = y$ so $y = -1$

$x = 4$ and $y = -1$

Check: in ②: $2 \times 4 + 3 \times (-1) = 8 - 3 = 5$ ✓

Alternatively you can use substitution to solve these equations: you are given $x = y + 5$ so substitute $y + 5$ for x in equation ②: $2(y + 5) + 3y = 5$.
This gives a linear equation in y which you can solve.
Then find x by substituting your value of y into $x = y + 5$.

Exam practice 4A

1 Solve these simultaneous equations.

a $x + y = 8$, $x - y = 2$
b $3x + 2y = 7$, $2x - 2y = 8$
c $x + y = 10$, $2x - y = 8$
d $2x + y = 11$, $7x + y = 21$
e $x + 3y = 11$, $x - 2y = 1$
f $x + y = 3$, $x + 3y = 5$

2 a $x + y = 3$, $5x - 2y = 1$
b $2x + y = 6$, $x - 2y = 8$
c $2x + 3y = 4$, $4x + 5y = 6$
d $2x - y = 4$, $5x - 3y = 5$
e $3x + 2y = 8$, $4x + 3y = 9$
f $2a - 3b = 12$, $3a - b = 11$

3 a $2x + 3y = 5$, $3x - 2y = 1$
b $5x + 2y = 1$, $2x + 3y = 7$
c $5x - 3y = 1$, $7x + 5y = 6$
d $4x - 3y = 12$, $5x - 4y = 13$
e $4x + 5y = 8$, $5x + 6y = 9$
f $3s - 4t = 6$, $7s - 6t = 4$

4 a $x = y + 1$, $2x + y = 8$
b $a + b = 2$, $2a = 10 + b$
c $y = 2x + 1$, $2y = 3x + 1$
d $5x + y + 1 = 0$, $4x + 3y - 8 = 0$
e $y = 2x - 14$, $3x = 8 - 5y$
f $p = 2q - 1$, $3p + 4q - 12 = 0$

5 a The length of this rectangle is twice its width.
Show that $2y - x = 2$.
b The perimeter of the rectangle is 18 cm.
Show that $x + y = 10$.
c Find the length of the rectangle.

UAM

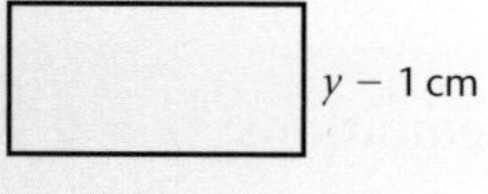

Use the information given to form an equation. Then simplify your equation and rearrange it.

6 One of the angles in this triangle is 90°.
One of the other angles is four times the size of the third angle.
Find the value of x and y.

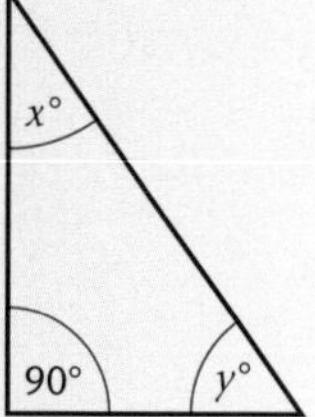

Use the information given and the fact that the sum of the angles in a triangle is 180° to form two equations.

7 The sum of two whole numbers is 30.
The difference between twice the smaller number and the larger number is 12.
Find the smaller number.

UAM

There are 2 possible answers to this question. Try to find them both.

4.2 Quadratic equations

A **quadratic equation** in one unknown can be written as $ax^2 + bx + c = 0$ where a, b and c are constants and a is not zero.

The graphical solution of quadratic equations is covered in Module 3. This section shows you how to solve quadratic equations using algebra.

The equation $5x^2 - 7x + 2 = 0$ is a quadratic equation.
Equations like this usually have two solutions or **roots**.

A **root** of an equation is a value of the unknown that satisfies the equation.

Solution by factorisation

You can solve a quadratic equation when the expression $ax^2 + bx + c$ factorises.
The solution uses the fact that the product of two numbers is zero only when one of the numbers is zero.

Example 4

Solve the equation $5x^2 - 7x + 2 = 0$.

$5x^2 - 7x + 2 = 0$

$(5x - 2)(x - 1) = 0$

$5x - 2 = 0$ or $x - 1 = 0$

$5x = 2$ $\quad$ $x = 1$

$x = \frac{2}{5}$

so $x = \frac{2}{5}$ or $x = 1$

Factorise $5x^2 - 7x + 2$.
Then use the fact that one of the factors must be zero.

Check that the answers satisfy the given equation.

The equation must be in the form $ax^2 + bx + c = 0$ so you may need to rearrange the equation before you try to factorise.

Example 5

Solve the equations: **a** $x(2x + 1) = 15$ **b** $\frac{8}{x-1} - \frac{15}{x+2} = 2$

a $x(2x + 1) = 15$

Multiply out the bracket.

$2x^2 + x = 15$

$2x^2 + x - 15 = 0$

Collect all the terms on the left-hand side. Then factorise.

$(2x - 5)(x + 3) = 0$

$2x - 5 = 0$ or $x + 3 = 0$

$2x = 5$ $\quad x = -3$

$x = \frac{5}{2} = 2\frac{1}{2}$

so $x = 2\frac{1}{2}$ or -3

b $\frac{8}{(x-1)} - \frac{15}{(x+2)} = 2$

Put brackets round the denominators. Then multiply each side by a common multiple of the denominators to get rid of the fractions. $(x - 1)(x + 2)$ is a common multiple of $(x - 1)$ and $(x + 2)$.

$(x-1)(x+2)\left(\frac{8}{(x-1)} - \frac{15}{(x+2)}\right) = (x-1)(x+2) \times 2$

$\cancel{(x-1)}(x+2) \times \frac{8}{\cancel{(x-1)}} - (x-1)\cancel{(x+2)} \times \frac{15}{\cancel{(x+2)}} = 2(x-1)(x+2)$

You can do some of these steps in your head but make sure you are confident about your accuracy.

$8(x + 2) - 15(x - 1) = 2(x^2 + x - 2)$

$8x + 16 - 15x + 15 = 2x^2 + 2x - 4$

$0 = 2x^2 + 2x - 8x + 15x - 4 - 15 - 16$

$0 = 2x^2 + 9x - 35$

$0 = (2x - 5)(x + 7)$ so $x = 2\frac{1}{2}$ or -7

Remember to check the answers in the given equation.

Exam practice 4B

1 Solve these equations.

a $x^2 - 5x + 6 = 0$
b $x^2 - 13x + 42 = 0$
c $x^2 + 13x + 36 = 0$
d $x^2 + 12x + 35 = 0$
e $x^2 + x - 30 = 0$
f $x^2 + 8x - 48 = 0$
g $2x^2 + 13x + 15 = 0$
h $3x^2 - 11x + 10 = 0$
i $5x^2 + 29x - 6 = 0$
j $6x^2 + 17x + 12 = 0$
k $8x^2 + 14x - 15 = 0$
l $3x^2 - 26x + 48 = 0$

2 Solve these equations.

a $x(x + 1) = 12$
b $x^2 = 3x + 40$
c $(x - 1)^2 = 9$
d $x^2 = 6 - x$
e $2x(x - 1) = 3(x + 1)$
f $(x - 3)(x - 2) = 30$
g $(4x - 5)(x - 2) = 1$
h $x^2 = 3x$
i $x(x - 2) = 3(x - 2)$
j $(x - 1)(x - 2) = (2x - 8)(x + 1)$

3 Solve these equations.

a $x - \frac{4}{x} = 3$

b $x + 2 = \frac{15}{x}$

c $x = \frac{12}{x + 1}$

d $\frac{15}{x + 1} = 4x$

e $\frac{4}{x} + \frac{5}{x + 2} = 1$

f $\frac{6}{x} + \frac{3}{x + 1} = 4$

g $\frac{2}{x - 1} + \frac{2}{x + 2} = 1$

h $\frac{6}{x - 2} - \frac{7}{x + 2} = 1$

i $\frac{8}{x + 2} + \frac{7}{2x - 1} = 3$

j $\frac{x}{x + 3} + \frac{6}{x + 8} = 1$

k $\frac{x}{x + 4} - \frac{4}{2x - 9} = 1$

l $\frac{2x}{x + 1} + \frac{6}{x + 2} = 3$

Put brackets round the denominator, then multiply both sides of the equation by the denominator.

UAM 4 The product of two consecutive positive integers is 132.
Find the smaller integer.

Start by writing 'The smaller integer is n'. Then the next (consecutive) integer is $n + 1$. Next form an equation.

UAM 5 The area of this rectangle is $36\,\text{cm}^2$.
Find the length of the shorter side.

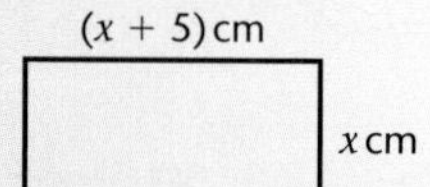

Make sure your solution fits the problem. In question 4 you are told that the integers are positive, so do not give a negative answer.

UAM 6 The product of two consecutive odd numbers is 483.
Find the numbers.

Can you find the numbers by trial and error? Start by using the $\sqrt{\ }$ button on your calculator.

4.3 Completing the square

You may not be able to solve the equation $x^2 + px + q = 0$ by factorisation because some quadratic expressions do not factorise.

You can write the equation as $x^2 + px = -q$ and then add a number to both sides so that the left-hand side is a perfect square.
The number you add is $(\frac{1}{2}p)^2$.

This gives a perfect square because $(x + k)^2 = x^2 + 2kx + k^2$
i.e. the constant term is (half the number multiplied by x)^2.

This process is called **completing the square**.

If the number on the right-hand side is positive, you can then solve the equation by finding the square root of both sides.

When $ax^2 + bx + c = 0$ and a is not 1, divide both sides by a.

$x^2 - 6x + 4 = 0$ can be written as $x^2 - 6x = -4$.
Adding 9 to both sides gives
$x^2 - 6x + 9 = -4 + 9$
$(x - 3)^2 = 5$ so $x - 3 = \pm\sqrt{5}$
$x = 3 \pm \sqrt{5}$

Example 6

a $x^2 - 8x - 3 = (x + a)^2 + b$.
Find the values of a and b.

b Hence solve the equation $x^2 - 8x - 3 = 0$.
Give an exact answer.

a $x^2 - 8x - 3 = 0$

$x^2 - 8x = 3$

$x^2 - 8x + 16 = 3 + 16 \Rightarrow (x-4)^2 = 19$

$(x-4)^2 - 19 = 0$

so $x^2 - 8x - 3 = (x-4)^2 - 19$

$a = -4$ and $b = -19$

Start by writing $x^2 - 8x - 3 = 0$.

You need to add $(\frac{8}{2})^2 = 16$ to $x^2 - 8x$ to make perfect square. So add 16 to both sides.

The symbol $\Rightarrow$ means 'gives'.

Alternatively:

$x^2 - 8x - 3 = (x + a)^2 + b$

$x^2 - 8x - 3 = x^2 + 2ax + a^2 + b$

So $-8 = 2a$ and $-3 = a^2 + b$

$a = -4$ $\quad -3 = 16 + b$

$b = -19$

When confident you could write:

$x^2 - 8x - 3$

$= (x-4)^2 - 16 - 3$ (halve the 8)

$= (x-4)^2 - 19$

b $(x-4)^2 - 19 = 0$

$(x-4)^2 = 19$

$x - 4 = \pm\sqrt{19}$

$x = 4 \pm \sqrt{19}$

'Hence' means use the result from part **a**.
So replace $x^2 - 8x - 3 = 0$ with $(x-4)^2 - 19 = 0$.

Exam practice 4C

1 What number needs to be added to each expression to make a perfect square?

a $x^2 - 4x$ b $x^2 + 12x$ c $x^2 - 5x$

2 Find the values of a and b for which:

a $x^2 - 8x + 4 = (x + a)^2 + b$ b $x^2 + 6x + a = (x + b)^2$

3 a Write each expression in the form $(x + a)^2 + b$.

i $x^2 - 4x + 2$ ii $x^2 + 10x - 2$

iii $x^2 + 7x - 3$

b Hence solve the equations:

i $x^2 - 4x + 2 = 0$ ii $x^2 + 10x - 2 = 0$

iii $x^2 + 7x - 3 = 0$

Give exact answers.

Class discussion

Try to solve the equation $x^2 + 3x + 3 = 0$. What happens? What can you say about the values of x for which $x^2 + 3x + 3 = 0$?

4.4 Using the formula

You can use completing the square to find a formula for solving a quadratic equation. The derivation of this formula is shown on page 53. The solution of the equation $ax^2 + bx + c = 0$ is

$$x = \frac{-b \pm \sqrt{b^2 - 4ac}}{2a}$$

You can solve a quadratic equation by substituting the values for a, b and c into the formula.

The two roots of a quadratic equation are: $\frac{-b + \sqrt{b^2 - 4ac}}{2a}$ and $\frac{-b - \sqrt{b^2 - 4ac}}{2a}$

Adding them gives $-\frac{b}{a}$. You can use this to check your answers.

Using surds and rounding

When the roots of an equation contain surds, they cannot be written as an exact decimal. You will need to round them.

$\sqrt{5}$ and $2\sqrt{3}$ are surds.

To round a number to a given decimal place or significant figure, look at the next digit:

- if it is 5 or more, round up
- if it is less than 5, round down.

For rounding to 1 decimal place look at the digit in the second decimal place:
$1.67 \Rightarrow 1.7$
$1.64 \Rightarrow 1.6$

Example 7

Solve the equation $x^2 - 6x - 2 = 0$.
Give your answers to two decimal places.

$x^2 - 6x - 2 = 0$

$a = 1, b = -6, c = -2$

$$x = \frac{-(-6) \pm \sqrt{(-6)^2 - 4(1)(-2)}}{2(1)}$$

$$x = \frac{6 \pm \sqrt{36 + 8}}{2} = \frac{6 \pm \sqrt{44}}{2}$$

$$\text{So } x = \frac{6 + \sqrt{44}}{2} \text{ or } \frac{6 - \sqrt{44}}{2}$$

$x = 6.32$ or -0.32 to 2 d.p.

Check: sum of roots $= 6.32 - 0.32 = 6, -\frac{b}{a} = -\frac{6}{1} = 6$ ✓

Compare $x^2 - 6x - 2 = 0$ with $ax^2 + bx + c = 0$ to find the values of a, b and c.
Then substitute these values into the formula.
Use brackets round the numbers to avoid mistakes.

When you are asked to give an exact answer, leave the values in surd form, but simplify them where possible.
For this equation, the exact values are:

$$x = \frac{6 \pm \sqrt{44}}{2} = \frac{6 \pm \sqrt{4} \times \sqrt{11}}{2} = \frac{6 \pm 2\sqrt{11}}{2} = 3 \pm \sqrt{11}$$

so $x = 3 + \sqrt{11}$ or $3 - \sqrt{11}$

Exam practice 4D

1 Solve the following equations. Give your answers to 2 d.p.
a $x^2 + 4x + 2 = 0$ b $x^2 + 5x + 3 = 0$ c $x^2 - 5x + 2 = 0$
d $x^2 - 9x + 5 = 0$ e $x^2 - 7x - 6 = 0$ f $x^2 + 6x - 5 = 0$

2 Solve the following equations. Give your answers to 2 d.p.
a $3x^2 + 5x + 1 = 0$ b $2x^2 + 7x + 4 = 0$
c $5x^2 + 7x - 3 = 0$ d $3x^2 - 6x - 4 = 0$
e $4x^2 - 2x - 3 = 0$ f $9x^2 - 15x + 1 = 0$

3 Find the roots of the following equations. Give your answers correct to 2 d.p.
a $x^2 = 5x - 1$ b $x^2 = 3x + 2$ c $x(x + 4) + 1 = 0$
d $5x = 3x^2 - 6$ e $2x - 1 = \frac{4}{x}$ f $\frac{x}{x - 1} = 4x + 1$

4 Solve the following equations. Give exact answers.
a $x^2 - 7x + 2 = 0$ b $x^2 - 5x - 4 = 0$ c $5x^2 + 8x + 2 = 0$
d $6x = 2 - x^2$ e $2x(x + 4) = 3$ f $2x + \frac{5}{2x + 5} = 0$

5 The area of a rectangle is 11 cm². The length is twice the width, less 1 cm. Find the width of the rectangle.
Give an exact answer.

Class discussion
Use the formula to try to solve the equation $x^2 + 3x + 5 = 0$.
What happens?
What can you say about the roots of this equation?

You must arrange these equations in the form $ax^2 + bx + c = 0$ before you write down the values of a, b and c.

4.5 Simultaneous equations, one linear and one quadratic

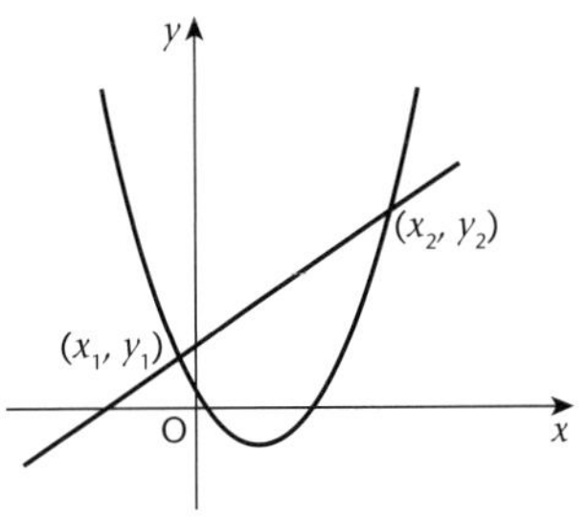

When one equation is quadratic and the other is linear, you have to use the substitution method to solve them.

There are usually two pairs of solutions, (x_1, y_1) and (x_2, y_2) as shown in the diagram.

Example 8 Solve the equations: $x^2 + 2y = 10$
$3y - 2x = 5$

$$x^2 + 2y = 10 \quad ①$$
$$3y - 2x = 5 \quad ②$$

> $x^2 + 2y = 10$ is a quadratic equation in two unknowns.
> $3y - 2x = 5$ is a linear equation in two unknowns.
> Use the linear equation to give one letter in terms of the other.

② gives
$$3y = 5 + 2x$$
$$y = \frac{5 + 2x}{3} \quad ③$$

③ in ①: $$x^2 + 2 \times \left(\frac{(5 + 2x)}{3}\right) = 10$$

> Substitute $\frac{5 + 2x}{3}$ for y in the quadratic equation.
> This gives a quadratic equation in one unknown that you can solve.

$$3x^2 + \frac{\cancel{3} \times 2 \times (5 + 2x)}{\cancel{3}} = 30$$
$$3x^2 + 2(5 + 2x) = 30$$
$$3x^2 + 10 + 4x - 30 = 0$$
$$3x^2 + 4x - 20 = 0$$
$$(x - 2)(3x + 10) = 0$$
$$x = 2 \text{ or } x = -\frac{10}{3}$$

> Substitute these values of x into ③ to find the corresponding values of y.

When $x = 2$, $y = \frac{5 + 4}{3} = 3$

When $x = -\frac{10}{3}$, $y = \frac{5 - \frac{20}{3}}{3} = \frac{15 - 20}{9} = -\frac{5}{9}$

The solutions are $x = 2$, $y = 3$ and $x = -\frac{10}{3}$, $y = -\frac{5}{9}$

> Check the answers.

Exam practice 4E

1 Solve these simultaneous equations.

a $xy = 12$
$x - y = 1$

b $x^2 + y = 3$
$x + y = 1$

c $xy = 15$
$2x - 3y = 1$

d $y^2 = 8x$
$3x + y = 10$

e $x^2 - y = 4$
$2x - y = 1$

f $y^2 + 2x - 33 = 0$
$3x - 2y = 2$

2 Solve these simultaneous equations.

a $x^2 + y^2 = 8$
$x + y = 4$

b $x^2 + y^2 = 10$
$2x - y = 7$

c $x^2 + y^2 = 169$
$x + 2y = 29$

3 The perimeter of this rectangle is 54 cm and its area is 180 cm². Find the length of the rectangle. UAM

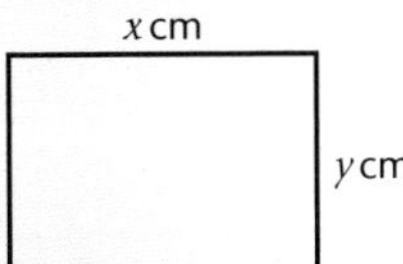

4 The product of two positive numbers is 238 and their difference is 3. Find the two numbers. UAM

4.6 Trial and improvement

Some equations cannot be solved using algebra.
You can find a solution to 1 (or more) decimal places by trying some values. You can use the result of the first two tries to improve the accuracy of your next try. This method is called **trial and improvement**.

Example 9

Use trial and improvement to complete the table to find a solution of the equation $x^3 - x = 20$. Give your answer correct to 1 decimal place.

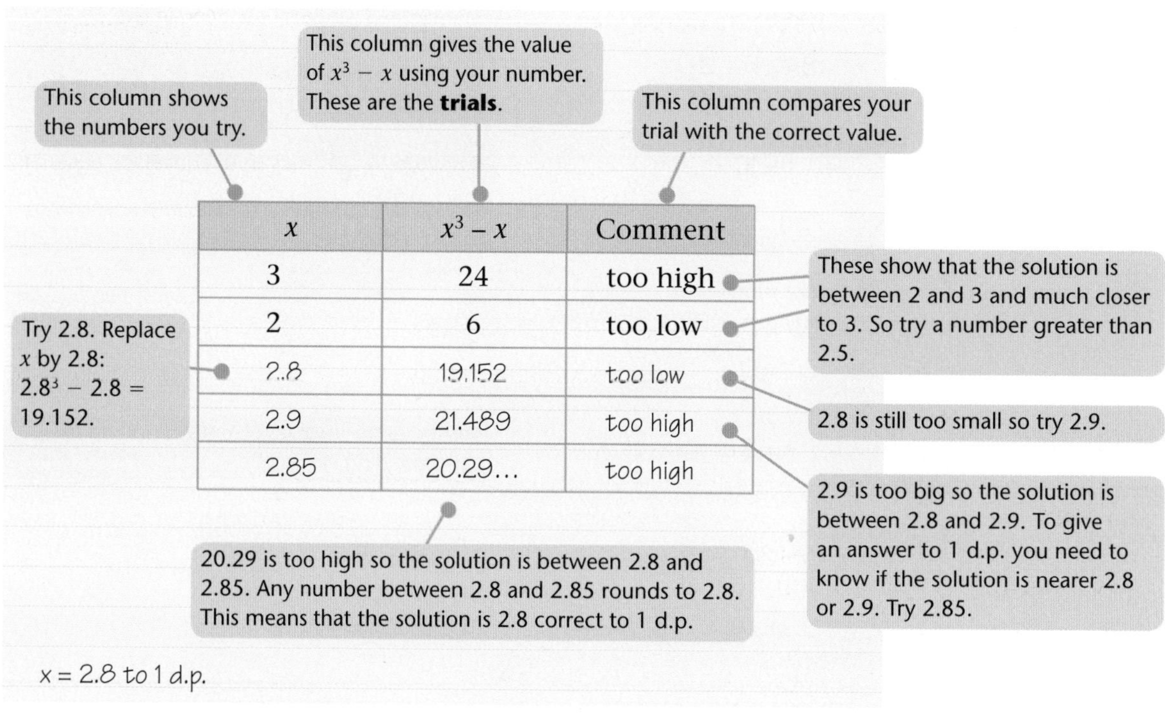

x	$x^3 - x$	Comment
3	24	too high
2	6	too low
2.8	19.152	too low
2.9	21.489	too high
2.85	20.29…	too high

$x = 2.8$ to 1 d.p.

Exam practice 4F

Copy and complete these tables using trial and improvement to find a solution to the equations. Give your answers correct to 1 d.p.

1 $x^3 + x = 50$

x	$x^3 + x$	Comment
3	30	too low
4	68	too high
3.6		

Start by replacing x with 3.6. If the value of $x^3 + x$ is bigger than 50, choose a number below 3.6. If the value is smaller than 50 try a number above 3.6. You may have to add some rows to the table.

2 $x^3 + x = 4$

x	$x^3 + x$	Comment
1	2	too low
2		

WWW **3** $x^3 + 3x = 40$

x	$x^3 + 3x$	Comment
3	36	too low
4	76	too high

4 $x^2 - \frac{1}{x} = 5$

x	$x^2 - \frac{1}{x}$	Comment
2	3.5	too low
3	8.66...	too high

WWW **5** $x^3 - 5x = 6$

x	$x^3 - 5x$	Comment
3	12	too high

ICT task

You can use a spreadsheet program to do the calculations for trial and improvement. You can find values for $x^3 - x$ like this.

	A	B	C	D
1	x	$x^3 - x$		
2	3	24		
3	2			
4				
5				

Enter the formula A2^3 − A2 in this cell.

Find out how to use the 'fill' function to work out values in this column.

Decide what value to try here, then use the fill function again.

Use this method to find a solution to these equations. Give your answers correct to 3 d.p.

a $x^3 - x = 5$ **b** $x^3 - x = 1$ **c** $x^3 - x = -30$

Summary of key points

- You can solve a pair of linear simultaneous equation by adding or subtracting equations to eliminate one of the letters:
  - you **add** when the signs of the terms to eliminate are **different**
  - you **subtract** when the signs of the terms to eliminate are the **same**.
- To solve a quadratic equation first arrange it so that it is in the form $ax^2 + bx + c = 0$ then factorise the left-hand side if possible.
- When the left-hand side of a quadratic equation does not factorise, you can solve it by completing the square or by using the formula:

  $$x = \frac{-b \pm \sqrt{b^2 - 4ac}}{2a}$$
- To solve a pair of simultaneous equations when one of them is quadratic, use the linear equation to find one letter in terms of the other then substitute this expression into the quadratic equation.
- You can find an approximate solution to an equation by trying values and then improving the values you try until you have an answer that is accurate enough.

Most candidates who get GRADE C or above can:

- use trial and improvement.

Most candidates who get GRADE A or above can also:

- form and solve a quadratic equation by factorising
- solve a pair of simultaneous equations when one of them is quadratic.

Glossary

Completing the square adding a number to an expression to make a perfect square

Quadratic equation an equation of the form $ax^2 + bx + c = 0$ where a, b and c are constants and $a \neq 0$

Simultaneous equations equations having solutions in common

Roots the values of the unknowns that satisfy an equation

Trial and improvement using the result of one trial solution to find a more accurate solution

Derivation of the formula for solving a quadratic equation

$$ax^2 + bx + c = 0$$

$$x^2 + \frac{b}{a}x + \frac{c}{a} = 0$$

Subtract $\frac{c}{a}$ from both sides.

$$x^2 + \frac{b}{a}x = -\frac{c}{a}$$

$$x^2 + \frac{b}{a}x + \left(\frac{b}{2a}\right)^2 = -\frac{c}{a} + \left(\frac{b}{2a}\right)^2$$

Add ($\frac{1}{2}$ the coefficient of x)^2 to both sides to complete the square on the left-hand side.

$$\left(x + \frac{b}{2a}\right)^2 = -\frac{c}{a} + \frac{b^2}{4a^2}$$

$$\left(x + \frac{b}{2a}\right)^2 = \frac{-4ac + b^2}{4a^2}$$

Combine the fractions on the right-hand side.

$$x + \frac{b}{2a} = \pm\sqrt{\frac{-4ac + b^2}{4a^2}}$$

Take the square root of both sides.

$$x = -\frac{b}{2a} \pm \sqrt{\frac{-4ac + b^2}{4a^2}}$$

Subtract $\frac{b}{2a}$ from both sides.

$$= -\frac{b}{2a} \pm \frac{\sqrt{b^2 - 4ac}}{2a}$$

Simplify the right-hand side.

so $$x = \frac{-b \pm \sqrt{b^2 - 4ac}}{2a}$$

5 Sequences

This chapter will show you:
✓ what a sequence is
✓ how to generate a sequence from a formula
✓ how to find a particular term in a sequence
✓ how to find a formula for the nth term of a sequence

Before you start you need to know:
✓ what even, odd and square numbers are
✓ how to recognise powers of 2 and powers of 10
✓ how to substitute values in an expression
✓ the meaning of n^2
✓ how to solve linear and quadratic equations

5.1 Sequences

A **sequence** is a list with a first member, a second member, a third member, and so on.
The members are called the **terms** of the sequence.
The terms can be any objects, such as numbers, expressions or shapes.

These are sequences:
2, 4, 6, 8, …
$x + 1$, $2x + 2$, $3x + 3$, …
□ □□ □□□ …

Continuing a sequence of numbers

There is usually a pattern or rule that you can use to continue the sequence. You can spot this rule in simple cases.

The house numbers on this street form a sequence

- even numbers — 8, 10, 12, 14, … is a sequence of even numbers.
- odd numbers — 7, 9, 11, 13, … is a sequence of odd numbers.
- square numbers — 4, 9, 16, 25, … is a sequence of square numbers.
- powers of 2 — 2, 4, 8, 16, 32, … are powers of 2.
- powers of 10 — 10, 100, 1000, 10 000, … are powers of 10.
- numbers that increase by the same amount — Each number in 2, 5, 8, 11, … is 3 more than the number before it.

Example 1

Here is a sequence of patterns.

pattern 1: •
pattern 2: • / • •
pattern 3: • / • • / • • •
pattern 4: • / • • / • • • / • • • •

The number of dots in each pattern make this sequence of numbers:
1, 3, 6, 10, …
These are called **triangular numbers**.

a Draw the next pattern in the sequence.
b How many dots are needed for the seventh pattern? Explain your answer.

a 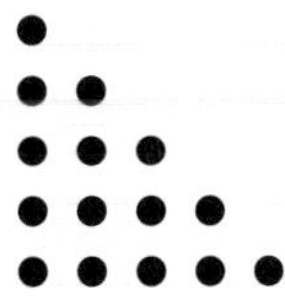

The sequence of patterns continues by adding a row of dots with one more dot than the row above. The last row of pattern 4 has 4 dots so the last row of pattern 5 has 5 dots.

b 28

Pattern 5 has 15 dots, pattern 6 has 6 more dots and pattern 7 has 7 more dots.

Pattern 7 has $15 + 6 + 7 = 28$ dots.

A sequence can also be a list of expressions or equations.

Example 2

This is a sequence of expressions.

$x + 10, 2x + 9, 3x + 8, \ldots$

a Write down the next two terms in this sequence.

b Prove that the difference between consecutive terms is always the same.

a $4x + 7, 5x + 6$

The number multiplied by x goes up by 1 each time and the number on its own goes down by 1 each time.

b Any term is in the form $ax + b$ where a and b are constants.

The next term is $(a + 1)x + (b - 1)$.

The difference between consecutive terms is

$$(a + 1)x + (b - 1) - (ax + b) = ax + x + b - 1 - ax - b$$
$$= x - 1.$$

$x - 1$ is the same for any two consecutive terms.

Exam practice 5A

1 Write down the next two numbers in each sequence.

a 6, 8, 10, 12, …
b 16, 25, 36, 49, …
c 16, 32, 64, …
d 1, 4, 7, 10, …
e 5, 4, 3, 2, …
f 10, 100, 1000, …
g 3, 7, 11, 15, …
h 80, 40, 20, …

2 Write down the value of a and b in each sequence.

a 2, 4, 8, a, 32, b, …
b 12, 15, a, 21, 24, 27, b, …
c 100, 81, 64, a, 36, 25, b, …
d 10, 7, 4, a, −2, −5, b, …
e a, 8, 10, 12, 14, 16, b, …
f a, 2, 5, 8, 11, b, …

3 This is a sequence of expressions.

$x + 4, x + 6, x + 8, \ldots$

a Write down the next two terms in this sequence.

b Show that the difference between consecutive terms is constant.

4 These are the first few equations in a sequence.

$x + 4 = 3, x + 3 = 2, x + 2 = 1$

a Write down the next two equations in this sequence.

UAM b Explain why x has the same value in every term.

5 These are the first three patterns in a sequence.

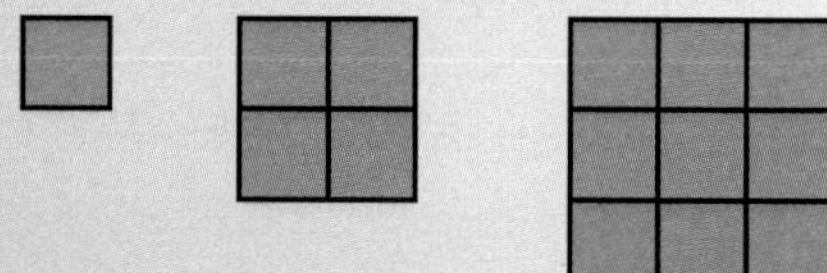

a Write down the number of squares in the fourth pattern.

UAM b Explain why there is no pattern with 30 squares in this sequence.

6 This is the start of a sequence of blocks.

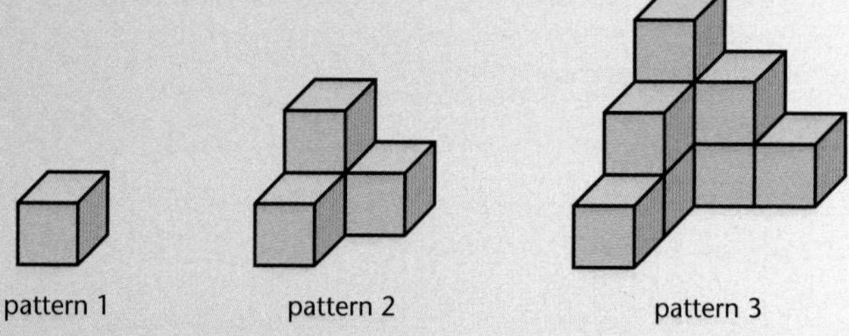

a Copy and complete this table.

Pattern number	1	2	3	4	5
Number of blocks	1	4	9		

b How many blocks are added to pattern 6 to make pattern 7?

c How many blocks are there in pattern 9?

UAM Explain your answer.

7 Write down the next two terms in each of these sequences.

a $3x, 5x, 7x, \ldots$

b $x + 1, x + 4, x + 9, \ldots$

c $x + 20, 2x + 19, 3x + 18, \ldots$

d $2x = 4, 4x = 8, 8x = 16, \ldots$

e $2(x + 5), 3(x + 3), 4(x + 1), \ldots$

f $x + 1 = 5, x = 4, x - 1 = 3, \ldots$

g $(2, 5), (3, 7), (4, 9), (5, 11), \ldots$

5.2 Generating a sequence

Each term in a sequence has a term number. The first term is term number 1, the second term is term number 2, and so on.

The ***n*th term** is term number n where n stands for any number.

You can **generate a sequence** if you know a rule to find the nth term. You can also generate a sequence using a term you know and the **term-to-term** rule.

The nth term is usually given as an expression with n in it.
You can use this expression to find any term in a sequence.

nth term = $3n$
The sequence is 3, 6, 9, …
The 10th term is the value of $3n$ when $n = 10$;
so the 10th term = $3 \times 10 = 30$.

The term-to-term rule is usually given in words. To generate a sequence using the term-to-term rule you need to know at least one term of the sequence.

First term = 2
Term-to-term rule: multiply previous term by 5 then add 5.
The sequence is 2, 15, 80, …

To generate a sequence you need to be able to write down the 1st term, the 2nd term, … and so on.

Example 3

A sequence starts 3, 6, 9, …
Each term is found by adding the previous two terms.
Write down the next two terms in the sequence.

4th term = 2nd term + 3rd term = 6 + 9 = 15
5th term = 3rd term + 4th term = 9 + 15 = 24

Did you know
that the sequence in example 3 is called a Fibonacci sequence? It is named after Leonardo da Pisa (known as Fibonacci) who also introduced the Arabic number system to Europe.

Enrichment task
This is the start of a Fibonacci sequence:

3, 4, 7, 11, 18, …

Another sequence is formed by dividing a term by the next term,
i.e. $\frac{3}{4} = 0.75$, $\frac{4}{7} = 0.5714\ldots$, $\frac{7}{11} = 0.6363\ldots$, $\frac{11}{18} = 0.6111\ldots$,

Find the next 5 terms of this sequence. What do you notice?

Investigate what happens when you choose different starting numbers for a Fibonacci sequence.

Example 4

The nth term of a sequence is $n(2n - 1)$.

a Write down the first two terms of the sequence.

b Is 125 a term in this sequence? Explain your answer.

a 1st term = $1(2-1)=1$

2nd term = $2(4-1)=2\times3=6$

The 1st term is the value of $n(2n-1)$ when $n=1$.

b $n(2n-1)=125$

$2n^2-n=125$

$2n^2-n-125=0$

$$n=\frac{-(-1)\pm\sqrt{(-1)^2-4\times2\times(-125)}}{4}=\frac{1\pm\sqrt{1001}}{4}$$

1001 is not a perfect square so the roots of this equation are not integers. 125 is not a term in this sequence.

n represents the term number, so n can only be a positive integer. Find out if such a value of n exists when $n(2n-1)=125$.

You can see from this that the solutions are not integers so you do not need to find them.

Example 5

The nth term of a sequence is 2^n.

a Write down an expression for the $(n+1)$th term.

b Prove that the product of any two consecutive terms of this sequence is an odd numbered term of this sequence.

a $(n+1)$th term = 2^{n+1}

Replace n by $n+1$ to give an expression for the $(n+1)$ term.

b nth term × $(n+1)$th term = $2^n\times2^{n+1}=2^{2n+1}$

2^{2n+1} is the $(2n+1)$th term of the sequence and $2n+1$ is an odd number.

The nth and $(n+1)$th terms are consecutive. Remember you add the powers when you multiply powers of the same number.

Exam practice 5B

1 The first term of a sequence is 3.
Write down the next three terms of the sequence whose term-to-term rule is:
- a multiply the previous term by 2 then add 1
- b add one to the previous term then multiply by 2
- c square the previous term then add 1

2 A sequence starts 4, 6, 12, …
The term-to-term rule is 'subtract 2 then multiply by 3'.
- a Work out the next three numbers.
- UAM b Explain why 200 is not a term in this sequence.

3 Write down the first three terms of the sequence whose nth term is

a $3n-1$	b $4n+5$	c $\frac{1}{2}n(n-1)$
d $4-3n$	e $n+n^2$	f n^2-1

4 a Write down the first two terms of the sequence whose nth term is $5n+1$.
- b What is the 10th term in this sequence?
- UAM c Is 37 a term in this sequence? Give a reason for your answer.

5 The nth term of a sequence is $n^2 + 1$.
  a Write down the first three terms of this sequence.
  b Work out the 12th term of this sequence.
UAM c Explain why 100 cannot be a term in this sequence.

6 The nth term of a sequence is $n(n + 1)$.
  a Find the 20th term of this sequence.
  b Show that 56 is a term in this sequence.
UAM c Explain why 60 cannot be a term in this sequence.

7 The nth term of a sequence is $10 - 2n$.
  a Write down an expression for the $(n - 1)$th term.
  b Show that the difference between any two consecutive terms is 2.

8 The nth term of the sequence of triangular numbers is $\frac{1}{2}n(n + 1)$.
  a Write down an expression for the $(n + 1)$th term.
UAM b Prove that the sum of any two consecutive triangular numbers is a square number.

5.3 Finding the nth term

You can find an expression for the nth term of a sequence when the difference between consecutive terms is constant.

Example 6

These are the first three patterns of a sequence.

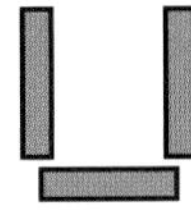
pattern 1

pattern 2

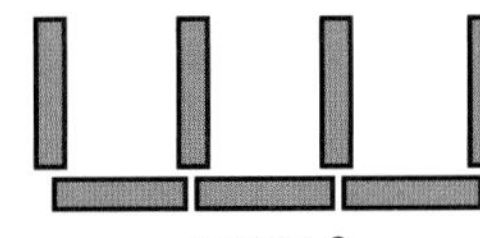
pattern 3

a Find the number of sticks in pattern n.
b Carly has 50 sticks.
What is the largest pattern number she can make?

Start by making a table showing the pattern number and the number of sticks.

a

Pattern number	1	2	3	4	5	6	…n
Number of sticks	3	5	7	9	11	13	
Pattern number × 2	2	4	6	8	10	12	…$2n$

The number of sticks increases by 2 each time.
Try multiplying the pattern number by 2. Add another row to the table to show these numbers.

You can see that you get these numbers by adding 1 to the numbers below.

Number of sticks in pattern $n = 2 \times n + 1$
$= 2n + 1$

Check: (number of sticks in pattern 6) $= 2 \times 6 + 1 = 13$ ✓

b All the patterns use an odd number of sticks, so 49 is the largest number of sticks that Carly can use.
$49 = 2n + 1$
$48 = 2n$
So the pattern number is 24.

You can use the rule from part **a** to form an equation.

Example 7

A sequence starts 7, 5, 3, 1, −1, …
Find the nth term of the sequence.

Term number	1	2	3	4	5	6	…n
Term	7	5	3	1	−1	**−3**	
Term number × (−2)	**−2**	**−4**	**−6**	**−8**	**−10**	**−12**	**…−2n**

Make a table showing the term numbers and the terms.

The terms decrease by 2 each time so add a row for (term number × −2). The terms are 9 more than these numbers.

The nth term $= -2n + 9$

$= 9 - 2n$

Check: 6th term = 9 − 2(6) = 9 − 12 = −3 ✓

Exam practice 5C

1 A sequence starts 7, 9, 11, …
Find the nth term of the sequence.

2 Explain how to generate each sequence.

You need to find the term-to-term rule.

a 1, 4, 7, 10, …
b 15, 13, 11, 9, …
c 64, 32, 16, 8, …
d 100, 10, 1, 0.1, …
e 12, 18, 24, 30, 36, …
f 100, 90, 80, 70, …

3 These are the first three patterns in a sequence.

pattern 1 pattern 2 pattern 3

UAM Find the number of dots in pattern n.

4 This is a sequence of patterns made with matchsticks.

pattern 1
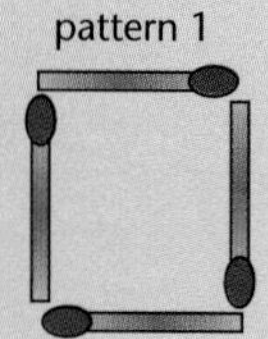
pattern 2
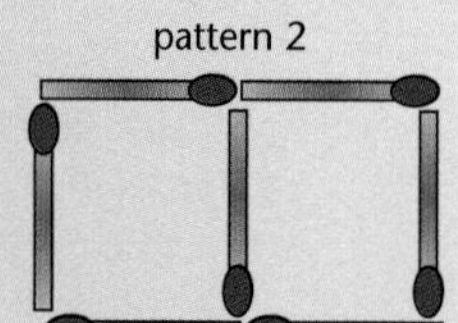
pattern 3
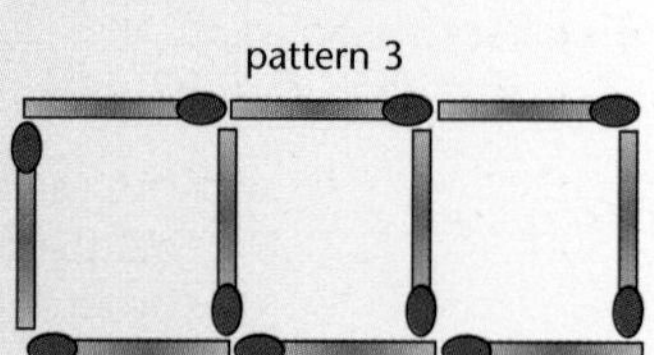

UAM How many matchsticks are there in pattern n?

5 These are the first three patterns in a sequence.

pattern 1
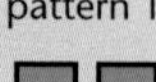

pattern 2
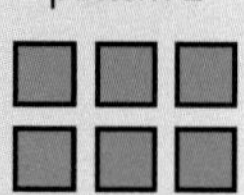
pattern 3
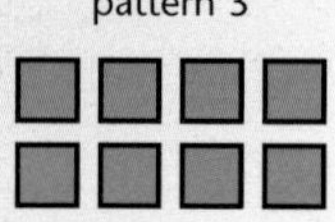

UAM Find the number of squares in pattern n.

6 Patterns are made with sticks.
These are the first three patterns in a sequence.

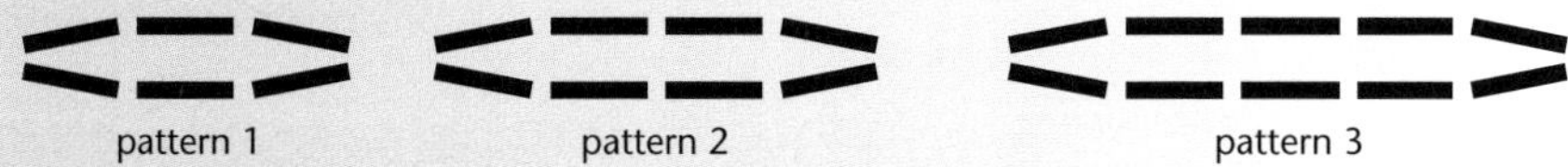

a Find the number of sticks in pattern n.

UAM b What is the largest pattern number you can make with 40 sticks?

7 These are the first three patterns in a sequence.

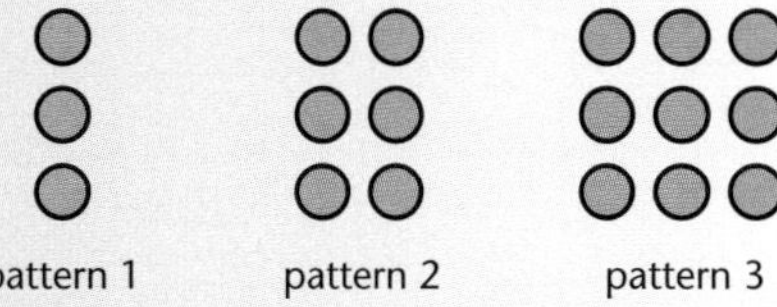

a Find the number of circles in pattern n.

b Chas has 100 circles.

i What is the largest pattern number he can make?

ii Does he have any circles left?

UAM Explain your answers.

UAM 8 These are the first three arrangements in a sequence of tables and chairs.

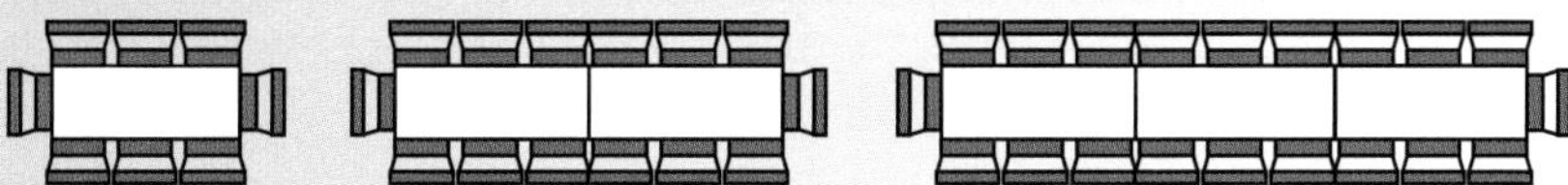

a Find the number of chairs that can be placed round n tables.

b How many tables are needed in an arrangement to seat 78 people?

c How many spare seats are there?

UAM 9 Square stones of side 1 foot are used to surround square flower beds.

a Find the number of stones needed, N, to surround a bed whose sides are w feet.

b Petra uses 80 stones to surround a square flower bed.
How wide is the bed?

10 This is a number grid.

1	2	3	4	5	6
7	8	9	10	11	12
13	14	15	16	17	18
19	20	21	22	23	24
25	26	27	28	29	30

a The shaded cross is called X_{15} because 15 is the number in the centre.

This is X_n:

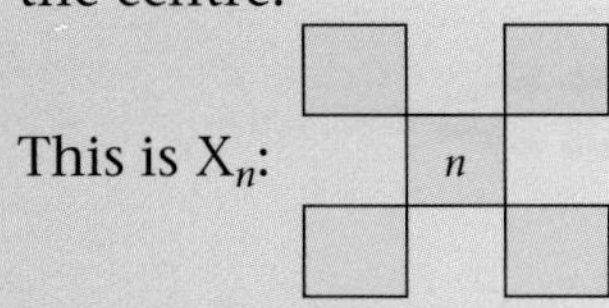

Copy the diagram and fill in the remaining squares.

UAM b Find the nth term of the sequence that starts 1, 8, 15, …

The numbers in a column form a sequence, so do the numbers in a diagonal.

11 This is a number grid.

1	2	3	4	5
6	7	8	9	10
11	12	13	14	15
16	17	18	19	20

a The shaded shape is called T_8 because 8 is the number in the middle of the top row of the T.
Draw T_n and fill in the numbers in each square.

UAM b Show that, for any three consecutive numbers, the square of the middle number is one greater than the product of the other two numbers.

Enrichment task

This is a sequence of calculations.

$3 \times 9 = 27$

$33 \times 9 = 297$

$333 \times 9 = 2997$

a Write down the next three calculations.

b Write down the value of $3\,333\,333 \times 9$.

c Find the sequence of calculations starting with $4 \times 9 = 36$, $44 \times 9 = \ldots$

d What do you think is the value of $777\,777 \times 9$?

Summary of key points

- A sequence has a first member, a second member and so on.
- The term-to-term rule tells you how to continue a sequence given one or more terms.
- The rule for finding the nth term in a sequence can be used to find any term.

Most candidates who get GRADE C or above can:

- write down the nth term of a linear sequence.

Most candidates who get GRADE A or above can also:

- use information given about a sequence to form equations or expressions involving terms other than the nth term.

Glossary

Generate a sequence	write the terms of a sequence from a rule
***n*th term**	the general term in a sequence
Sequence	a set of numbers or objects made and written in order, according to some mathematical rule
Term of a sequence	one of the numbers or patterns in the sequence
Term-to-term rule	a rule to find the next term of a sequence from previous terms
Triangular numbers	numbers that can be shown as a triangle of dots. For example 6: ● ●● ●●● 15: ● ●● ●●● ●●●● ●●●●●

6 Triangles, quadrilaterals and polygons

This chapter will show you:

- ✓ the different types of angles obtained when a straight line cuts two or more parallel lines
- ✓ the different types of triangle
- ✓ what the sum of the angles of any triangle is
- ✓ the properties of isosceles and equilateral triangles
- ✓ what the sum of the angles of any quadrilateral is
- ✓ the names and properties of the special quadrilaterals
- ✓ what a polygon is
- ✓ what the sum of the interior and exterior angles of a polygon are
- ✓ the properties of regular polygons

Before you start you need to know:

- ✓ how to add, subtract, multiply and divide whole numbers
- ✓ how to find a fraction of a quantity
- ✓ how to solve equations
- ✓ what a line segment is
- ✓ how to distinguish between **acute**, **obtuse** and **reflex** angles
- ✓ that **vertically opposite** angles are equal
- ✓ that angles on a straight line add up to 180°
- ✓ that **supplementary angles** add up to 180° and **complementary angles** add up to 90°

6.1 Angles and parallel lines

Parallel lines are lines that are always the same distance apart however far they are drawn.

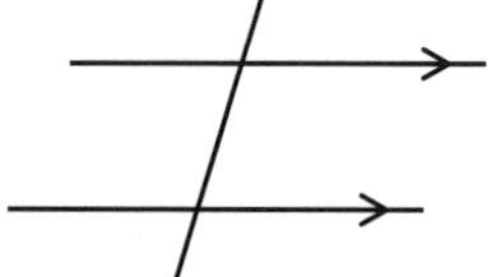

You mark pairs of parallel lines with arrows.

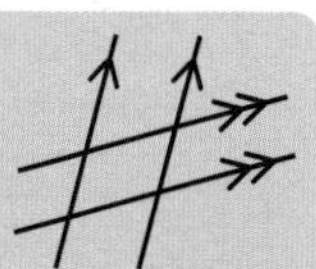

When a straight line cuts a pair of parallel lines several different types of angles are formed.

The line crossing parallel lines is called a **transversal**.

These two angles are called **corresponding angles**. They are equal.

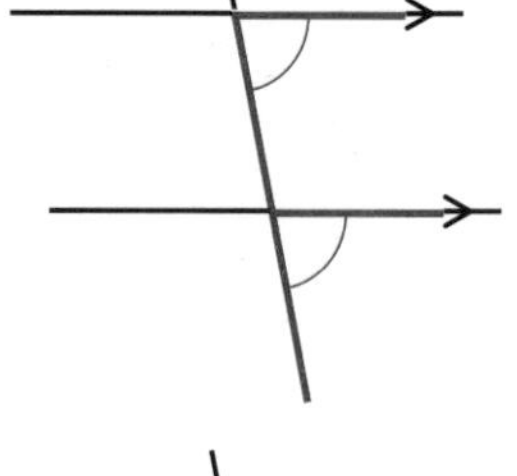

Look for the letter F which you can draw around corresponding angles.

Did you know

that the Babylonians divided one complete revolution into 360 degrees? Maybe this was because there were 360 days in their year.

These two angles are **alternate angles**. They are equal.

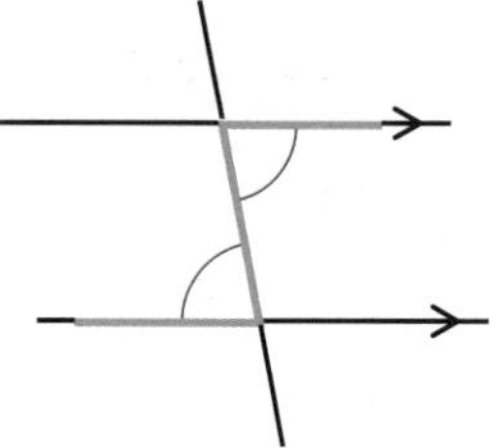

Look for the letter Z which you can draw round alternate angles.

Example 1

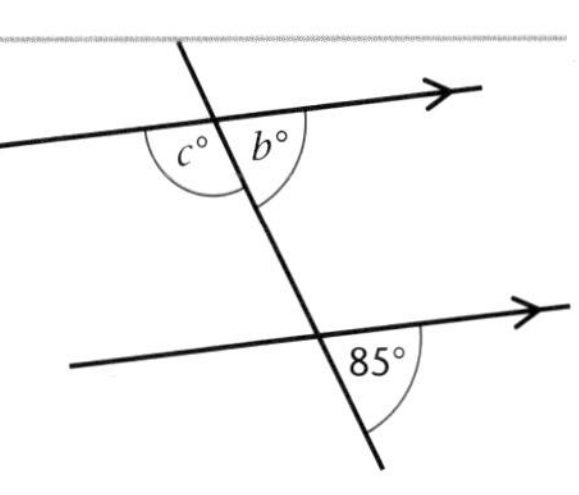

Find the value of c.
Give a reason for each step in your working.

$b = 85$ because corresponding angles are equal

$b + c = 180$ because angles on a straight line add up to 180°
$c = 180 - 85$
$c = 95$

You need to combine two facts to find c. First look for any two angles that are equal.

Exam practice 6A

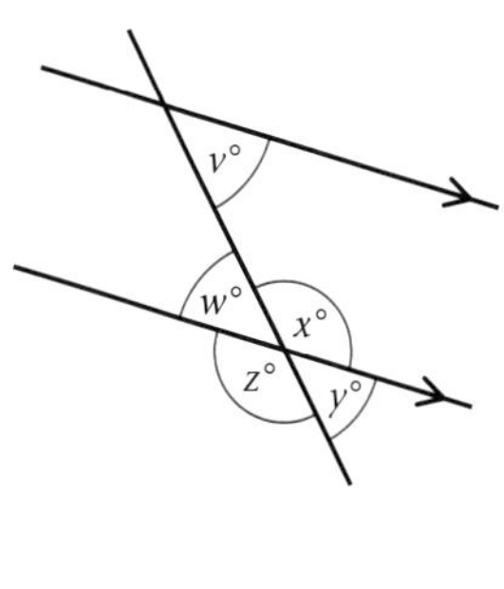

1 a Write down the angle that is alternate to $w°$.
b Write down the angle that corresponds to $y°$.
c Write down the angle that is vertically opposite $z°$.

In questions 2 to 13 find the value of each letter.

Give reasons for your answers.

2
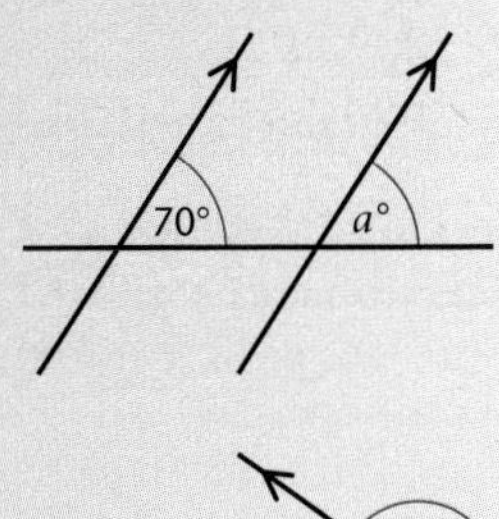

3
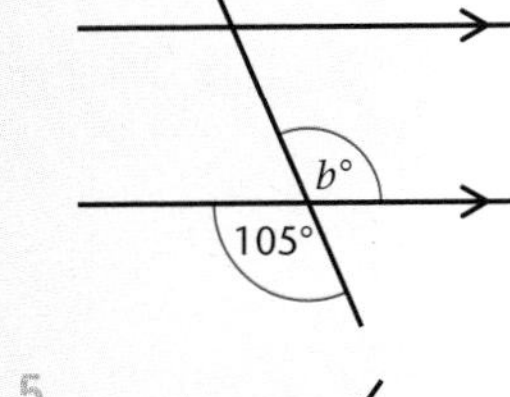

4
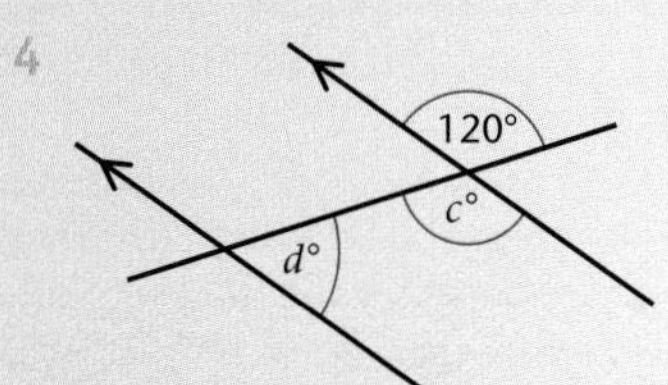

5
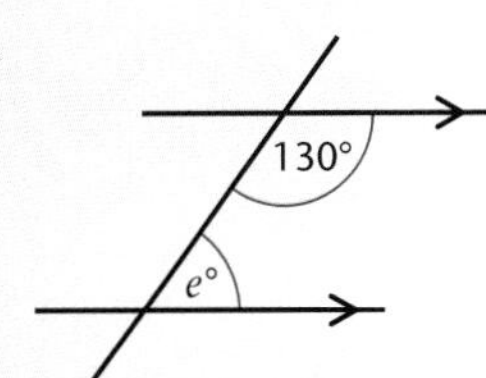

6
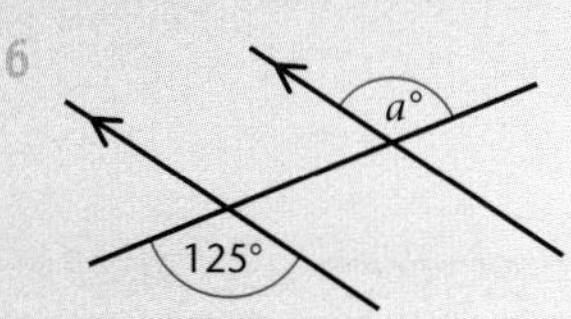

7
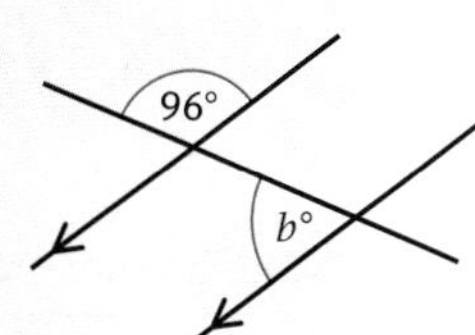

8
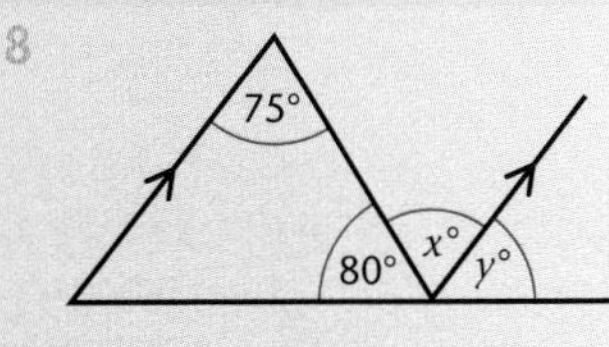

9
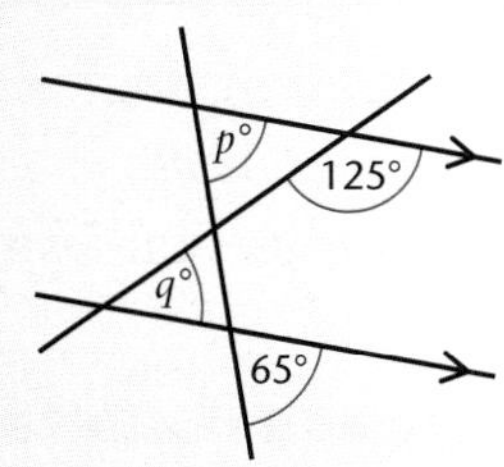

10
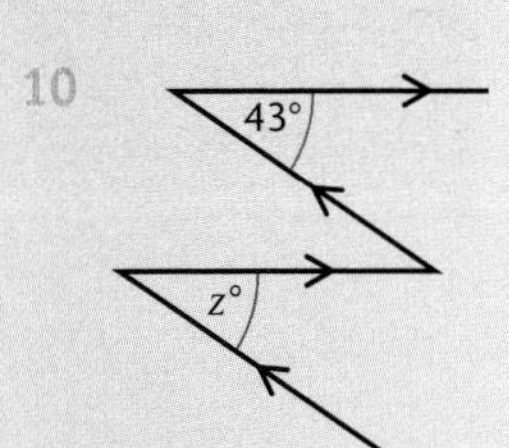

11
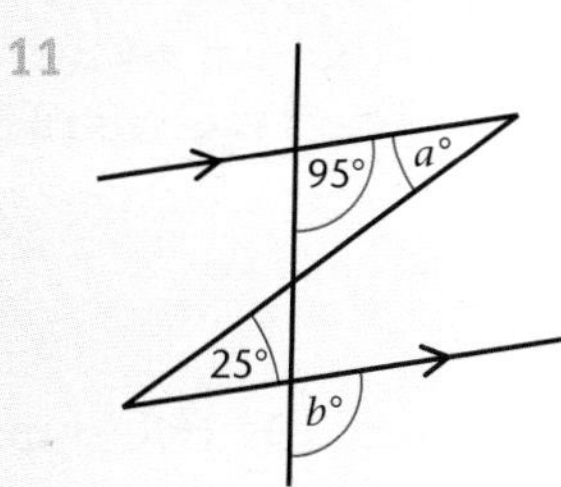

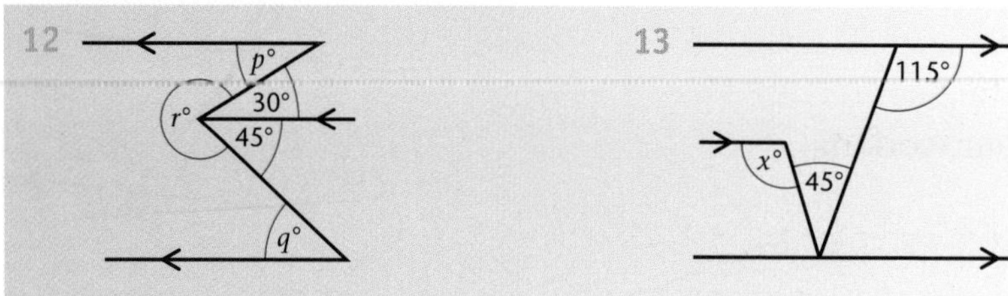

6.2 Triangles

A triangle has three sides and three angles.

Capital letters are used to label the corners.
These letters are used to name the triangle.
Each side is named using the letters at its ends.

In a **scalene triangle**, the three sides have different lengths.

The diagram shows triangle ABC.

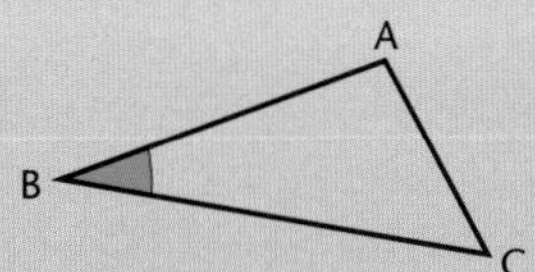

B is the **vertex** of the green angle.
AB and BC are the arms of the angle.
This angle is called ∠ABC, $\widehat{ABC}$, ∠B or $\hat{B}$.

The plural of vertex is **vertices**.
Every triangle has three vertices.

Angles of a triangle

The three angles of any triangle add up to 180°.

$a + b + c = 180$

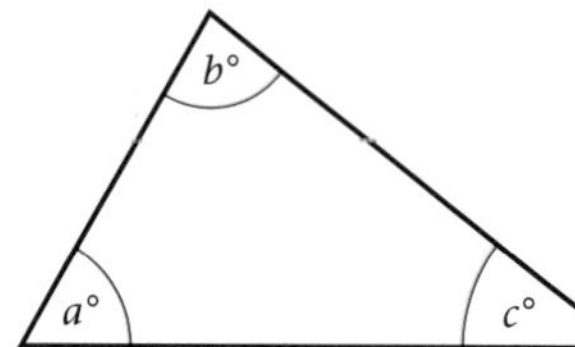

The difference between a demonstration and a proof.
A demonstration shows that a fact is true for a particular case.
A proof shows that a fact is true in all cases.
You can draw a triangle, measure the three angles and add them up. This demonstrates that the three angles of your triangle add up to 180°. It does not prove that the three angles of any triangle add up to 180°.

You can prove this for any triangle.

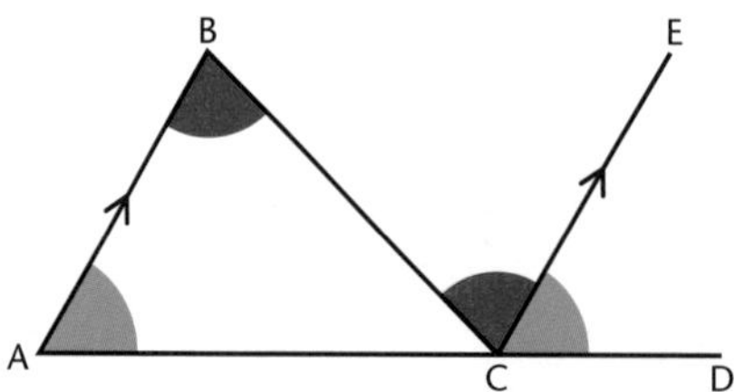

In this triangle ∠A = ∠ECD (corresponding angles)
∠B = ∠BCE (alternate angles)
The three angles at C add up to 180° (angles on a straight line)
so ∠A + ∠B + ∠C = 180°.

Therefore the **angles of a triangle add up to 180°**.

You can also use this diagram to prove that **an exterior angle of a triangle is equal to the sum of the two inside opposite angles**.

Exterior angle ∠BCD = ∠BCE + ∠ECD
= ∠B + ∠A

So the exterior angle ∠BCD = the sum of the two opposite interior angles.

An exterior angle is formed when a side is extended in either direction.

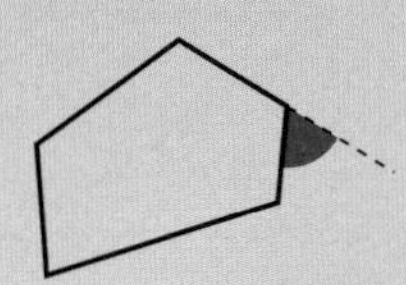

Example 2

Work out the value of **a** a **b** b.
Give reasons for each step in your working.

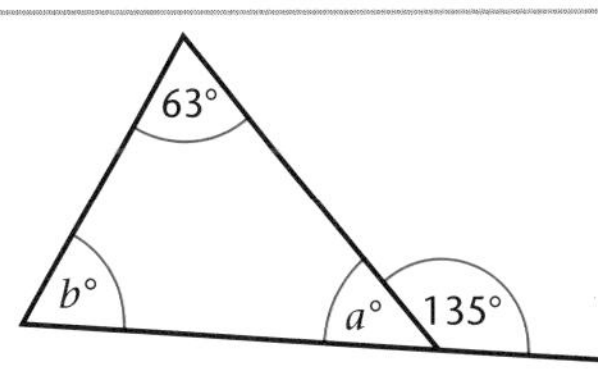

a $a + 135 = 180$ because $a°$ and $135°$ are angles on a straight line
so $a = 45$

b $b + 63 + 45 = 180$ because the three angles in a triangle add up to 180°
$b = 180 - 108$
$b = 72$

Use the facts that the sum of two angles on a straight line is 180° and the sum of the angles of a triangle is also 180°.

Exam practice 6B

In questions 1 to 10 find the value of each letter.

An angle marked with a square is a right angle. A right angle is 90°.

1

2

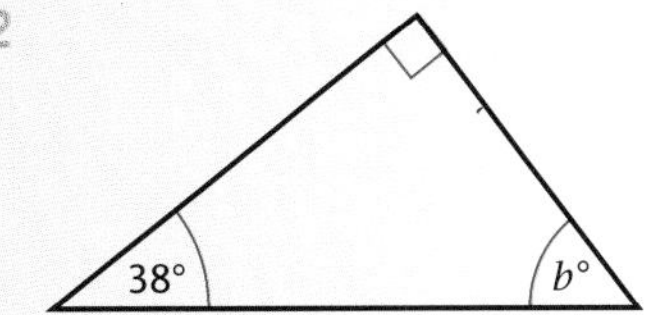

3

4

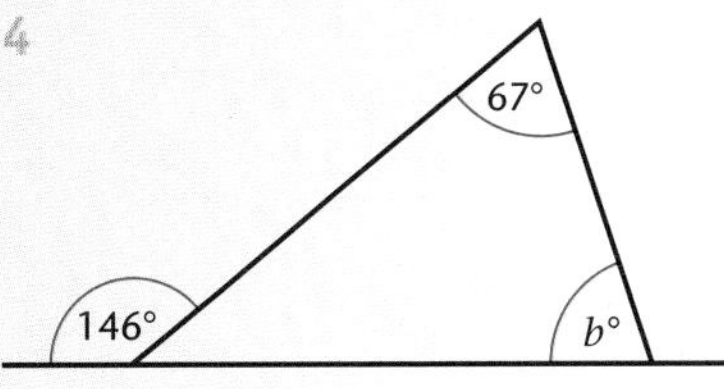

5

6

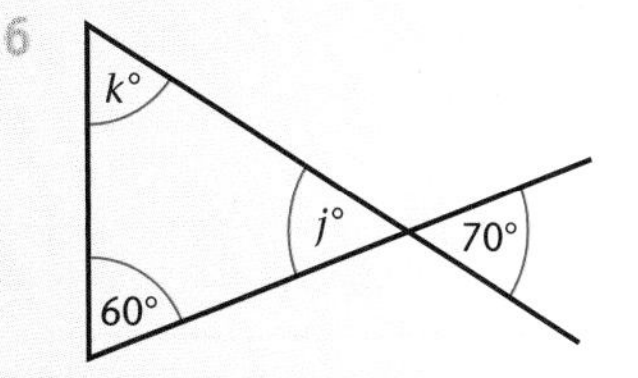

7

8

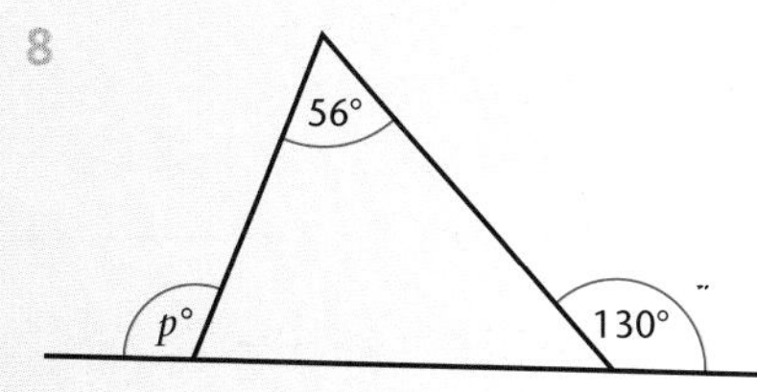

9

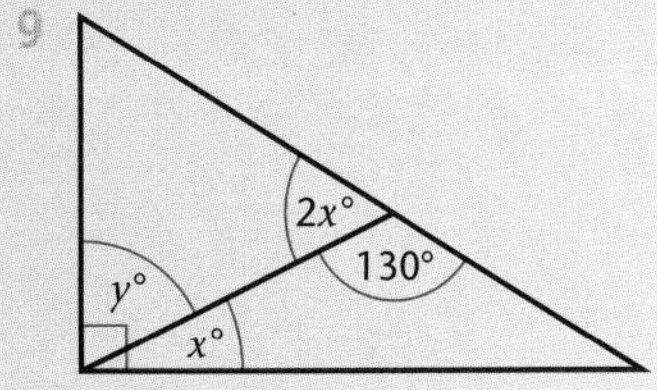

10

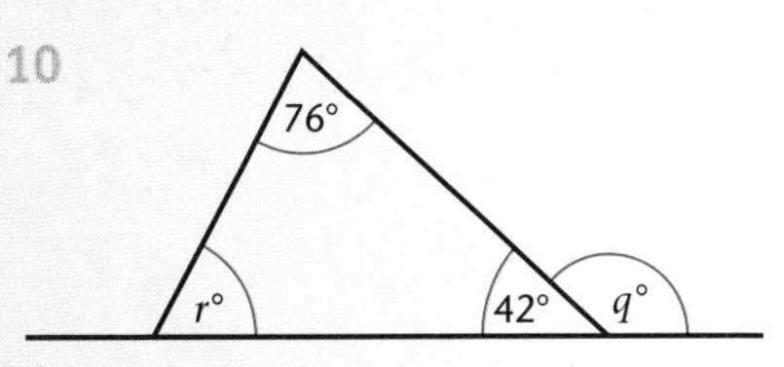

Class discussion

Can you draw a triangle on a sheet of paper with more than one right angle?
Can you draw a triangle with more than one right angle on a curved surface?
On a globe draw two lines at right angles from the north pole to the equator. Join their ends along the equator. What can you say about the sum of the angles in this figure?
Look up the definition of a triangle and a straight line. What does this tell you about the figure you have drawn on a globe?

In questions 11 and 12 form an equation in x and solve it. Hence write down the value of each angle in the triangle.

11

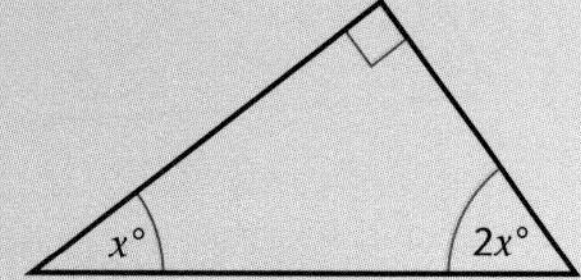

12

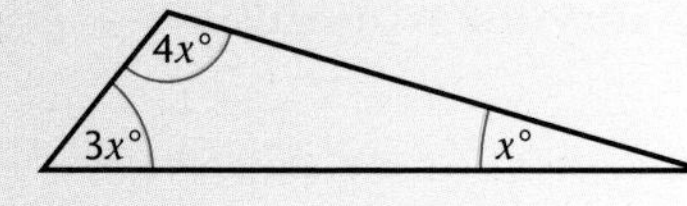

6.3 Special triangles

An **isosceles** triangle has two equal sides and two equal angles.
The equal angles are called the **base angles** of the triangle.

You know that a triangle is isosceles if you know that two sides are equal or that two angles are equal.

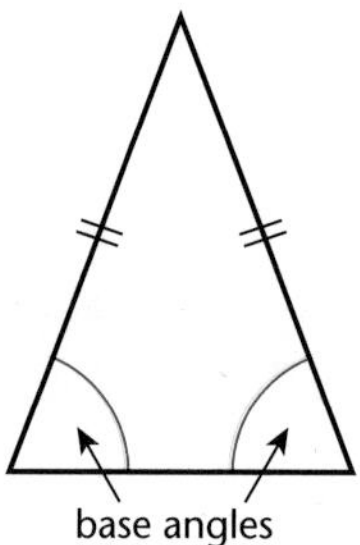

The equal sides and the base angles on this isosceles triangle are marked.
You can see that neither of the base angles is between the equal sides.

An **equilateral** triangle has three equal sides and three equal angles. Each angle is 60°.

You know that a triangle is equilateral if the three sides are equal or if all the angles are 60°.

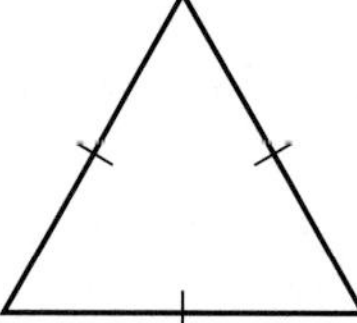

In a **right-angled triangle** one of the angles is 90°.

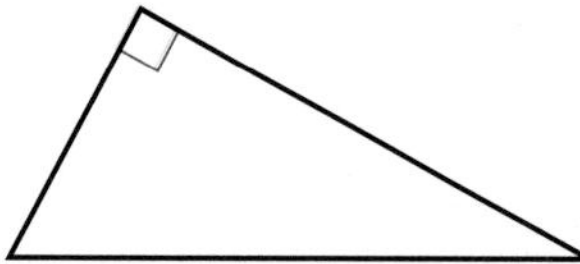

Example 3

Work out the value of p.
Give reasons for your working.

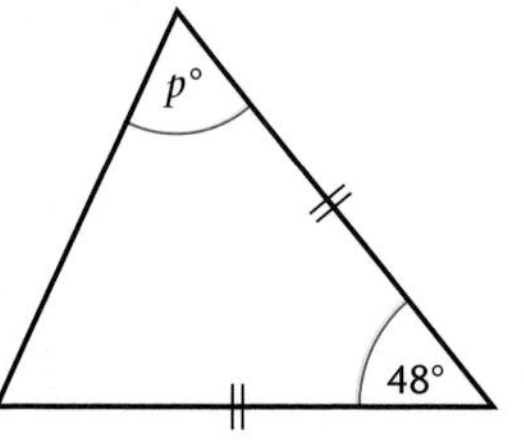

The triangle has two equal sides so it is isosceles.

The base angles of an isosceles triangle are equal so the unmarked angle is $p°$. The angles of the triangle add up to 180°,

so $p + p + 48 = 180$

$2p = 180 - 48$

$2p = 132$

$p = 66$

Exam practice 6C

1 Write down the mathematical name of each triangle.

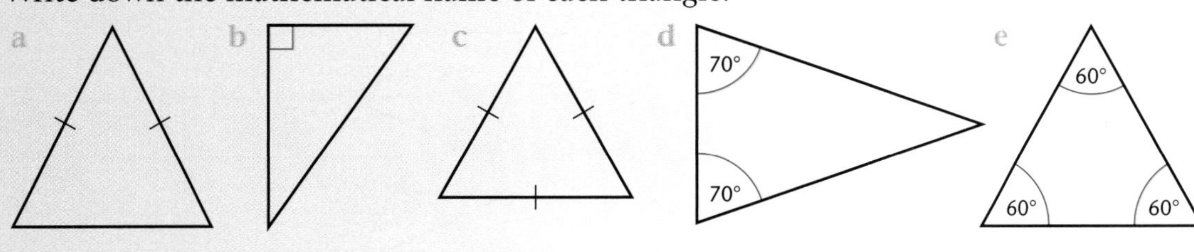

2 Anna said that this triangle is equilateral.
UAM Explain why Anna is correct.

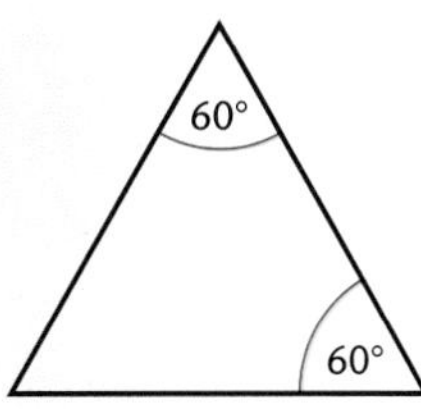

3 Kay said that two sides of this triangle are the same length.
Is Kay correct?
UAM Give a reason for your answer.

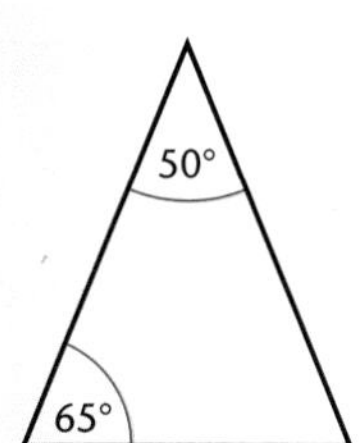

In an equilateral triangle all the angles are equal.

UAM In questions 4 to 10 find the value of each letter. Give reasons for your working.

4 $g°$, 48°

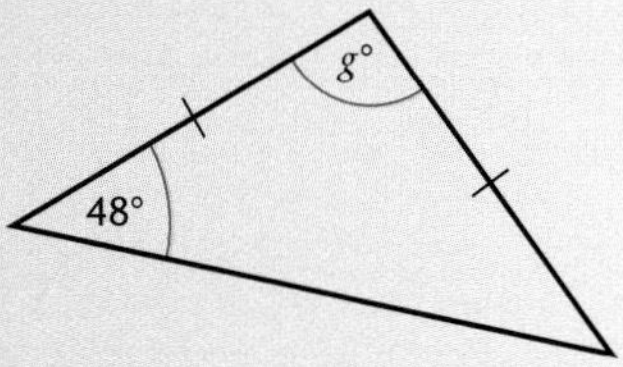

5 108°, $h°$, $i°$

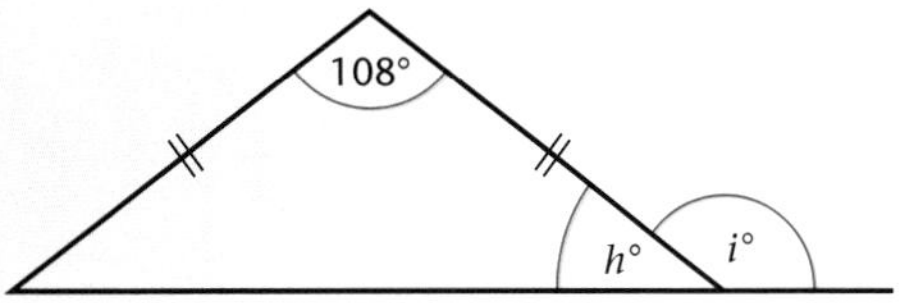

6 50°, $i°$, $h°$

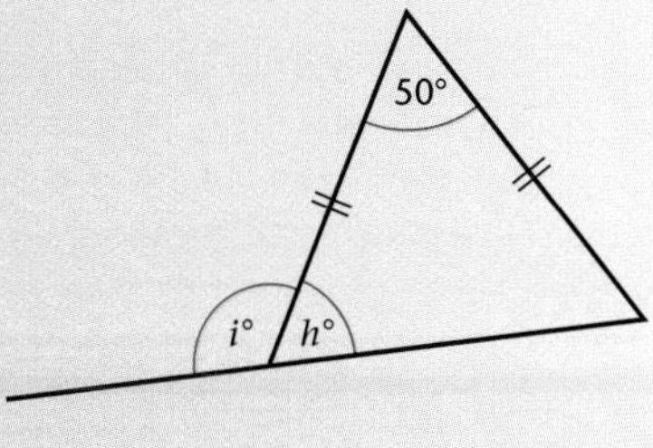

7 $j°$, $k°$, 130°

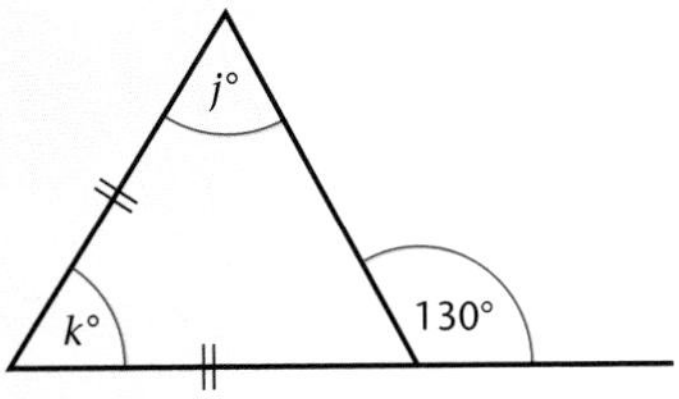

8 $k°$, 25°

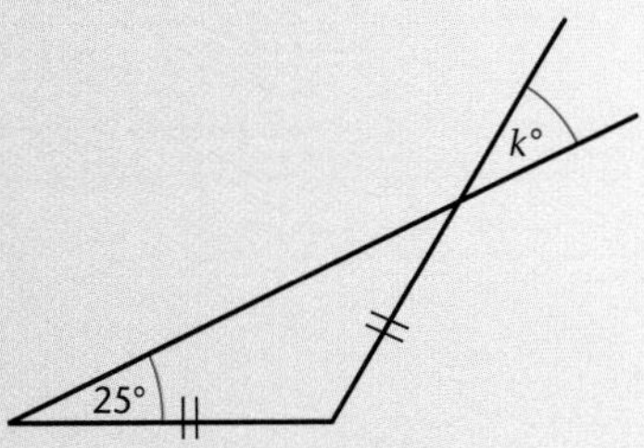

9 $m°$

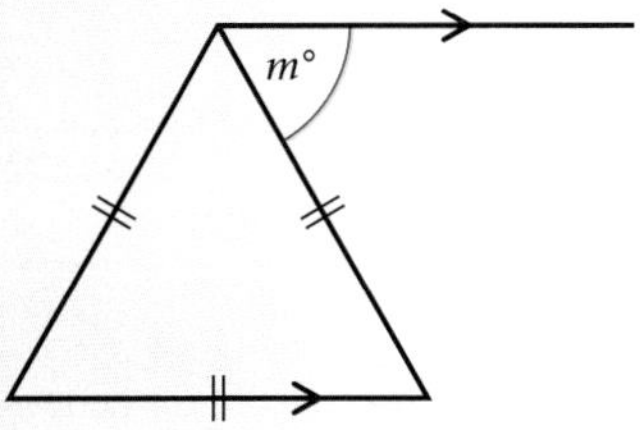

10 110°, $b°$, $a°$

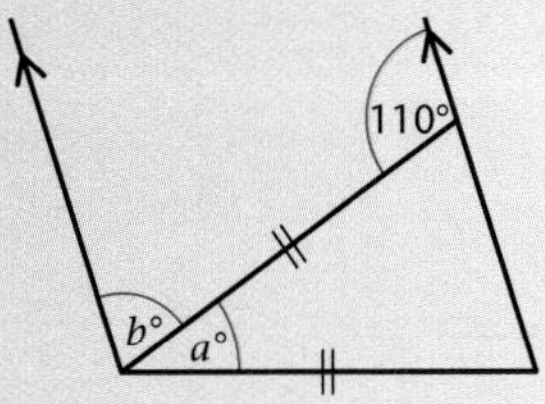

6.4 Quadrilaterals

A **quadrilateral** is a flat shape bounded by four straight lines.

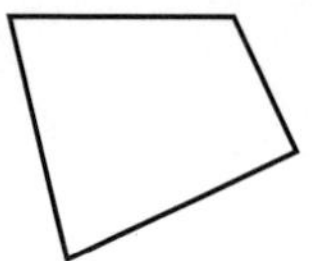

A **diagonal** is a line joining two opposite vertices.

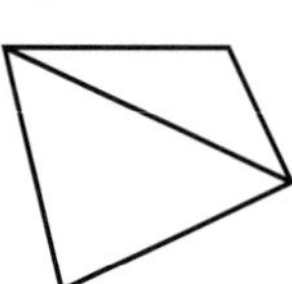

Every quadrilateral has two diagonals.

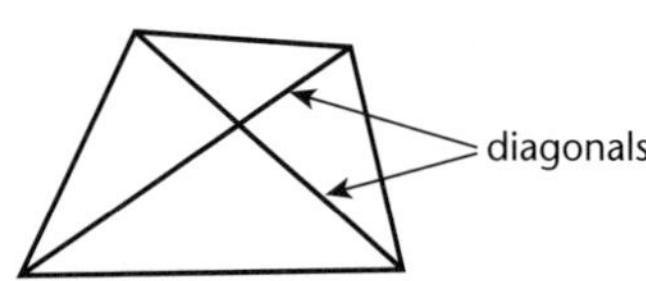

Each diagonal divides a quadrilateral into two triangles.
The sum of the angles in any triangle is 180°
so **the sum of the angles of a quadrilateral is 360°**.

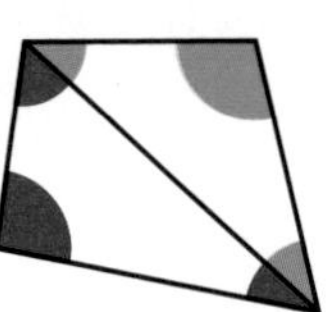

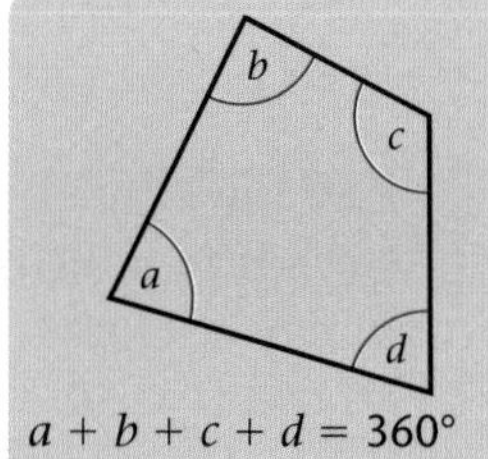

$a + b + c + d = 360°$

Example 4

Work out the value of p.

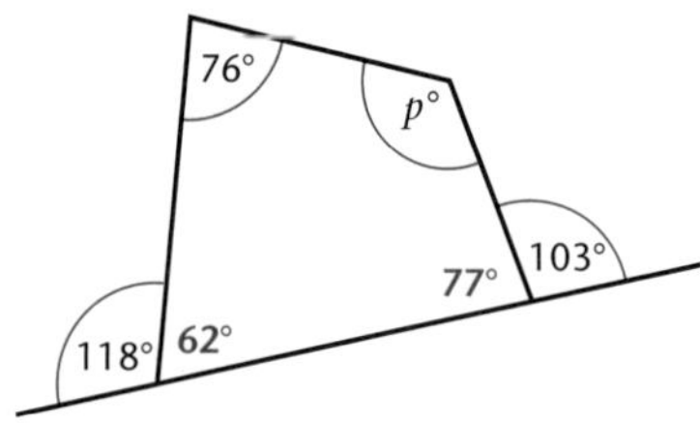

$180 - 118 = 62$ and $180 - 103 = 77$

$77 + 76 + p + 62 = 360$

$215 + p = 360$

$p = 360 - 215$

$p = 145$

First find the size of the unknown angles inside the quadrilateral. You can use the fact that angles on a straight line add up to 180°.

Then use the fact that angles in a quadrilateral add up to 360°.

Exam practice 6D

Work out the value of each letter.

1

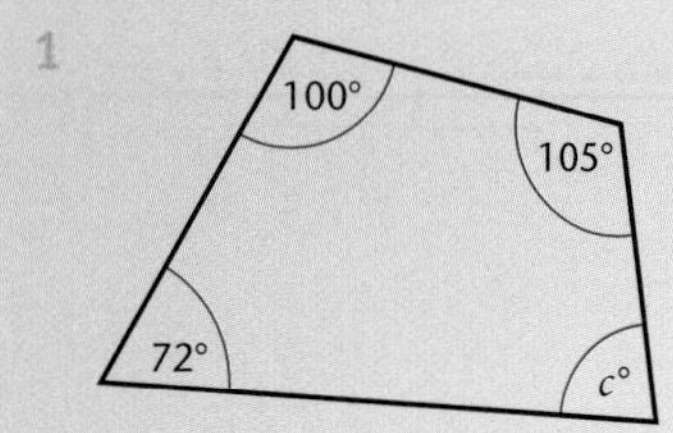

2

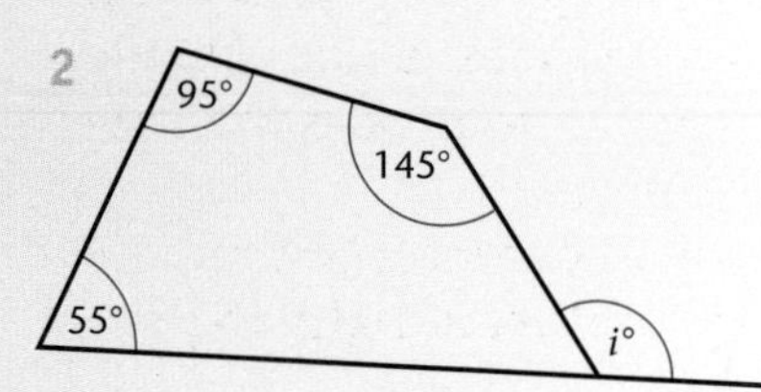

In question 2 find the value of the unmarked angle in the quadrilateral first.

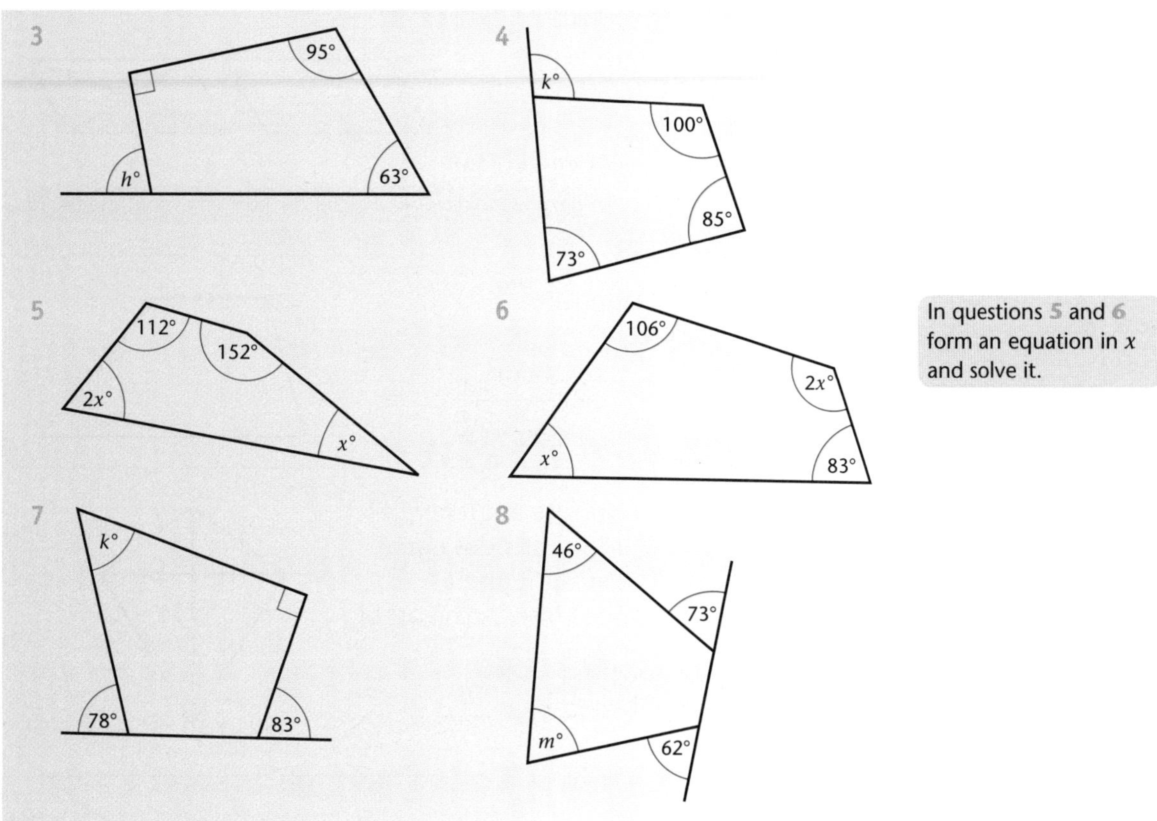

In questions 5 and 6 form an equation in x and solve it.

6.5 Special quadrilaterals

Some quadrilaterals have special names.

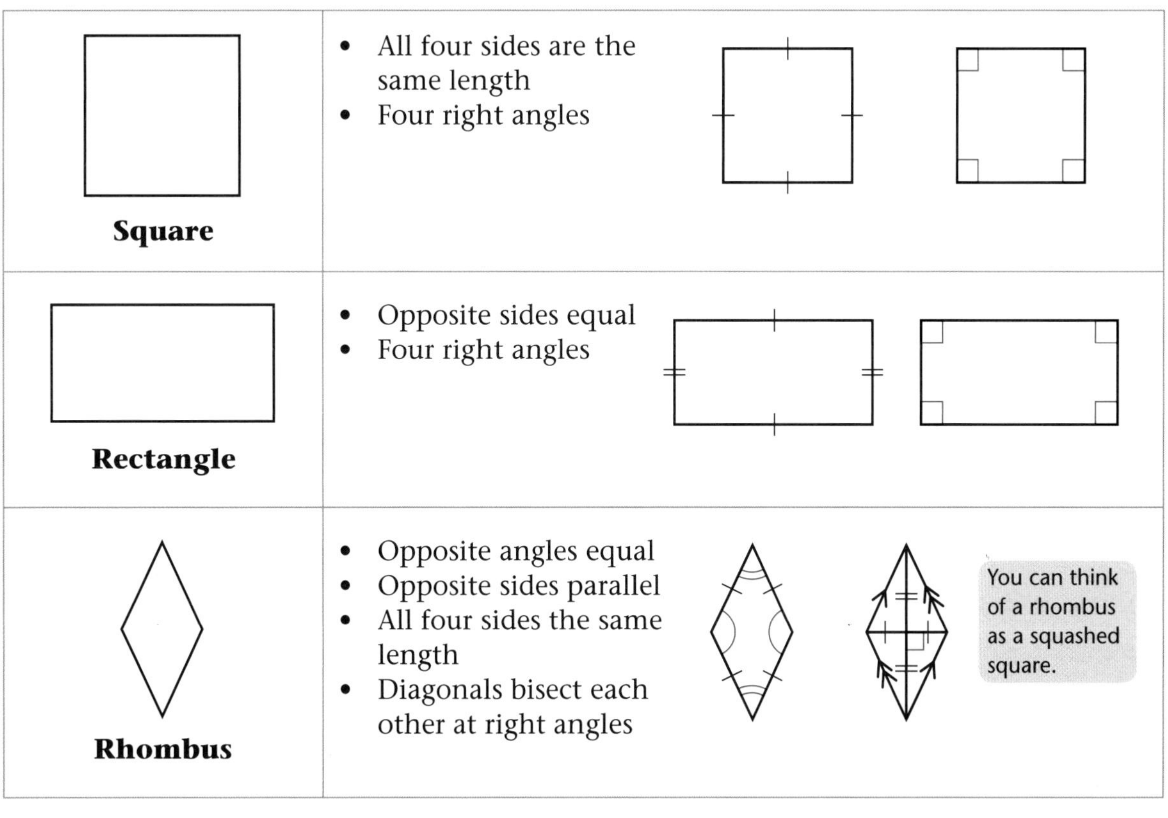

Square	• All four sides are the same length • Four right angles
Rectangle	• Opposite sides equal • Four right angles
Rhombus	• Opposite angles equal • Opposite sides parallel • All four sides the same length • Diagonals bisect each other at right angles

You can think of a rhombus as a squashed square.

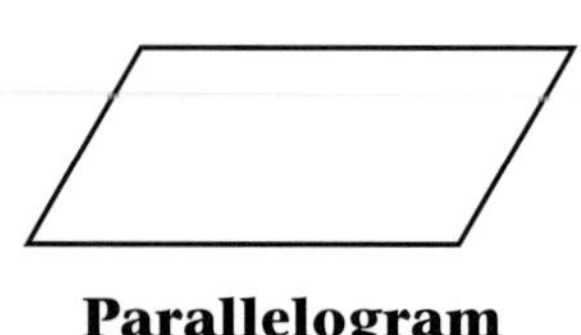 **Parallelogram**	• Opposite angles equal • Opposite sides equal and parallel • Diagonals bisect each other A parallelogram is like a rectangle pushed over at the top.
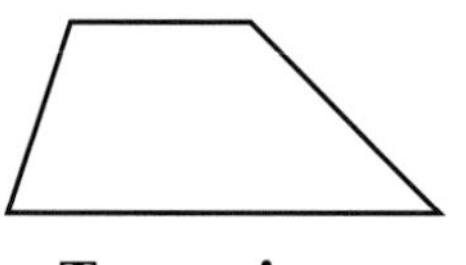 **Trapezium**	• One pair of opposite sides parallel 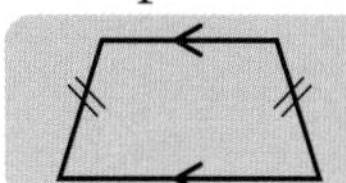 is called an isosceles trapezium 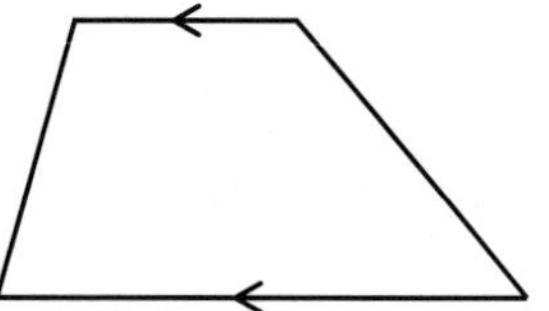
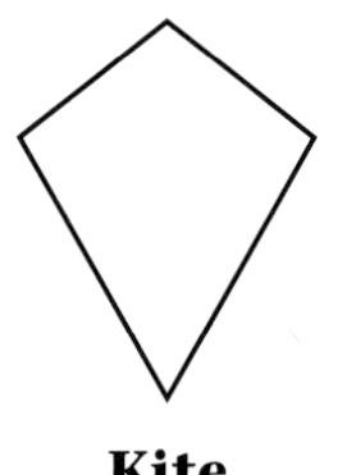 **Kite**	• One pair of opposite angles equal • Two pairs of adjacent sides equal • Diagonals cut at right angles • Just one diagonal bisects the other A kite is two isosceles triangles joined at their bases. 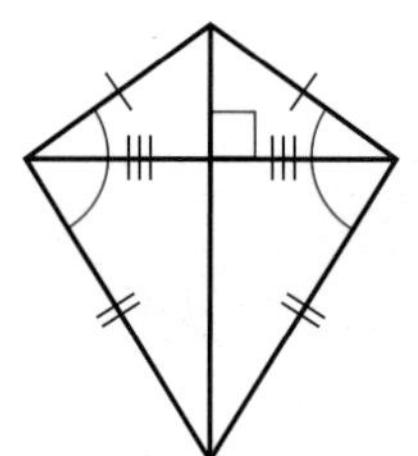

You can prove that the opposite angles of a parallelogram are equal

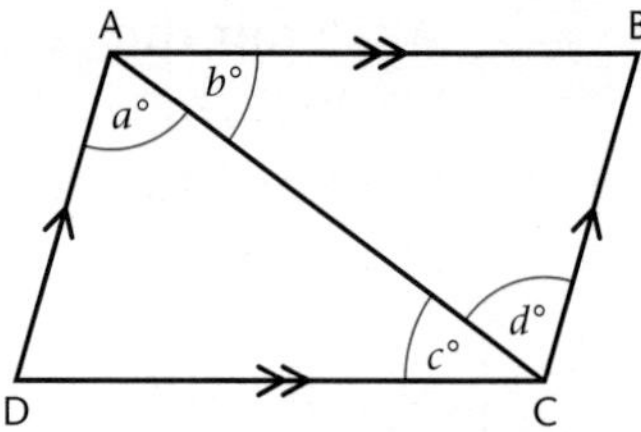

In this parallelogram $\angle DAB = a° + b°$ and $\angle DCB = c° + d°$.
But $a° = d°$ and $b° = c°$ (alternate angles)
$\therefore \angle DAB = a° + b° = d° + c° = \angle DCB$.

Also $\angle ADC = 180° - a° - c°$ and $\angle ABC = 180° - b° - d°$.
But $a° = d°$ and $b° = c°$
so $\angle ADC = 180° - a° - c° = 180° - b° - d° = \angle ABC$.
In both cases the opposite angles are equal.

Other properties of a parallelogram are proved later.

Example 5

Work out the value of each letter.

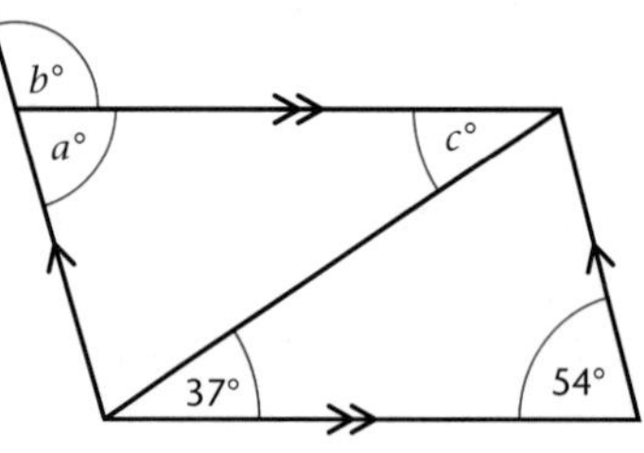

$a = 54$

$a°$ and 54° are opposite angles of a parallelogram so they are equal.

$b = 180 - 54$
$b = 126$

$a°$ and b° are angles on a straight line so they add up to 180°.

$c = 37$

$c°$ and 37° are alternate angles so they are equal.

Exam practice 6E

In questions 1 to 6 find the value of each letter.

1

2

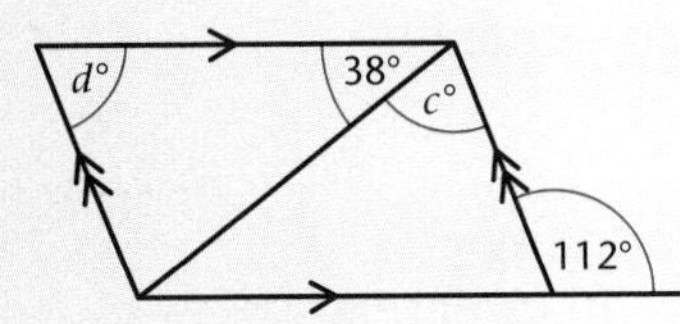

3

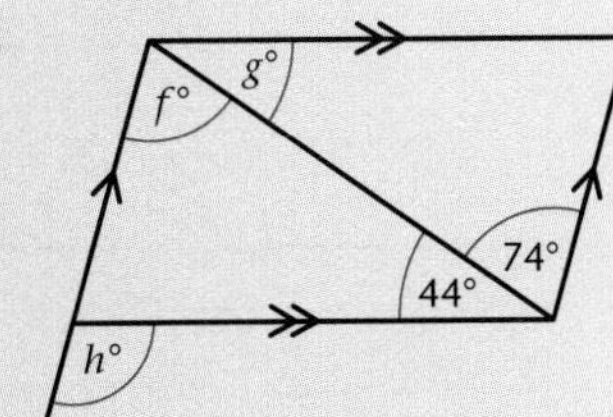

4

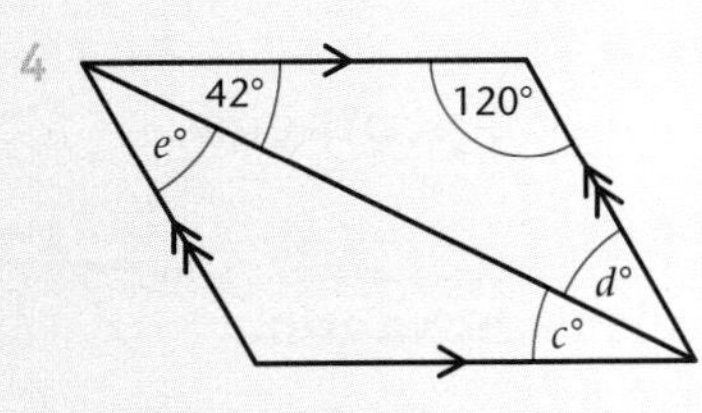

5

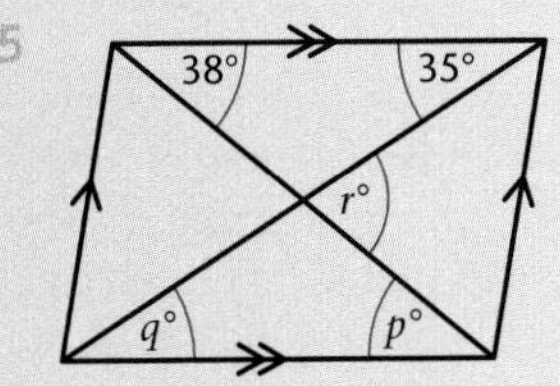

6

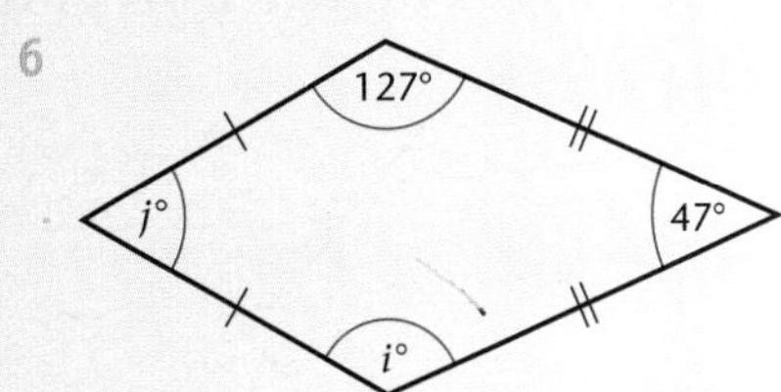

UAM

7 a A chevron is made from two identical parallelograms placed edge to edge. Work out the values of a and b in the first chevron.

b Work out the value of x in the second chevron.

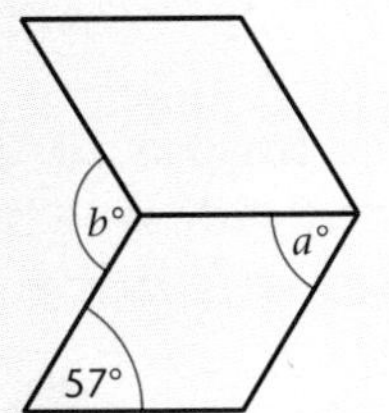

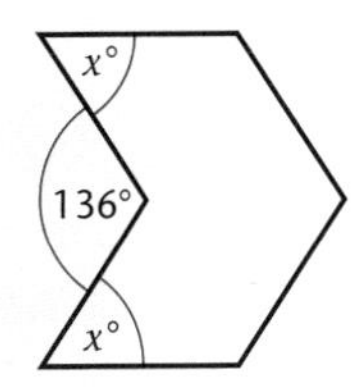

8 Show how two of these triangles can be put together to form:

a an isosceles triangle

b a rectangle

c a parallelogram

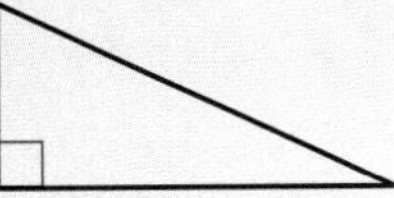

UAM

9 a Jamie said that a quadrilateral with both diagonals the same length must be a rectangle.
Is Jamie correct? Give a reason for your answer.

b Colleen said that if a parallelogram has one angle equal to 90°, all the angles must be 90°.
Is Colleen correct? Give a reason for your answer.

10 What is the mathematical name of each of these quadrilaterals?

a Both pairs of its opposite sides are parallel.

b It is a parallelogram in which one angle is a right angle.

c It is a parallelogram with both its diagonals the same length.

d Its diagonals are the same length, bisect each other, and cross at right angles.

e It is a parallelogram with four equal sides.

Sketch each shape. Do not assume that the shape has any other properties.

6.6 Polygons

A **polygon** is a flat shape bounded by straight lines.

A polygon with 3 sides is a triangle.
A polygon with 4 sides is a quadrilateral.

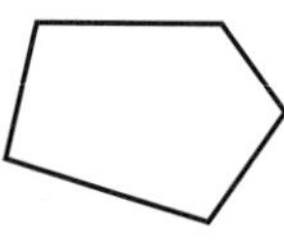

A polygon with 5 sides is a called a **pentagon**.

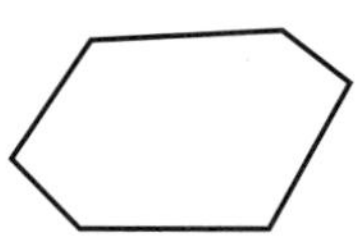

A polygon with 6 sides is called a **hexagon**.

The sum of the exterior angles of any polygon is 360°.

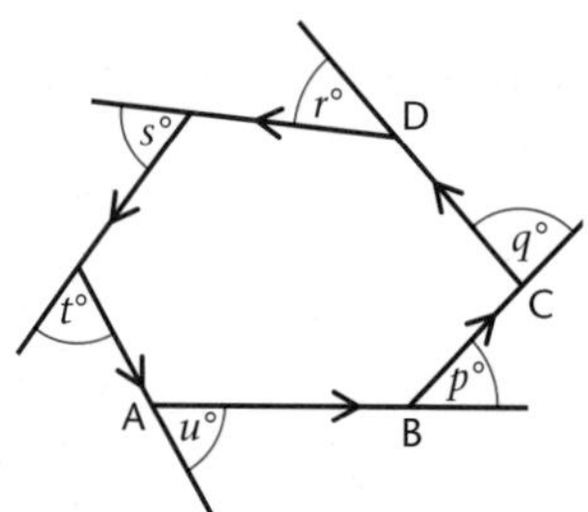

Think about walking around the polygon in the direction of the arrows, starting at A walk to B. At B you turn through an angle $p°$ to walk to C, then an angle $q°$ to walk to D, and so on. By the time you get back to A and are facing B again, you have turned through 360°.
$p° + q° + r° + s° + t° + u° = 360°$

The sum of the interior angles in any polygon is
180° × (number of sides) – 360°
or 90° × (2 × number of sides – 4).

The formula for the sum of the interior angles of a polygon with n sides is usually written as $90° \times (2n - 4)$.

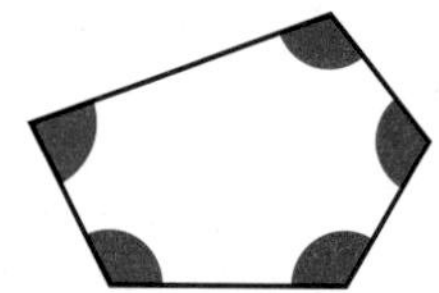

The sum of the interior and exterior angles is 180° × (number of sides). You know that the exterior angles add up to 360°, so the sum of the interior angles is 180° × (the number of sides) – 360°.

Example 6

a Calculate the values of p and q.
b What is the mathematical name of this quadrilateral? Give a reason for your answer.

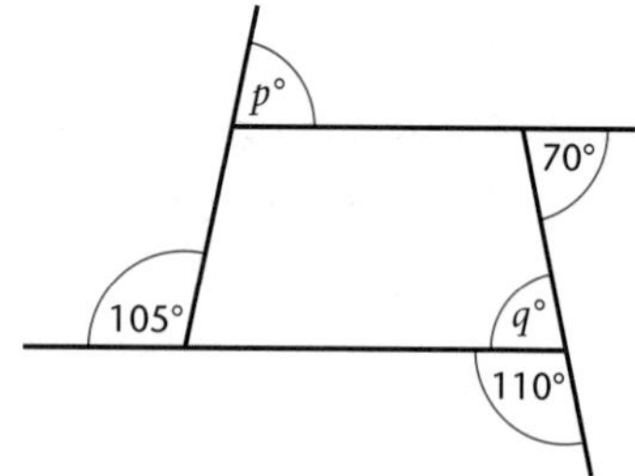

a $110 + 105 + 70 + p = 360$
$285 + p = 360$
$p = 75$

The exterior angles of a quadrilateral add up to 360°.

$110 + q = 180$
$q = 70$

Angles on a straight line add up to 180°.

b Trapezium.
70° and $q°$ are equal and are alternate angles so two of the sides are parallel.

Example 7

Find the sum of the interior angles of **a** a pentagon **b** a hexagon.

a In a pentagon
the sum of the interior angles is $90° \times (10 - 4)$
$= 90° \times 6$
$= 540°$

A pentagon has 5 sides.
$(2n - 4) = 2 \times 5 - 4 = 6$

b In a hexagon
the sum of the interior angles is $90° \times (12 - 4)$
$= 90° \times 8$
$= 720°$

A hexagon has 6 sides.
$(2n - 4) = 2 \times 6 - 4 = 8$

Regular polygons

A **regular polygon** has all its sides the same length and all it angles equal. These polygons are regular.

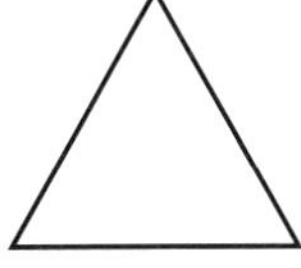
Equilateral triangle

Square

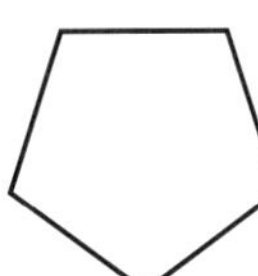
Pentagon

Hexagon

Did you know
that the United States Defence Department building is called The Pentagon because of its shape?

Example 8

a A regular polygon has 10 sides. Find the size of an interior angle
b Each interior angle of a regular polygon is 156°.
How many sides does it have?

Find an exterior angle first.
There are 10 of them, they are all equal, and their sum is 360°.

a Size of an exterior angle $= 360° \div 10 = 36°$
Size of an interior angle $= 180° - 36° = 144°$

Exterior angle + interior angle = 180°.

b Each exterior angle is $180° - 156° = 24°$
Number of sides $= 360 \div 24 = 15$

First find an exterior angle.
If the number of sides is n
$n \times 24 = 360$. So $n = 360 \div 24$.

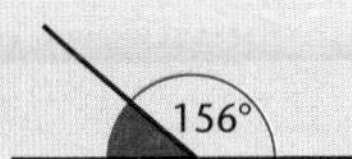

Exam practice 6F

1 Find the values of x.

a

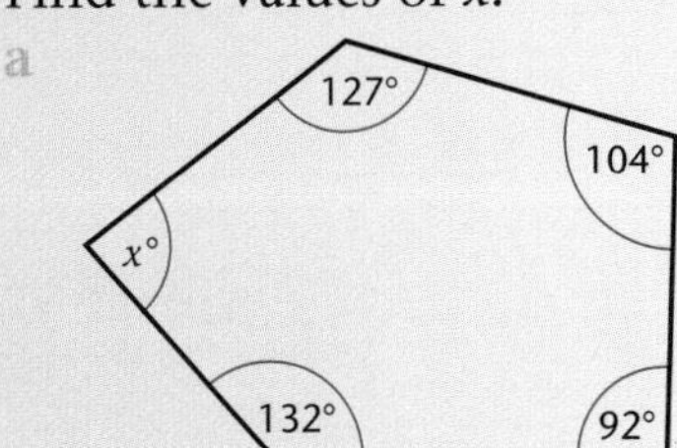

b

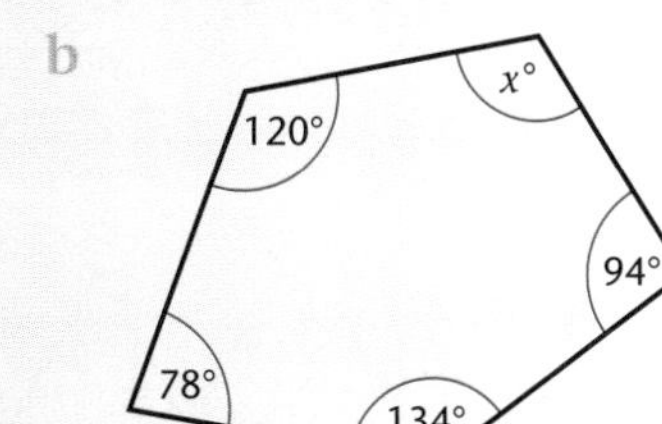

2 Find the values of x.

a b

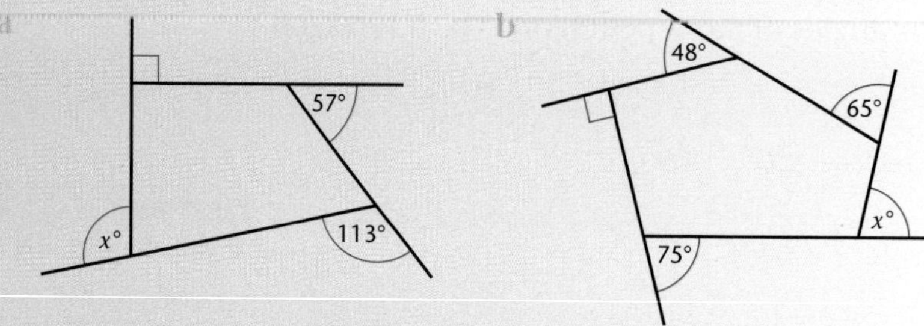

3 Find the size of each exterior angle of a regular polygon with
a 6 sides b 8 sides c 12 sides d 18 sides.

4 Find the size of each interior angle of a regular polygon with
a 5 sides b 8 sides c 12 sides d 20 sides.

5 How many sides does a regular polygon have if each exterior angle is
a 30° b 40° c 36°?

6 a Is it possible for the exterior angle of a regular polygon to be
i 40° ii 50° iii 70°?
b Is it possible for the interior angle of a regular polygon to be
i 130° ii 135° iii 165°?

UAM Give reasons for your answers.

7 Work out the value of x.

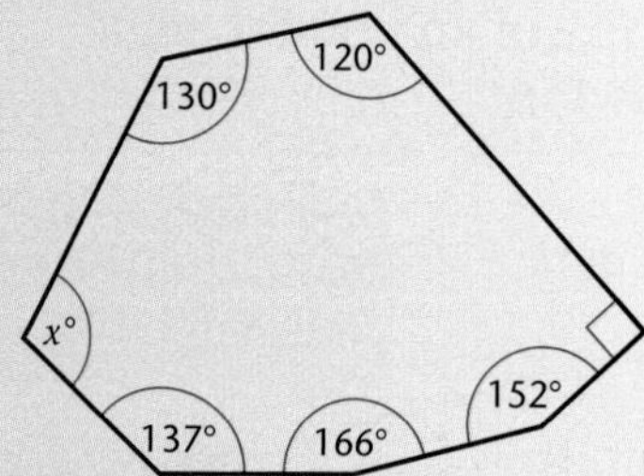

8 Find the values of x.

a b

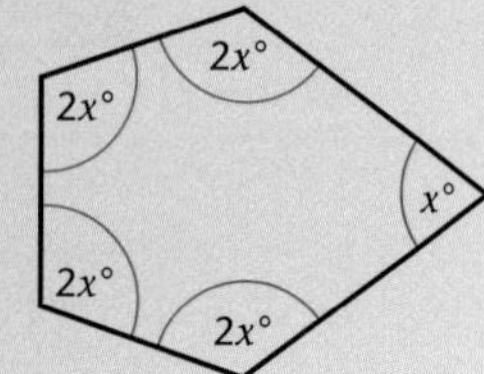

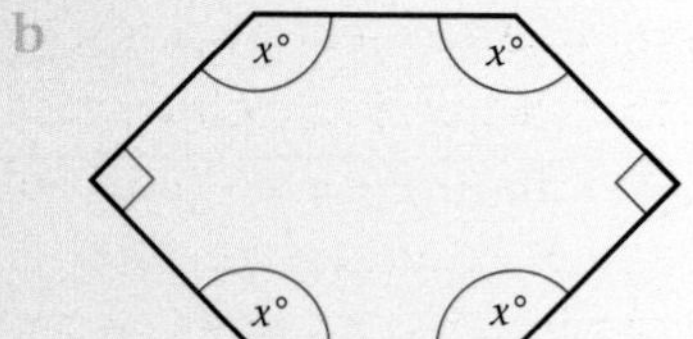

You need to form an equation in x and solve it.

9 a This is a regular polygon.
What is its mathematical name?
b O is the centre of the polygon.
Work out the value of p.
c Find the value of q.

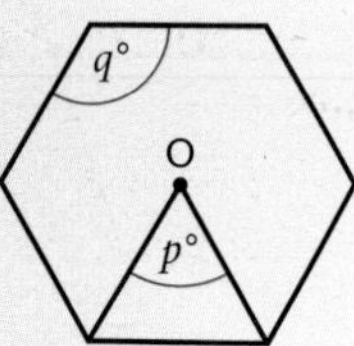

The angle at O is 360° divided by the number of sides.

UAM **10** Two sides of a regular pentagon are extended until they meet.
Calculate the value of
a x b y.

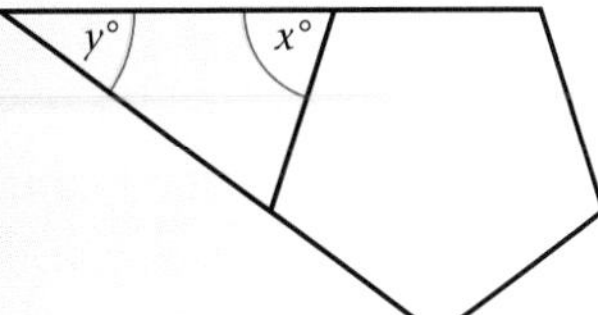

UAM **11** ABCDE is a regular pentagon.
a Work out the value of
i x ii y.
b Work out the angles of △EBD.
c What is the mathematical name of
i △ABE ii △EBD?

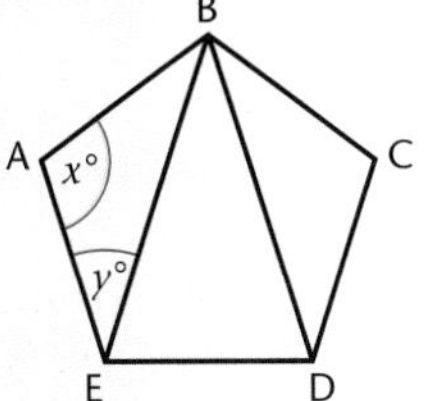

UAM **12** ABCDEF is a regular hexagon.
a Work out the value of
i x ii y.
b Work out the size of ∠CAF.
c What mathematical name can you give to
i △ABC ii quadrilateral ACDF?

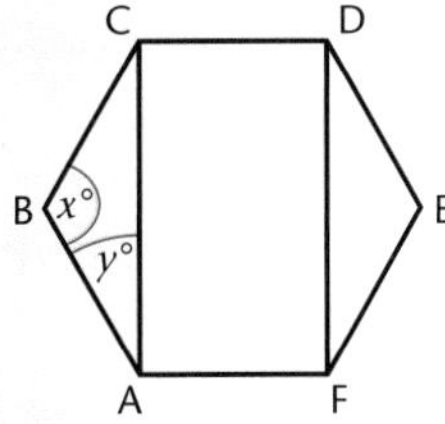

13 ABCDEF is a regular hexagon.
a Find the sizes of the angles in ABEF.
b What is the mathematical name for ABEF?

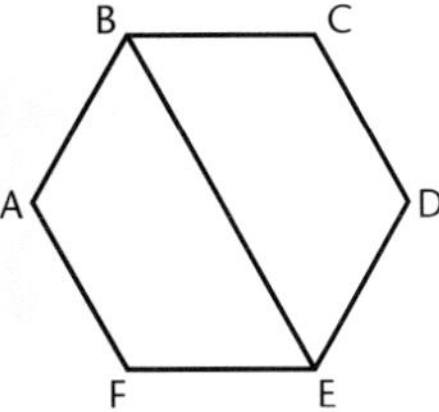

Summary of key points

- Corresponding angles are equal.
- Alternate angles are equal.
- The interior angles of any triangle add up to 180°.
- The interior angles in a quadrilateral add up to 360°.
- In a square all four sides are the same length and every interior angle is 90°.
- The exterior angle of a triangle is equal to sum of the interior opposite angles.
- In a rectangle the opposite sides are equal and all the interior angles are 90°.
- In a parallelogram the opposite sides are equal and parallel, the opposite angles are equal, and the diagonals bisect each other.
- A kite has one pair of opposite angles equal, two pairs of adjacent sides equal and just one diagonal bisects the other at right angles.
- In a trapezium just one pair of opposite sides are parallel.
- The sum of the exterior angles of any polygon is 360° and the sum of the interior angles is (180° × number of sides) − 360°.
- In a regular polygon, all the sides are equal, all the exterior angles are equal and all the interior angles are equal. Each exterior angle is equal to 360° ÷ the number of sides.

Most candidates who get GRADE C or above can:

- find the number of sides in a regular polygon given an exterior angle
- use the properties of parallel lines to find angles.

Glossary

Acute angle	an angle that is smaller than 90°
Alternate angles	a pair of angles formed by a straight line crossing a pair of parallel lines. Also known as Z angles
Base angles	the two equal angles of an isosceles triangle
Complementary angles	two acute angles whose sum is 90°
Corresponding angles	a pair of angles formed by a straight line crossing a pair of parallel lines. Also known as F angles
Diagonal	a line joining two opposite vertices
Equilateral triangle	a triangle with 3 sides of equal length and 3 equal angles of 60°
Hexagon	a polygon with six sides
Isosceles triangle	two sides are equal and the angles opposite those sides are equal
Kite	a quadrilateral that has two pairs of equal adjacent sides
Obtuse angle	an angle that is bigger than 90° but smaller than 180°
Parallel lines	lines that are always the same distance apart
Parallelogram	a quadrilateral with both pairs of opposite sides equal and parallel
Pentagon	a polygon with five sides
Polygon	a flat shape bounded by any number of straight sides
Quadrilateral	a flat shape bounded by four straight sides
Rectangle	a quadrilateral with all angles equal to 90°
Reflex angle	an angle greater than 180° but less than 360°
Regular polygon	all sides and angles are equal
Rhombus	a parallelogram that has all its sides equal
Right-angled triangle	has one angle equal to 90°
Scalene triangle	all the sides are different lengths
Square	a rectangle with equal sides
Supplementary angles	two angles whose sum is 180°
Transversal	a line that crosses parallel lines
Trapezium	a quadrilateral with only one pair of opposite sides parallel
Vertex (plural vertices)	the corner of a polygon where two sides meet
Vertically opposite angles	the angles formed when two straight lines cross

7 Areas

This chapter will show you:

- ✓ how to convert different units of length
- ✓ how to convert different units of area
- ✓ how to find the area of a square, rectangle, triangle, parallelogram and trapezium and of compound shapes combining some of these
- ✓ how to find the circumference and area of a circle
- ✓ how to find the length of an arc and the area of a sector of a circle

Before you start you need to know:

- ✓ how to calculate with a mixture of $+$, $-$, $\times$ and $\div$
- ✓ the properties of different triangles
- ✓ the properties of different quadrilaterals
- ✓ the different parts of a circle
- ✓ how to square a number
- ✓ how to solve linear and quadratic equations
- ✓ how to give an answer to an appropriate degee of accuracy

7.1 Units of length and area

There are two systems for measuring length.

Metric units

The metric units of length in everyday use are the kilometre (km), the metre (m), the centimetre (cm) and the millimetre (mm).

The relationship between these units are:

1 km = 1000 m
1 m = 100 cm = 1000 mm
1 cm = 10 mm

Imperial units

The mile is the only imperial unit of length in everyday use in the UK.
Yards, feet and inches are other imperial units of length that are used occasionally.

The relationships between these units are:

1 foot = 12 inches
1 yard = 3 feet

You need to know these relationships.

You can use these relationships to convert between different units.
To convert to a smaller unit, you multiply.
To convert to a larger unit, you divide.

You can convert between imperial and metric units of length using:

5 miles $\approx$ 8 km
2 inches $\approx$ 5 cm

You need to know these conversions.

Example 1

Convert:
a 5.5 km to metres
b 154 cm to metres
c 7843 mm to centimetres.

a $5.5\text{ km} = 5.5 \times 1000\text{ m} = 5500\text{ m}$

A metre is smaller than a kilometre, so multiply by 1000. (1 km = 1000 m)

b $154\text{ cm} = 154 \div 100\text{ m} = 1.54\text{ m}$

You are changing to a larger unit so divide by 100. (1 m = 100 cm)

c $7843\text{ mm} = 7843 \div 10\text{ cm} = 784.3\text{ cm}$

You are changing to a larger unit so divide by 10. (1 cm = 10 mm)

Example 2

Convert:
a 60 miles into kilometres
b 120 kilometres into miles.

a $60 \times 8 \div 5 = 96$ so 60 miles $\approx$ 96 km

5 mile $\approx$ 8 km so 1 mile $\approx 8 \div 5$ km and 60 miles $\approx 60 \times 8 \div 5$ km

b $120 \times 5 \div 8 = 75$ so 120 km $\approx$ 75 miles

8 km $\approx$ 5 miles so 1 km $\approx 5 \div 8$ miles and 120 km $\approx 120 \times 5 \div 8$ miles

Units of area

Area is measured in squares.
The area covered by this square is called **1 square centimetre** (1 cm^2).

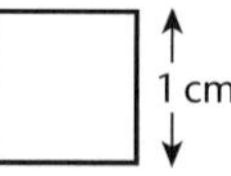

The dark square has a side of 1 mm. The area covered by this square is called **1 square millimetre** (1 mm^2).

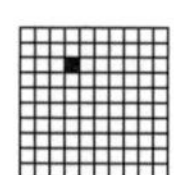

The relationships between metric units of area are:

$1\text{ cm}^2 = 10 \times 10\text{ mm}^2 = 100\text{ mm}^2$
$1\text{ m}^2 = 100 \times 100\text{ cm}^2 = 10\,000\text{ cm}^2$
$1\text{ km}^2 = 1000 \times 1000\text{ m}^2 = 1\,000\,000\text{ m}^2$

Areas of land are measured in **hectares** (ha):

$1\text{ ha} = 10\,000\text{ m}^2$.

In the imperial system areas of land are measured in **acres**:

1 acre = 4840 square yards.

To convert between hectares and acres use:

1 hectare $\approx$ 2.47 acres.

To convert from hectares to acres multiply by 2.47.
To convert from acres to hectares divide by 2.47.

Class discussion

The unit used to describe an area depends on what is being measured. For a very large area, such as a country, use km^2, for the area of a farm use hectares, for the area of a small garden use m^2, for the area of a page in a book use cm^2 and for the area of a postage stamp use mm^2.

Which unit would you use for measuring:
- the area of an oak leaf?
- a bedroom window?
- the bedroom floor?
- a county?
- a fingernail?
- a carpet?
- a postcard?
- a playing field?
- an ocean?
- a supermarket receipt?

Exam practice 7A

1 Convert each length into the unit given in brackets.

a 10 cm (mm) b 7600 m (km) c 70 mm (cm)
d 4500 mm (m) e 800 cm (m) f 2 m (mm)
g 178 mm (cm) h 3.5 km (m)

2 Convert each length into the unit given in brackets.

a 36 inches (feet) b 9 feet (yards)
c 40 miles (km) d 64 km (miles)

3 Convert, approximately, into the unit given in brackets.

a 12 inches (cm) b 60 cm (inches) c 30 inches (cm)

4 a Arrange these lengths in order of size, longest first.
30 inches, 2 feet, 1 metre, 120 cm

b Ed said that 120 kilometres was more than 80 miles.
Is Ed correct? Give a reason for your answer.

UAM

You can do this without converting them into the same unit if you know that 1 metre is slightly longer than 1 yard.

5 Convert each area into the unit given in brackets.

a 1.2 cm^2 (mm^2) b 450 mm^2 (cm^2)
c 0.5 km^2 (m^2) d 5600 m^2 (km^2)
e 0.4 km^2 (m^2) f 564 mm^2 (cm^2)
g 100 hectares (acres) h 24.7 acres (hectares)

7.2 Areas of squares and rectangles

Area of a square = (the length of a side)^2.

Area of a rectangle = length × breadth.

Example 3

Find the area of each shape.

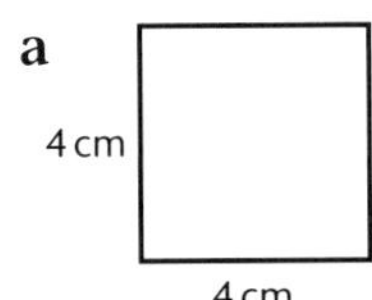

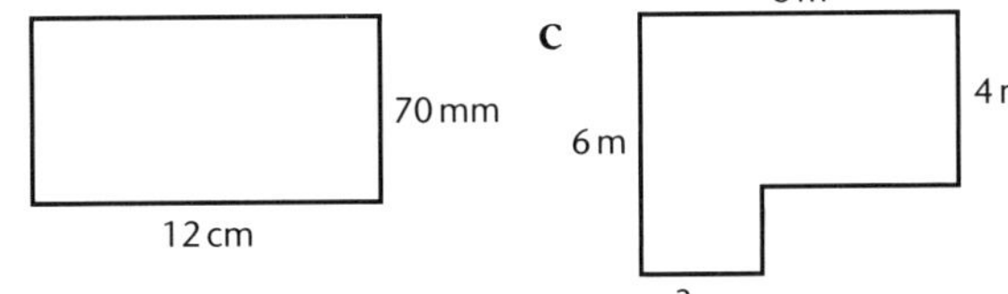

a $4 \times 4 = 16$
Area of square = 16 cm^2

b 70 mm = 7 cm
$12 \times 7 = 84$
Area of rectangle = 84 cm^2

Both lengths must be in the same units. Convert 70 mm into cm by dividing by 10.

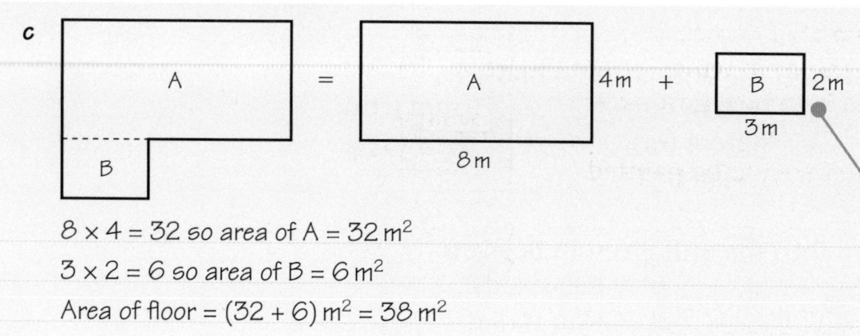

Divide the area into two rectangles and label each one. Make a shape equation. Put the measurements on each rectangle.

This is a shape equation.

Exam practice 7B

1 a Find the area of a square of side
   i 6 cm ii 90 mm iii 0.4 km.
 b Find the area of a rectangle measuring
   i 6 cm by 10 cm ii 50 m by 35 m iii 6.7 cm by 5 cm.
 c Find the area of a rectangle measuring 9 cm by 45 mm.

Both lengths must be measured in the same unit. Convert 45 mm to cm.

2 Find the area of each shape. All measurements are in centimetres.

a

b

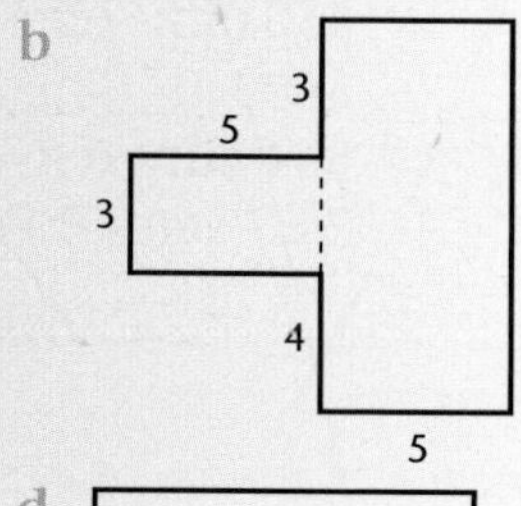

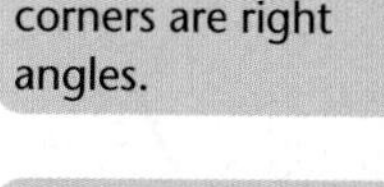

These shapes can be divided into two or more rectangles.

c

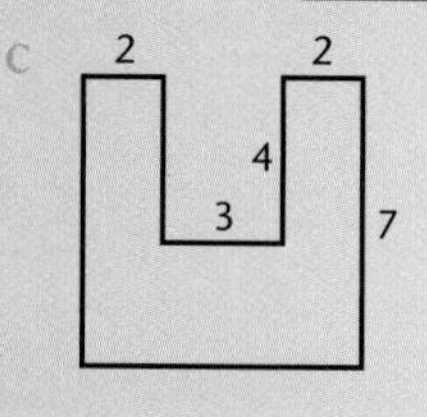

d

e

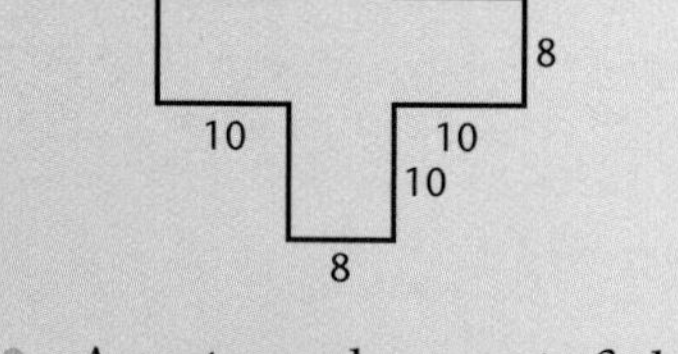

f

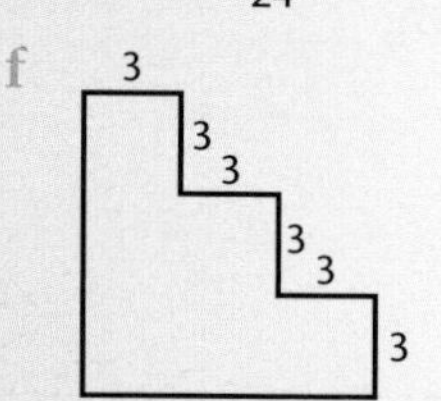

3 A rectangular sports field measures 400 m by 320 m.
 a Find its perimeter.
 b Find its area i in square metres ii in hectares.

The **perimeter** is the distance round the edge of a shape.

4 This diagram shows a frame for a photograph made out of card.
Work out the area of:
 a the card b the space available for a photograph
 c the card showing when the photograph is on it.

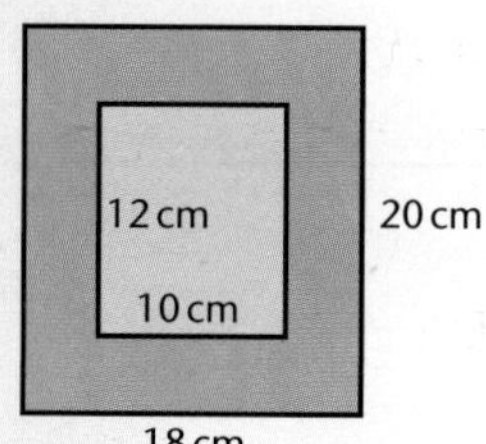

5 A wooden door has a glass panel.
  a Find the area of the glass panel.
  b The wooden area is to be painted on both sides.
  Work out the total area to be painted.

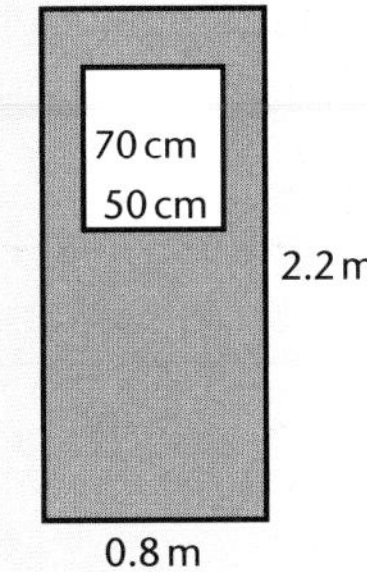

6 The length of a rectangle is twice its width.
The area of the rectangle is $32\,\text{cm}^2$.
  a Show that the length of the rectangle is 8 cm.
  b Work out the perimeter of the rectangle.

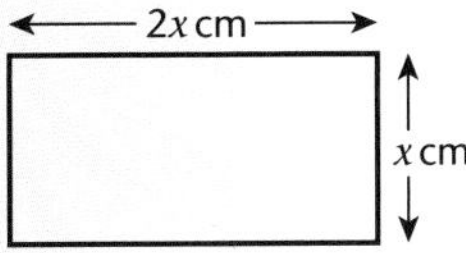

Form an equation and solve it.

7 A rectangular patio is 3 metres longer than it is wide.
The area of the patio is $40\,\text{m}^2$.
Work out the dimensions of the patio.

UAM

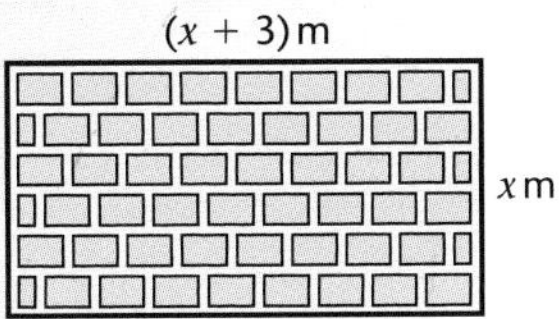

8 The area of this rectangular piece of plywood is $96\,\text{cm}^2$.
The piece is 4 cm narrower than it is long.
How long is it?

UAM

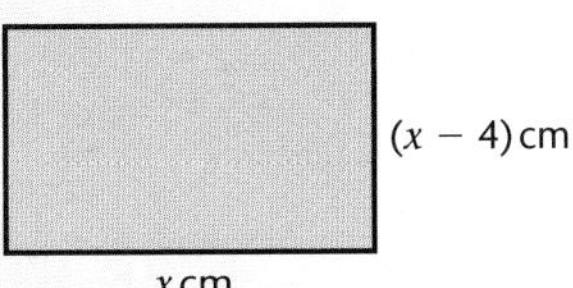

7.3 Areas of other shapes

Triangle

Area of a triangle $= \frac{1}{2} \times$ base $\times$ height

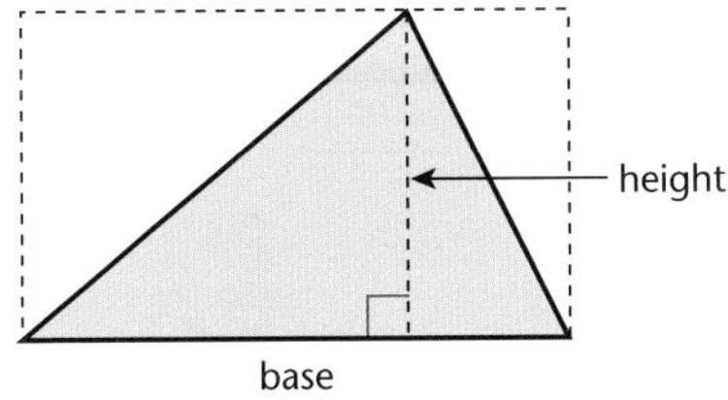

The area of the shaded triangle is equal to half the area of the rectangle that surrounds it.

Height means perpendicular height to the base.

Parallelogram

Area of a parallelogram = base $\times$ height

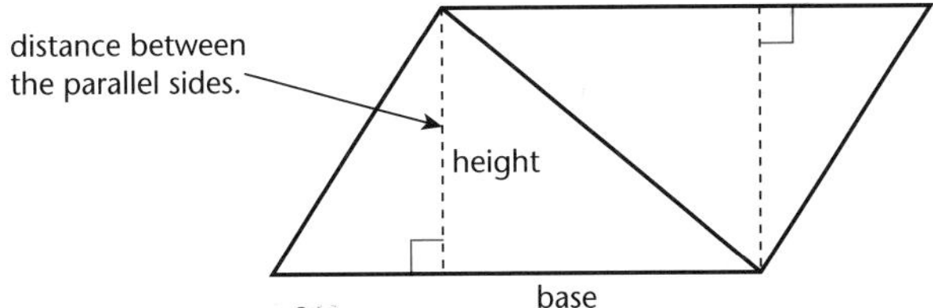

A diagonal of a parallelogram divides it into two identical triangles.
Area of one triangle $= \frac{1}{2} \times$ base $\times$ height.
The area of the parallelogram is twice this.

Trapezium

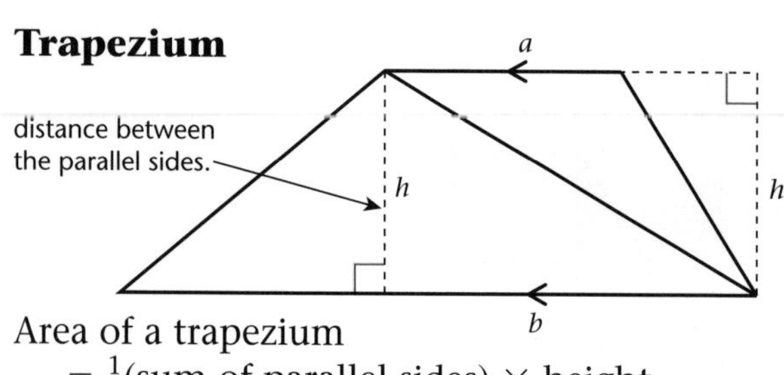

Area of a trapezium
$= \frac{1}{2}$(sum of parallel sides) × height

This diagonal divides the trapezium into two triangles. The area of the bottom triangle is $\frac{1}{2}bh$ and the area of the top triangle is $\frac{1}{2}ah$.
So the area of trapezium $= \frac{1}{2}ah + \frac{1}{2}bh$.
$= \frac{1}{2}(a + b) \times h$.

Example 4

Find the area of each triangle.

a

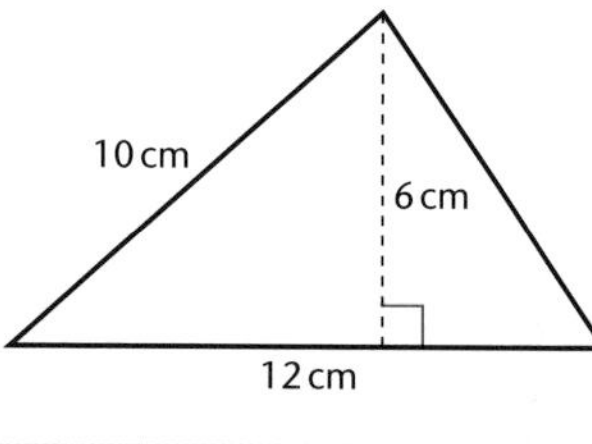

b

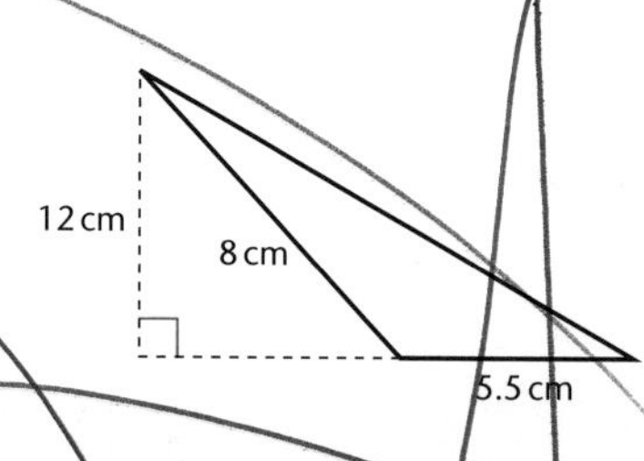

a Area of triangle $= \frac{1}{2} \times 12 \times 6\ \text{cm}^2$
$= 36\ \text{cm}^2$

The base is 12 cm and the perpendicular height 6 cm. The length 10 cm is not needed.

b Area of triangle $= \frac{1}{2} \times 5.5 \times 12\ \text{cm}^2$
$= 33\ \text{cm}^2$

The base is 5.5 cm and the perpendicular height 12 cm. The length 8 cm is not needed.

Example 5

Find the area of this parallelogram.

15 cm, 20 cm, 12 cm

Area $= 15 \times 20\ \text{cm}^2$
$= 300\ \text{cm}^2$

One side of the parallelogram is 15 cm. The distance between this side and the side opposite it is 20 cm. You can use these two measurements to find the area. The measurement of 12 cm is not needed to answer the question.

Exam practice 7C

1 Find the area of each shape.

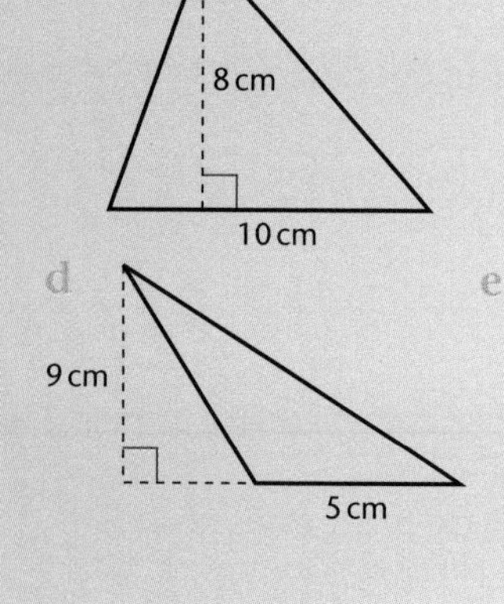

b 6 cm, 9.5 cm

c 16 cm, 20 cm

e 10 cm, 8 cm, 15 cm

f 14 cm, 14 cm, 12 cm

Sometimes it helps if you turn the page around.

When three measurements are given in a question and you only need two, make sure that you choose the right two. You need the base and the perpendicular height from this base.

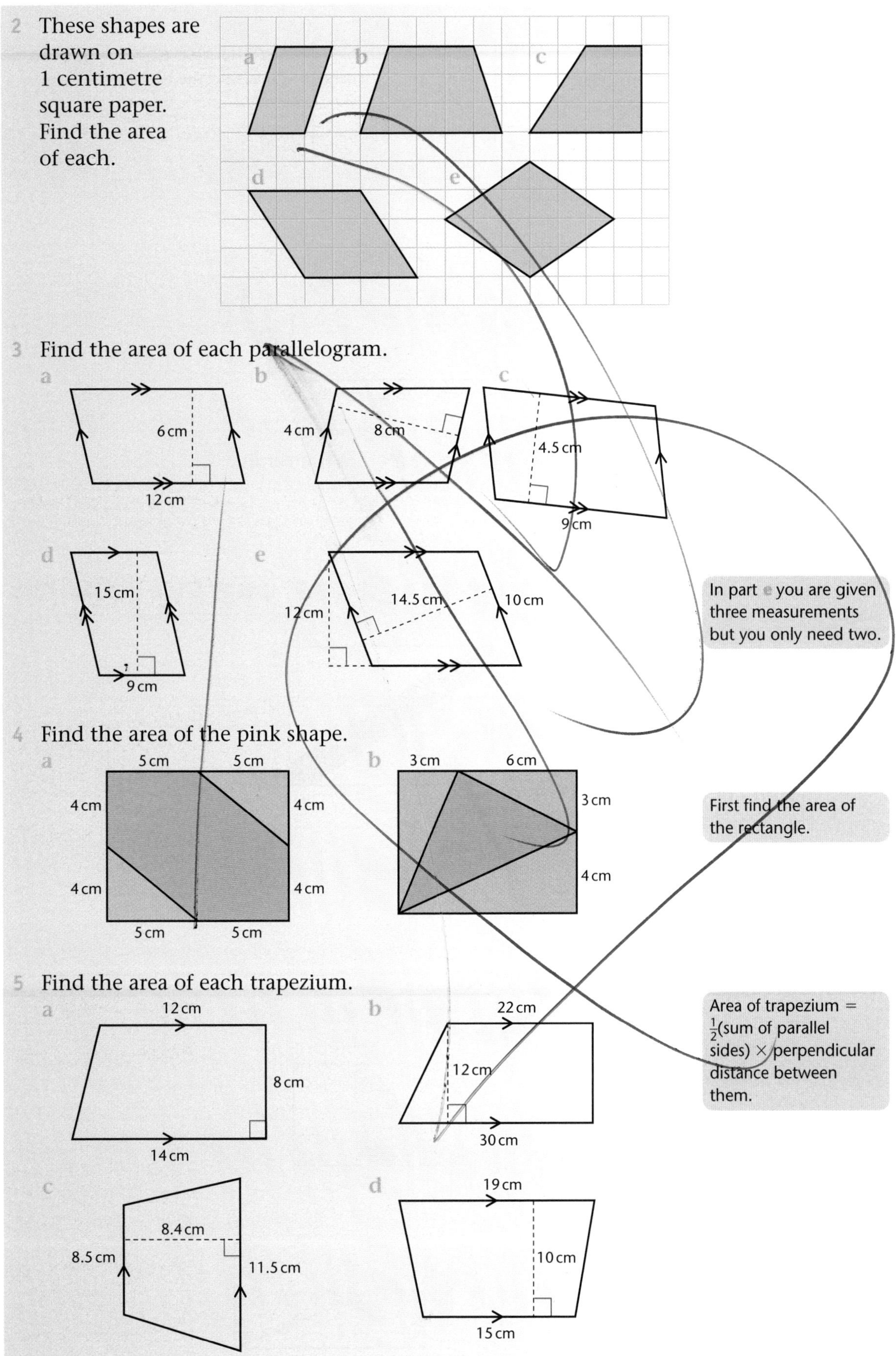
2 These shapes are drawn on 1 centimetre square paper. Find the area of each.
a
b
c
d
e
3 Find the area of each parallelogram.
a
6 cm
12 cm
b
4 cm
8 cm
c
4.5 cm
9 cm
d
15 cm
9 cm
e
12 cm
14.5 cm
10 cm
In part e you are given three measurements but you only need two.
4 Find the area of the pink shape.
a
5 cm
5 cm
4 cm
4 cm
4 cm
4 cm
5 cm
5 cm
b
3 cm
6 cm
3 cm
4 cm
First find the area of the rectangle.
5 Find the area of each trapezium.
a
12 cm
8 cm
14 cm
b
22 cm
12 cm
30 cm
Area of trapezium = ½(sum of parallel sides) × perpendicular distance between them.
c
8.4 cm
8.5 cm
11.5 cm
d
19 cm
10 cm
15 cm

6 Find the area of each shape.

a

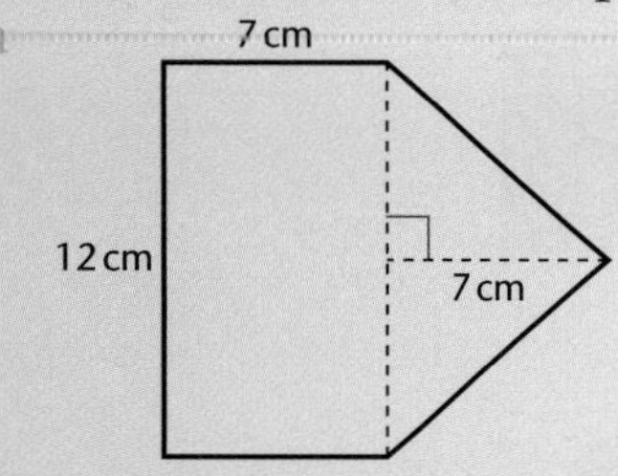

b

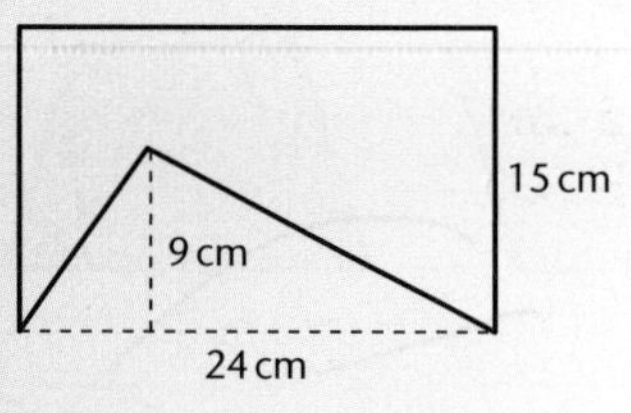

7 The diagram shows the end wall of a bungalow. Find its area.

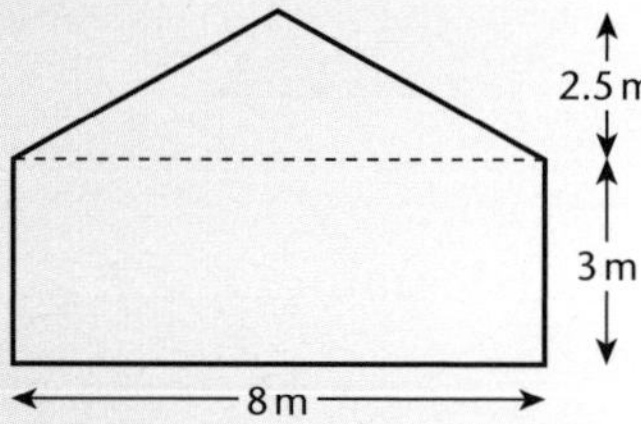

8 Each part of this shape is a trapezium. Find its area.

9 This white rectangular flag has a red diagonal band across it. Find:

a the length and width of the rectangle
b the area of the rectangle
c the area of the flag that is white
d the area of the shaded band.

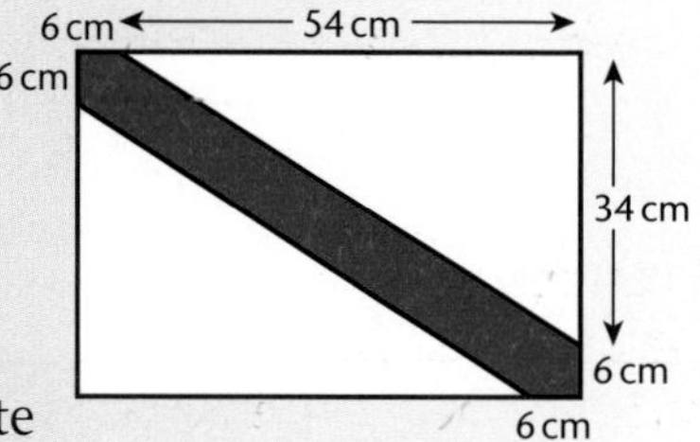

10 This hexagon is made from a rectangle and a trapezium. Find its area.

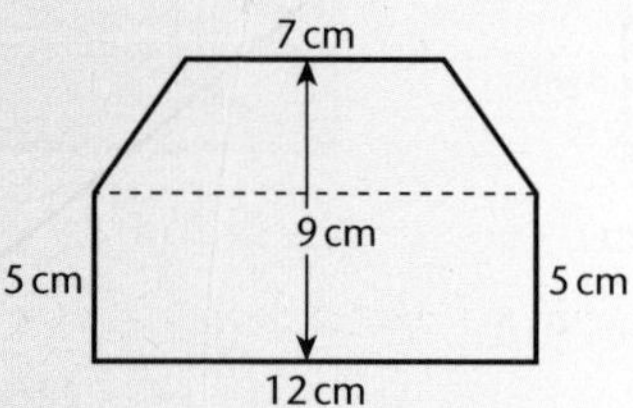

11 Two-fifths of this area is shaded. Work out the area that is:

a shaded b not shaded.

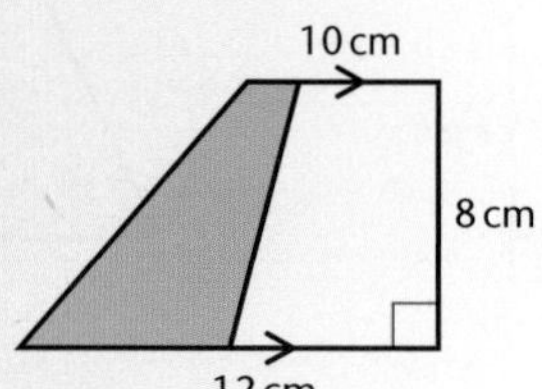

12 The area of △ABC is $\frac{5}{8}$ the area of △ADC. DC = 12 cm. Work out the length of AB.

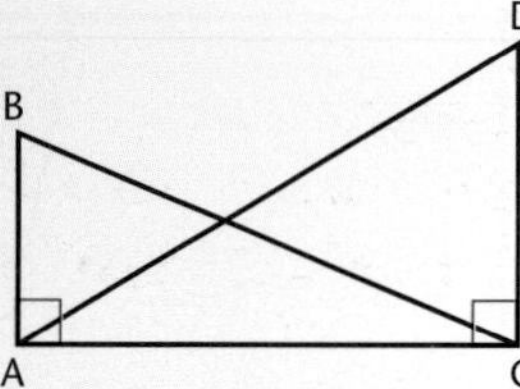

UAM

13 ABCD is a parallelogram.
C is the midpoint of BE.
The area of △CDE is 8.5 cm^2.
Work out the area of ABCD.

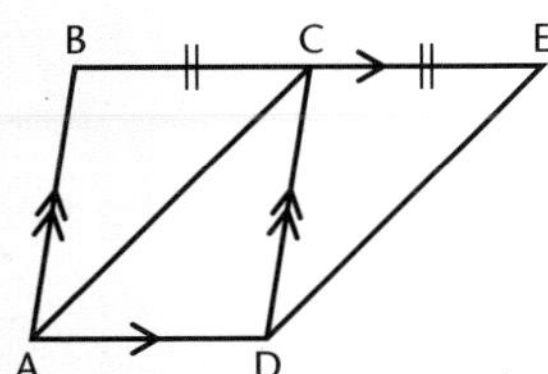

7.4 Circumference and area of circles

In a circle:

Diameter = 2 × radius

Circumference = 2 × π × radius
= π × diameter

Area = π × (radius)^2

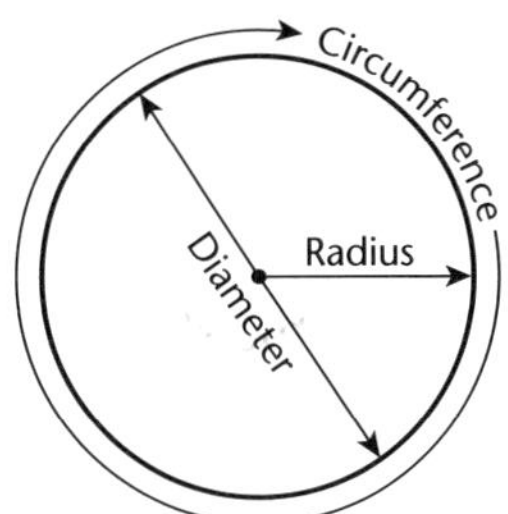

The **circumference** of a circle is the perimeter of the circle.

The formula for the circumference of a circle is $C = 2\pi r$ or $C = \pi d$.
The formula for the area of a circle is $A = \pi r^2$.

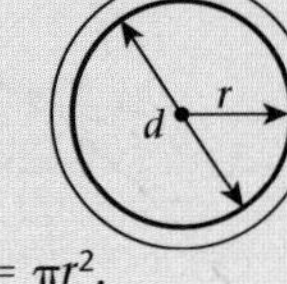

π is a number – it is the ratio of the circumference of a circle to its diameter.
π cannot be written exactly either as a fraction or as a decimal.
Sometimes you are asked to give your answer in terms of π.

For estimates use 3 as the value of π.

Example 6

The diameter of a wheel is 60 cm.
Find **a** an estimate for the circumference
b the circumference to the nearest centimetre.

a Estimate of circumference = 3 × 60 cm = 180 cm

Circumference = π × diameter.

b Circumference = π × 60 cm
= 188.4… cm
= 188 cm to the nearest cm.

Use your calculator. Press [π] [×] [6] [0] [=]

Example 7

Find the area of this semicircle.
Give your answer in terms of π.

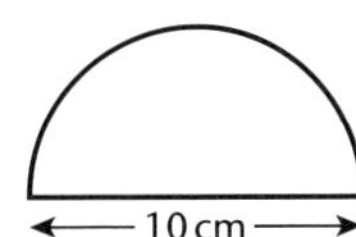

A semicircle is half a circle.

This means leave π in your answer.

Radius = 5 cm
Area of circle = π × (radius)^2
= π × (5)^2 = π × 25 = 25π
Area of semicircle = $\frac{1}{2}$ × 25π cm^2 = 12.5π cm^2.

radius = $\frac{1}{2}$ diameter

Work out the value of 5^2 but leave π as a symbol.

Example 8

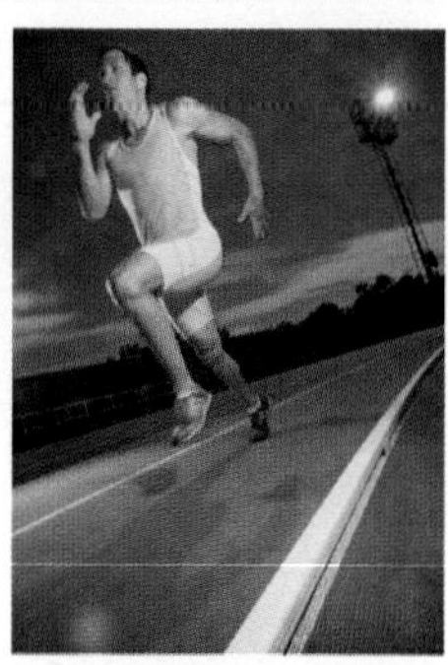

The distance round a circular running track is 400 m.
Work out the diameter of the track to the nearest metre.

$400 = \pi \times d$

$d = \frac{400}{\pi} = 127.3\ldots$

Diameter of track is 127 m to the nearest metre.

Circumference = π × diameter.
Use d for the diameter and replace 'circumference' by 400.

Press
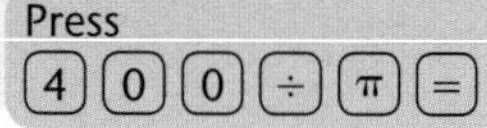

Example 9

The diameter of the circular top of a tin is 8 cm.
Find its area to the nearest cm^2.

Area = $\pi \times (\text{radius})^2$

$\pi \times 4^2 = 50.2\ldots$

Area of top = 50 cm^2 to the nearest cm^2.

Radius is half diameter = $\frac{1}{2}$ of 8 = 4.

Exam practice 7D

1 Use $\pi = 3$ to estimate the circumference of a circle with radius
a 10 cm b 8 m c 30 mm.

2 Estimate the circumference of this wheel.

3 The radius of a circular clock face is 12 cm.
a What is its diameter?
b Use $\pi = 3$ to estimate its circumference.

4 Use $\pi = 3$ to estimate the diameter of a circle with a circumference of
a 180 cm b 7.5 m c 96 mm.

5 Find, in terms of π,
a the circumference of a circle of radius 4 cm
b the area of a circle of radius 3 m
c the diameter of a circle with a circumference of 60 cm.

Did you know
that mathematicians over the ages have spent a lot of time trying to find the exact value of π?
You can use the π button on your calculator to see the value to several decimal places.
The earliest known reference to π is around 1650 BC in a papyrus. Around 200 BC, Archimedes said that π is a number between $3\frac{10}{71}$ and $3\frac{1}{7}$.
The first person to use the Greek letter for the number was a Welsh mathematician, William Jones, in 1706.

In the remaining questions give answers to an appropriate degree of accuracy.

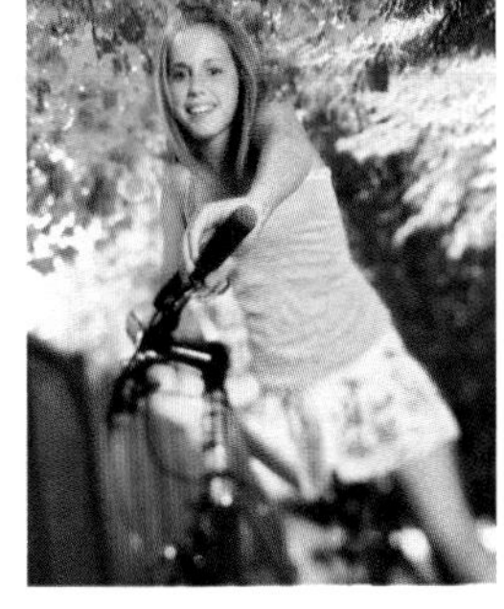

6 The diameter of Kayleigh's bicycle wheel is 60 cm.
  a Calculate the circumference of the wheel.
  b Kayleigh cycles 100 metres.
    How many revolutions does the wheel make?

7 This circular kitchen table top has a plastic strip around the edge.
  a How long is the strip?
  b Work out the area of the table.

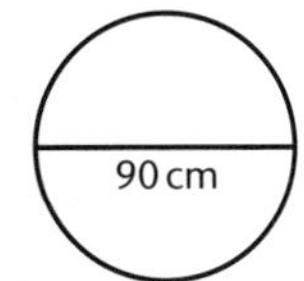

8 The diameters of three different sized plates are
  16 cm, 21 cm and 27 cm.
  Find the circumference of each.

9 This is a semicircle.
  Work out a the perimeter b the area.

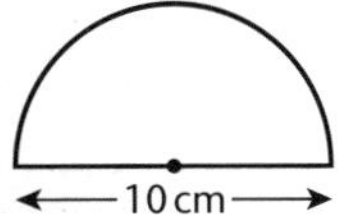

A semicircle is half a circle.

10 a The radius of a circular flower bed is 22 metres. Find its area.
   b The diameter of a circular brooch is 38 mm. Find its area.

11 a The diameter of a plate is 17 cm. Find its area.
   b Flo said that the area of another plate which had a diameter of 25 cm was more than twice as much. Was Flo correct?
   UAM Give a reason for your answer.

12 This window is made from a square and a semicircle.
   Find its area.

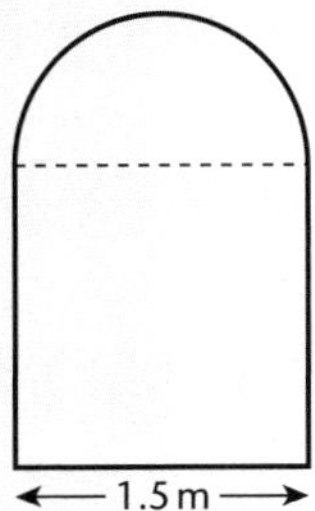

13 This is the cross-section through a piece of skirting board. It is made from a rectangle and a quadrant. Work out the area of the cross-section.

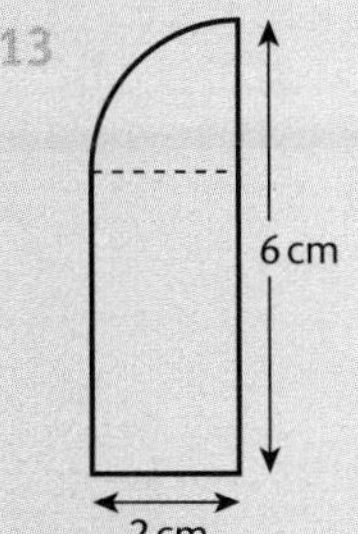

A quadrant is one quarter of a circle.

14 The diagram shows a mount for a photo frame.
   A circle, diameter 14 cm, has been removed from a square of side 20 cm.
   Find
   a the area of the original square card
   b the circular area cut out
   c the area of the mount.

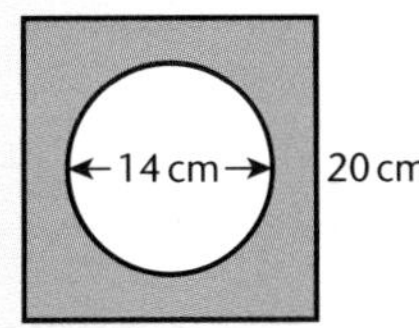

15 In her garden Jan has a circular swimming pool, diameter 8 metres, surrounded by a square paved area. The side of the square is 14 metres.
Work out
a the total length of the edge of the paved area
b the area that is paved.

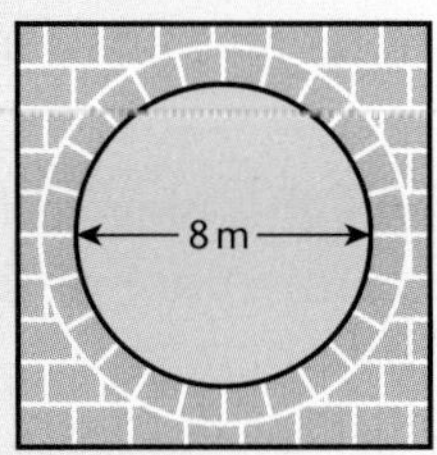

The paved area has two edges – an inside edge and an outside edge.

16 This is a Pembroke table. It has two semicircular leaves that hang vertically when the table is not wholly opened out.
Find
a the area of the rectangular top
b the area of one semi circular leaf
c the surface area of the top of the table when it is opened out.

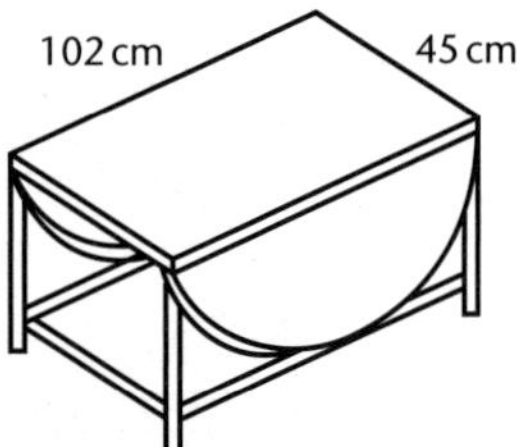

7.5 Arcs and sectors of circles

The shaded area OAB is a **sector**. It is bounded by two radii and an arc.

$$\text{Length of arc AB} = 2\pi r \times \frac{\angle AOB}{360°}$$

$$\text{Area of sector} = \pi r^2 \times \frac{\angle AOB}{360°}$$

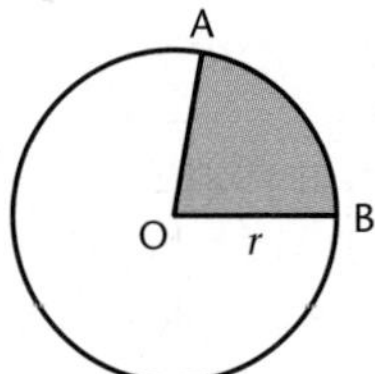

The **arc** AB bounding the sector is a **minor arc**. The arc AB bounding the unshaded part of the circle is a **major arc**.

Radii is the plural of radius.

Example 10

This circle has a radius of 5 cm.
Work out
a the value of x
b the area of the sector.

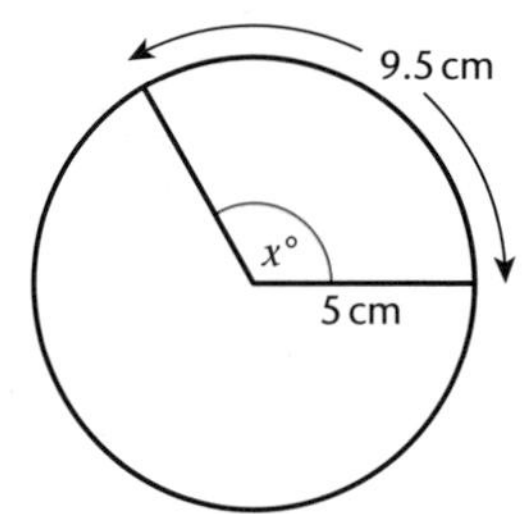

a arc length $= 2\pi r \times \frac{x}{360}$

$9.5 = (2\pi \times 5)\frac{x}{360}$

$\frac{360 \times 9.5}{2\pi \times 5} = x$ so $x = 108.86\ldots$

$\therefore x = 109$ to the nearest whole number.

b area of sector $= \pi r^2 \times \frac{x}{360}$

$\pi \times 5^2 \times \frac{108.86\ldots}{360} = 23.75$

Area of sector is $23.75\ \text{cm}^2$

Exam practice 7E

1 For each sector find
i the length of the arc ii the area of the sector.

a
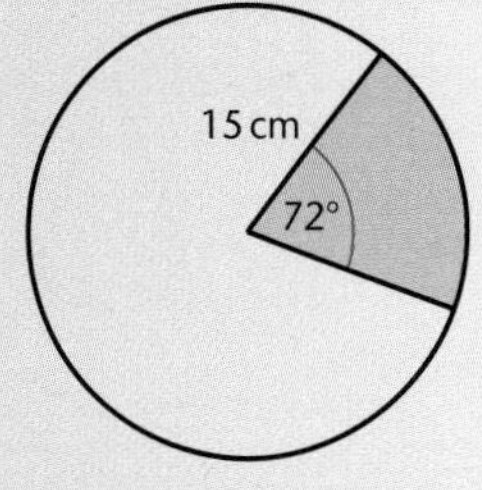

b
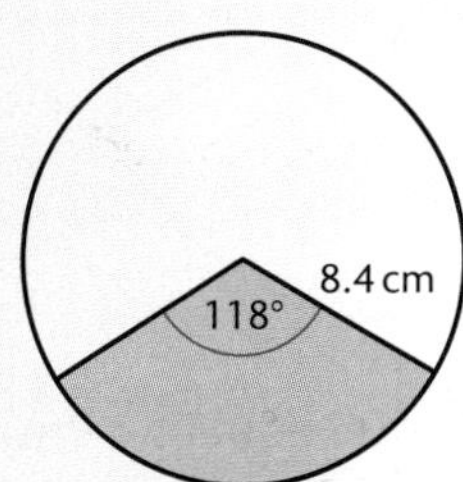

c
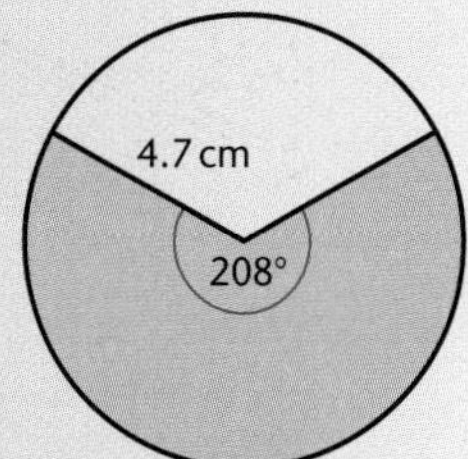

d
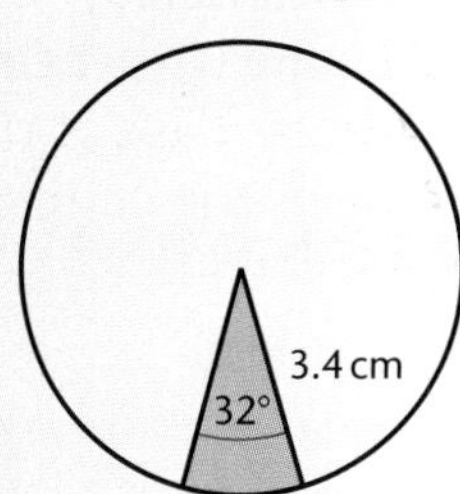

2 Find the angle marked at the centre of each circle.

a
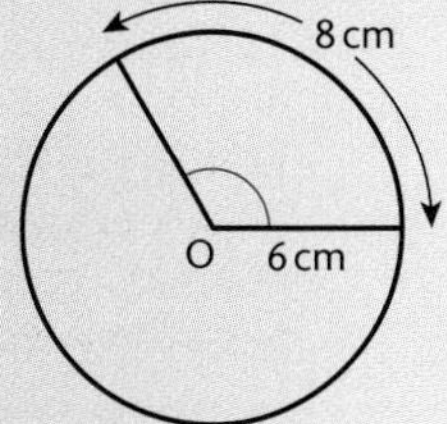

b
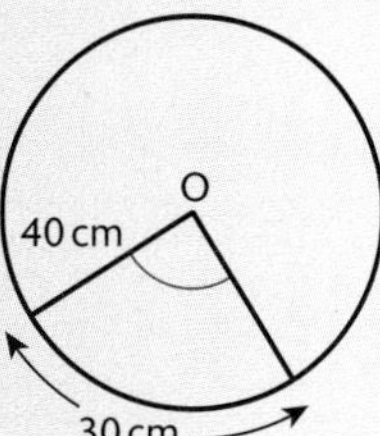

c
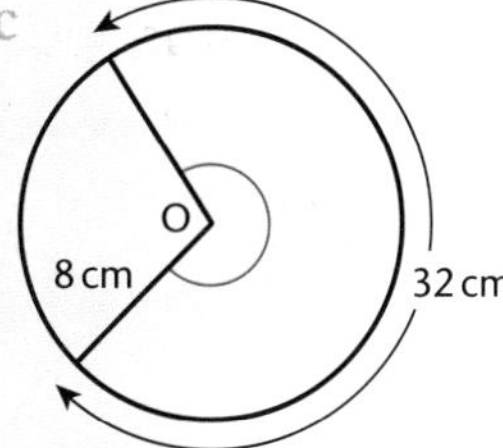

3 Find the radius of each circle.

a
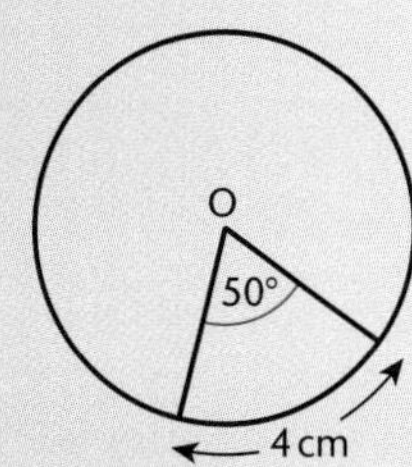

b
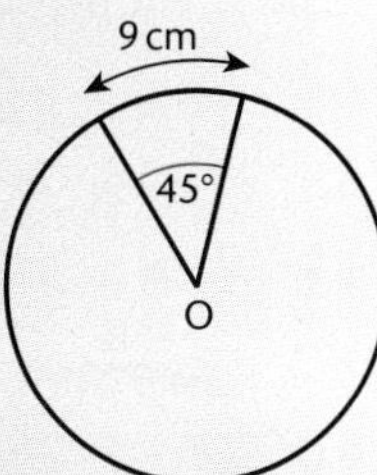

c
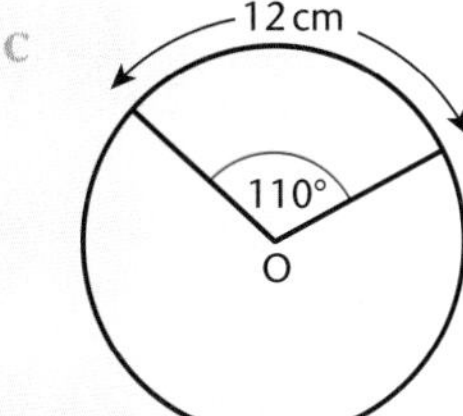

4 O is the centre of this circle.
Find, in terms of π,
a ∠AOB
b the area of the shaded sector.

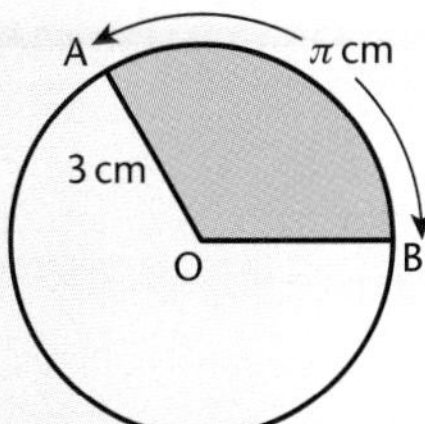

5 The radius of this circle is 20 cm.
Find
a the length of the major arc AB
b the area of the minor sector OAB.

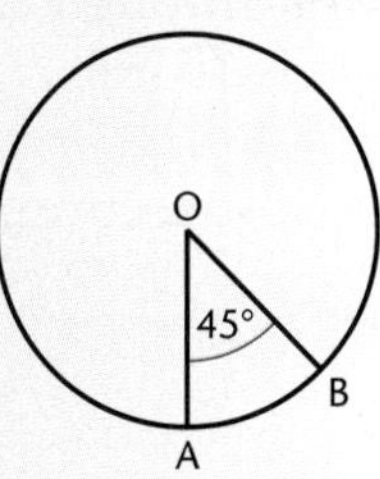

major arc + minor arc = circumference.

6 OAB is a sector of a circle of radius 12 cm.

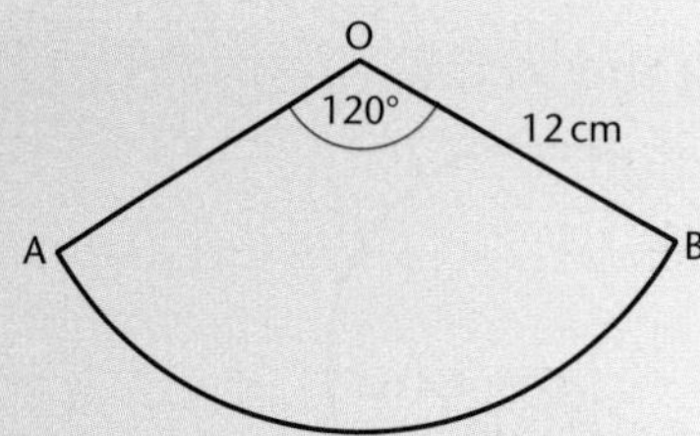

The length of the arc AB becomes the circumference of the circular base.

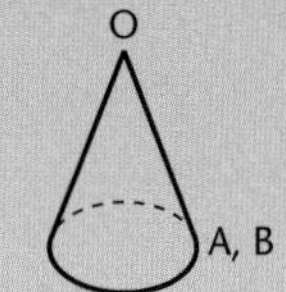

a Show that the length of the arc AB is 8π cm.
b Find, in terms of π, the area of the sector.
c The sector is folded to make a cone with a circular base added. Calculate the radius of the circular base of the cone.
d Work out the total surface area of the cone.

7 Kelly has a circular pond in her garden. Its diameter is 7 metres.

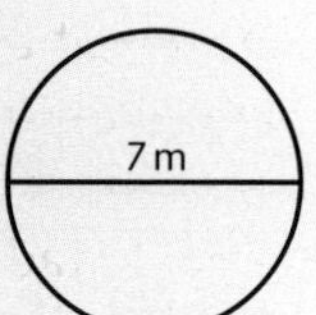

Remember to give the units.

a Find the circumference of the pond
i in terms of π ii correct to 1 d.p.
b Work out the area of the pond
i in terms of π ii correct to 3 s.f.

8 Work out the area that is coloured.

The coloured area is called a **segment**. First find the area of the sector AOB. Now find the area of $\triangle$OAB.

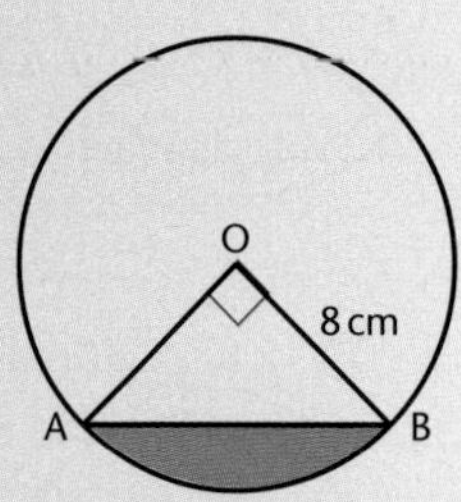

9 Four drop-down flaps will convert a square table into a round one. The diameter of the circular table is 2 metres.
a Work out the the area of the four flaps.
b Show that the area of the square is increased by 57% by raising the flaps.

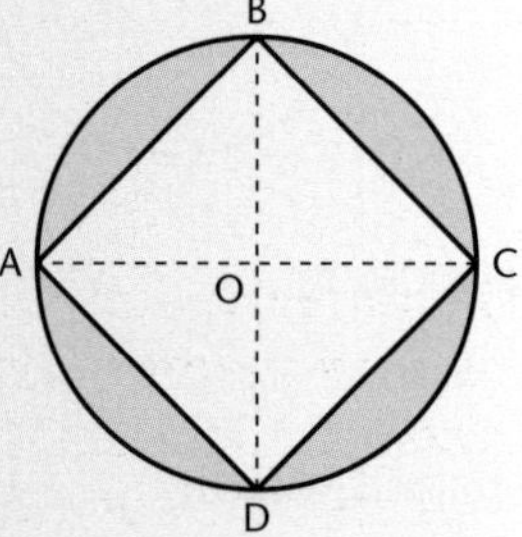

10 This sketch shows the cross-section through a metal pipe. The bore of the pipe is 10 mm and the diameter 16 mm.
Work out the area of the shaded cross-section.

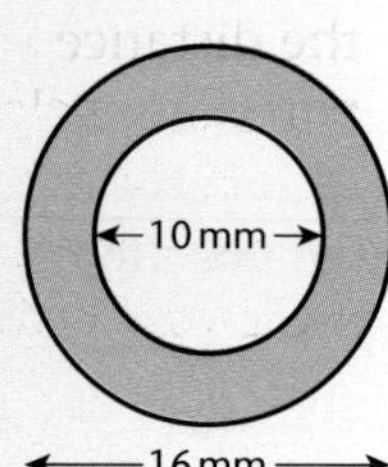

Summary of key points

- You need to know these relationships between units:
  1 km = 1000 m, 1 m = 100 cm, 1 cm = 10 mm
  1 yard = 3 feet, 1 foot = 12 inches
  5 miles ≈ 8 km, 2 inches ≈ 5 cm
- To convert a large unit to a smaller unit multiply.
- To convert a small unit to a larger unit divide.
- The perimeter of a shape is the total distance around its sides.
- Area of a rectangle = length × breadth.
- Area of a triangle = $\frac{1}{2}$ base × perpendicular height.
- Area of a parallelogram = length of one side × the perpendicular distance between that side and the other parallel side.
- Area of a trapezium = $\frac{1}{2}$ the sum of the parallel sides × height perpendicular to them.
- The area of a compound shape can often be found by dividing it into shapes whose areas you can find.
- Circumference of a circle = 2π × radius.
- Area of a circle = $\pi \times (\text{radius})^2$.
- Arc length = $2\pi r \times \frac{x}{360}$ where r is the radius of the circle and $x°$ the angle at the centre.
- Area of a sector of a circle = $\pi r^2 \times \frac{x}{360}$ where r is the radius of the circle and $x°$ the angle at the centre.

Most candidates who get GRADE C or above can:

- convert between metric and imperial units
- find the perimeter and area of a rectangle
- find the perimeter and area of a semicircle.

Most candidates who get GRADE A or above can also:

- find the length of a major arc given the radius and angle at the centre.

Glossary

Acre	an imperial unit for measuring area
Arc	part of an unbroken curved line
Circumference	the perimeter of a circle
Hectare	a metric unit of area
Major arc	the longer arc when the circle is divided into two unequal parts
Minor arc	the shorter arc when the circle is divided into two unequal parts
Perimeter	the distance around a shape
Sector	part of a circle bounded by two radii and an arc
Segment	one of the two regions a circle is divided into by a chord
Square centimetre	the area covered by a square with side 1 cm
Square millimetre	the area covered by a square with side 1 mm

8 3-D Shapes

This chapter will show you:

- ✓ what a cube, cuboid, prism, cylinder, pyramid, cone and sphere are
- ✓ how to draw the plan, front and side elevations for different solids
- ✓ how to find the surface area and volume of a cube, cuboid, right prism, cylinder, cone and sphere
- ✓ how to convert one unit of volume to another
- ✓ how to find the volume of a compound shape
- ✓ the relationship between volume and capacity
- ✓ how to convert between units of mass
- ✓ the meaning of density
- ✓ how to use dimensions to distinguish between formulae that give lengths, areas or volumes

Before you start you need to know:

- ✓ how to draw shapes accurately
- ✓ how to find the area of a square, a rectangle, a triangle, a parallelogram and a trapezium
- ✓ how to find the circumference and area of a circle
- ✓ the relationship between metric units of length and area
- ✓ how to work with fractions and decimals

8.1 Cubes, cuboids, prisms and cylinders

This is a **cube**. It has:

- 6 **faces** (top, bottom and 4 sides)
- 12 **edges** (an edge is where two faces meet)
- 8 vertices or corners (a **vertex** is where 3 or more faces meet).

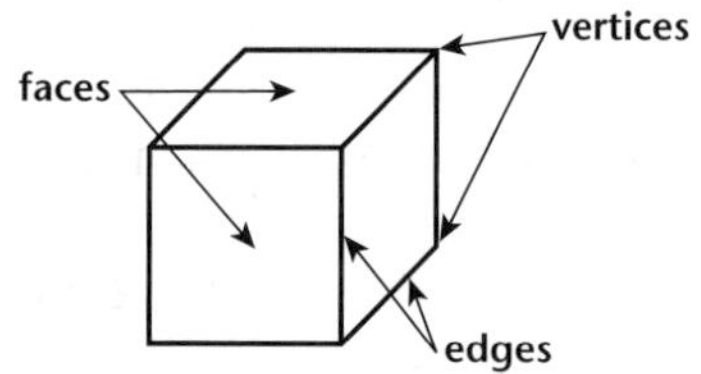

The faces are all squares and the edges are all the same length.

This is a **cuboid**. It has the same number of faces, edges and vertices as a cube. The edges are not all the same length.
The faces are rectangles, but not all the same size.
Each pair of opposite faces are congruent rectangles.

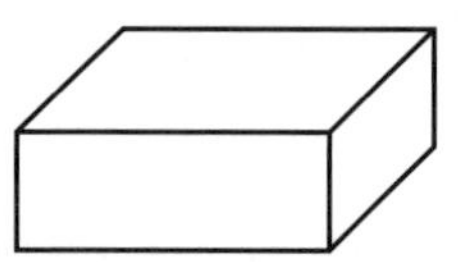

A cuboid is a rectangular block like a brick.
A cube is a special type of cuboid.

These are **prisms**. The two ends of a prism are parallel and the same shape. This can be any shape. When the ends are polygons the other faces are rectangles.

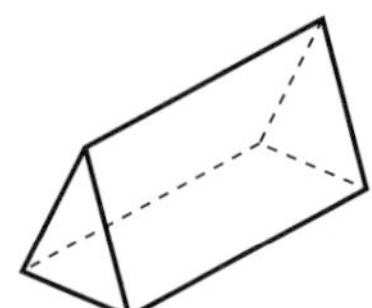

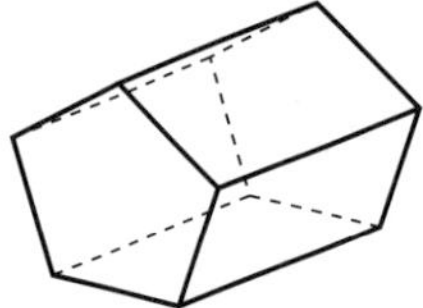

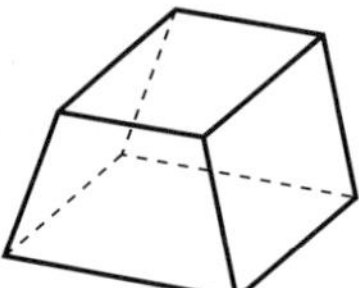

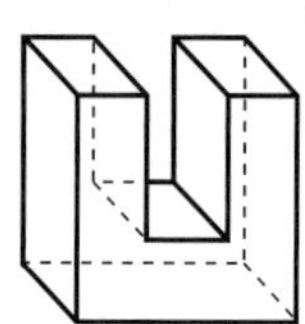

A cuboid is a rectangular prism.
Its cross-section is a rectangle.

When a prism is cut parallel to its ends the shape of its cut face is called its **cross-section**.

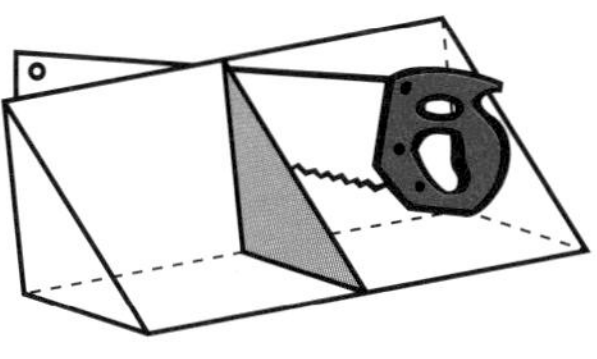

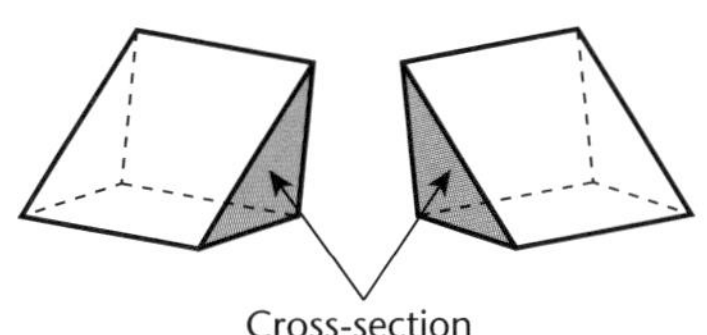

In this example the cross-section is a triangle.

The cross-section of a prism is **uniform**.
This means it is exactly the same throughout.

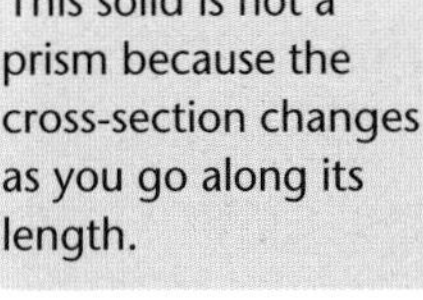

This solid is not a prism because the cross-section changes as you go along its length.

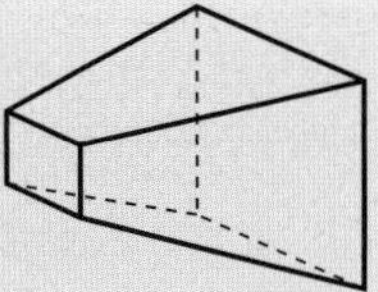

The cross-section of this shape is a circle.
It is called a **cylinder**.

Planes of symmetry

A plane of reflective symmetry cuts a solid into two parts, one of which is the reflection of the other in the plane.

Class discussion

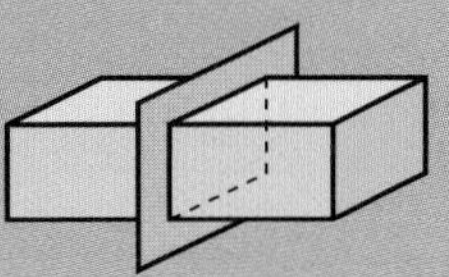

a A cuboid has 3 planes of symmetry. This is one. Can you find the other two?
b Describe the planes of symmetry of a cylinder.

Exam practice 8A

1 This is a cuboid.

a How many faces does it have?
b How many faces meet at A?
c How many faces are rectangles measuring 6 cm by 3 cm?
d How many edges are 5 cm long?
e Nikki said that the sum of the lengths of all the edges is 56 cm. Is Nikki correct? Give a reason for your answer.

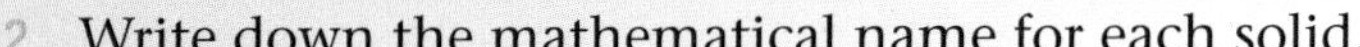

2 Write down the mathematical name for each solid.

a 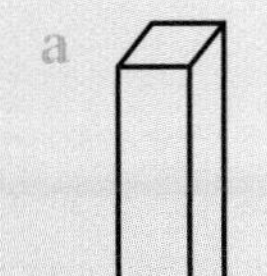 b 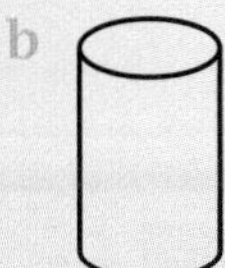 c 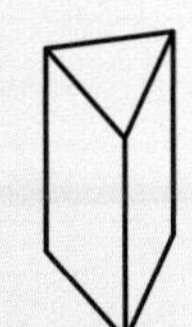 d 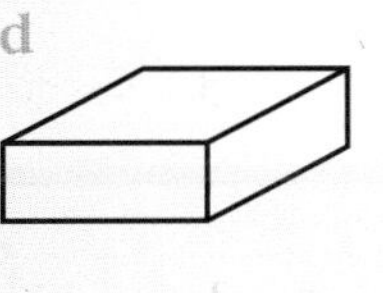 e 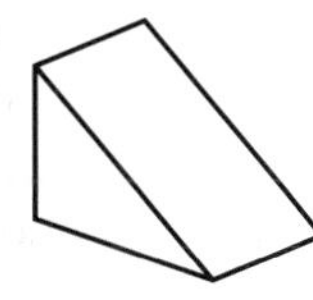

3 The cross-section of this prism is a trapezium.

a Write down the number of
i faces ii edges iii vertices.
b How many planes of symmetry are there?

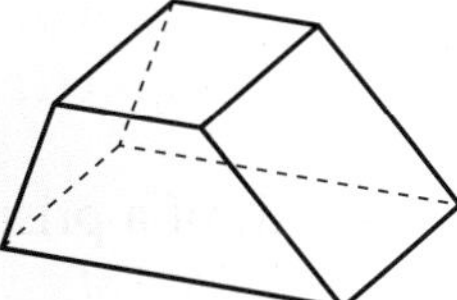

4 The cross-section of this prism is a regular hexagon.
Write down the number of
a faces b edges c vertices.

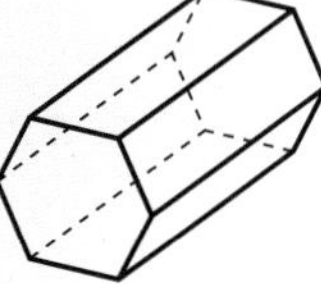

8.2 Plans and elevations

When you look at a solid from different directions, you see different shapes.

This beaker looks different depending on which way you look at it.

When you look directly from above you see two circles.

This is called a **plan**.

When you look from the side you see this shape.

This is called an **elevation**.

Example 1

This solid is made from 10 cubes.
Draw the view

a from direction A

b from direction B.

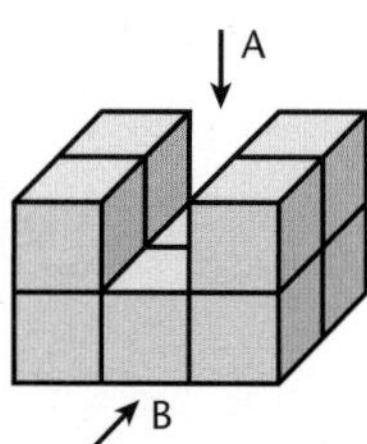

a

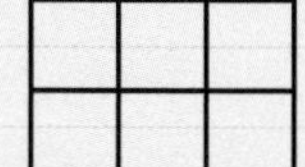

Looking from direction A (above) you can see the tops of 6 cubes. This is the plan.

b

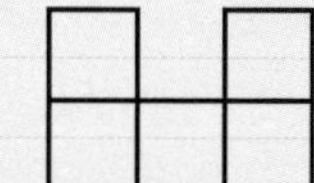

Looking from direction B (the front) you can see the front faces of 5 cubes. This is the front elevation.

Example 2

a Draw the plan of this solid.

b Draw the elevation of this solid from direction B.

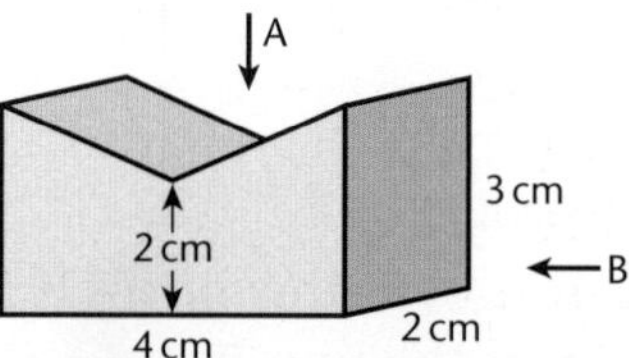

a

When you look from above you can see the edges shown in red. The sloping edges shown in green look shorter than they are. They look flat.

b

The broken line shows that there is an edge that you cannot see.

Example 3

The top of this solid is a cube.
It is drawn on a 5 mm isometric grid.

a Draw the plan

b Draw the elevation from the direction of the arrow.

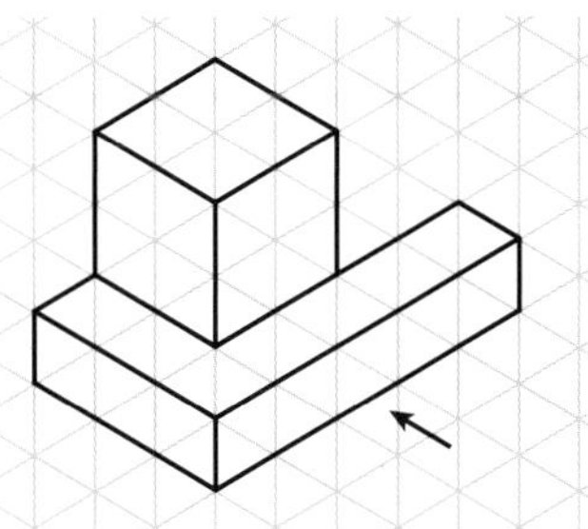

An isometric grid gives a way of drawing a 3-D solid by preserving lengths. Every line on this grid is 5 mm long and represents the true length of an edge on the solid.

a

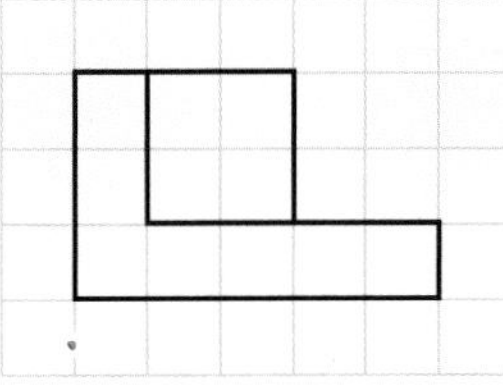

From above, you can see the shaded faces.

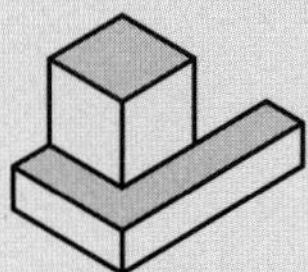

The top face is a square of side 1 cm.

b

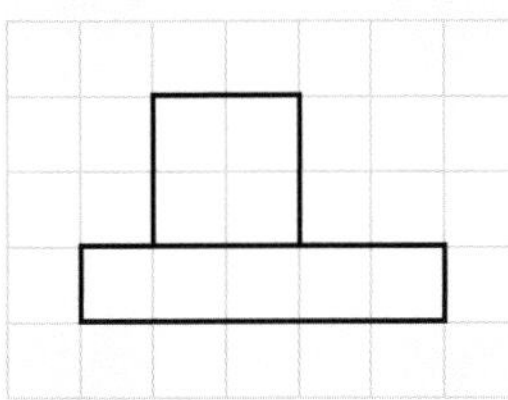

From the direction of the arrow you can see the shaded square and rectangle.

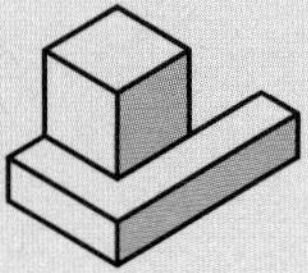

Exam practice 8B

Use 1 cm squared or dotted paper for this exercise.

1 This solid is made from 5 cubes.
  a Draw the plan.
  b Draw the view from direction B.

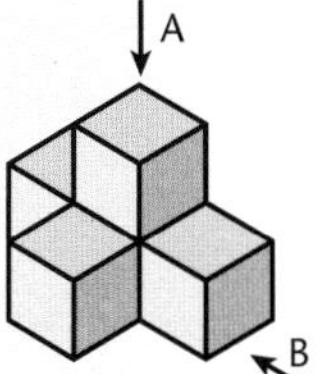
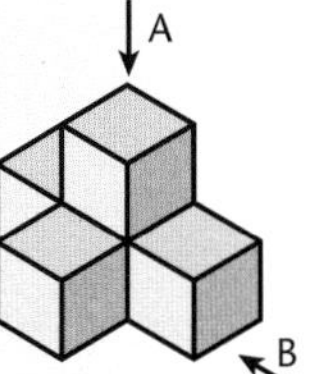

The plan is the view from direction A.

2 This solid is made from 7 cubes.
  Draw the view
  a from direction A
  b from direction B.

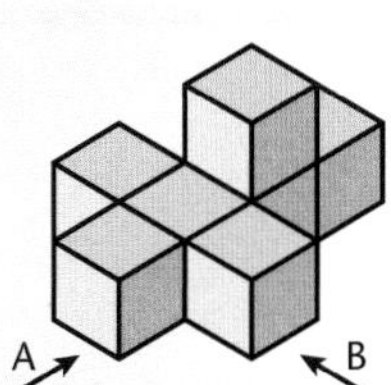

3 This solid is made from 7 cubes.
  Draw the view
  a from direction A
  b from direction B.

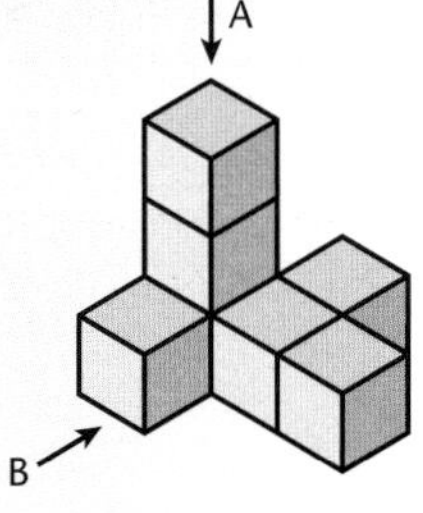

4 This shape is made from 10 cubes.

a Draw the elevation

i from direction A

ii from direction B.

b Draw the plan.

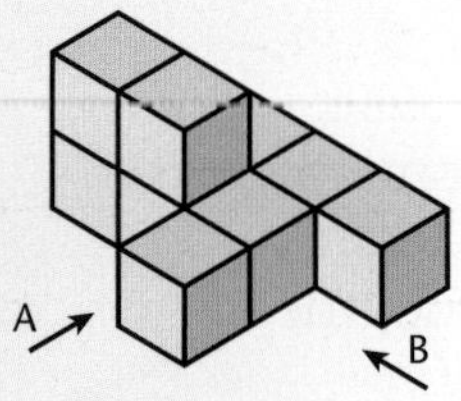

5 This shape is made from 10 cubes.

a Draw the elevation

i from direction A

ii from direction B.

b Draw the plan.

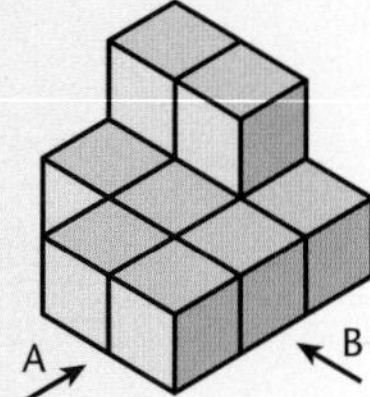

6 Draw the views from the directions labelled.
All measurements are given in centimetres.

a

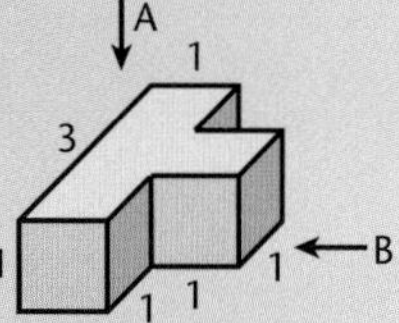

b

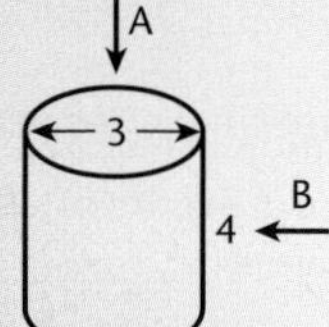

c

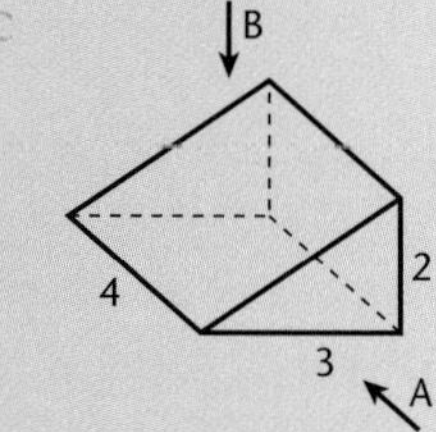

d

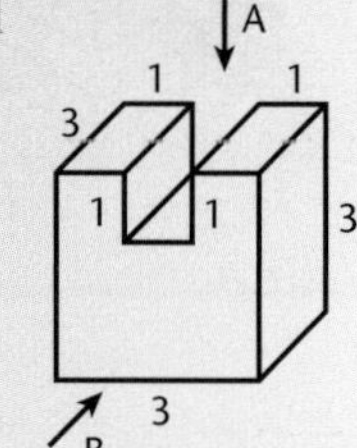

7 Draw the elevation of each solid from the direction shown by the arrow.

a

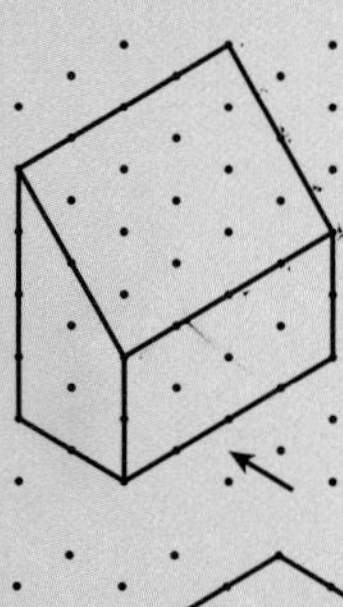

b

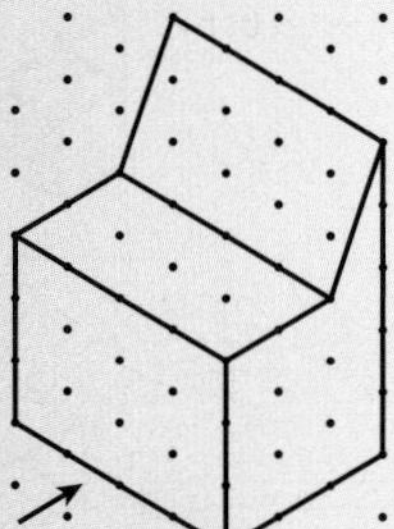

c

These solids are drawn on an isometric grid. The dots are 5 mm apart in all directions.

8 Sketch the solid with the following plan, front and side elevations.

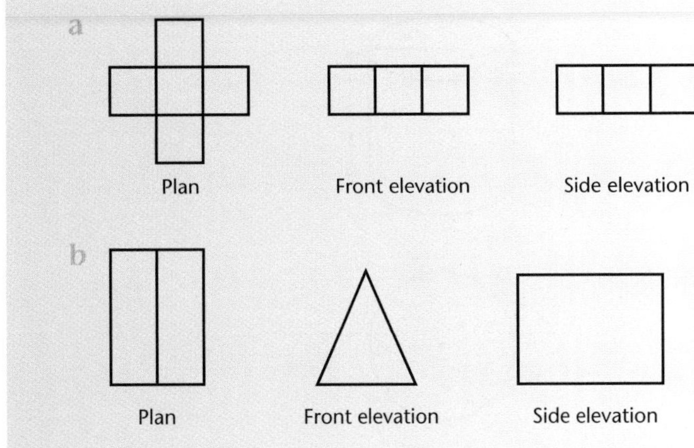

8.3 Surface area of a cuboid, prism and cylinder

You can find the total surface area of a prism by adding together the areas of the faces.

Example 4

The cross-section of this prism is a trapezium.
Find the total surface area of this prism.

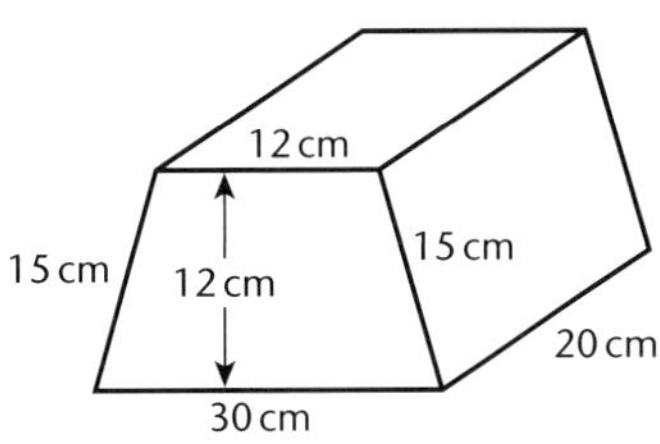

	Front	Back	Top	Bottom	Side	Side
Area (cm^2)	$\frac{1}{2}(12 + 30) \times 12$ = 252	$\frac{1}{2}(12 + 30) \times 12$ = 252	12×20 = 240	30×20 = 600	15×20 = 300	15×20 = 300

Area of a trapezium
= $\frac{1}{2}$(sum of the parallel sides) × (distance between them)

The front and back are trapeziums.
The other 4 sides are rectangles.

You can use a table to make sure you do not miss any faces.

$252 + 252 + 240 + 600 + 300 + 300 = 1944$

Total surface area = 1944 cm^2.

Surface area of a cylinder

This cylinder has radius r and height h.

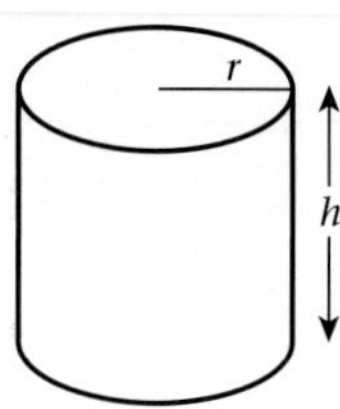

The ends are circles so the area of each end is πr^2.

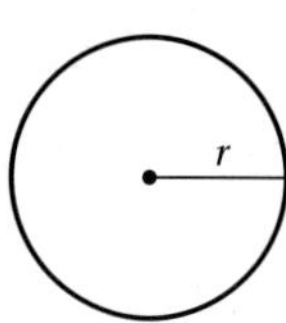

The curved part opens out into a rectangle measuring $2\pi r$ by h.
So the area of the curved surface is $2\pi rh$.

Total surface area $= 2\pi r^2 + 2\pi rh = 2\pi r(r + h)$

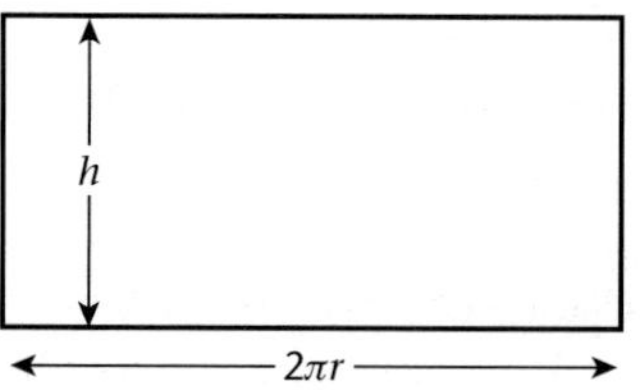

Example 5

A cylindrical water tank is 1.24 m high and has a radius of 54 cm.

a Find the curved surface area of the tank.

b Find its total surface area.

Give your answer in square metres to 1 decimal place.

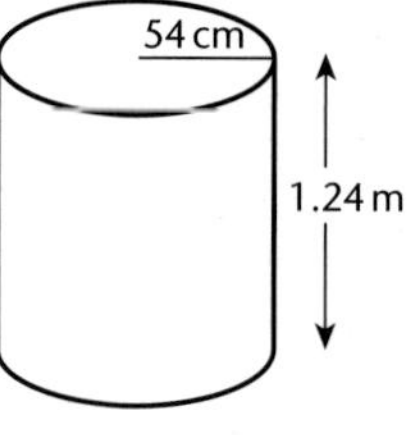

a Height of cylinder = 1.24 m

Radius of cylinder = 0.54 m

Curved surface area $= 2\pi rh$

$= 2 \times \pi \times 0.54 \times 1.24\ \text{m}^2$

$= 4.207\ldots\ \text{m}^2$

$= 4.2\ \text{m}^2$ to 1 d.p.

Both dimensions must be in the same units. The answer is asked for in square metres, so convert 54 cm to metres.

b Area of one end $= \pi r^2$

$= \pi \times (0.54)^2\ \text{m}^2$

$= 0.916\ldots\ \text{m}^2$

Total surface area $= (0.916\ldots + 0.916\ldots + 4.207\ldots)\ \text{m}^2$

$= 6.03\ldots\ \text{m}^2$

$= 6.0\ \text{m}^2$ to 1 d.p.

Do not use rounded answers in calculations.

Exam practice 8C

Find the total surface area of each cuboid.

> The area of a rectangle = length × breadth.

1 2 3

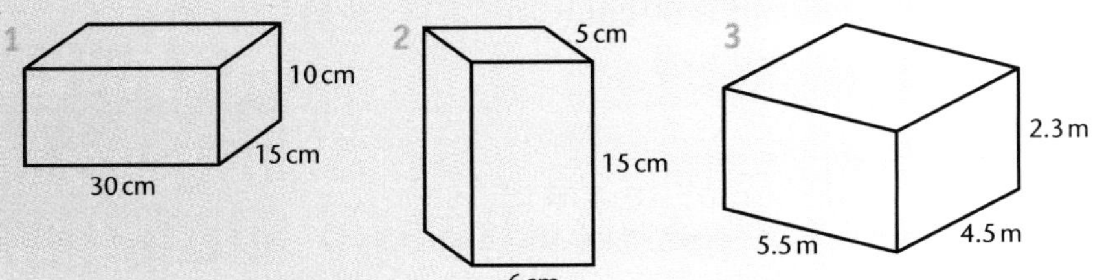

4 This is a box for sending wedding cake through the post .
Work out its total surface area.

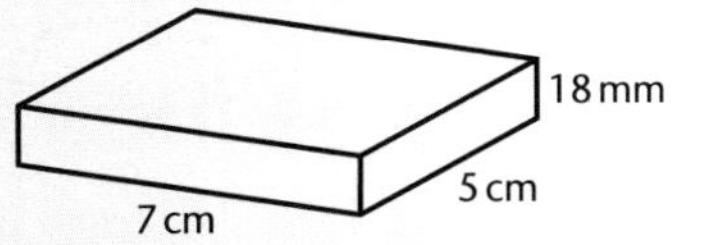

> The lengths must be in the same units. Change 18 mm to cm.

5 This is a child's building block.
The blocks are to be painted yellow.
One can of paint will cover an area of 1 m².
Eli says that the paint in one can is enough to paint more than 100 blocks.
Is Eli correct? Give a reason for your answer.

6 Find the total surface area of each shape.

a

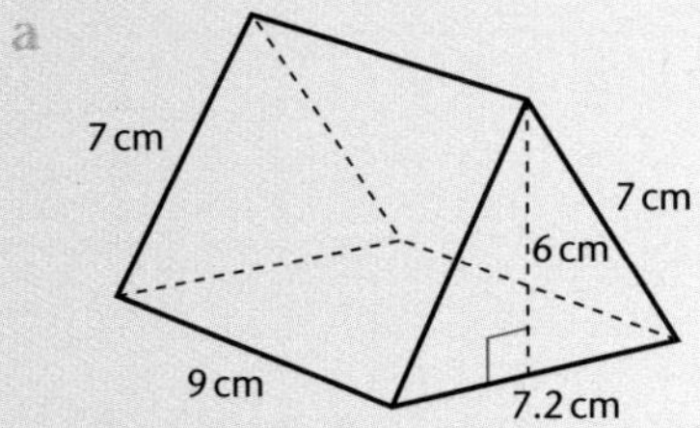

b

7 This is a water trough.
It is made from three rectangular planks with trapeziums at each end.
Find
a the outside area of each end piece
b the total area of the outside of the trough.

> It does not have a top.

8 The curved surface of a cylindrical can is covered by a label.
The diameter of the tin is 7.4 cm and it is 10 cm high.
Work out
a the circumference of the tin
b the area of the label.
Give your answer to the nearest cm and cm² respectively.

9 The radius of a cylinder is 4 cm. It is 12 cm long.
Work out
a the area of one end
b its curved surface area
c the percentage of its total surface area that is curved.
Give your answers to 1 d.p.

10 A coin is 1.5 mm thick and has a diameter of 2.5 cm.
Find the total surface area of the coin. Give your answer to 3 s.f.

Take care with units.

11 A garden roller has a radius of 35 cm and is 60 cm wide.

a Find, in square metres, the area rolled by
  i one complete turn of the roller
  ii 100 complete turns of the roller.

b How many revolutions are needed to roll an area of 800 square metres? Give your answer correct to the nearest whole number.

12

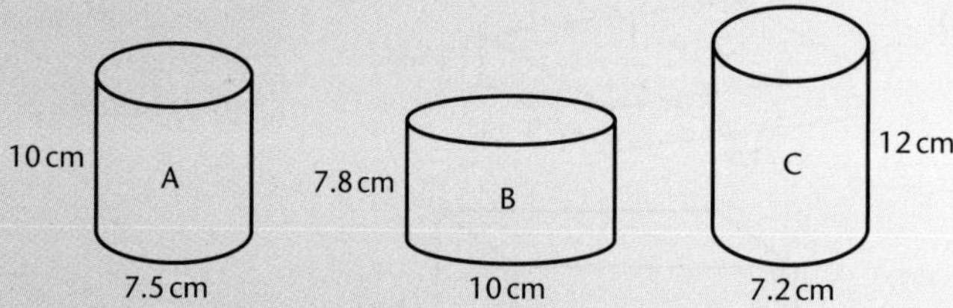

Kobi has three cylinders. Which cylinder has

a the largest curved surface area
b the smallest curved surface area
c the smallest total surface area?

Give reasons for your answers.

8.4 Volume

Volume measures the space occupied by a solid.
Volume is measured in standard sized cubes.

1 cubic centimetre is written 1 cm^3.

A cube of side 1 cm has a volume of 1 cubic centimetre (1 cm^3).
A cube of side 1 mm has a volume of 1 cubic millimetre (1 mm^3).
A cube of side 1 m has a volume of 1 cubic metre (1 m^3).

The relationships between these units are:

$$1\,cm^3 = 10 \times 10 \times 10\,mm^3 = 1000\,mm^3$$
$$1\,m^3 = 100 \times 100 \times 100\,cm^3 = 1\,000\,000\,cm^3$$

Example 6

Convert

a 0.0073 cm^3 into mm^3 **b** 6540 cm^3 into m^3.

a $1\,cm^3 = 1000\,mm^3$
so $0.0073\,cm^3 = 0.0073 \times 1000\,mm^3 = 7.3\,mm^3$

You are converting to a smaller unit, so multiply.

b $1\,m^3 = 1\,000\,000\,cm^3$
so $6540\,cm^3 = \frac{6450}{1\,000\,000}\,m^3 = 0.006\,54\,m^3$

You are converting to a larger unit, so divide.

Volume of cuboid = length × breadth × height

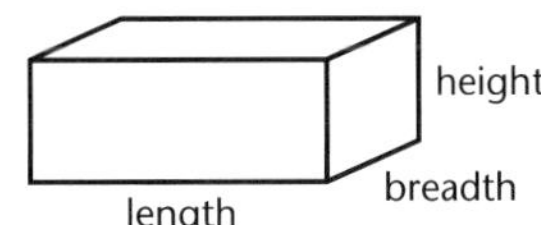

Example 7

Find the volume of each solid.

a

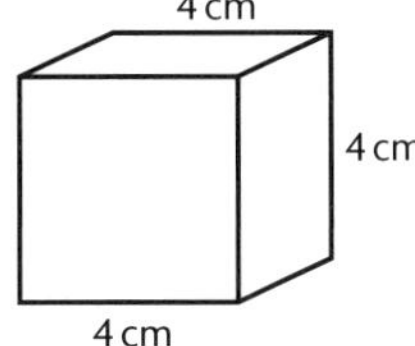

b

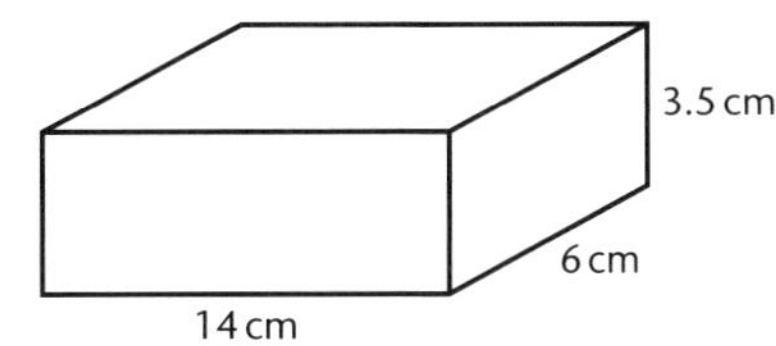

a Volume of cube = $4 \times 4 \times 4\ cm^3 = 64\ cm^3$

b Volume of cuboid = $14 \times 6 \times 3.5\ cm^3 = 294\ cm^3$

The length, breadth and height of a cube are all the same.

Example 8

The cross-section of this piece of wood is a T. Find its volume.

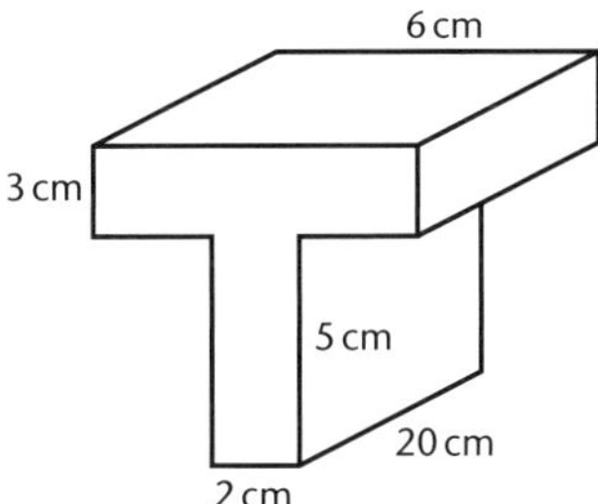

Volume of A is $6 \times 3 \times 20\ cm^3 = 360\ cm^3$

Volume of B is $5 \times 2 \times 20\ cm^3 = 200\ cm^3$

$360 + 200 = 560$

Volume of wood = $560\ cm^3$

This solid can be divided into two cuboids.

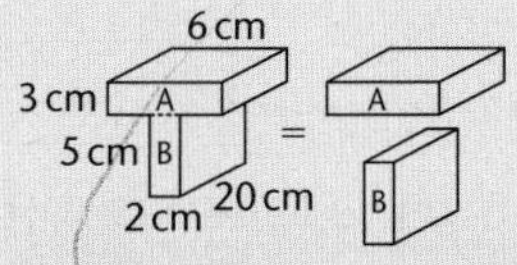

Cuboid A measures 6 cm × 3 cm × 20 cm.
Cuboid B measures 5 cm × 2 cm × 20 cm.

Exam practice 8D

1 These solids are made from cubes of side 1 centimetre. Find their volumes.

a

b

c

Class discussion

Which unit would you use to measure the volume of:

- the room you are in
- a brick
- a teaspoonful of water
- a 10p coin
- a paving slab
- a garden shed?

2 Convert

a $2.5\ m^3$ into cm^3
b $6\ cm^3$ into mm^3
c $5000\ m^3$ into cm^3
d $7500\ cm^3$ into mm^3
e $0.079\ cm^3$ into mm^3
f $8500\ mm^3$ into cm^3.

3 Work out the volume of each cuboid.

a

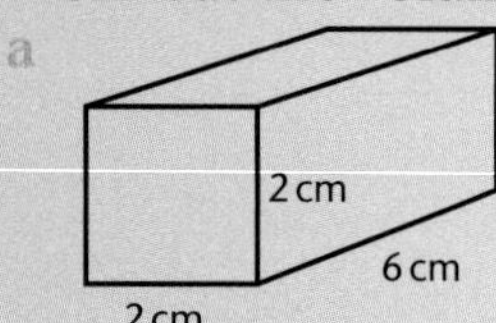

b

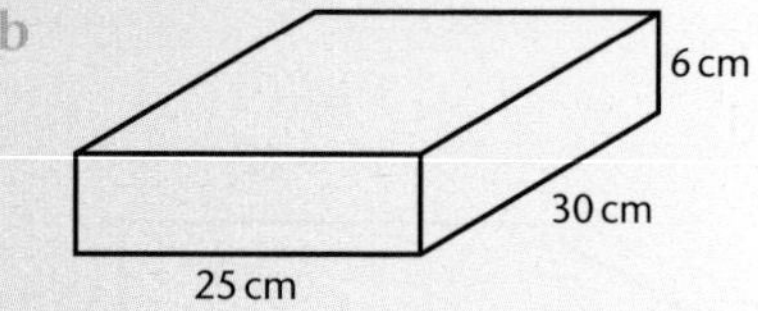

c

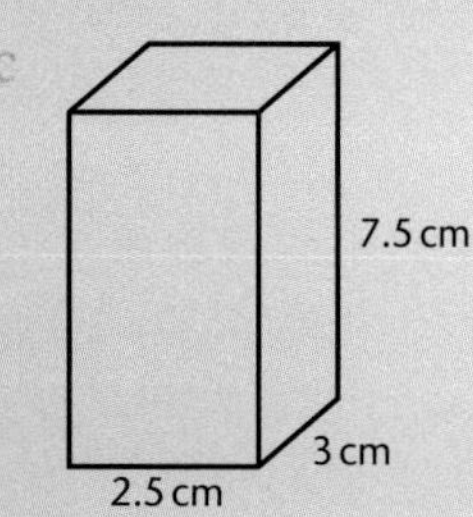

4 Each solid is made from two or more cubes or cuboids.
Find the volume of each one.

Divide each solid into two cuboids.

a

2 cm
4 cm
8 cm
2 cm
2 cm
6 cm

b

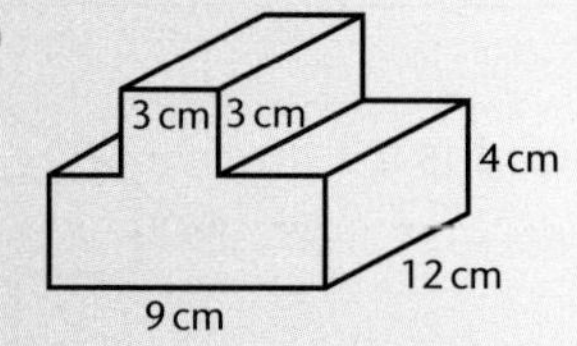

c

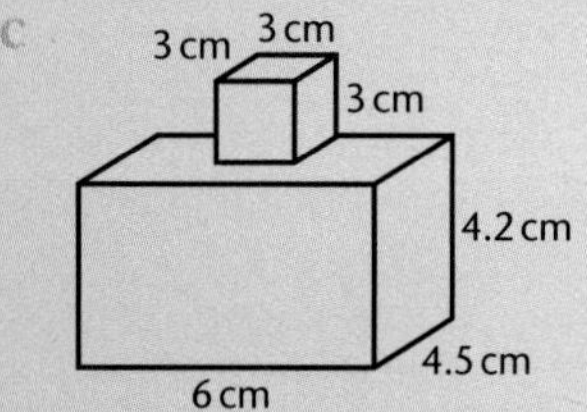

5 a How many small cubes, of side 2 cm, are needed to make the large cube?

b Work out the volume of
 i the small cube
 ii the large cube.

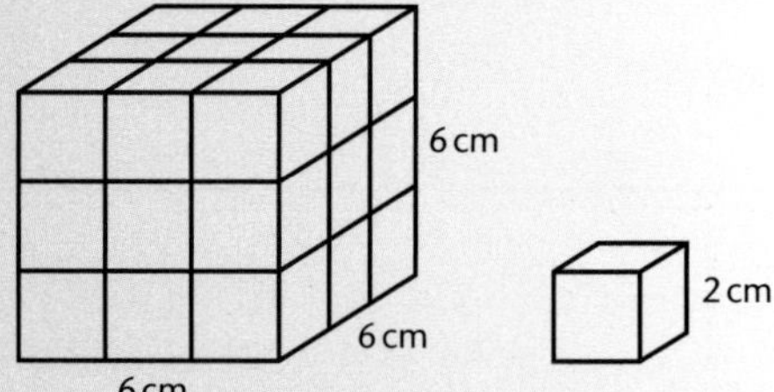

6 Find the volume of this concrete block in cubic centimetres.

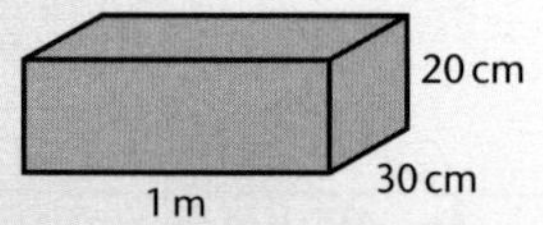

Be careful with the units.

7 A flat-packed wardrobe measures 15 cm by 1.5 m by 2 m.
Maryse said that its volume was 45 cubic metres.
Was Maryse correct? Give a reason for your answer.

8 The volume of a rectangular box is $360\,\text{cm}^3$.
The base of the box measures 12 cm by 6 cm.
Mark said that the depth of the box was 8 cm.
   a Is Mark correct?
   UAM b Give a reason for your answer.

The volume of box = $12 \times 6 \times d\,\text{cm}^3$ where d cm is the depth. Form an equation using the fact that the volume is $360\,\text{cm}^3$.

9 Bob digs a rectangular hole 5 m by 3 m to lay the base for a new garage. He wants the base to be at least 35 cm thick.
He orders $5\,\text{m}^3$ of concrete. Tony says this will not be enough.
   a Will there be enough concrete?
   UAM b Give a reason for your answer.

10 This rectangular gift box is tied up with ribbon.
Find
   a its volume
   b the total surface area of the box
   c the length of ribbon needed if 5 cm extra is allowed for tying.

12 cm
20 cm
25 cm

11 The volume of a cube is $64\,\text{cm}^3$.
Work out its surface area, clearly stating the units.

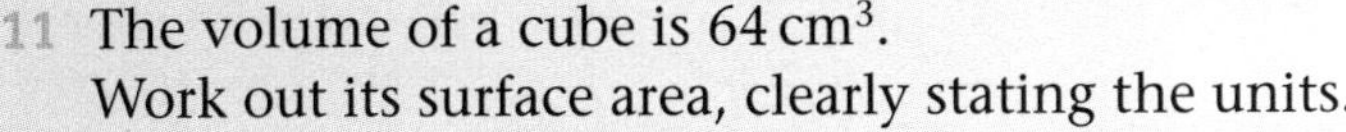

8.5 Prisms, cylinders and compound shapes

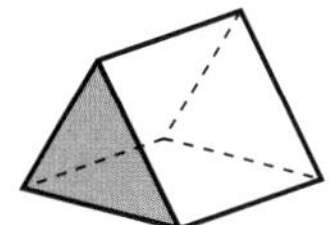 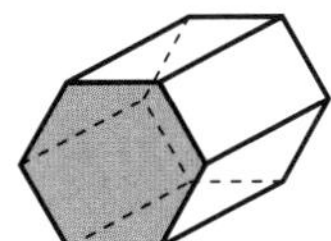 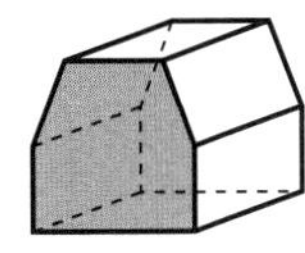 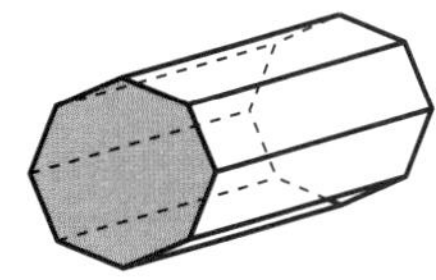

All four shapes have uniform cross-sections. They are all prisms.

Volume of a prism = area of cross-section × length.

Example 9

The cross-section of this prism is a trapezium. Find its volume.

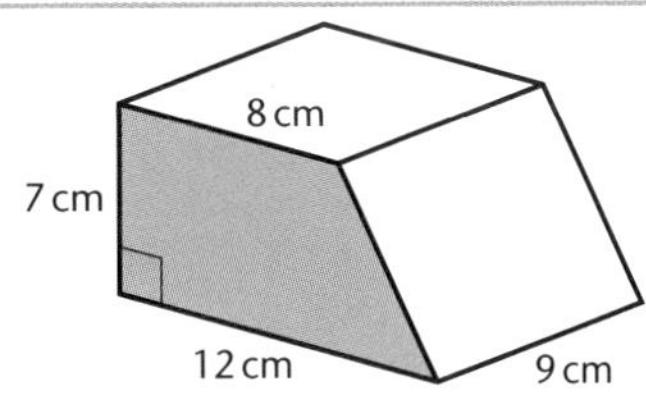

Area of cross-section $= \frac{1}{2}(8 + 12) \times 7\,\text{cm}^2$
$= 10 \times 7\,\text{cm}^2$
$= 70\,\text{cm}^2$

Area of a trapezium $= \frac{1}{2}$(sum of parallel sides) × (distance between them).

Volume of prism = area of cross-section × length
$= 70 \times 9\,\text{cm}^3$
$= 630\,\text{cm}^3$

Volume of a cylinder

A cylinder is a prism with a circular cross-section.

Volume of cylinder = area of cross-section × height.

The formula for the volume, V, is $V = \pi r^2 h$.

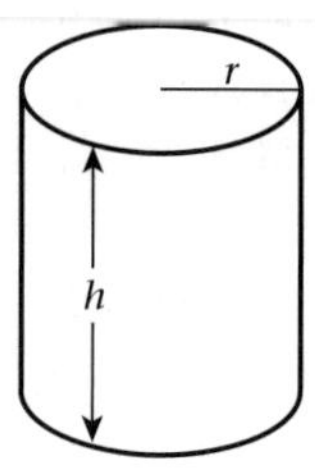

The cross-section is a circle.
Its area is πr^2 so the volume is $\pi r^2 \times h$.

When a prism is standing on one end the length becomes the height.

Exam practice 8E

1 Find the volume of each prism.

You are given the areas of the cross-sections.

a
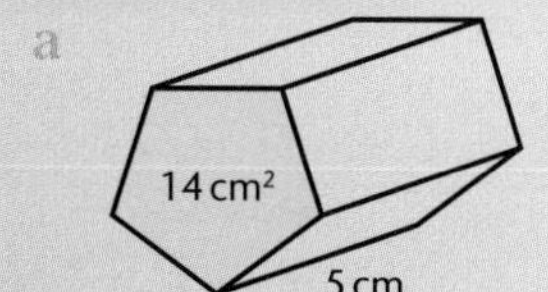

b
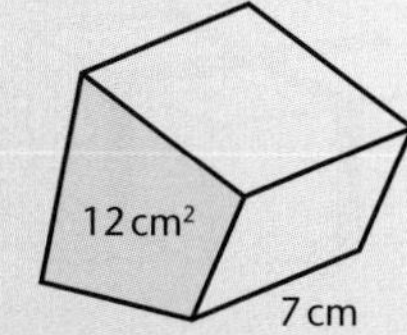

c
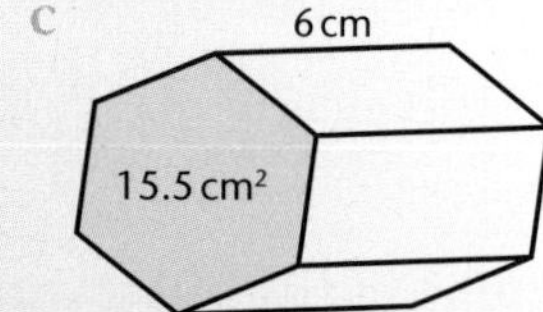

2 Find the volume of each prism.

First work out the area of the cross-section.

a
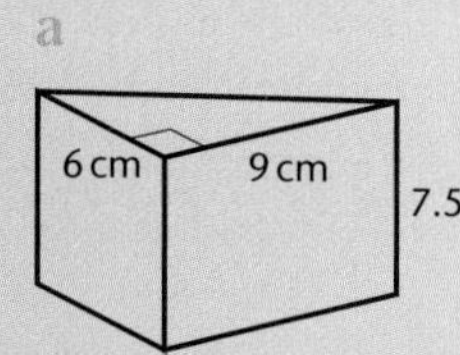

b

3.5 m 2.5 m 3 m 4 m

c
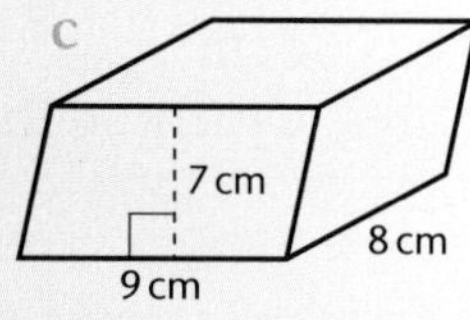

3 Find the volume of each cylinder.
Give your answers to 3 s.f.

a
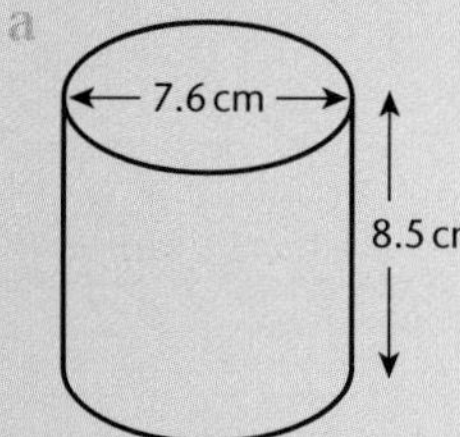

b
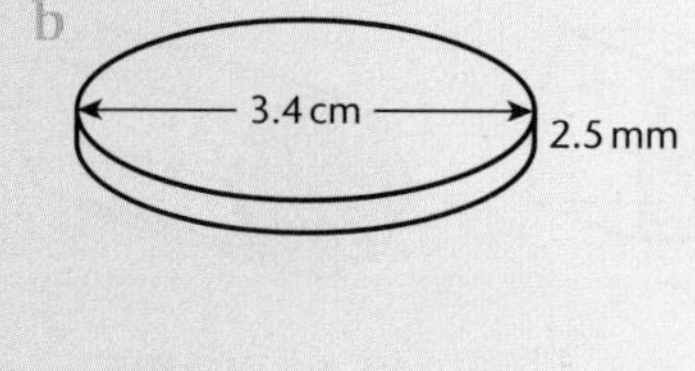

c
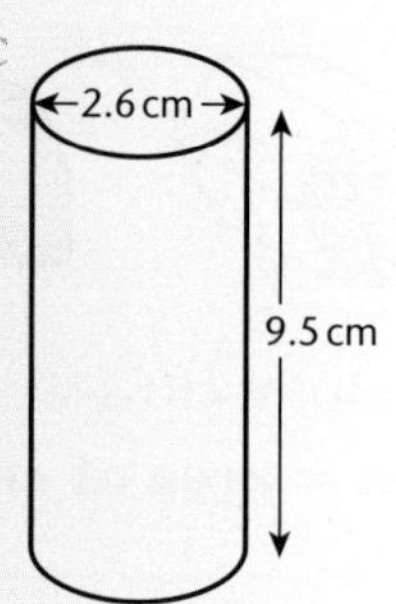

4 Find the volume of each solid. Give your answers to 1 d.p.

a
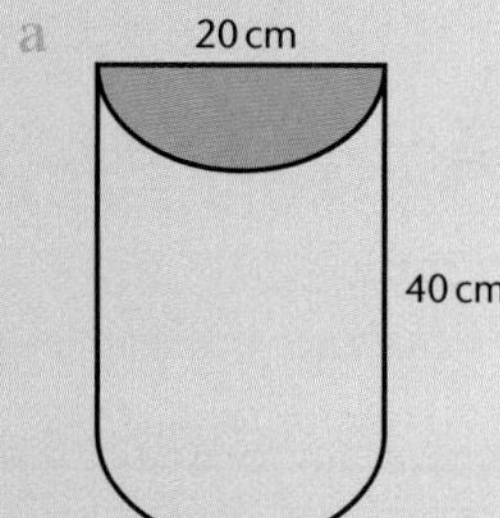

The cross-section of this solid is a semicircle.

b
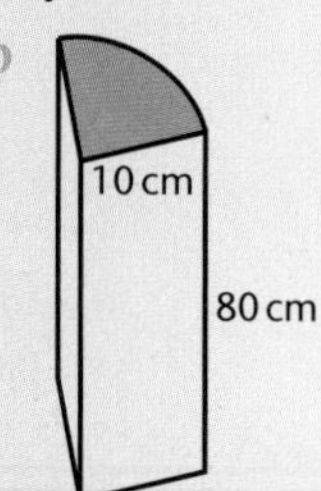

The cross-section of this solid is a quadrant.

A quadrant is a quarter of a circle.

5 Six discs of radius 3 cm are pressed out of a rectangular sheet of metal measuring 18 cm by 12 cm.
The sheet is 0.8 mm thick.
Work out

a the volume of metal wasted

b the percentage of metal wasted.

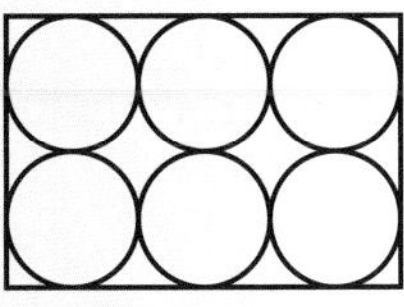

6 a Find the area of the cross-section of this solid.

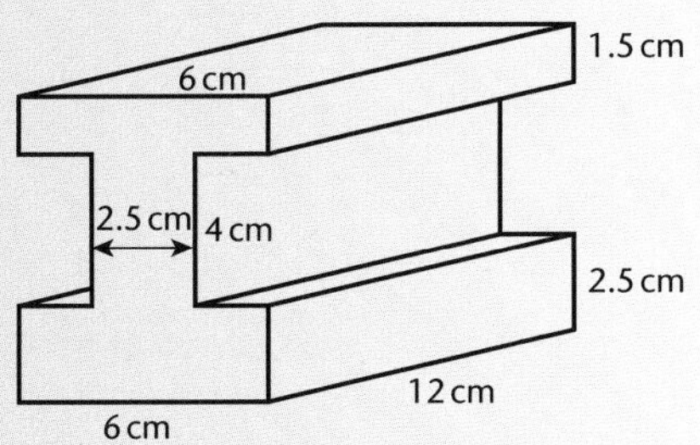

b Find the volume of the solid.

You can find the area of the cross-section by dividing it into three rectangles.

Class discussion

You can find the volume using the answer to part **a**, or you can divide the solid into three cuboids. Now look again at question 4 in Exam Practice 8D and decide whether using 'area of cross-section × length' or dividing it into cuboids is the easier method.

8.6 Pyramids, cones and spheres

A **pyramid** is a solid with a flat base which comes up to a point (the vertex).

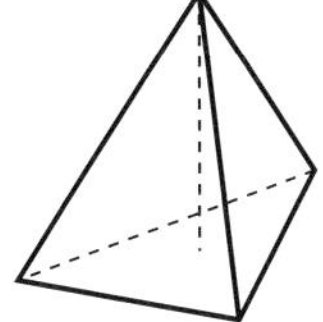 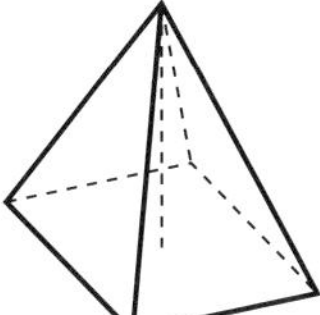 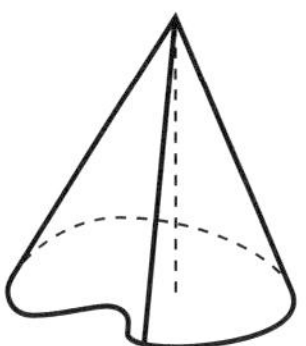 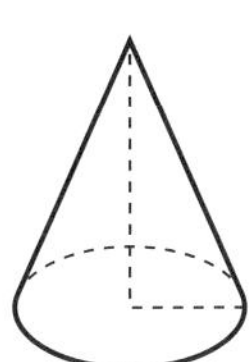

A pyramid with a triangular base is a **tetrahedron**.

Volume of a pyramid $= \frac{1}{3} \times$ area of base $\times$ height

A **cone** is a pyramid with a circular base.
This is a **right cone**.

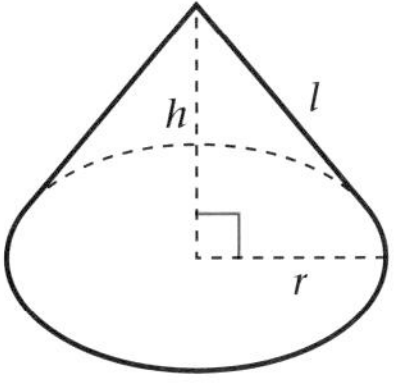

- Volume of a cone $= \frac{1}{3}\pi r^2 h$
- Curved surface area of a cone $= \pi r l$
- Total surface area of a cone $= \pi r^2 + \pi r l$

A right cone or right pyramid has its vertex vertically above the centre of its base.

l is the length of the sloping surface. It is called the slant height.

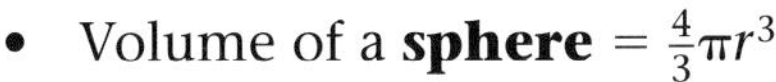

- Volume of a **sphere** $= \frac{4}{3}\pi r^3$
- Surface area of a sphere $= 4\pi r^2$

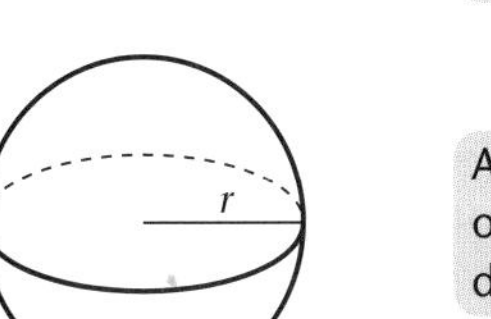

All the points on the surface of a sphere are the same distance from the centre.

Example 10

This cone has height 8 cm, base radius 6 cm and slant height 10 cm.
Find

a its volume in terms of π
b its curved surface area in terms of π
c its total surface area correct to 3 s.f.

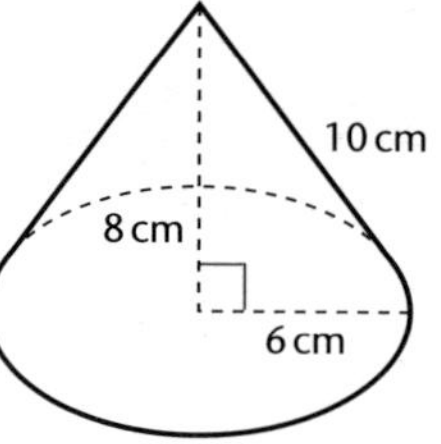

a $V = \frac{1}{3}\pi r^2 h = \frac{1}{3}\pi \times 6^2 \times 8\ \text{cm}^3 = 96\pi\ \text{cm}^3$

b Curved surface area $= \pi r l = \pi \times 6 \times 10\ \text{cm}^2 = 60\pi\ \text{cm}^2$

c Total surface area = area of base + curved surface area

$$= \pi \times 6^2 + 60\pi\ \text{cm}^2$$
$$= 36\pi + 60\pi\ \text{cm}^2$$
$$= 96\pi\ \text{cm}^2$$
$$= 302\ \text{cm}^2 \text{ to 3 s.f.}$$

Exam practice 8F

1 Work out the volume of each shape.

You are given the area of the base and the height.

a 12 cm, 9.5 cm²

b
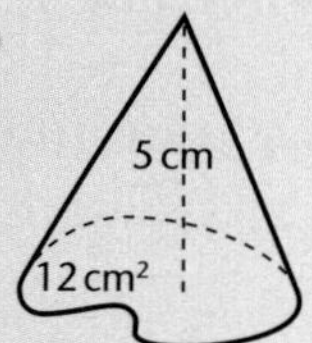

c
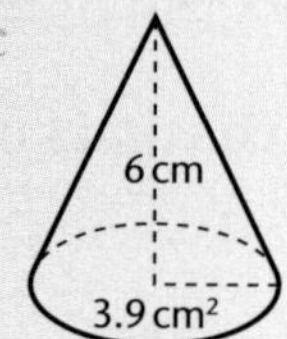

d
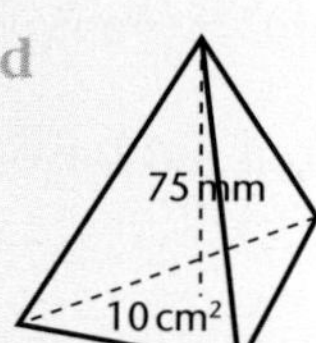

2 For each cone find

i the volume
ii the curved surface area
iii the total surface area.

Find the slant height by using Pythagoras' theorem (see chapter 9)

a
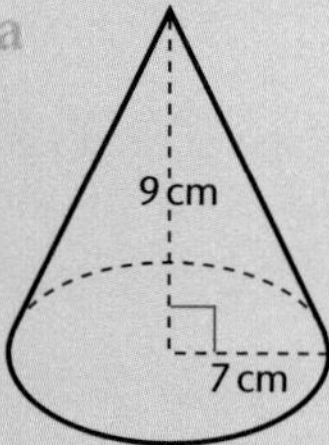

b 7.5 cm, 3.6 cm

c
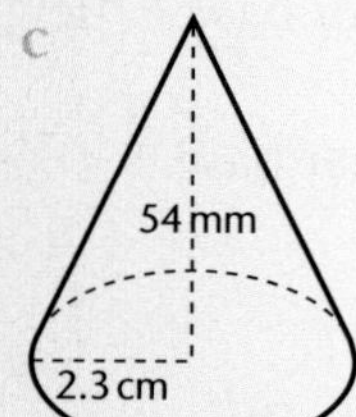

3 The volume of this cone is $100\ \text{cm}^3$.
Find its height.

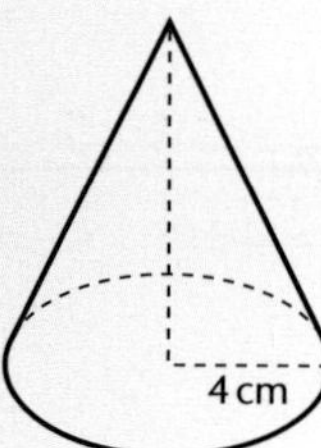

4 A conical shape is drilled out of a cylindrical block of wood.
Calculate
a the original volume of the cylindrical block
b the volume of the conical shape removed
c the percentage of the original block remaining.

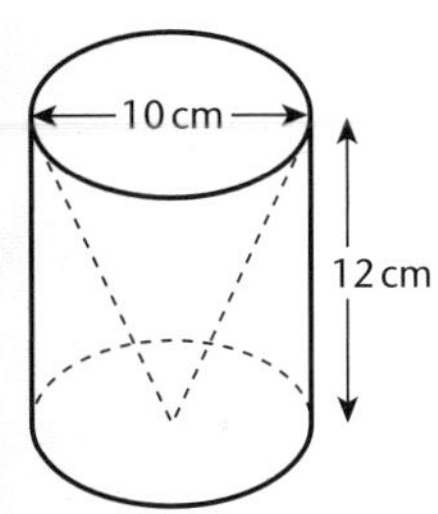

UAM

5 This shows a **frustum** of a cone.
Work out its volume.

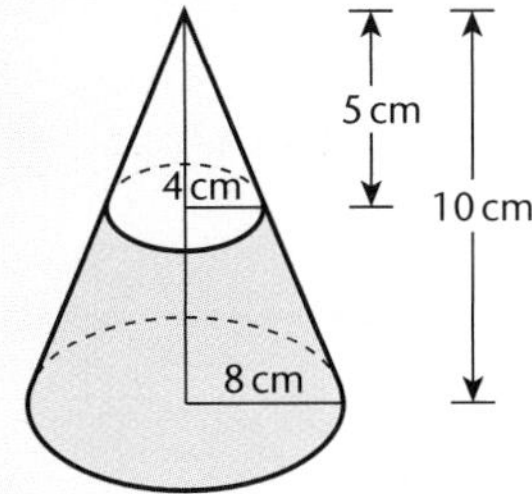

A frustum of a cone or pyramid is the shape you get when the top is removed by a cut parallel to the base. A frustum of a cone is sometimes called a truncated cone.

6 Find i the surface area and ii the volume of a sphere of radius:
a 10 cm b 6 cm c 0.8 m

7 This is a hemisphere.
Find
a its volume
b its total surface area.

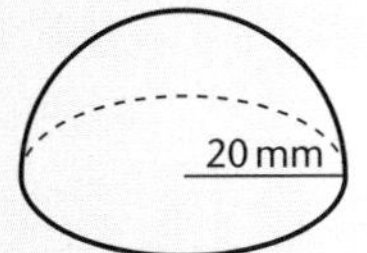

A hemisphere is half a sphere.

8 A salt cellar is made from a cylinder and a hemisphere.
The diameter of the bottom is 3 cm and the height of the salt cellar is 6 cm.
Calculate its volume.

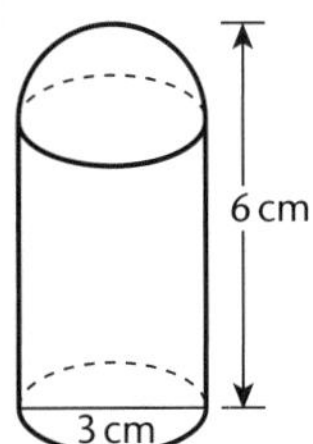

UAM

9 Twelve tennis balls, each of diameter 62 mm, are packed into a rectangular box, in layers of 6.
a Find, in cm, the dimensions of the smallest possible box.
b Find the volume of the space taken up by the balls.
c What percentage of the space in the box is occupied by the balls?

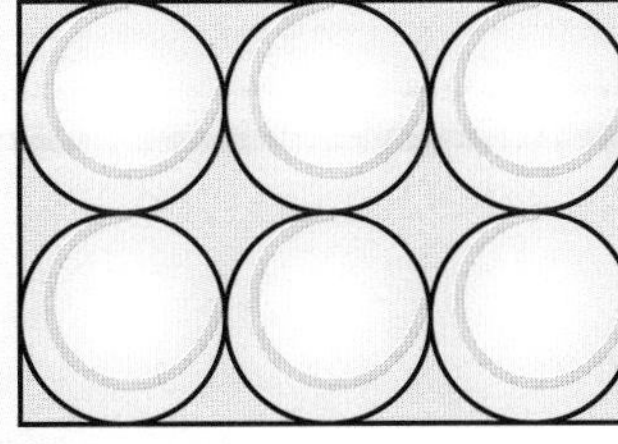

10 A pyramid has a rectangular base measuring 9 cm by 5 cm.
It is 8 cm high.
Calculate its volume.

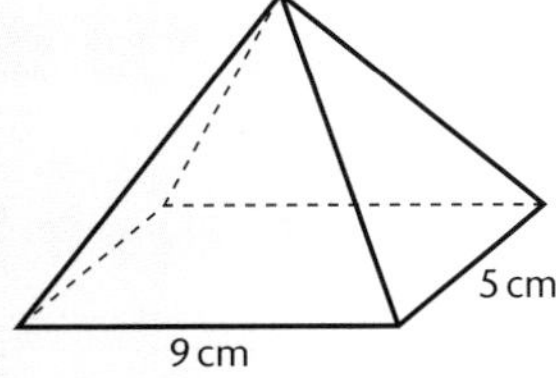

11 ABCD is a tetrahedron. AC = 6 cm, BC = 8 cm, DC = 7 cm and ∠ACB = ∠BCD = ∠ACD = 90°.
Work out
a the area of the base
b the volume of the tetrahedron.

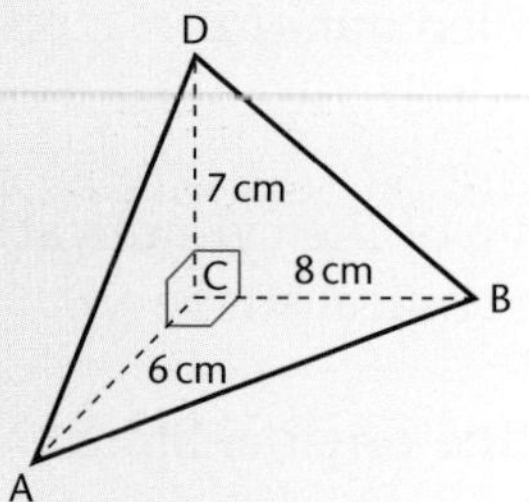

UAM 12 This spinning top is made by attaching a hemisphere to a cone.
The radius of the hemisphere is 6.5 cm.
The volume of the solid is 1018 cm^3.
Calculate the height of the cone.

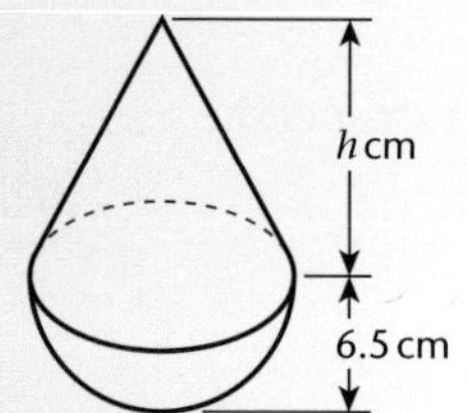

8.7 Capacity

The **capacity** of a container is the amount it can hold.

Petrol is sold in litres. The capacity of a teaspoon is about 5 ml.

The units of capacity in everyday use are the litre, the centilitre (cl) and the millilitre (ml). The relationships between them are:

1 litre = 1000 ml and 1 cl = 10 ml

Capacity is a measure of volume.
The relationships between units of capacity and units of volume are:

1 litre = 1000 cm^3 and 1 millilitre = 1 cm^3

The imperial units of capacity still used are pints and gallons.

1 gallon = 8 pints

You can convert between metric and imperial units of capacity using:

1 litre ≈ 1.75 pints and 1 gallon ≈ 4.55 litres.

Example 11

a Convert 1.3 litres to ml.
b Jane needs 1 pint of water.
How far should she fill this jug?
Explain your answer.

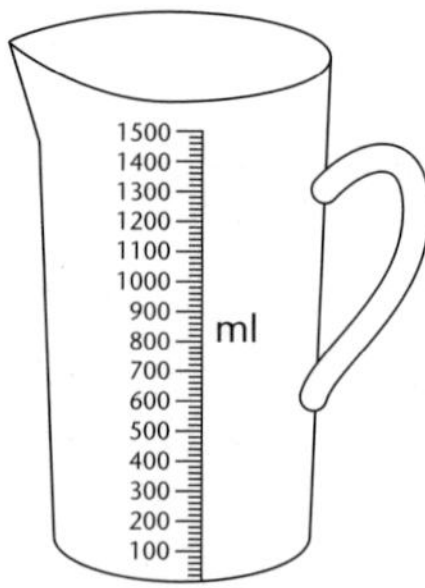

a 1.3 litres = 1.3 × 1000 ml = 1300 ml

You are changing to a smaller unit so multiply.

b 1 pint ≈ 1000 ÷ 1.75 ml = 571.4… ml
She should fill the jug to between 560 and 580 ml.

1.75 pints ≈ 1000 ml so 1 pint ≈ 1000 ÷ 1.75 ml.

The subdivisions on the jug are 20 ml apart.
She cannot measure more accurately than between two subdivisions.

Example 12

Find the capacity of this cylindrical drum.
Give your answer in litres to the nearest litre.

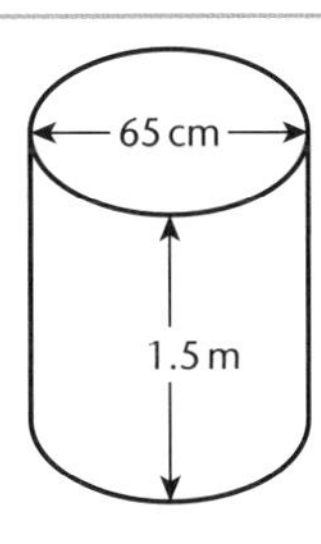

First find the volume. You need the radius and the height in the same units.

Radius = 65 ÷ 2 = 32.5 cm
Height = 1.5 × 100 cm = 150 cm
Volume = $\pi \times (\text{radius})^2 \times$ height
$\pi \times 32.5^2 \times 150 = 497\,746.0\ldots \text{cm}^3$

497 746.0… ÷ 1000 = 497.7…

To change cm³ to litres, divide by 1000.

Capacity = 498 litres to the nearest litre.

Exam practice 8G

1 a A carton holds 4 litres of milk. How many millilitres is this?

1 litre = 1000 millilitres.

b Sam buys a $2\frac{1}{2}$ litre can of oil. How many cubic centimetres is this?

1 litre = 1000 cubic centimetres.

c A carton contains 250 ml of soup. What fraction of a litre is this?

ml is the abbreviation for millilitre.

d Cherie buys $1\frac{1}{2}$ litres of cola. How many millilitres is this?

2 a The volume inside a jug is 2000 cm³. How many litres is this?

b A bag contains 0.02 cubic metres of bulb fibre. How many cubic centimetres is this?

c A bottle holds 75 centilitres of wine. What fraction of a litre is this?

1 litre = 100 centilitres.

d A petrol can hold 5 litres. How many cubic centimetres is this?

3 A medicine bottle holds 200 ml and a medicine spoon holds 5 ml.
Peter must take 10 ml of this medicine twice a day.

a How many spoonfuls must Peter take each day?
b How many days will the medicine last?

UAM 4 a Helen wants 8 gallons of diesel but the pump shows litres. Jo says that if she buys 40 litres she will have more than 8 gallons.

1 gallon ≈ 4.55 litres.

i Is Jo correct?
ii Give a reason for your answer.

b Some drinks are still sold by the pint. Harry says that 2 litres is more than 3 pints.

1 litre ≈ 1.75 pints.

i Is Harry correct?
ii Give a reason for your answer.

5 The cross-section of a water trough is a trapezium whose parallel sides are 56 cm and 44 cm and are 30 cm apart.
The trough is 1.5 m long.

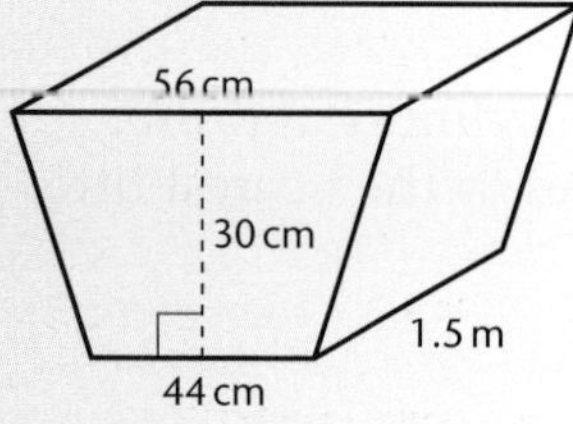

a Work out the volume of the trough. Give your answer in cubic metres.
b What is the capacity in litres?

6 The diameter of a cylinder is 50 cm. The cylinder is 160 cm high.
Work out its capacity in
a cm^3 b litres.

7 The capacity of the tank on a milk tanker is 50 000 litres. It is 800 cm long. Work out the area of its cross-section.

8 A machine takes 4 seconds to fill a can that holds 25 ml. At the same rate it takes 1 hour 24 minutes to fill a tank. Find the capacity of the tank in litres.

9 The area of cross-section of a cylindrical pipe is $5\ cm^2$.
Water flows out of the pipe at a speed of 1 metre per second.
Calculate

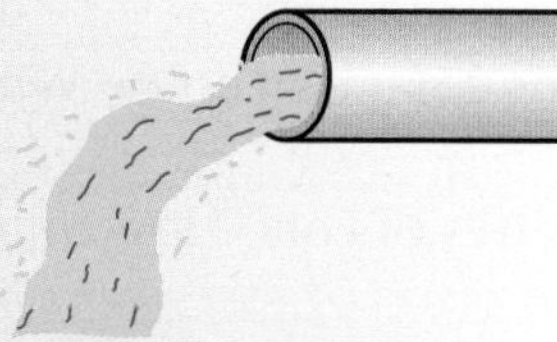

a the volume of water that comes out of the pipe in 1 minute
b how long it takes to fill a tank with a capacity of 600 litres.

10 Bath essence is sold in spheres with a diameter of 2 cm. They are sold in rectangular boxes. Each box holds two layers with six spheres in each layer. They just fit into the box.
Work out

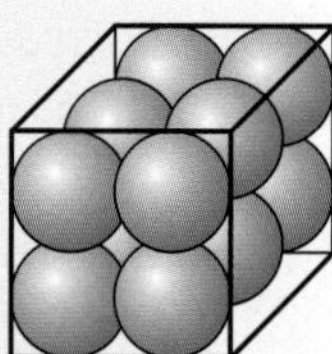

a the dimensions of the box
b the total capacity of bath essence in the box.

8.8 Mass and density

Mass is the scientific name for the amount of matter in an object. In everyday language we usually talk about the weight of something rather than its mass.

In science, weight is a force caused by gravity. It is measured in Newtons.

The units of mass in common use are the kilogram (kg), the gram (g), the milligram (mg) and the tonne (t).
The relationships between them are:

$1\ t = 1000\ kg,\ 1\ kg = 1000\ g,\ 1\ g = 1000\ mg$

The pound is an imperial unit still used.
You can convert between pounds (lb) and kilograms using $1\ kg \approx 2.2\ lb$.

Density measures the mass of 1 unit of volume of a material. The unit of volume usually used for density is the cubic centimetre (cm^3).

g/cm^3 means 'grams per cubic centimetre'.

The density of gold is 19.3 g/cm^3.

This means that 1 cm^3 of gold has a mass of 19.3 g.

You can work out density using: Density $= \frac{\text{mass}}{\text{volume}}$

Example 13

a A block of wood has a mass of 200 grams and its volume is 250 cm^3.
Find the density of the wood.

b The density of copper is 8.9 g/cm^3.
The volume of a block of copper is 400 cm^3. What is the mass of the block?

a 250 cm^3 weighs 200 g
1 cm^3 weighs 200 ÷ 250 g = 0.8 g
The density of the wood is 0.8 g/cm^3.

The density of the wood is the mass of 1 cubic centimetre.

b 400 × 8.9 = 3560
So 400 cm^3 has a mass of 3560 g = 3.56 kg.

The density tells you that 1 cm^3 has a mass of 8.9 grams. 400 cm^3 has 400 times as much mass.

Exam practice 8H

1 Convert the given quantity into the unit in brackets.

a	2 kg (g)	b	3.2 t (kg)
c	7460 g (kg)	d	2450 kg (t)
e	500 g (kg)	f	583 kg (t)
g	0.05 kg (g)	h	1400 g (kg)
i	3000 mg (g)	j	0.06 g (mg)
k	0.008 kg (g)	l	0.0075 t (kg)

2 a A bag of cement has a mass of 50 kg. A lorry is loaded with 150 bags.
How many tonnes of cement is this?

b Louis buys a 1 kg bag of weedkiller. The instructions say 'Use 25 g with 5 litres of water'. How many litres of weedkiller can Louis mix?

1 tonne = 1000 kg.

3 a The volume of a silver ingot is 56 cm^3.
The density of silver is 10.5 g/cm^3. What is the mass of the ingot?

b A jug holds 35 cubic centimetres of mercury. The density of mercury is 13.6 g/cm^3. What is the mass of the mercury in the jug?

4 a 1 cm^3 of platinum has a mass of 21.5 g. Work out the mass of a cuboid of platinum measuring 15 cm by 5 cm by 2.2 cm.

b The density of milk is 0.98 grams per cubic centimetre. Connie said that 2 litres of milk weighs more than 1 kilogram.

1 litre = 1000 cm^3.

i Is Connie correct?

ii Give a reason for your answer.

5 The area of cross-section of this wooden triangular prism is 6.5 cm^2. The prism is 10 cm long and has a mass of 58.5 g. Work out the density of the wood.

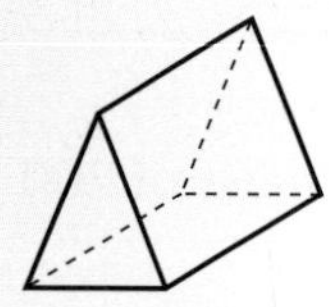

6 A solid metal sphere has a radius of 8.5 cm. It is made from metal of density 7.8 g/cm^3.
Work out

a the volume of the sphere

b its surface area

c its mass in kilograms correct to 3 s.f.

7 This prism is made of wood. Its cross-section is a triangle.

a Work out the volume of the block.

b The prism weighs 800 grams. Find the density of the wood.

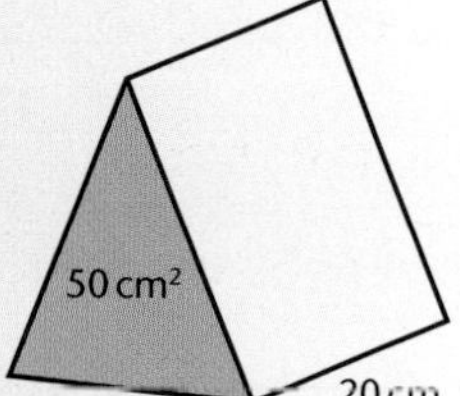

8 This glass paperweight is in the shape of a pyramid. It weighs 225 grams.

a Calculate the volume of the paperweight.

b Work out the density of the glass from which it is made.

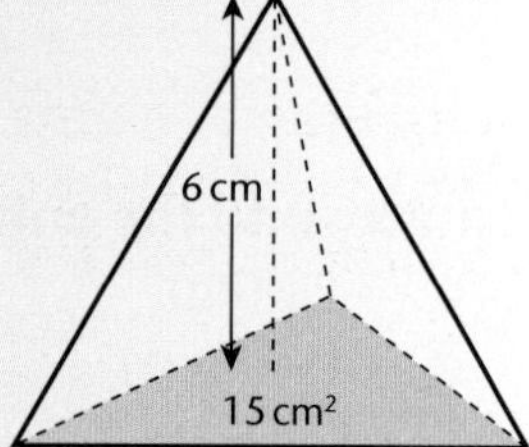

8.9 Formulae and dimensions

Formulae for finding the areas and volumes of shapes and solids contain letters that represent length, area or volume units. Some formulae also contain numbers or symbols that stand for numbers, such as π.

A length is **1-dimensional**.
An expression with single letters representing lengths must give a length.

The letters a and b stand for lengths. The expressions $a + b$ and $2\pi a$ give lengths.

An area is **2-dimensional**.
You find an area by multiplying two lengths together.
An expression with two letters representing lengths multiplied together must give an area.

The letters a and b stand for lengths. The expressions ab and πa^2 give areas.

A volume is **3-dimensional**.
You find a volume by multiplying three lengths together.
An expression with three letters representing lengths multiplied together must give a volume.

The letters a, b and c stand for lengths. The expressions abc and a^2b give volumes.

Example 14

b and c represent lengths, and A represents an area.
State whether each expression represent a length, an area or a volume.

a bc **b** Ab **c** $2\pi b^2c$

a bc represents an area.

length × length is 2-dimensional.

b Ab represents a volume.

area × length is 3-dimensional.

c $2\pi b^2c$ represents a volume.

$b \times b \times c$ is three-dimensional. 2 and π are numbers.

Exam practice 8I

1 Write true or false for each of these.

a 5 km is a length
b 15 cm is an area
c 4 cm^3 is a volume
d 2π cm^2 is an area
e 3 km^2 is a length
f 54 mm^2 is a volume

2 Write down whether each of these is a length, an area or a volume.

a the region inside a square
b the distance around a pond
c the space inside a box
d the diameter of a circle
e the region within a circle
f the space inside an egg
g the surface of a cube
h a perimeter

3 The letters p, q and r each represent a number of centimetres. Write down the unit (cm, cm^2 or cm^3) for the capital letter in each formula.

a $A = pq$
b $P = p + q + r$
c $B = \pi q^2$
d $X = pqr$
e $P = \pi q^2 r$
f $D = 2p + 3r$
g $T = p^2 + q^2$
h $W = pq + qr$

4 a, b and c represent lengths.
Which two of these formulae give a volume?

a $E = 4\pi a^2$ b $F = 2\pi^2 abc$ c $G = \pi a^2 b$ d $H = 3(a^3 + b^2)$

5 Two lengths are given as p cm and q cm. Write down whether each expression represents a length, an area, a volume or none of these.

a $\dfrac{p^2 - q^2}{p}$ b $pq - p$ c $pq^2 - p^2q$ d $p^2 + 3pq$ e $q^3 - 4pq$

6 Mike said that the formula for the volume of a solid was $V = \pi(r^3 + h^2)$.
Kim said that it could not be.
UAM Is Kim correct? Give a reason for your answer.

Summary of key points

- The relationship between metric units are:
volume: $1\,m^3 = 1\,000\,000\,cm^3$ and $1\,cm^3 = 1000\,mm^3$
capacity: 1 litre = 1000 ml
where 1 litre = $1000\,cm^3$ and 1 ml = $1\,cm^3$
mass: 1 t = 1000 kg, 1 kg = 1000 g, 1 g = 1000 mg
- The relationships between imperial units and metric units are:
1 gallon ≈ 4.55 litres
1 kg ≈ 2.2 lb (pounds)
- Volume of a cuboid = length × breadth × height.
- Volume of a prism = area of cross-section × length.
- Volume of a cylinder = $\pi \times (\text{radius})^2 \times$ height.
- Volume of a pyramid = $\frac{1}{3} \times$ area of base × height.
- Volume of a cone = $\frac{1}{3}\pi \times (\text{radius})^2 \times$ height.
- Volume of a sphere = $\frac{4}{3}\pi \times (\text{radius})^3$.
- You can find the surface area of a cube, cuboid or prism by finding the sum of the areas of the faces.
- Curved surface area of a cylinder = $2\pi \times$ radius × height.
- Curved surface area of a cone = $\pi \times$ radius × slant height.
- Surface area of a sphere = $4\pi \times (\text{radius})^2$.

Most candidates who get GRADE C or above can:
- find the volumes and surface areas of prisms and cylinders
- calculate density.

Most candidates who get GRADE A or above can also:
- find the volume and surface area of a sphere.

Glossary

Capacity	a measure of volume
Cone	a solid with a circular base tapering to a point
Cross-section	a slice through a solid
Cube	a solid whose six faces are squares
Cuboid	a solid with six faces whose opposite faces are identical rectangles
Cylinder	a prism with a circular cross-section
Density	the mass of one unit of volume of a material
Edge	the line where two faces meet
Elevation	what you see looking at the side of an object
Face	flat surface enclosed by edges or a curved edge
Frustum	a frustum of a cone/pyramid is the shape you get when the top is removed by a cut parallel to the base

Glossary (continued)

Mass	the amount of matter in an object
One-dimensional	a description of a length
Plan	what you see by looking down on an object
Prism	a solid whose cross-section is always the same
Pyramid	a solid with a flat base, tapering to a point
Right cone	a cone whose vertex is above the centre of the base
Sphere	a closed surface with every point on its surface the same distance from its centre
Tetrahedron	a pyramid with a triangular base
Three-dimensional	a description of volume
Two-dimensional	a description of area
Uniform	always the same
Vertex	a corner
Volume	the space occupied by a solid

9 Pythagoras' theorem

This chapter will show you:

- ✓ how to work out the length of the hypotenuse of a right-angled triangle when the lengths of the other sides are known
- ✓ how to work out a side of a right-angled triangle when one side and the hypotenuse are known
- ✓ how to solve problems involving right-angled triangles in two and three dimensions

Before you start you need to know:

- ✓ how to find the square and square root of a number
- ✓ the main compass directions
- ✓ properties of cuboids, prisms and pyramids
- ✓ how to solve quadratic equations

9.1 Pythagoras' theorem

Pythagoras' theorem connects the lengths of the sides in a right-angled triangle. The side opposite the right angle is called the **hypotenuse**.

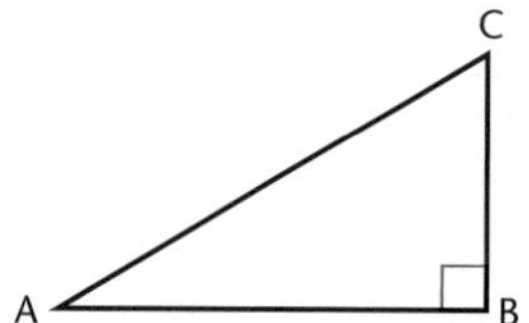

The side AC is opposite the right angle in this triangle, so AC is the hypotenuse.

Pythagoras was a famous Greek mathematician, astronomer, scientist and philospher who lived approximately 2500 years ago.

Pythagoras' theorem states that

> **In a right-angled triangle the square of the hypotenuse is equal to the sum of the squares of the other two sides.**

For this triangle $AC^2 = AB^2 + BC^2$.

Example 1

Triangle LMN has a right angle at M.
Find the length of LN.

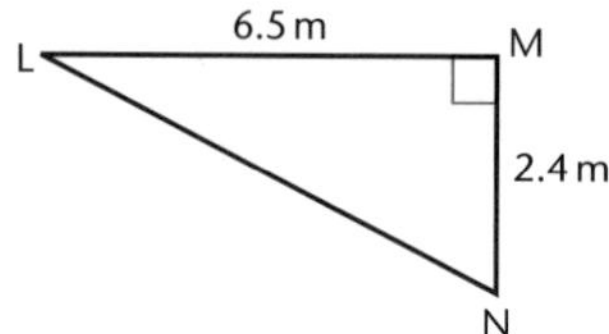

$LN^2 = 2.4^2 + 6.5^2$

$= 48.01$

$LN = \sqrt{48.01}$

$= 6.928\ldots = 6.9$ m to 1 d.p.

Press

Press

Exam practice 9A

In questions 1 to 8 find the length of the hypotenuse.
Give answers that are not exact correct to 1 decimal place.

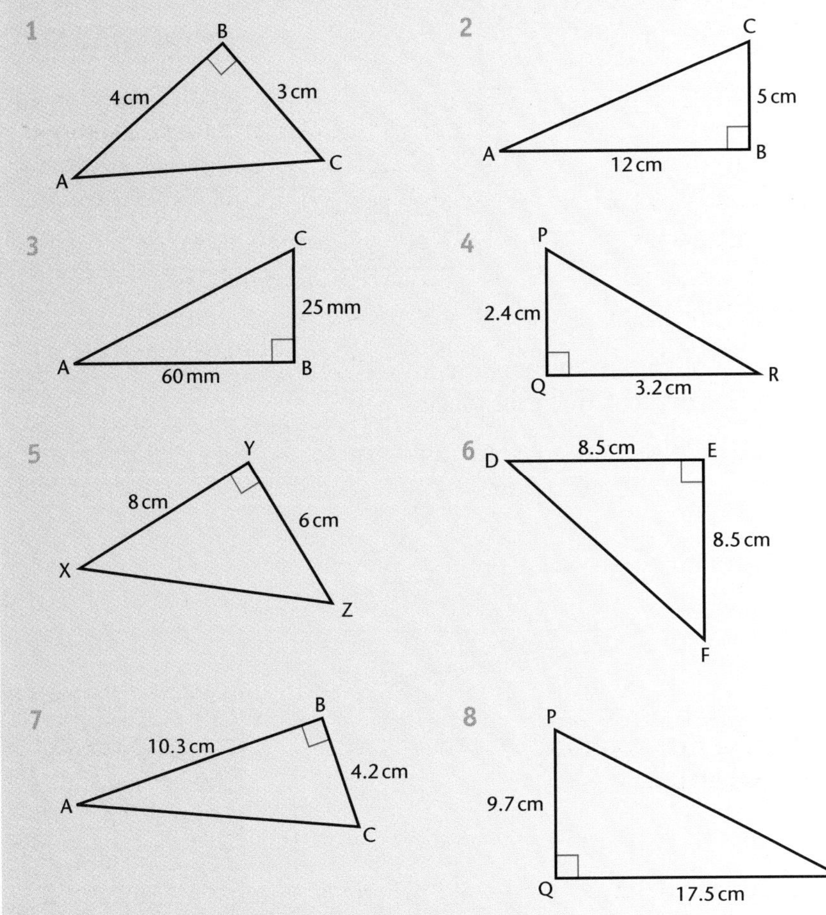

9 a Form an equation in x and solve it.
b Write down the lengths of the unknown sides.

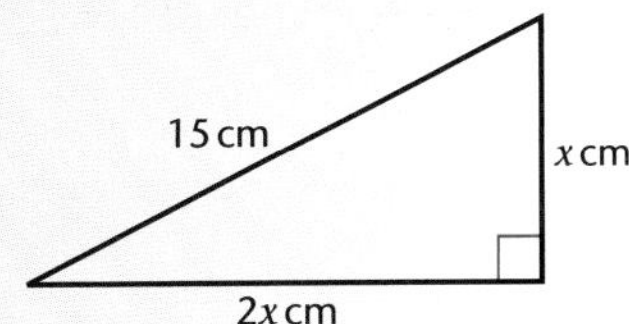

10 Work out the lengths of the unknown sides.

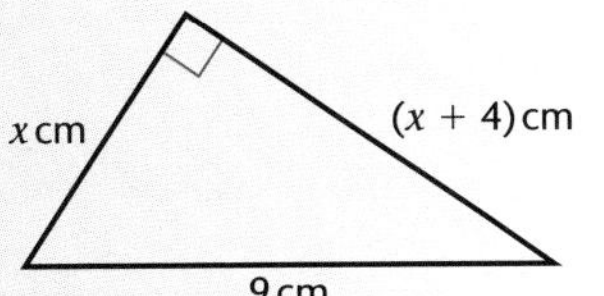

Did you know

that thousands of years ago the Egyptians used knotted ropes to make sure the angles at the corners of large buildings were right angles?

With 12 knots in the rope equally spaced in a loop, they could fold it to give a triangle with sides 3, 4 and 5 units long.

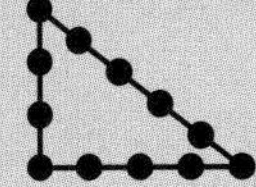

The triangle has a right angle between the two shorter side.

To find x you must solve a quadratic equation.

9.2 Finding a shorter side

You can use Pythagoras' theorem to find one of the shorter sides of a right-angled triangle when you know the lengths of the other two sides.

Example 2

Triangle XYZ has a right angle at X.
Find the length of XY.

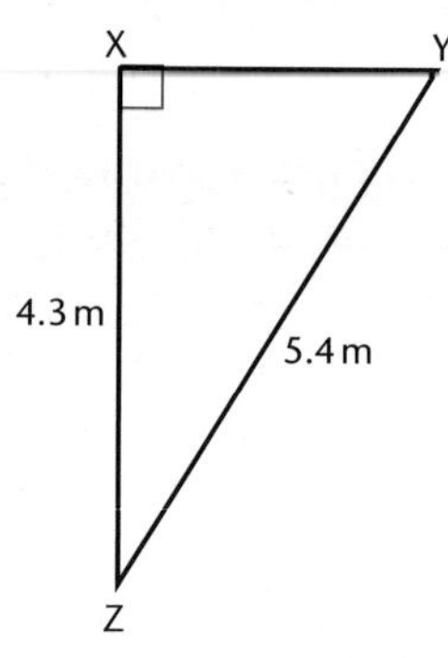

$$5.4^2 = 4.3^2 + XY^2$$
$$29.16 = 18.49 + XY^2$$
$$10.67 = XY^2$$
$$XY = \sqrt{10.67}$$
$$= 3.266\ldots$$
$XY = 3.3$ m to 1 d.p.

YZ is the hypotenuse so $YZ^2 = XY^2 + XZ^2$ from Pythagoras' theorem. Substitute 5.4 for YZ and 4.3 for XZ.

Exam practice 9B

In questions 1 to 6 find the length of the unknown side. Give answers that are not exact correct to 1 decimal place.

1
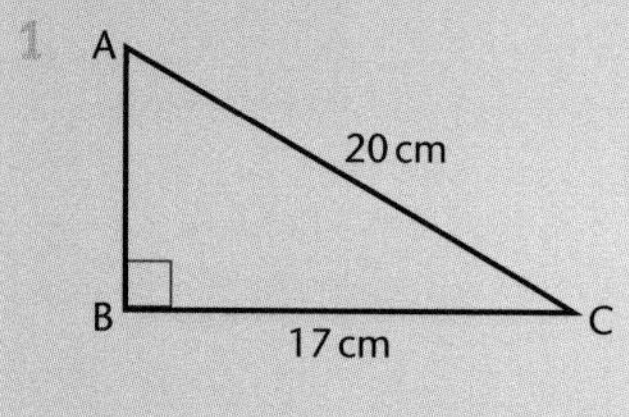

2

3
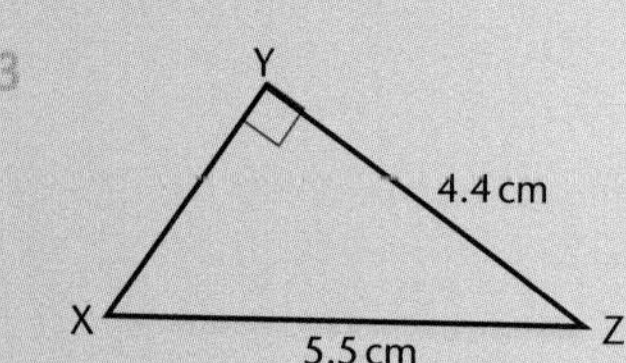

4
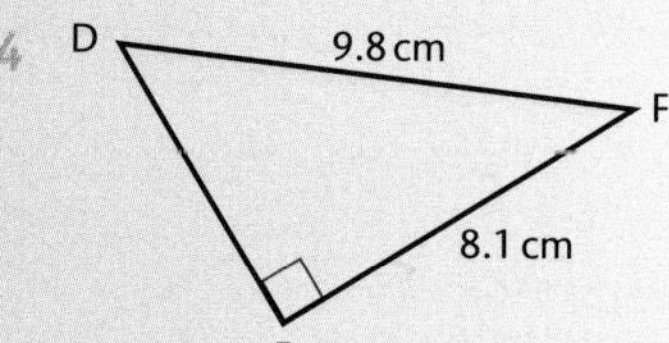

5
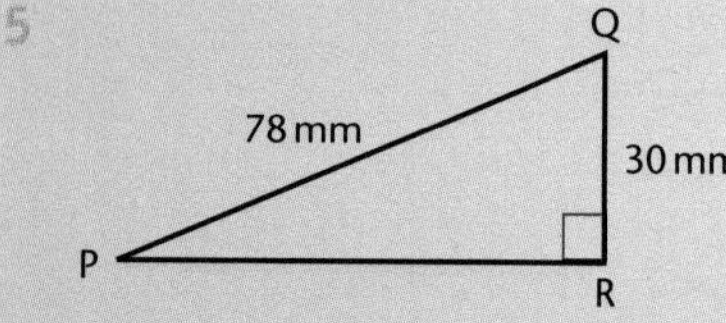

6
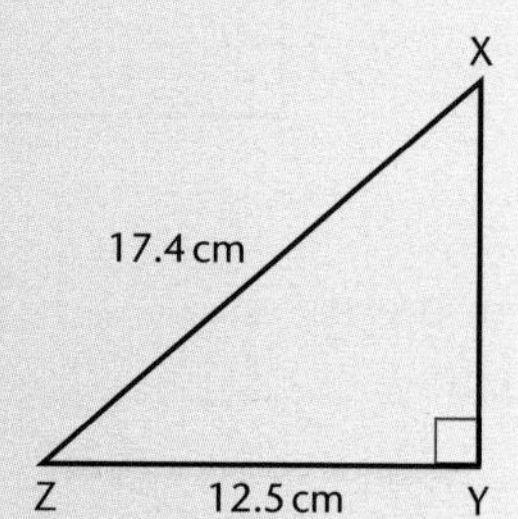

7 In this question find the lengths of both unknown sides.

a
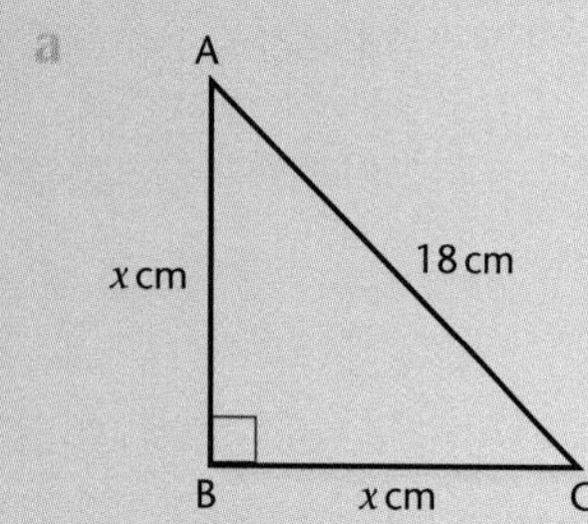

b
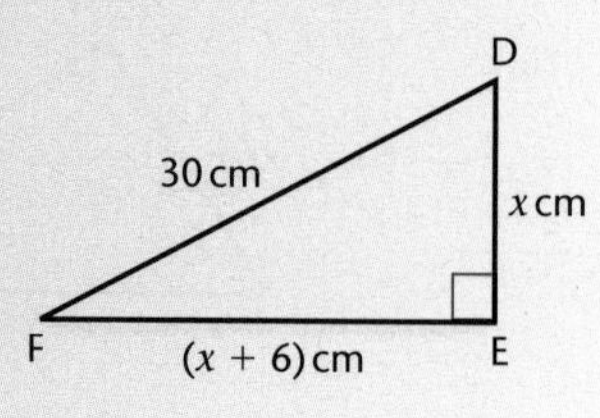

Form an equation in x and solve it.

8 Work out the length of
a BD
b AC.

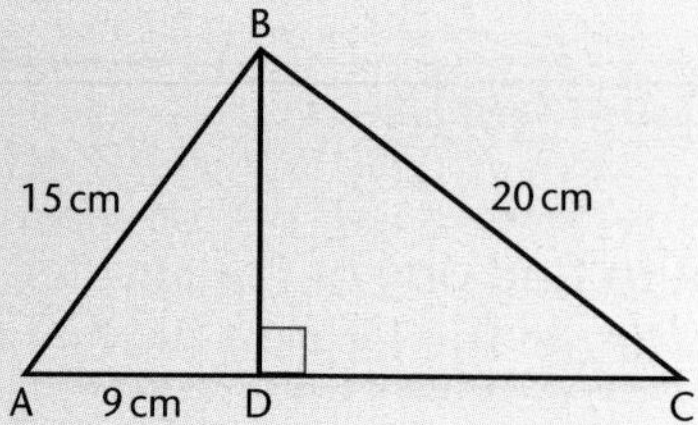

9.3 Converse of Pythagoras' theorem

If the square of the longest side in a triangle is equal to the sum of the squares of the other two sides the triangle contains a right angle.
The right angle is opposite the longest side.

Converse means a statement that is reversed.
The converse of the statement
'All cows have four legs'
is
'All creatures with four legs are cows'.
The converse of a true statement is not always true.

Example 3

Work out whether or not this triangle contains a right angle.
If it does, name the right angle.

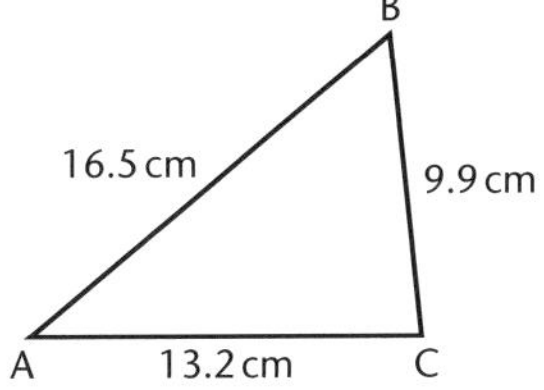

Square of the longest side = $16.5^2 = 272.25$

Sum of squares of the other two sides $= 9.9^2 + 13.2^2$

$= 98.01 + 174.24$

$= 272.25$

The triangle contains a right angle and this is $\angle C$.

The right angle is opposite the longest side.

Exam practice 9C

1 Work out whether each triangle contains a right angle.
If it does, name the right angle.

a

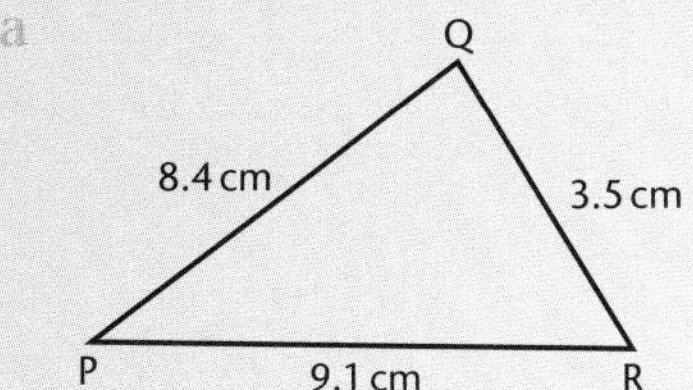

b

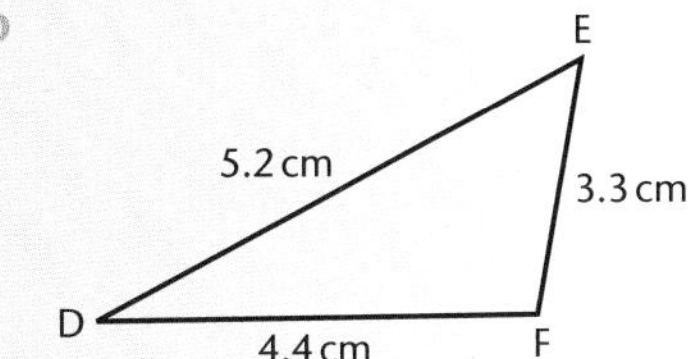

c

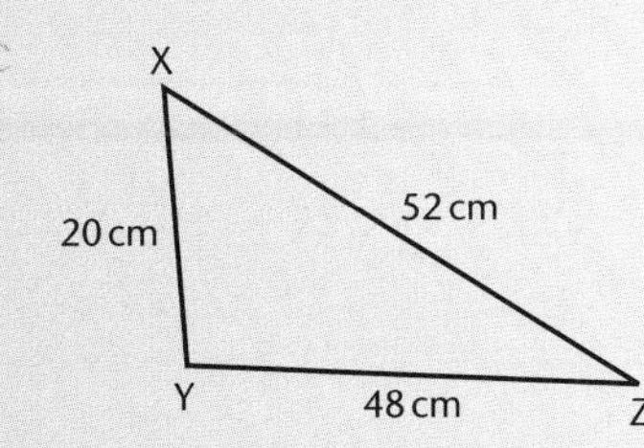

d

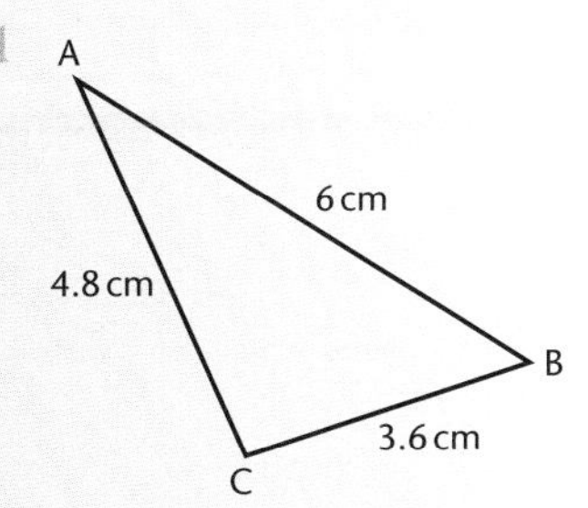

e

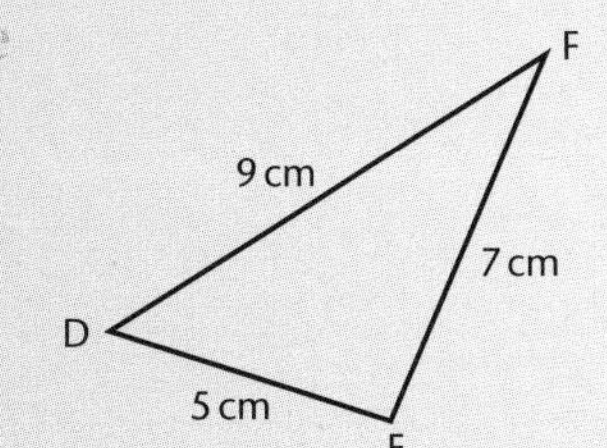

f

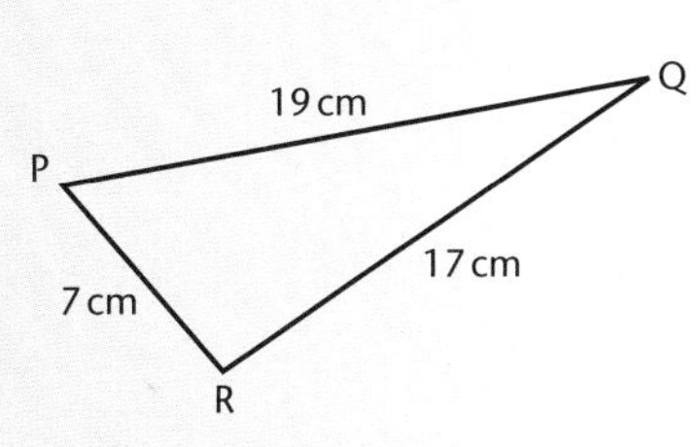

Class discussion

Each of these statements is true.
What is the converse of each statement and is it true?

1 The sum of two odd numbers is always an even number.
2 When $x = 3$, $x^2 = 9$.
3 The square of an even number is an even number.
4 When a rectangle has sides 3 cm long and 4 cm long, its area is 12 cm^2.

9.4 Using Pythagoras' theorem to solve problems

Many problems can be solved using Pythagoras' theorem.

Example 4

A carpenter checks that a frame is rectangular by measuring the diagonals. They should be the same length. What should the length of each diagonal be? Give your answer to the nearest tenth of a centimetre.

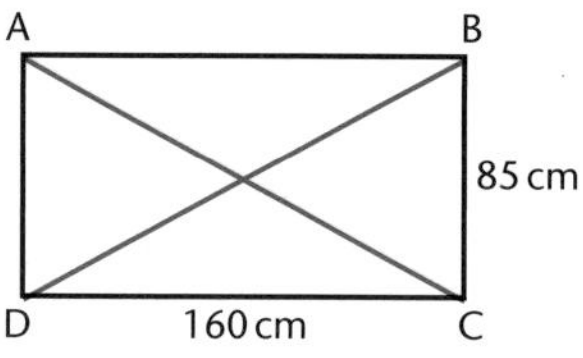

$BD^2 = 160^2 + 85^2$

$= 25\,600 + 7225$

$= 32\,825$

$AC = BD = \sqrt{32\,825} = 181.17...$

The length of each diagonal should be 181.2 cm.

Using Pythagoras' theorem in triangle BCD.

Exam practice 9D

1 Zoe walks 3 km due north, then 4 km due west. How far is she from her starting point?

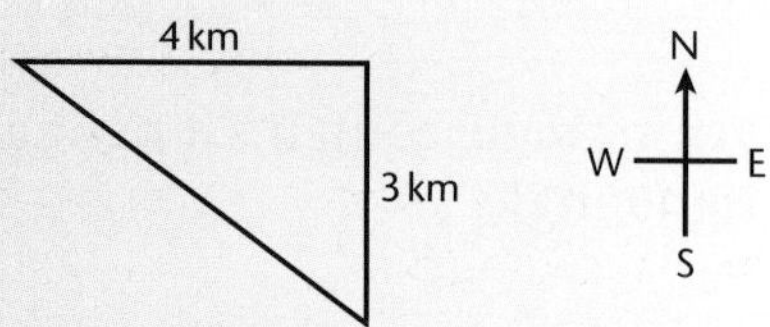

2 Alan walks 5 km due south, then 3 km due east. How far is Alan from his starting point?

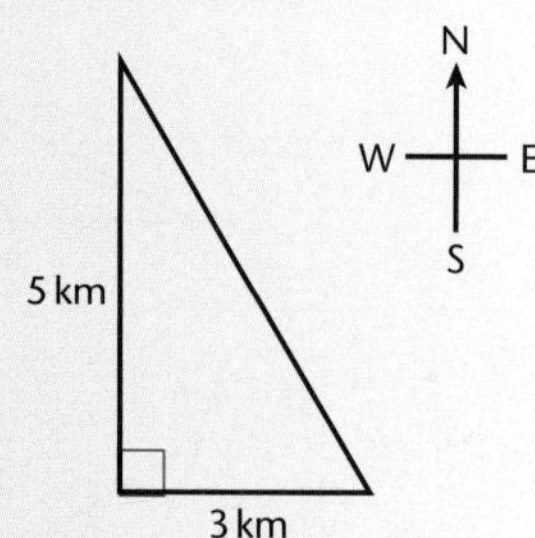

3 This is a rectangular football pitch.

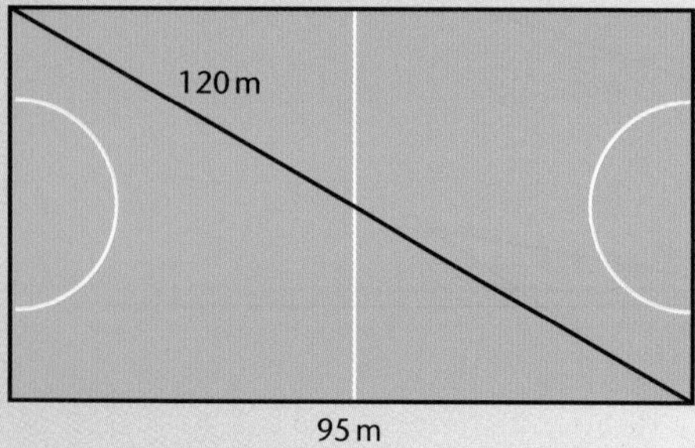

Find its width to the nearest metre.

4 This ladder is leaning against a vertical wall. How far up the wall does the ladder reach?

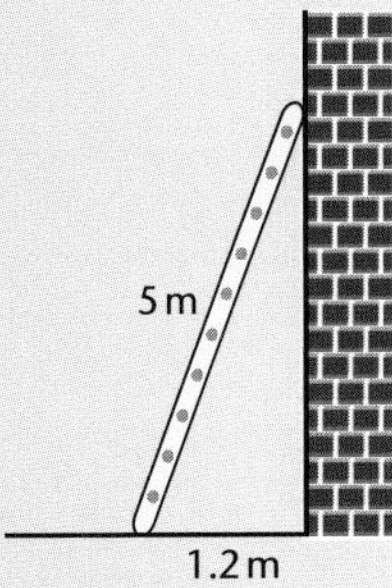

5 A, B and C are three houses. Work out

a ∠BAC

b the distance from B to C.

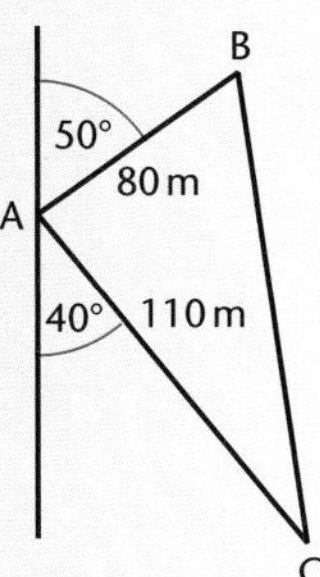

6 Find the length of the longest straight line that can be drawn on this square.

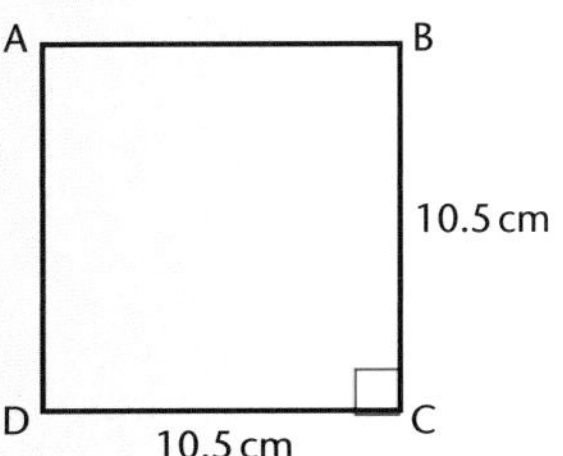

The longest line is one of the diagonals. This gives a right-angled triangle that you can use Pythagoras' theorem in.

7 A door is 2.1 m high and 0.9 m wide. Work out the length of the diagonal.

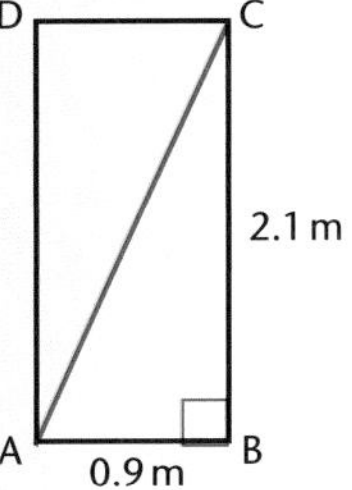

8 A rectangle measures 58 cm by 33 cm. Find the length of a diagonal.

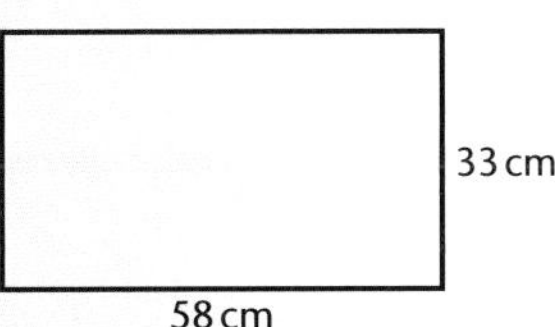

UAM

9 a What is the mathematical name of this quadrilateral? Give a reason for your answer.

b One diagonal is 6 cm and the other is 4.5 cm. Work out

i the length of AB

ii the perimeter of the quadrilateral.

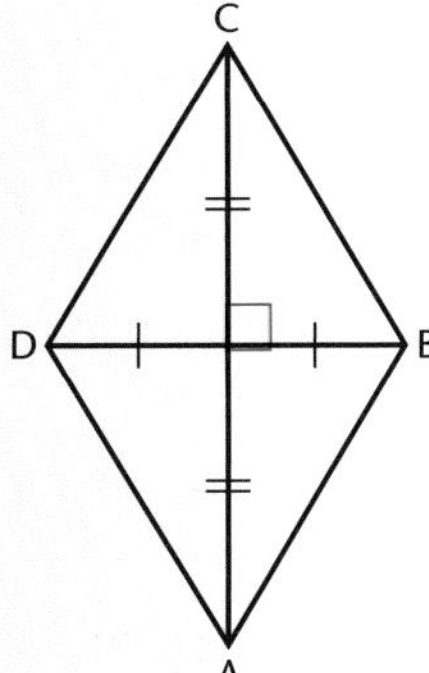

10 This drawing shows the cross-section of a storage shed. Find the length of each sloping edge of the roof.

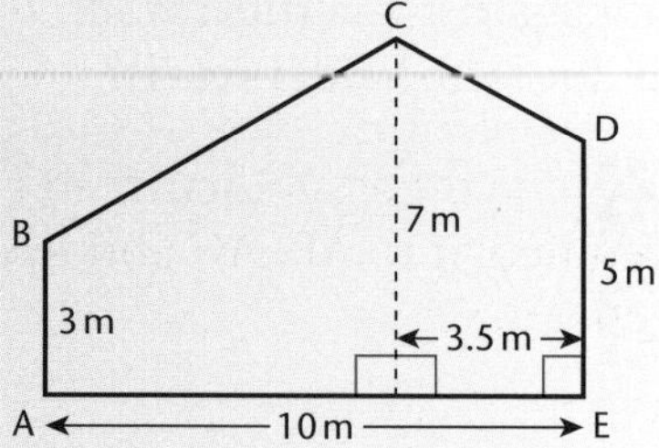

11 This diagram shows a square field of side 200 m. It is divided into four enclosures by a triangular fence AEF. Work out the length of the fence.

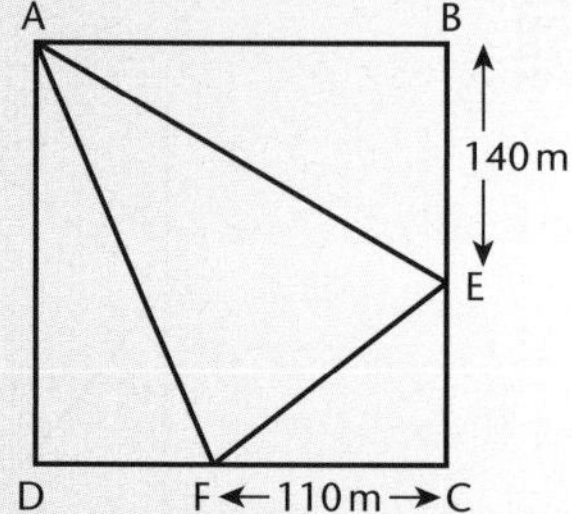

12 A ladder, AB, rests on level ground between two vertical walls. The foot of the ladder is 3.5 m from the base of one wall and the ladder rests against that wall at a height of 7.2 m.

a How long is the ladder?

b The ladder is now turned about A so that it rests against the other wall at C. How far is C above D?

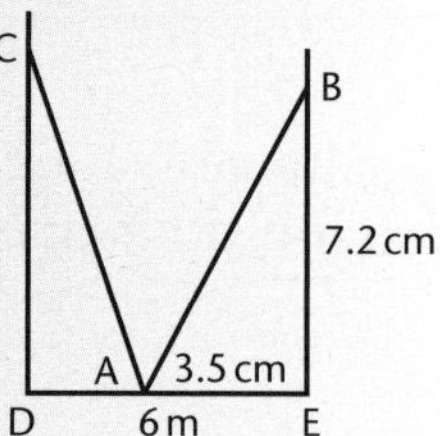

13 This is a sketch of the uniform cross-section of a skip.

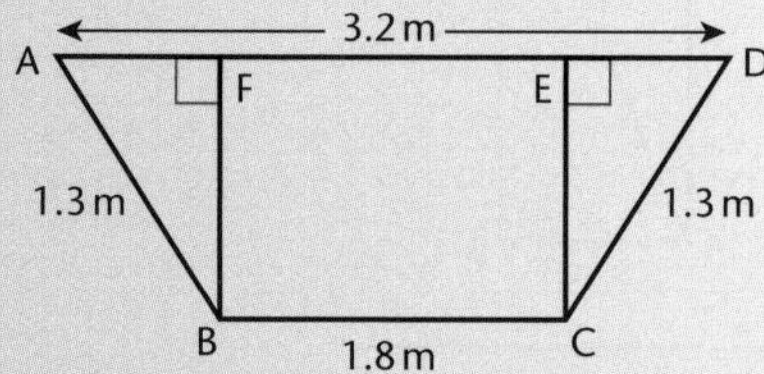

a What is the mathematical name of this shape?

b Find the length of AF.

c Work out

i the depth of the skip, EC.

ii The area of the entire cross-section.

d The skip is 1.6 m wide. Find its capacity in cubic metres.

14 Jonathan cuts the corners off a square of plyboard of side 90 cm to create a regular octagon. Work out the length of one side of the octagon.

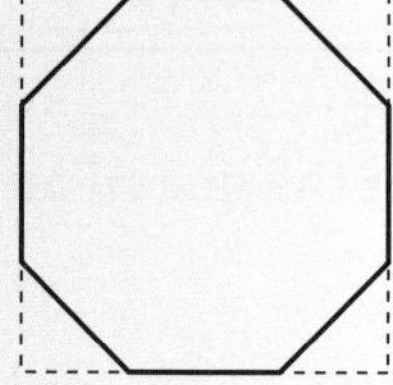

9.5 Three-dimensional problems

A line perpendicular to a plane is perpendicular to every line in that plane. AE is perpendicular to AB, AC and AD, and to any other line drawn on the base.

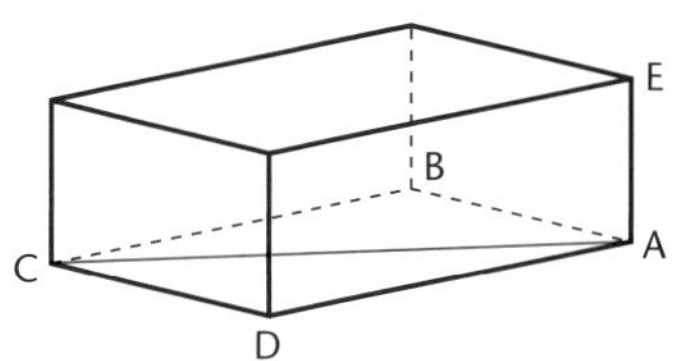

When you draw a diagram remember to:

- draw vertical lines vertically in your diagram
- mark angles that are right angles, particularly when they do not look like right angles on your diagram
- draw parallel lines so that they look parallel
- use broken lines for lines that cannot be seen.

Example 5

This rectangular box measures 7 cm by 6 cm by 5 cm.

a Calculate the length of
i AH **ii** EG.

b What is the length of the longest straight stick that will fit into this box?

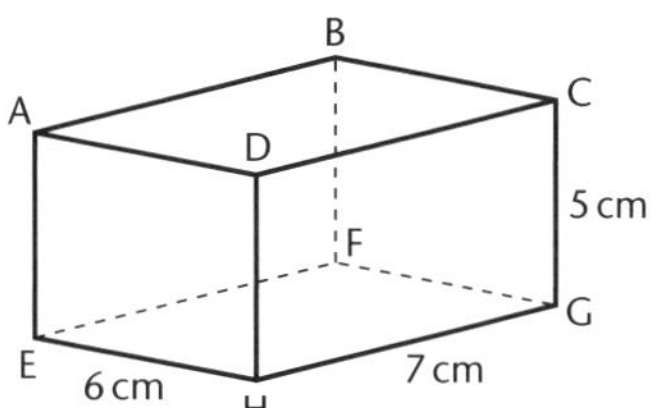

Give your answers correct to 3 s.f.

a i $AH^2 = AE^2 + EH^2$
$= 25 + 36$
$= 61$
$AH = \sqrt{61} = 7.810\ldots$
so length of AH is 7.81 cm.

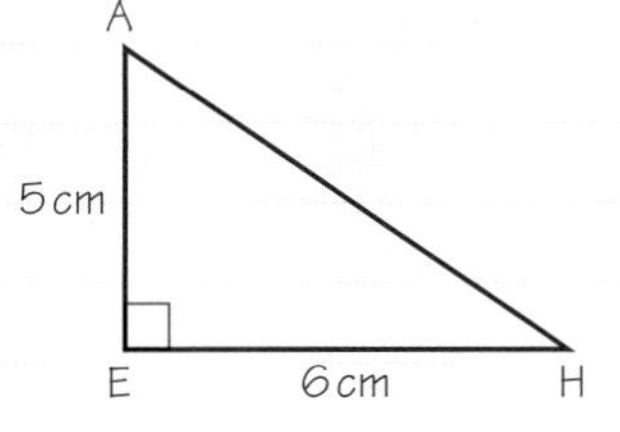

Find a right-angled triangle that has AH as a side.
Draw this triangle and put the measurements on it.

ii $EG^2 = EH^2 + HG^2$
$= 36 + 49$
$= 85$
$EG = \sqrt{85} = 9.219\ldots$
so length of EG is 9.22 cm.

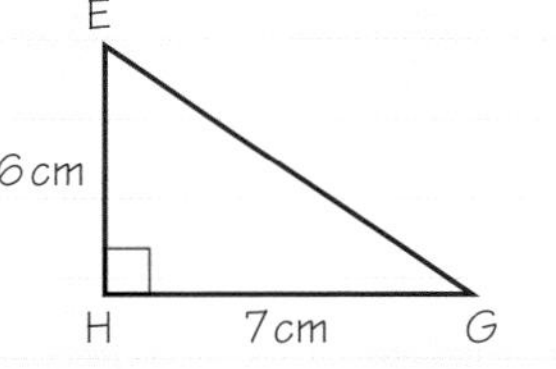

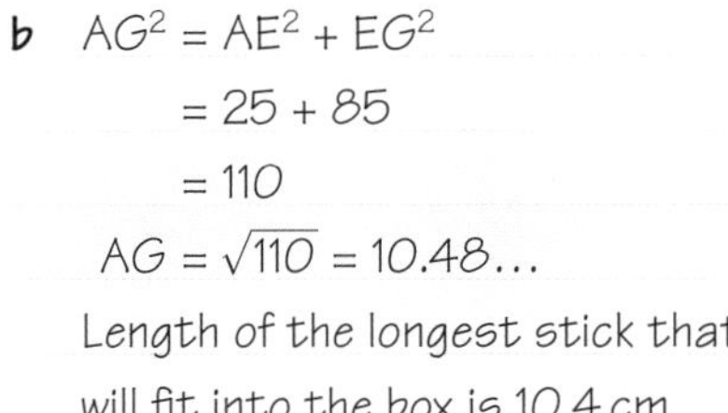

b $AG^2 = AE^2 + EG^2$
$= 25 + 85$
$= 110$
$AG = \sqrt{110} = 10.48\ldots$
Length of the longest stick that will fit into the box is 10.4 cm.

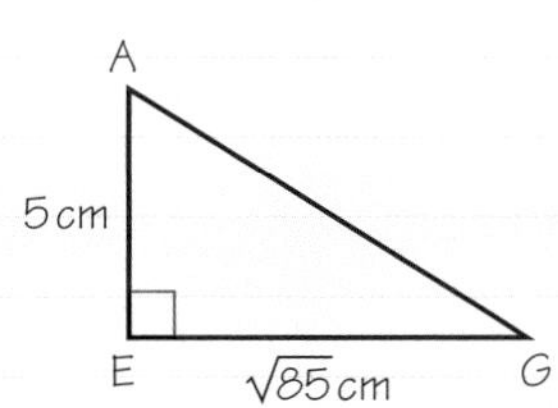

The longest line is a diagonal from a top vertex to the opposite bottom vertex such as AG. Draw a right-angled triangle with AG as one side and put the measurements you know on it.

Exam practice 9E

1 The inside measurements of this rectangular box are 40 cm × 30 cm × 20 cm.
Find the length of the longest straight stick that will
a lie on the bottom of the box
b fit into the box.

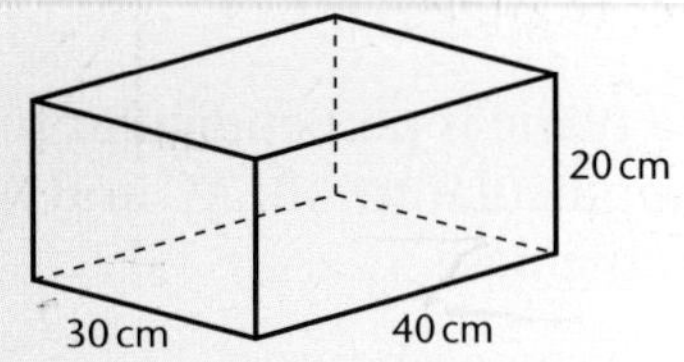

2 This is a cube. Each edge is 6 cm.
Find the length of
a EG b EC.

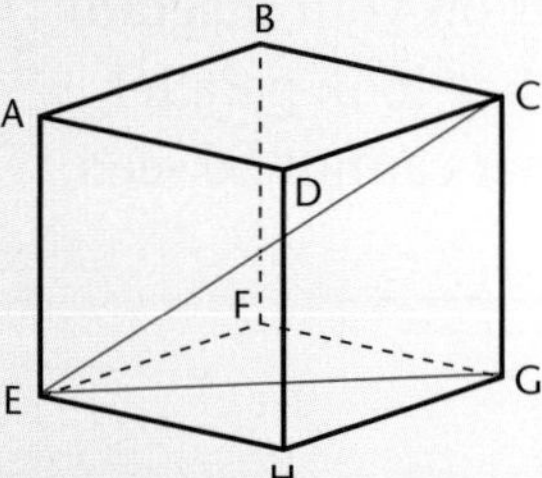

3 This is a cube. Each edge is 8 cm.
Find the length of
a AC b AG.

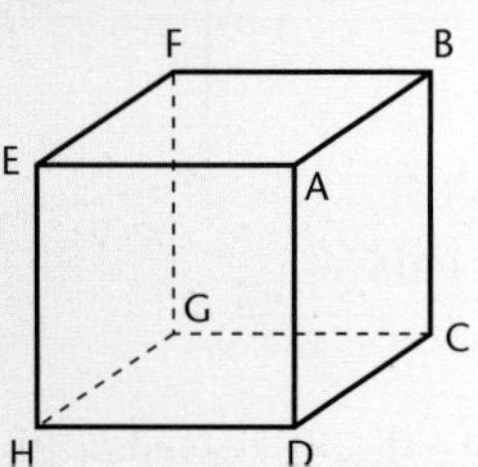

4 This rectangular block measures 5 cm by 4 cm by 3 cm.
Work out the length of
a BG b BH.

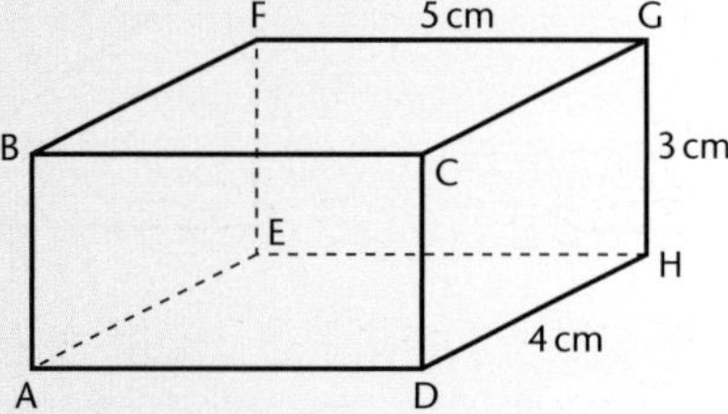

5 This is a triangular prism.
The cross-section is a right-angled triangle.
Work out the length of
a BD b DF c AD.

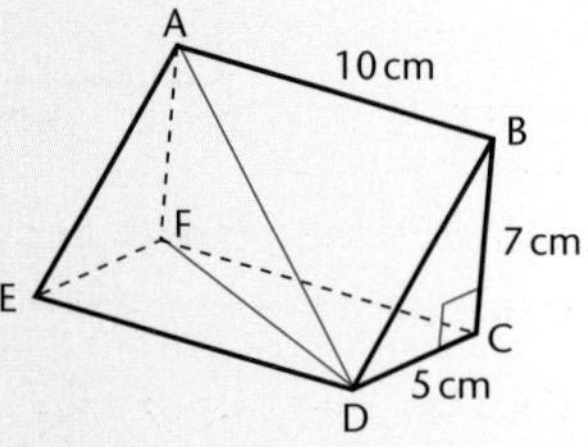

6 The cross-section of this prism is an isosceles triangle.
M is the midpoint of ED.
Work out the length of
a AM b MC c AC.

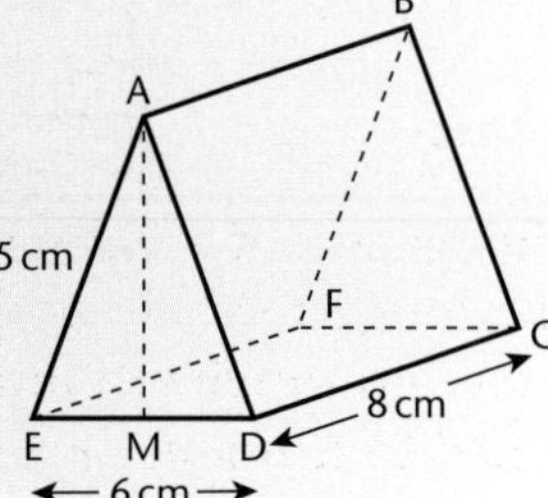

7 The base of this pyramid is a right-angled isosceles triangle.
V is vertically above A.
M is the midpoint of BC.
Work out the length of
a AM b VM.

To find AM draw △ABC. Add the measurements you know and mark the right angle.

8 This diagram shows a square-based pyramid.
V is vertically above the centre of the base, E.
Work out
a the length of BD
b the length of BE
c the height of V above the base.

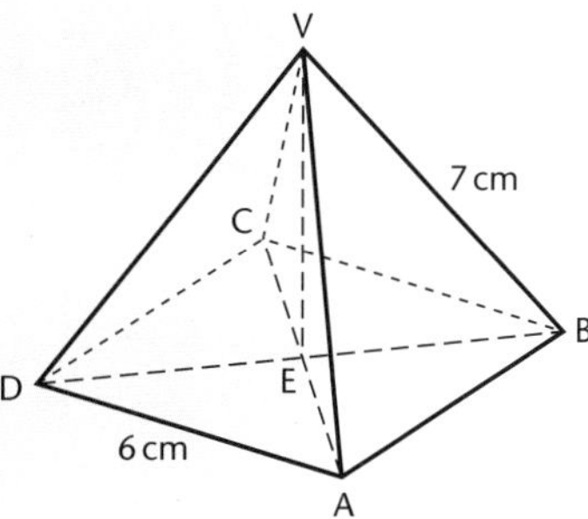

9 The dimensions of a rectangular box are exact numbers of centimetres. The volume of the box is 105 cm^3.
A metal rod 8.6 cm long will just fit inside the box lying on its base.
a How deep is the box?
b Work out the length of the longest rod that will just fit inside the box.

Summary of key points

- In a right-angled triangle the square of the longest side is equal to the sum of the squares of the other two sides.
- If any two sides in a right-angled triangle are known the third side can be found.
- When solving problems in 3-dimensions always draw and label the triangle you are using separately.

Most candidates who get GRADE C or above can:
- use Pythagoras' theorem to find a side in a right-angled triangle.

Most candidates who get GRADE A or above can also:
- use Pythagoras' theorem to find lengths in 3-dimensional problems.

Glossary

Converse	the reverse of a statement
Hypotenuse	the longest side in a right-angled triangle
Pythagoras' theorem	in a right-angled triangle the square of the hypotenuse is equal to the sum of the squares of the other two sides

10 Straight-line graphs

This chapter will show you:

✓ the meaning of coordinates
✓ how to find the midpoint and the length of a line segment
✓ what the equation of a straight line looks like and how to plot its graph
✓ how to find the gradient of a line
✓ how to recognise parallel and perpendicular lines
✓ how to find the equation of a line
✓ how to use graphs to solve simultaneous equations
✓ the relationship between distance, time and speed
✓ how to draw and use a distance–time graph

Before you start you need to know:

✓ the names and properties of the special triangles and quadrilaterals
✓ Pythagoras' theorem and how to use it
✓ how to change the subject of a formula
✓ how to work with negative numbers
✓ how to substitute numbers into an equation
✓ how to solve equations
✓ the units used for length and how to convert between them
✓ the units used for time and how to convert between them

10.1 Coordinates

You need one number to give the position of a point on a line.
You need two numbers to give the position of a point on a flat surface.
You need three numbers to give the position of a point in space.
These numbers are called **coordinates**.

The point A is at 2 on this number line.

The point B on this surface is 1 along and 2 up.

The point C inside this cuboid is 1 along, 2 across and 2 up.

The coordinates that give the position of the point on a grid are written as a pair of numbers in brackets.

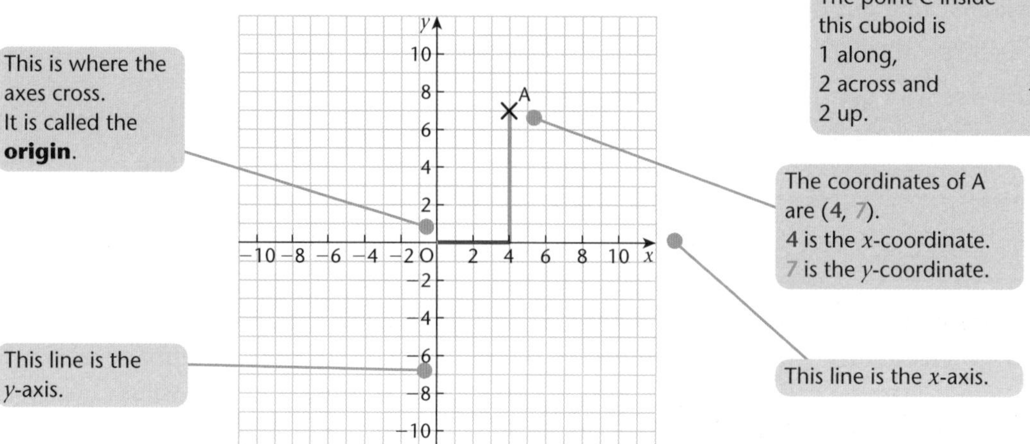

The midpoint of a line segment

A **line segment** is the line between two points. The **midpoint** of the line segment is the point halfway between these points.
You can find the coordinates of the midpoint from a graph.

The length of a line segment

You can find the length of a line that is parallel to the x- or y-axis by counting grid lines.
You can use Pythagoras' theorem to find the length of a sloping line.

Did you know

that coordinates that give the position of a point in relation to perpendicular axes are called Cartesian coordinates?
They are named after René Descartes (1596–1650).

Example 1

a Plot the points A(1, −3) and B(5, 5).
b Find the coordinates of the midpoint, M, of the line AB.
c Find the length of the line AB.

a

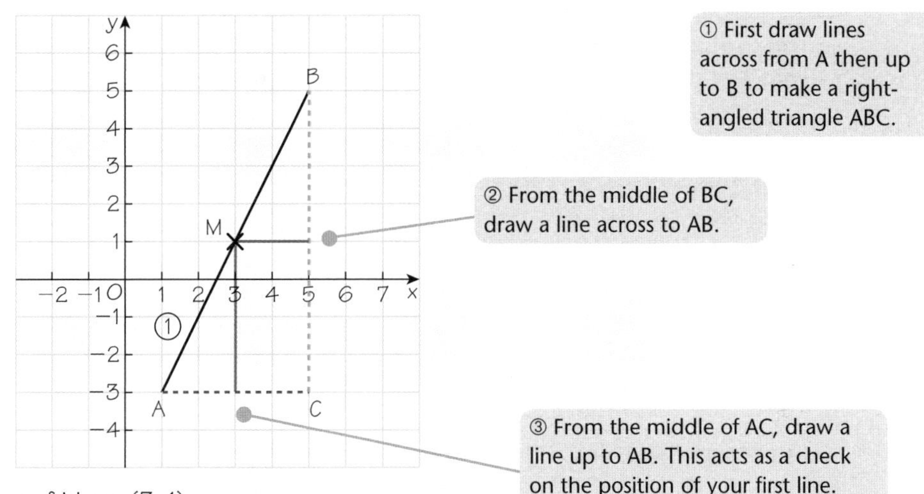

b The coordinates of M are (3, 1).

c AC = 4 and BC = 8

$AB^2 = AC^2 + BC^2$ Pythagoras' theorem

$= 16 + 64 = 80$

$AB = \sqrt{80} = 8.94$ to 3 s.f.

AC goes from 1 to 5 parallel to the x-axis so its length is 4.
BC goes from −3 to 5 parallel to the y-axis so its length is 8.

You can sometimes 'read' the coordinates of a midpoint by looking at the graph.

Alternatively you can use the fact that the coordinates of the midpoint are the means of the x-coordinates and of the y-coordinates of the endpoints.

For any two points $P(a, b)$ and $Q(c, d)$

$PQ = \sqrt{(a - c)^2 + (b - d)^2}$

and the mid point of PQ is the point $\left(\frac{a + c}{2}, \frac{b + d}{2}\right)$.

Exam practice 10A

1 a What is the mathematical name of the triangle ABC?
  b Find the length of
   i AB ii AC.
  c Find the coordinates of the midpoint of
   i AB ii AC.

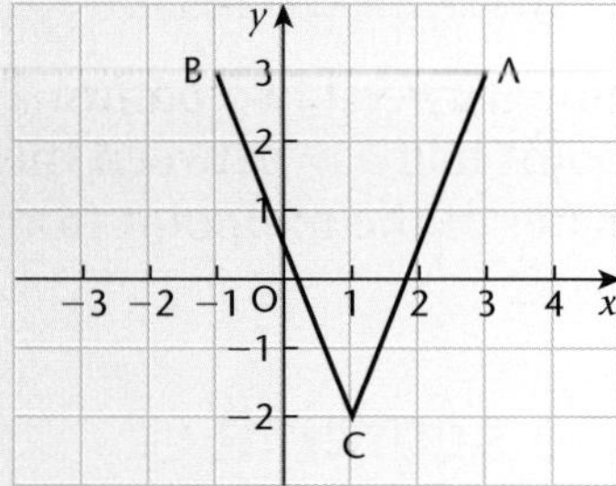

2 a What is the mathematical name of the quadrilateral ABCD?
  b On a copy of the diagram join
   i AC ii BD.
  c Mark the midpoint of BD and label it M.
  d What are the coordinates of M?

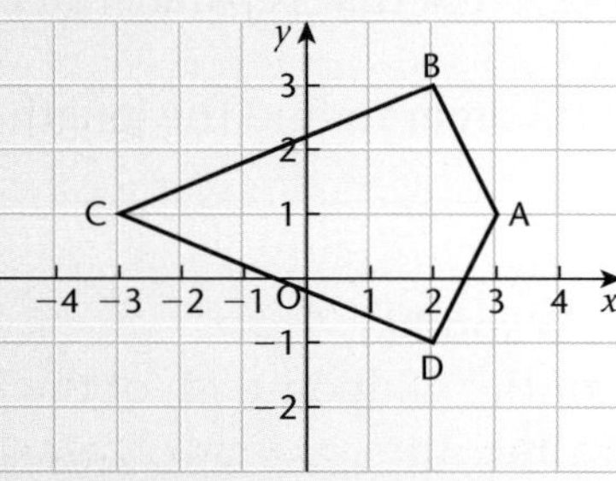

3 a Write down the coordinates of the midpoint of
   i PS ii QR.
  b Kwame said the line joining the midpoints of PS and QR is perpendicular to QR. Explain why Kwame is wrong.

UAM

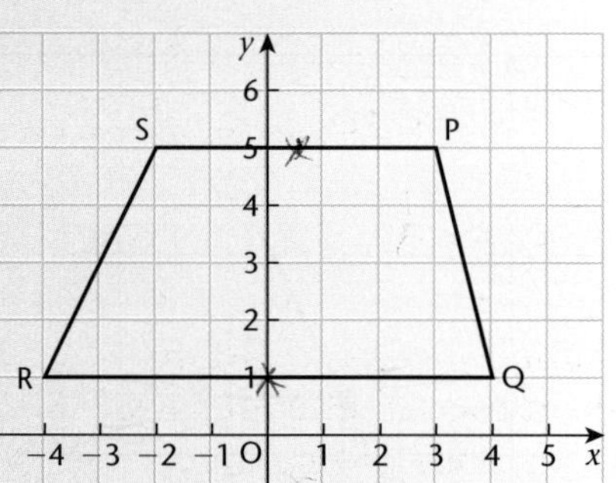

The coordinates of a point can be decimals or fractions.

4 a What is the mathematical name of the quadrilateral PQRS?
  b Write down the length of
   i PS ii SR.
  c Write down the coordinates of the midpoints of PQ and SR.
  d Explain why the line joining the midpoints of PQ and SR is parallel to SP and RQ.

UAM

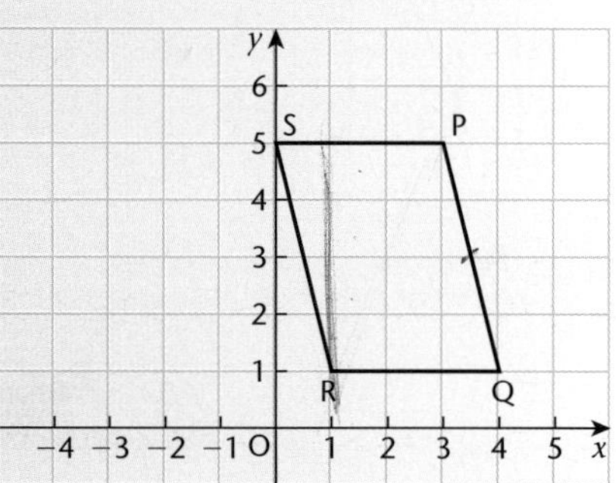

10.2 The graph of a straight line

Equations of the form $y = mx + c$, where m and c are constants, are called **linear equations**.

When you substitute any number for x you get a corresponding value for y. You can do this for different values of x to get pairs of values that you can use as coordinates to plot points on a graph. These points all lie on a straight line.

Any equation that can be written in the form $y = mx + c$ gives a straight line.

Example 2

Draw the graph of $y + 2x = 3$ for values of x from -2 to 4.

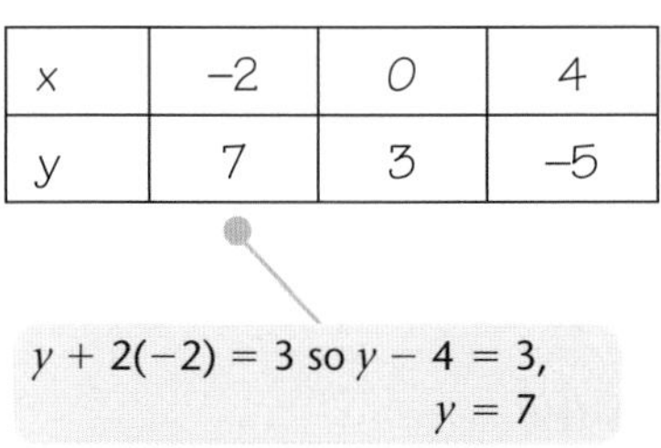

x	−2	0	4
y	7	3	−5

$y + 2x = 3$ gives a straight line because it can be written as $y = -2x + 3$.
Make a **table of values** of x and y. Use the highest and lowest values of x you need, and choose a third value to check your answer.

$y + 2(-2) = 3$ so $y - 4 = 3$,
$y = 7$

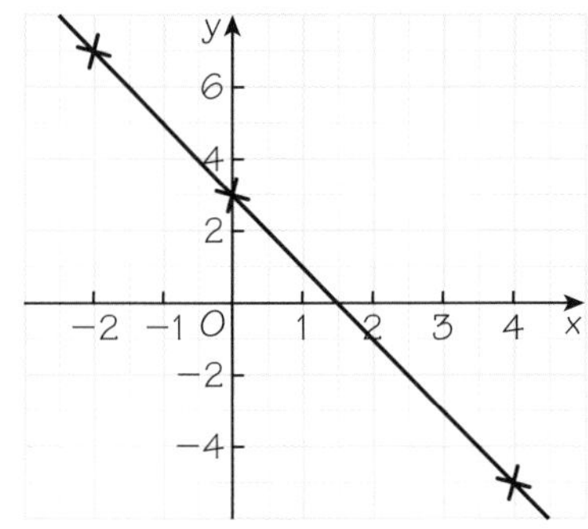

The values of x go from -2 to 4.
The table shows that the values of y go from -5 to 7.
Draw the x- and y-axes on graph paper. The range of values of y is twice the range of values of x so choose 1 cm for 2 units on the y-axis and 1 cm for 1 unit on the x-axis.

Use the pairs of values $(-2, 7)$, $(0, 3)$ and $(4, -5)$ as coordinates. Plot these points, draw a straight line through them and continue it to the edges of the grid. If your working and plotting are correct all these points will lie on a straight line.

You can solve a pair of simultaneous equations by drawing their graphs on the same set of axes. The values of x and y at the point where they cross are the solution of the simultaneous equations.

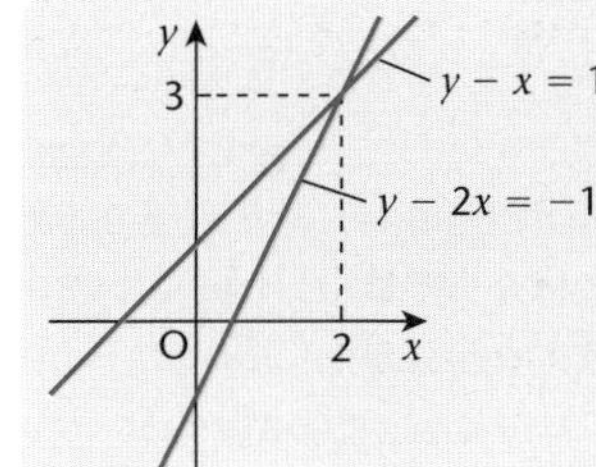

The solution of the simultaneous equations
$y - x = 1$
$y - 2x = -1$
is $x = 2$, $y = 3$.

Lines parallel to the axes

An equation of the form $y = c$, where c is a constant, is a line parallel to the x-axis.

An equation of the form $x = k$, where k is a constant is a line parallel to the y-axis.

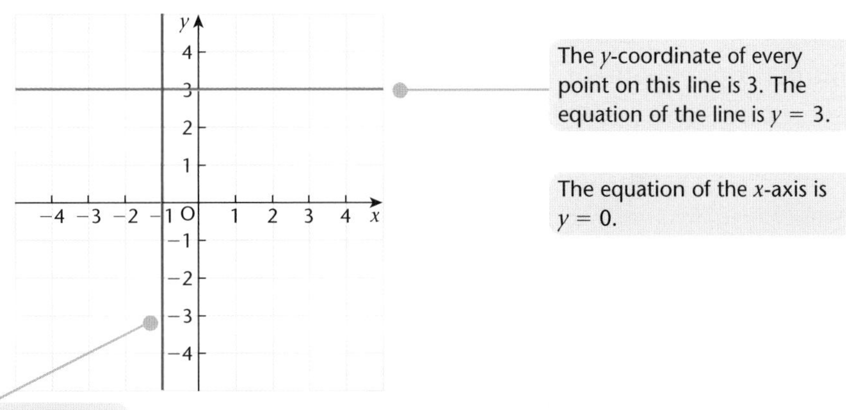

The y-coordinate of every point on this line is 3. The equation of the line is $y = 3$.

The equation of the x-axis is $y = 0$.

The x-coordinate of every point on this line is -1.
The equation of the line is $x = -1$.

The equation of the y-axis is $x = 0$.

Exam practice 10B

You need graph paper for these questions.

1 a Draw the graph of $y = x + 1$ for values of x from -4 to 4.
  b Draw the graph of $y + x = 3$ on the same set of axes.
  c Write down the solution of the simultaneous equations

$$y = x + 1$$
$$y + x = 3$$

2 a Draw the graph of $y = 2x - 4$ for values of x from -4 to 4.
  b Solve the equation $2 = 2x - 4$.
  c Fred said that the solution of the equation $2 = 2x - 4$ is the x-coordinate of the point on the line where the y-coordinate is 2.
UAM Explain why Fred is correct.

3 a Draw the graph of $y + 2x = 1$ for values of x between -1 and 3.
  b There is a point on the line where the x and y coordinates are equal.
    Write down the coordinates of this point.
  c On the same set of axes, draw the graph of $2y - x = 1$.
  d Write down the coordinates of the point where the two lines cross.
UAM e Explain why your answer to part d gives the solution of the simultaneous equations

$$y + 2x = 1$$
$$2y - x = 1$$

4 a Draw the graph of $y = \frac{1}{2}x + 1$ for values of x between -4 and 4.
  b There is a point on this line where the x coordinate is 1 more than the y coordinate.
    Write down the coordinates of this point.
UAM c Explain why the point (2, 4) is not on this line.

(2, 4) is on the line only if $y = 4$ when 2 is substituted for x in the equation of the line.

5 Which of the following points is on the line $3y - 2x = 8$?
  (3, 4), (−2, 4), (8, 8), (0, 4), (4, 0).

6 This is the graph of $2y + x = 3$.
  On a copy of this graph draw another line to solve the simultaneous equations

$$2y + x = 3$$
$$2y - x = 1.$$

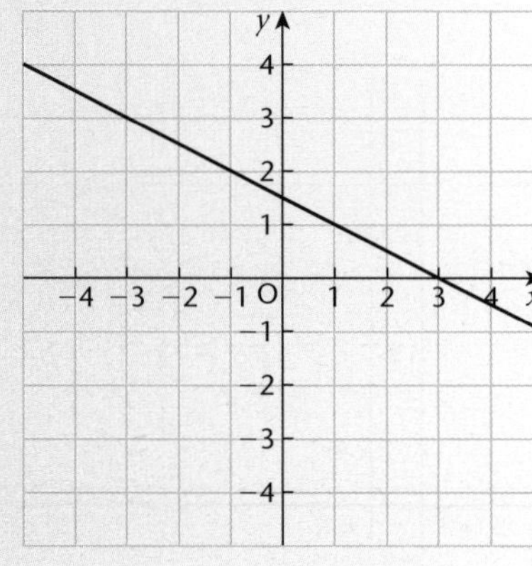

WWW

10.3 Gradient

The **gradient** of a line is a measurement of its slope. It is the amount by which y changes when x increases by 1 unit. You can calculate the gradient using $\frac{\text{vertical change}}{\text{horizontal change}}$ between two points on the line.

The gradient is positive when the line slopes up.

The equation of this line is $y = 2x - 1$. Its gradient is 2.

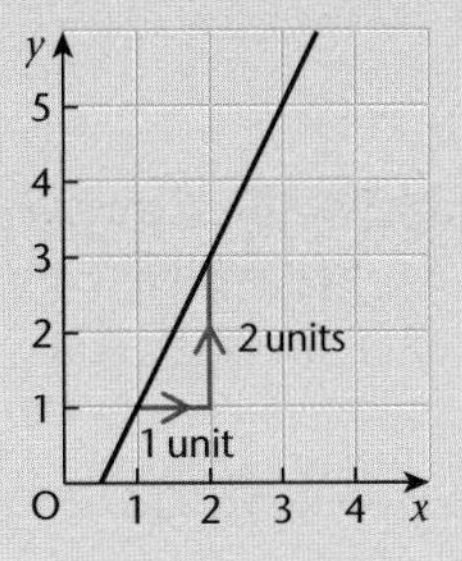

The gradient is negative when the line slopes down.

The equation of this line is $y = 6 - 3x$. Its gradient is -3.

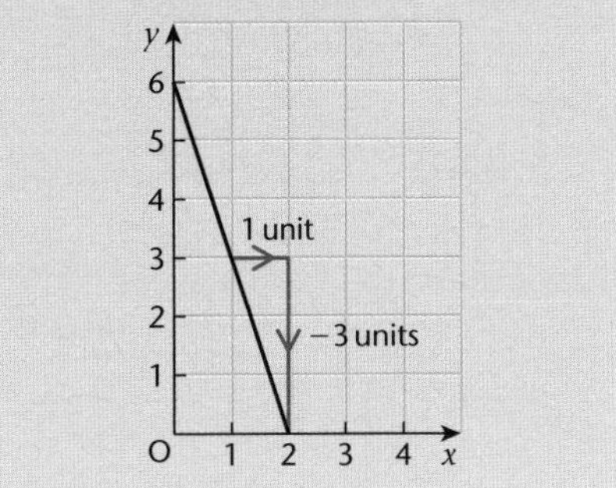

Example 3

Find the gradient of this line.

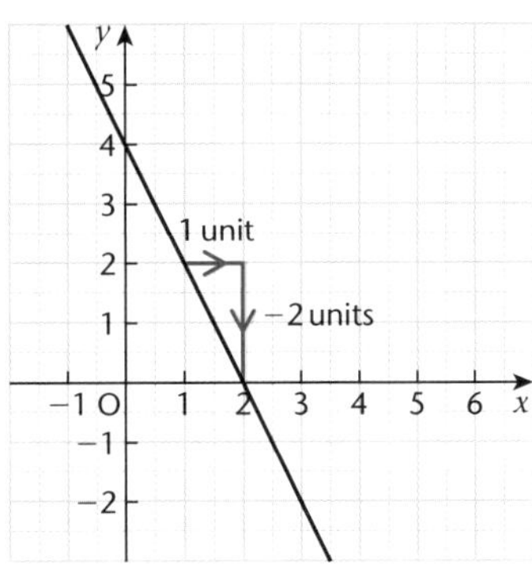

Choose a point on the line whose x-coordinate is a whole number. Go across one unit then down to the line. The amount by which y changes is the gradient of the line.

The gradient is −2.

You can find the gradient from any two points on the line.
On this line, y changes by -1.5 units when x increases by 0.5 units.
So the gradient is $-1.5 \div 0.5 = -3$.

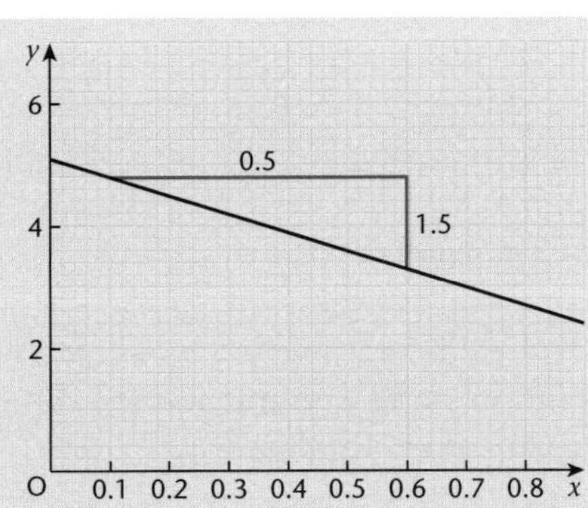

Always use the scales on the axes, not measurements with your ruler.
So $\frac{-7\frac{1}{2}}{25} = -0.3$ is wrong.

You can find the gradient of a line from its equation. When the equation is written in the form $y = mx + c$, the gradient of the line is the value of m.

> You must include the sign.
> $y = -4x + 1$: gradient $= -4$.
> $y = 2x - 3$: gradient $= 2$.

> When x increases from 0 to 1, y changes from c to $m + c$.
> So when x increases by 1 unit, y increases by m units, so the gradient is m.

Example 4

What is the gradient of the line

a $y = 4x - 2$ **b** $y = 7 - x$ **c** $y - \frac{1}{2}x = 5$?

a $y = 4x - 2$
The gradient is 4.

> Compare $y = 4x - 2$ with $y = mx + c$.

b $y = 7 - x$ or $y = -x + 7$
The gradient is -1.

> x is multiplied by 1 and the sign is negative, so the gradient is -1.

c $y - \frac{1}{2}x = 5$
$y = \frac{1}{2}x + 5$
The gradient is $\frac{1}{2}$.

> Write the equation in the form $y = mx + c$.

Parallel and perpendicular lines

Parallel lines have the same gradient.

> The lines $y = 2x - 1$ and $y = 2x + 3$ are parallel because they both have a gradient of 2.

The product of the gradients of perpendicular lines is -1.

This means that if the gradient of one line is m, the gradient of a perpendicular line is $-\frac{1}{m}$.

> The black line has gradient m.
> The black line is rotated by 90° about A, to give the green line.
> The gradient of the green line is $-\frac{1}{m}$.

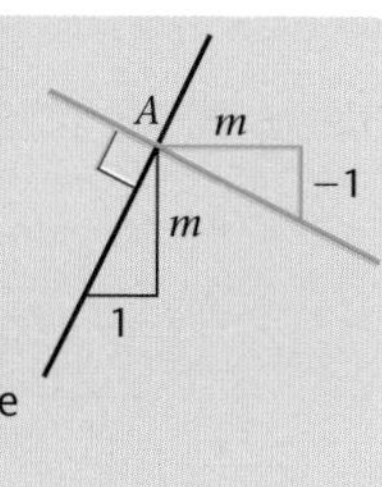

Exam practice 10C

1 Write down the gradient of each line.

a $y = 3x + 9$ b $y = 2x - 4$
c $y = 5 - x$ d $y + 2x = 4$
e $y = 3 - \frac{1}{2}x$ f $y = \frac{1}{3} - \frac{2}{3}x$.

2 Which two of the lines in question 1 are perpendicular?

> Look for two gradients whose product is -1.

3 Which of these lines are parallel?
$y = 3x - 1$, $y = 4x - 3$, $y = 4 + 3x$, $y = 6 - 3x$.

UAM 4 Imran said that the lines $y = 5x - 2$ and $y = 2 - 5x$ are parallel.
Is Imran correct? Explain your answer.

5 Find the gradient of each of these lines.

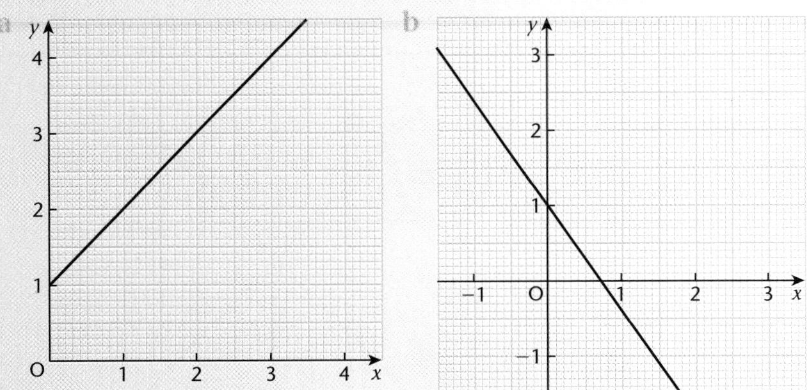

6 Find the gradient of a line perpendicular to each of the lines given in question 5.

10.4 Finding the equation of a line

You can write the equation of a line in the form $y = mx + c$, where m is the gradient of the line and c is a number.
When $x = 0$, $y = c$. This is the value of y where the line crosses the y-axis.

You can use this to find the equation of a line from its graph.

The point where a graph crosses the y-axis is called the ***y*-intercept**.

Example 5

Find the equation of this line.

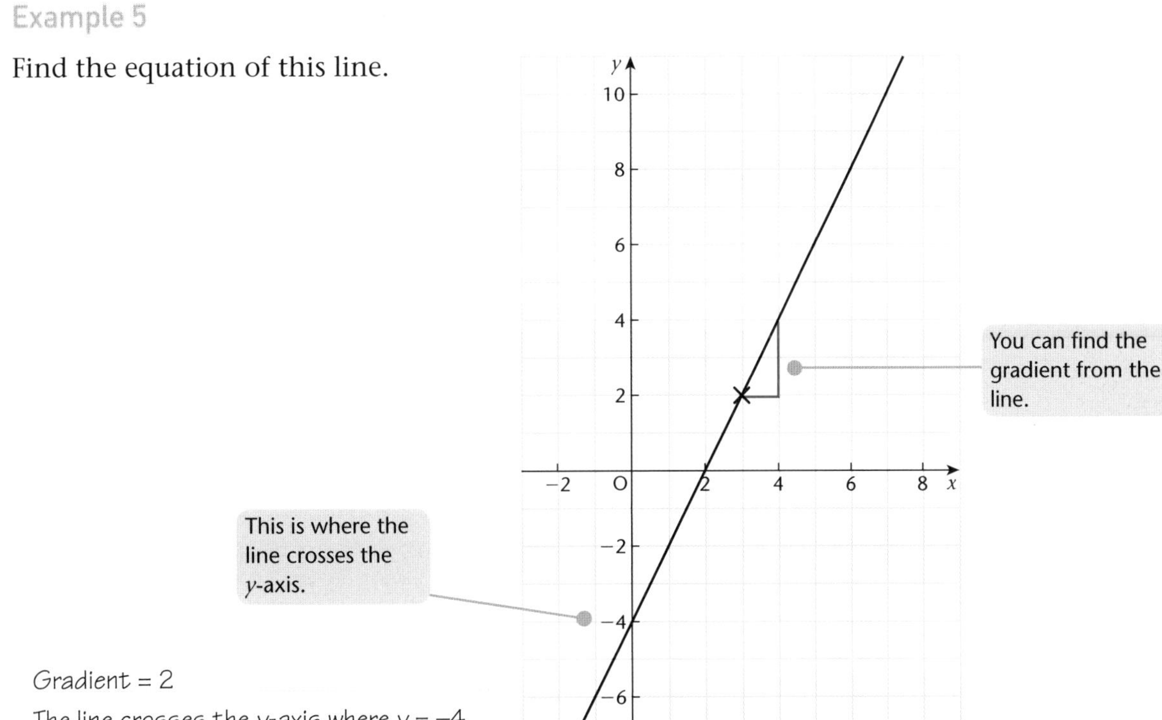

Gradient = 2

The line crosses the y-axis where $y = -4$.

The equation of the line is $y = 2x - 4$.

Sometimes you can write down the equation of a line without having to do any calculations.

Example 6

Write down the equation of each line.

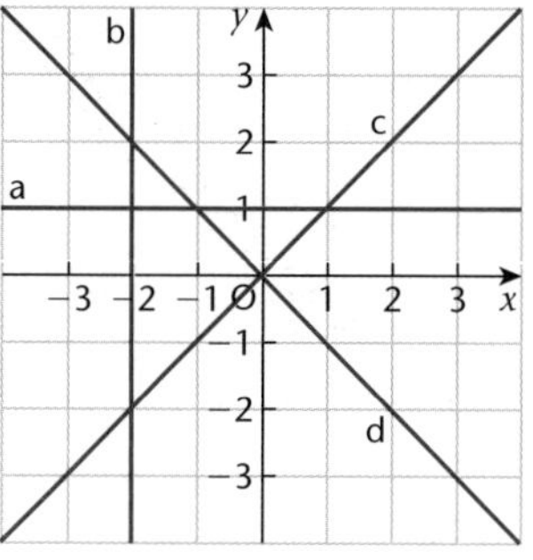

a $y = 1$

Every point on this line has a y-coordinate of 1.

b $x = -2$

Every point on this line has an x-coordinate of -2.

c $y = x$

y-coordinate = x-coordinate for every point on this line.

d $y = -x$

y-coordinate = − x-coordinate for every point on this line.

You need to be able to recognise the lines $y = x$ and $y = -x$.

You can find the equation of a line when you know its gradient and the coordinates of one point on the line.

Example 7

This diagram shows the points A(2, −3) and B(5, 6).

a Find the equation of the line through A and B.

b Find the equation of the line perpendicular to AB passing through the point (0, 5).

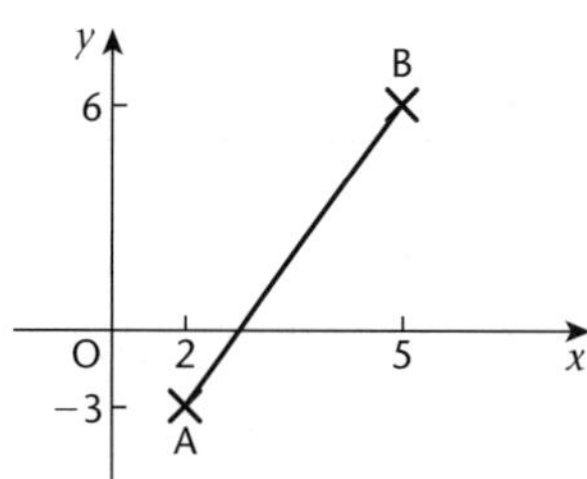

a The gradient of the line through A and B is $\frac{9}{3} = 3$

First work out the gradient. From A to B, x increases from 2 to 5, y increases from −3 to 6 so y increases by 9 units when x increases by 3 units.

The equation of the line is $y = 3x + c$.

B(5, 6) is on the line, so when $x = 5$, $y = 6$.

$6 = 15 + c$

$c = 6 - 15 = -9$

The equation of the line is $y = 3x - 9$.

You can find the value of c by substituting the coordinates of one point into $y = 3x + c$ and solving an equation.

b The gradient of the line perpendicular to AB is $-\frac{1}{3}$

The line crosses the y-axis where $y = 5$.

The equation is $y = -\frac{1}{3}x + 5$.

(0, 5) is on the y-axis.

Exam practice 10D

1 Write down the equation of each line.

a

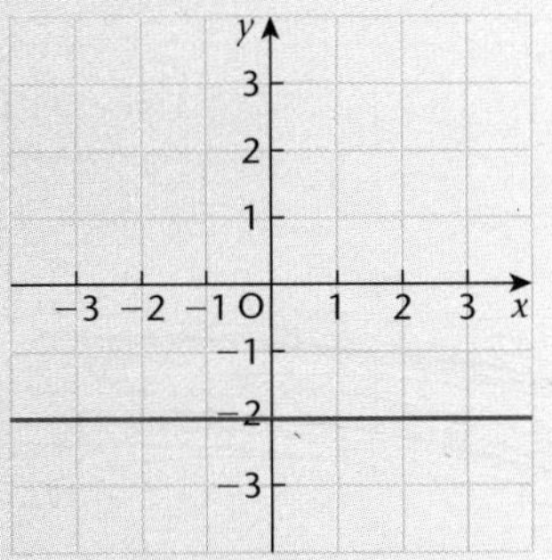

b

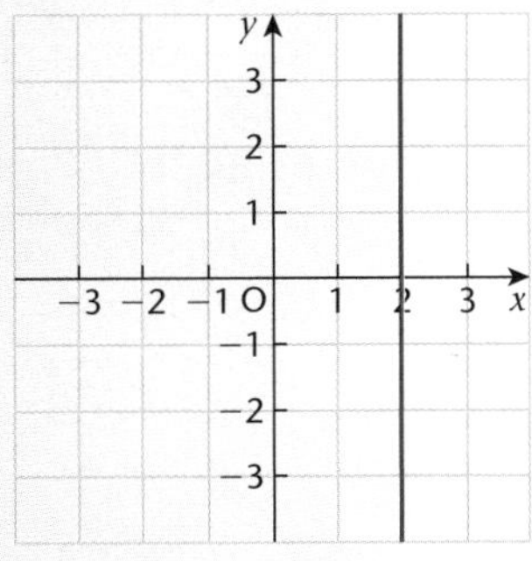

c

2 a Write down the coordinates of A and B.

b On a copy of the graph, draw the line through A and B.

c Work out the gradient of the line.

d Find the equation of the line.

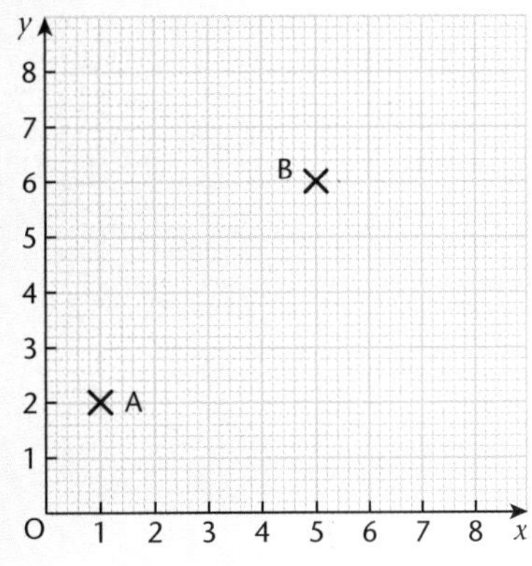

WWW

3 a Work out the gradient of the line through A and B.

b Find the equation of the line.

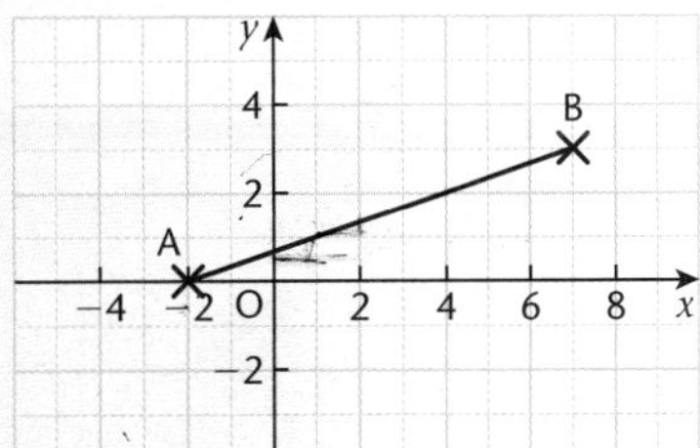

4 The diagram shows the points A(1, 5) and B(3, 1).

a Work out the gradient of the line through A and B.

b Find the equation of the line.

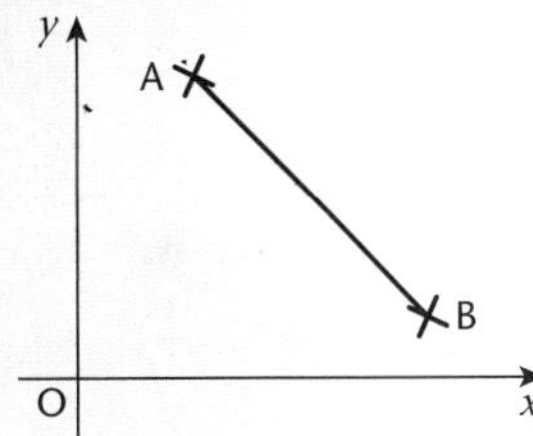

5 The diagram shows the points A(0, 2) and B(4, 4).

a Find the equation of the line through A and B.

b Find the equation of the line through (1, 5) that is parallel to the line through A and B.

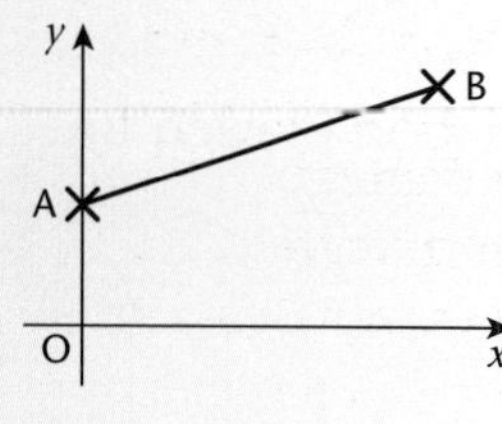

This line will have the same gradient as the line through A and B.

6 The diagram shows the points P(−2, −2) and Q(6, 2).

a Find the equation of the line through P and Q.

b Find the equation of the line that is perpendicular to PQ and goes through the point (4, −3).

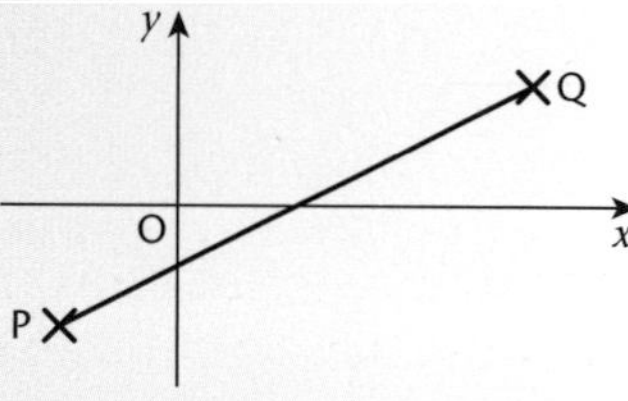

7 a Find the equation of the line through S(0, 8) and T(2, 0).

b Find the equation of the line through the point (−2, 0) that is parallel to the line through S and T.

c Find the equation of the line through the point (5, 2) that is perpendicular to the line through S and T.

UAM

8 The cost of a visit by an engineer to repair a washing machine is made up of two parts, a fixed call-out charge and a charge for each hour spent on the job. The graph shows the total bill (£P) for call-outs lasting up to 3 hours.

a Find the equation of the line.

b Write down the fixed call-out charge.

c How much is the hourly charge?

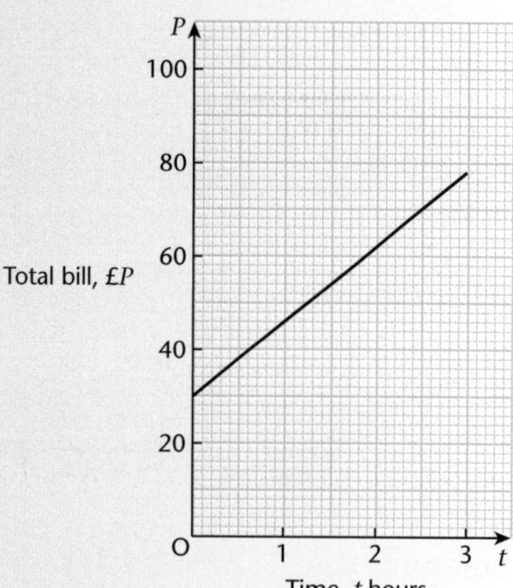

The equation is in the form $P = (\text{gradient}) \times t + c$.

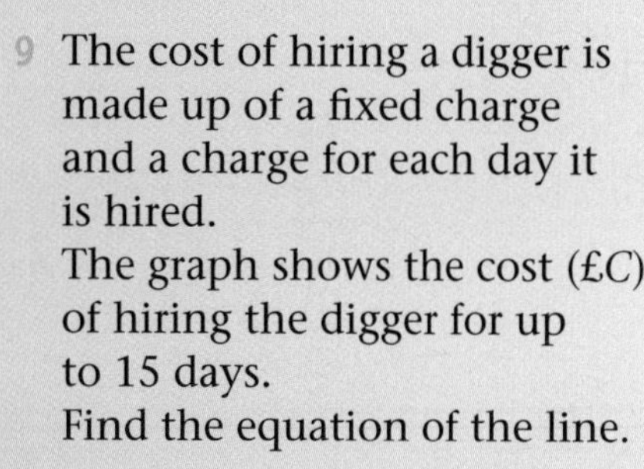

9 The cost of hiring a digger is made up of a fixed charge and a charge for each day it is hired. The graph shows the cost (£C) of hiring the digger for up to 15 days. Find the equation of the line.

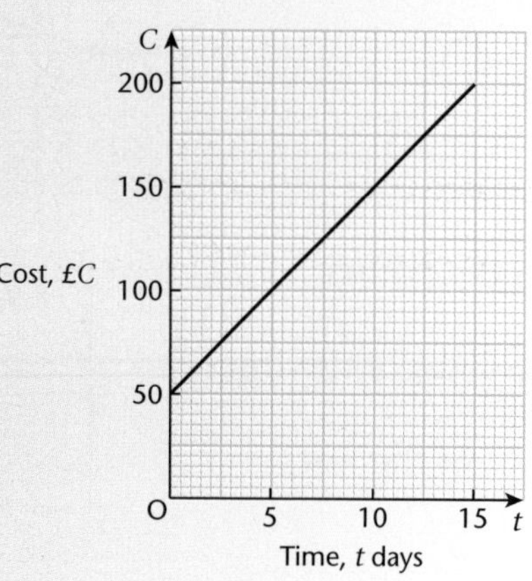

10 a Use the values 0°C = 32°F and 20°C = 68°F to draw a graph to convert between degrees Fahrenheit (°F) and degrees Celsius (°C) on a copy of this grid.
b Use your graph to convert 41°F to °C.
c Find the equation of the line.

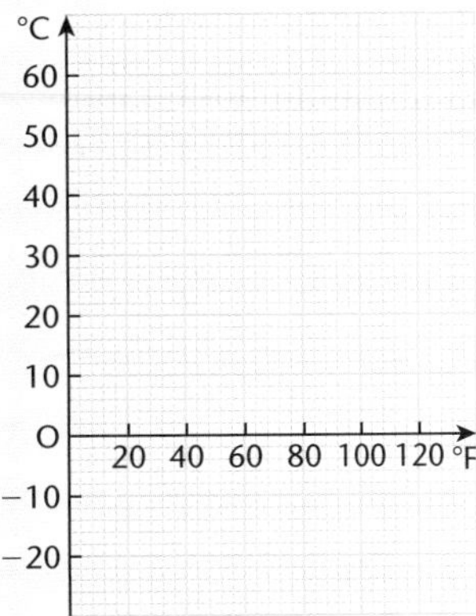

WWW

Graphs like this one, that can be used to convert a quantity measured in one unit to another unit are called **conversion graphs**.

11 a Use £10 = US$18 to draw a graph to convert between *D* dollars and *P* pounds for sums of money up to $100.
b Use your graph to convert
i £8 to dollars ii $45 to pounds.
c Find the equation of your line.

Use graph paper and choose the scales for your axes. Use scales where the subdivisions represent whole numbers such as 1 cm for $10.
Remember to label your axes.

12 This graph shows the amount of water in a reservoir over 10 weeks.

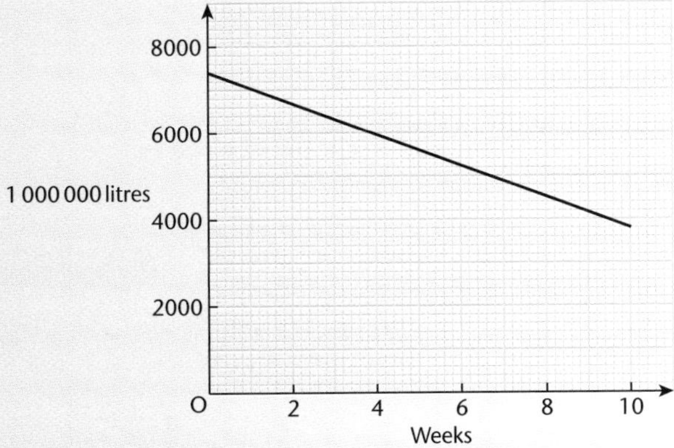

a Find the gradient of the line and explain what it represents.
b Find the equation of the line.
c Tim said 'The reservoir will be empty after another 11 weeks.' What assumption has Tim made?

UAM

10.5 Distance, time and speed

When something moves it covers distance.

Speed measures the distance covered per unit of time.

Speed is a **compound measure** because it combines distance and time.

$$\text{average speed} = \frac{\text{total distance covered}}{\text{time taken}}$$

A car travelling at a constant speed covers 80 miles in two hours.
The car travels 40 miles each hour so its speed is 40 mph (mph is short for miles per hour).

When you travel, your speed is likely to vary.
You can give an **average speed** for a whole journey.
You do this by finding the distance covered then dividing it by the time taken.

The most common metric units of speed are kilometres per hour (km/h) and metres per second (m/s).

The only imperial unit of speed in everyday use is miles per hour (mph).

You can use this diagram to find speed, distance or time when you know the other two.
Cover up the quantity you want to find.

D
S T

Example 8

Amy ran for 10 minutes and walked for 10 minutes to get to the station.
She covered a distance of $1\frac{1}{2}$ miles.
What was her average speed in mph.

To find a speed in mph, the distance must be in miles and the time in hours. So convert 20 min to hours.

Total distance = 1.5 miles.
Total time = 20 minutes = $\frac{1}{3}$ hour
$1.5 \div \frac{1}{3} = 1.5 \times \frac{3}{1} = 4.5$
Average speed = 4.5 mph.

To divide by a fraction, turn it upside down and multiply.

Example 9

a A car made a journey at an average speed of 50 mph.
How far did the car travel in 45 minutes?

b Convert a speed of 50 mph to km/h.

Use 5 miles ≈ 8 kilometres.

a Distance = speed × time
$= 50 \times \frac{3}{4}$ miles = 37.5 miles

The speed is in mph, so the time must be in hours.
45 min = $\frac{3}{4}$ hour.

b 50 mph ≈ 50 × (8 ÷ 5) km/h
= 80 km/h

5 miles ≈ 8 km, so 1 mile ≈ 8 ÷ 5 km.
This gives 50 miles ≈ 50 × (8 ÷ 5) km.

Exam practice 10E

1 Ashad cycled 30 km in 2 hours.
He rested for 30 minutes, then cycled 30 km in 75 minutes.
Find his average speed for the journey.

2 Use this conversion graph to convert
a 20 m/s to km/h
b 50 km/h to m/s.

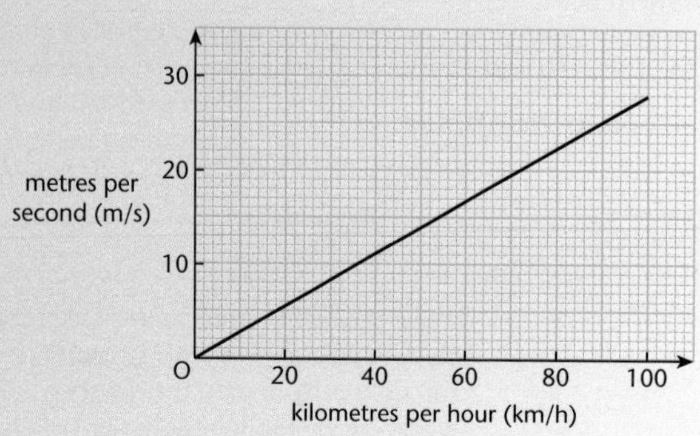

3 Convert a speed of 70 km/h to mph.

4 A cruise ship sailed for 5 days at an average speed of 18 knots.
  a How many nautical miles did the ship sail?
  b Convert a speed of 18 knots to mph.

A **knot** is a speed of 1 nautical mile per hour. 1 nautical mile ≈ 1.15 land miles.

10.6 Distance–time graphs

A **distance–time** graph shows a journey.
The vertical axis shows distance and the horizontal axis shows time.

A distance–time graph is also called a **travel graph**.

Example 10

This graph shows Gail's journey from home to work.
She left home at 7.30 a.m. and cycled to the station.
She caught a train to a station near her work and walked the rest of the way.

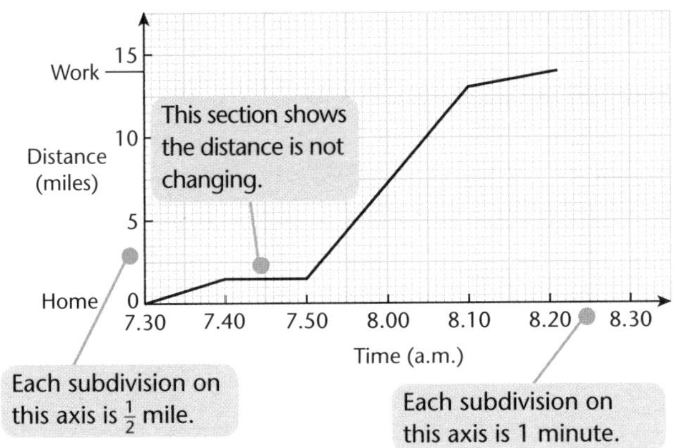

a How far is Gail's work from home?
b How long did Gail wait for a train?
c How long did Gail's journey to work take?
d What was the average speed of Gail's journey to work? Give your answer to 1 d.p.

a 14 miles

Gail's work place is at the top end of the graph. Read across from here to the distance axis.

b 10 minutes

Gail's distance from home does not change while she waits. This is the flat section. It starts at 7.40 and ends at 7.50.

c 51 minutes

She started at 7.30 and arrived at 8.21.

d Distance = 14 miles
Time = 51 minutes = $\frac{51}{60}$ hours
$14 \div \frac{51}{60} = 14 \times \frac{60}{51} = 16.47\ldots$
Average speed = 16.5 mph to 1 d.p.

Press
1 4 × 6 0 ÷ 5 1 =

Exam practice 10F

Make sure you know what each subdivision on each axis means.

1 This graph shows a car journey between two towns.

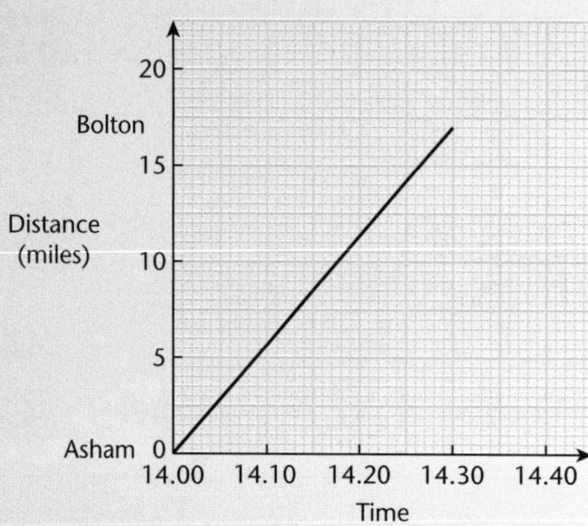

a How far is Bolton from Asham?
b How many minutes does the journey take?
c How far did the car travel in the first 10 minutes?
d Work out the average speed of the car in mph.

Remember to give units in your answers.

2 This graph shows Henry's journey from Birmingham to Manchester.
He leaves home at 10.30 and stops at motorway services on the way.

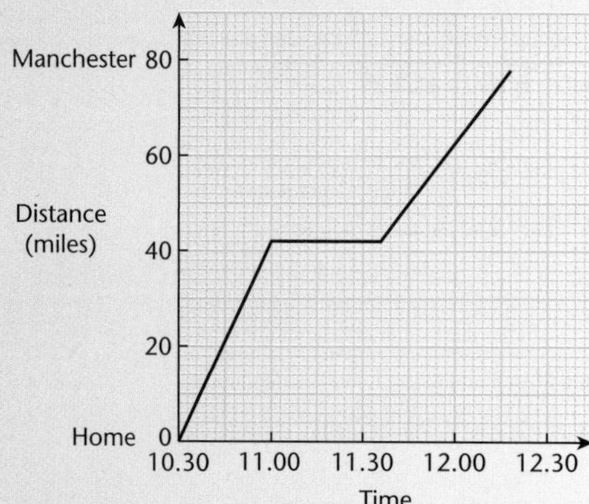

a How far was Henry's journey to Manchester?
b How far were the services from Henry's home?
c How long did Henry stay at the services?
d Work out Henry's speed from leaving the services to arriving in Manchester. Give your answer in mph to 1 decimal place.

3 This graph shows Kim's journey to school.
She waits for her friend and then they cycle to school together.
She leaves home at 08.35 and cycles to a friend's house.

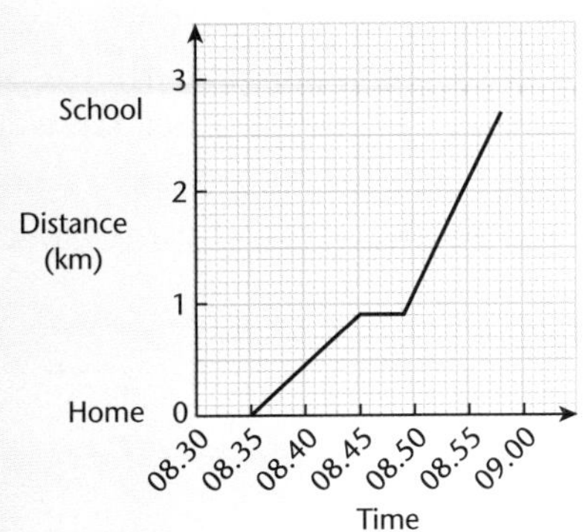

a What time does Kim gets to her friend's house?
b How far is it from Kim's home to the school?
c Work out the speed for the last part of the journey.
d Find Kim's average speed for the whole journey. Give your answer to 1 d.p.

4 This graph shows Freda's journey from work to a warehouse, and back to work.

a How far is the warehouse from work?
b How long did Freda stay at the warehouse?
c How long did the journey back to work take?
d How far did Freda travel in the first six minutes after leaving the warehouse?

> The part of the graph that goes down shows the journey from the warehouse back to work.

e Was Freda's speed greater on the journey to the warehouse or the journey back to work? Give a reason for your answer.

5 Adam leaves home at 07.30 and drives 8 miles to work.
He arrives at 07.45.
Draw a graph to show his journey.

Use a copy of this grid.

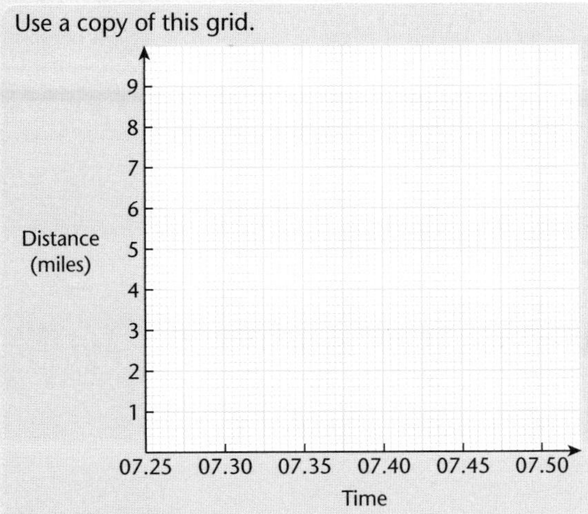

WWW

6 Dwaine walks from home to Pete's house. He waits 5 minutes for Pete to join him. They then walk together to the cinema which is 800 metres from Dwaine's home. They arrive at 18.53.

This graph shows Dwaine's walk from home to Pete's house.

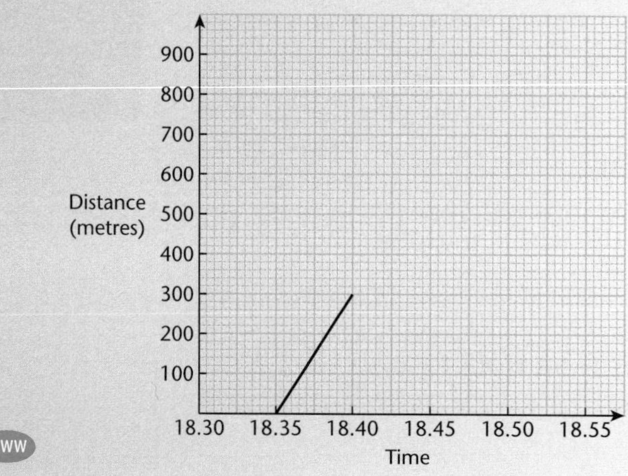

WWW

a Copy and complete the graph to show Dwaine's journey from home to the cinema.

b How far is the cinema from Pete's house?

7 Frank drives from his house to the bus station to pick up his daughter.
He waits for ten minutes. They then drive home at a constant speed, arriving there at 12.49.

a This graph shows part of Frank's journey.

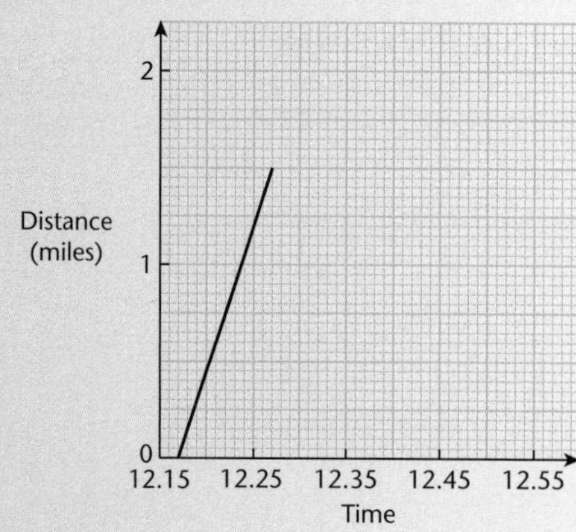

WWW

Copy and complete the graph to show Frank's journey.

b Work out Frank's speed from the bus station to home.

c How far does Frank travel between 12.39 and 12.49?

10.7 Coordinates in 3-dimensions

The coordinates that give the position of a point in 3-dimensions are written as three numbers in brackets.

You can use Pythagoras' theorem to find the length of the line between two points.

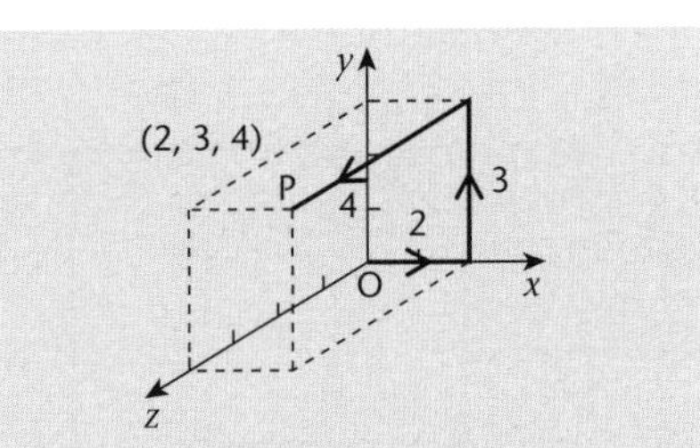

The point P is 2 units along the x-axis, 3 units up the y-axis and 4 units along the z-axis. The coordinates of P are (2, 3, 4).

Example 11

a Find the length of the line from the origin to the point P(2, 3, 4).
b A and B are the points (2, 4, 4) and (4, 5, 7). Find the length of AB.
c Find the coordinates of the midpoint of AB.

a $OP^2 = 2^2 + 4^2 + 3^2$
$= 4 + 16 + 9 = 29$
$OP = 5.39$ to 3 s.f.

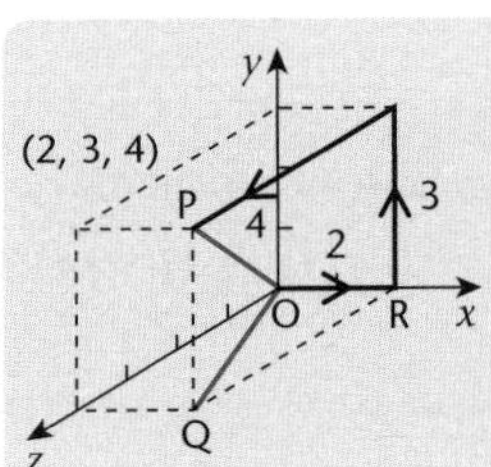

OP is the diagonal of a cuboid.
In triangle ORQ, $\angle R = 90°$, $OR = 2$, $RQ = 4$
so $OQ^2 = OR^2 + RQ^2$.
In triangle OQP, $\angle Q = 90°$, $QP = 3$
so $OP^2 = OQ^2 + QP^2 = OR^2 + RQ^2 + QP^2$
$= 2^2 + 4^2 + 3^2$.

b $AB^2 = 2^2 + 1^2 + 3^2$
$= 4 + 1 + 9 = 14$
$AB = 3.74$ to 3 s.f.

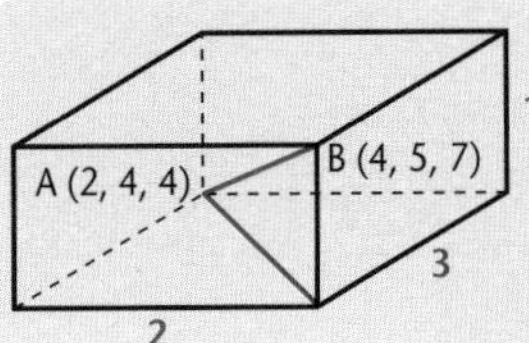

You can think of AB as the diagonal of a cuboid. The lengths of the sides of the cuboid are the differences between the coordinates of A and B. Using Pythagoras' theorem gives $AB^2 = (4 - 2)^2 + (5 - 4)^2 + (7 - 4)^2$.

c The midpoint of AB has coordinates
$\left(\frac{2+4}{2}, \frac{4+5}{2}, \frac{4+7}{2}\right) = (3, 4\tfrac{1}{2}, 5\tfrac{1}{2})$

You can find the coordinates of the midpoint from the diagram or you can use the fact that the coordinates are the mean values of the coordinates of A and B.

For any two points $P(a, b, c)$ and $Q(d, e, f)$,

$$PQ = \sqrt{(a-d)^2 + (b-e)^2 + (c-f)^2},$$

and the midpoint of PQ is the point $\left(\frac{a+d}{2}, \frac{b+e}{2}, \frac{c+f}{2}\right)$.

Exam practice 10G

1 Write down the coordinates of the point A. Find the length and the coordinates of the midpoint of AO.

a

b

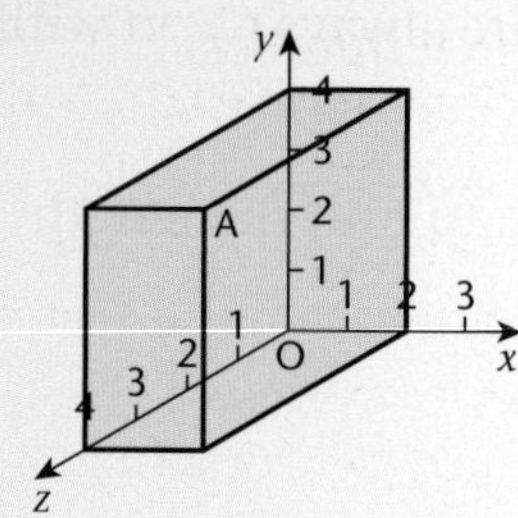

c

d

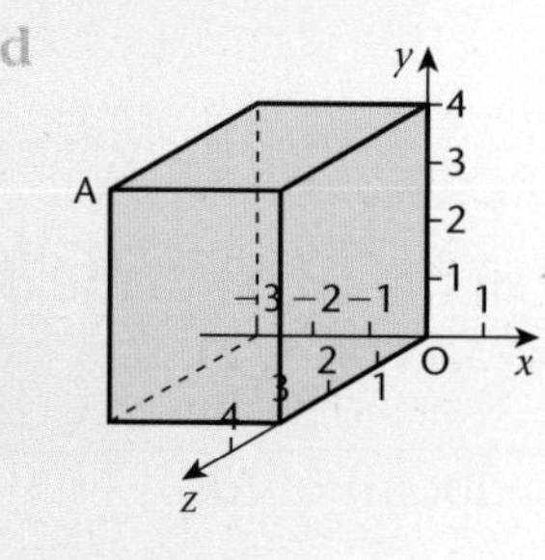

2 Find the distance between these pairs of points.

a (3, 5, 2) and (4, 6, 3)

b (5, 7, 0) and (8, 9, 2)

3 Find the coordinates of the midpoint of the line between the points given in question 2.

Summary of key points

- The coordinates of a point are always given with the distance along the x-axis first.
- You can use Pythagoras' theorem to find the length of a sloping line segment when you know the coordinates of its ends.
- You need to make a table of values to draw the graph of an equation.
- The equation of a straight line is $y = mx + c$ where m is the gradient and c is the value of y where the line crosses the y-axis.
- The gradient of a line is the amount by which y changes when the value of x increases by 1 unit.
- The gradient is positive when a line slopes up and negative when it slopes down.
- Two lines are parallel when they have the same gradient.
- Two lines are perpendicular when the product of their gradients is -1.
- You can find the equation of a line by working out its gradient then using the coordinates of a point on the line to find the value of c.
- You can solve simultaneous equations by finding the point where the lines of the equations cross.
- When you read values from the scales on the axes of a graph, make sure you know what each subdivision means.
- You can work out the speed for a journey or part of a journey from a travel graph. Read the time taken and the distance travelled from the scales on the axes.

Most candidates who get GRADE C or above can:

- find the gradient and the equation of a straight line
- find the average speed from a distance–time graph.

Most candidates who get GRADE A or above can also:

- find the equation of a line perpendicular to a given line and passing through a given point.

Glossary

Average speed	the total distance divided by the total time
Compound measure	combining two or more simple measures
Conversion graph	a graph that converts one quantity to another
Coordinates	values describing the position of a point on a grid
Distance–time graph	shows a journey with the distance on the vertical axis and the time on the horizontal axis
Gradient	measures the slope of a line
Intercept	the point where a line or curve cuts an axis
Knot	a speed of one nautical mile per hour
Line segment	a line between two points
Linear equation	an equation of the form $y = mx + c$
Midpoint	the point halfway between the ends of a line segment
Origin	the point where the axes cross
Speed	distance covered in one unit of time
Table of values	a table giving values of x and corresponding values of y
Travel graph	a graph showing a journey

11 Inequalities

This chapter will show you:
- ✓ how to solve an inequality in one unknown
- ✓ how to solve a set of inequalities in two unknowns

Before you start you need to know:
- ✓ how to draw the graph of a line from its equation
- ✓ how to find the equation of a line from a graph

11.1 Inequalities in one unknown

$x > 3$ is called an **inequality**. It means that x can stand for any number greater than 3.

The symbol $>$ means 'greater than'.
The symbol $<$ means 'less than'.

You can use a number line to show this inequality.

The open circle shows that 3 is not included.

$x \leqslant 2$ is a different type of inequality. It means that x can stand for any number less than or equal to 2.

The symbol $\geqslant$ means 'greater than or equal to.'
The symbol $\leqslant$ means 'less than or equal to.'

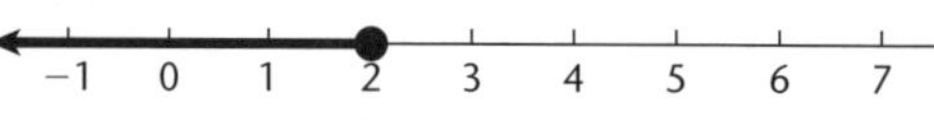

The closed circle shows that 2 is included.

Solving inequalities

Solving an inequality means finding the values of x for which it is true.

You can use these facts to help solve an inequality.

The solution will look like '$x <$ a number' or '$x >$ a number'.

You can add or subtract the same number to or from both sides.

$5 > 3$:
- adding 4 to both sides gives $9 > 7$ which is true
- subtracting 6 from both sides gives $-1 > -3$ which is also true.

You can multiply or divide both sides by the same positive number.

$5 > 3$:
- multiplying both sides by 2 gives $10 > 6$ which is true
- dividing both sides by 3 gives $1\frac{2}{3} > 1$ which is true.

If you multiply or divide by a negative number you have to change the direction of the inequality.

$5 > 3$:
- multiplying both sides by -2 and changing the direction of the inequality gives $-10 < -6$ which is also true.

Example 1

Solve these inequalities and show the solution on a number line.

a $2x < 7$ **b** $3x - 5 \geqslant 7$

a $2x < 7$ — Divide both sides by 2.

$x < 3.5$

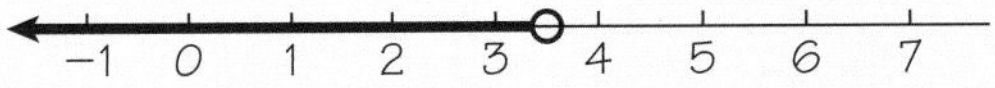

Draw an open circle because 3.5 is not included.

b $3x - 5 \geqslant 7$ — Add 5 to both sides.

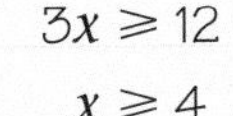

$3x \geqslant 12$ — Divide both sides by 3.

$x \geqslant 4$

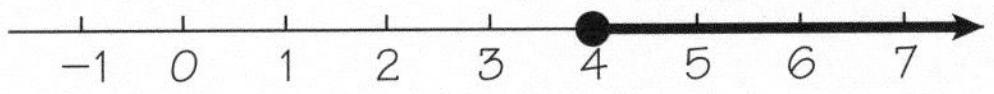

Draw an closed circle because 4 is included.

Sometimes two inequalities are combined.

Example 2

Find the integers that satisfy $6 < 5n \leqslant 15$.

$6 < 5n \leqslant 15$ — Divide all three expressions by 5.

$6 < 5n \leqslant 15$ means $6 < 5n$ and $5n \leqslant 15$. The values of n must make both inequalities true.

$1.2 < n \leqslant 3$

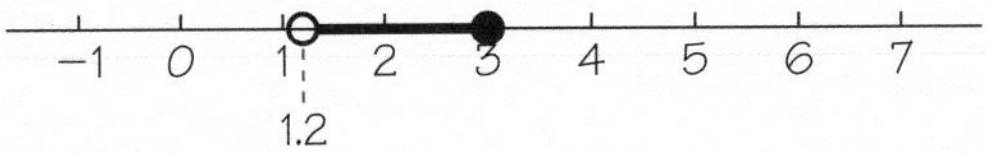

Show this on a number line. You can now see the integers for which both inequalities are true.

$n = 2$ and 3

Exam practice 11A

1 Write down the inequalities represented on these number lines.

a 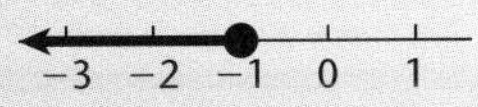

b 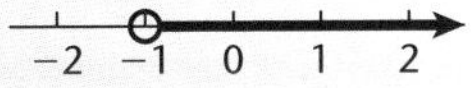

c 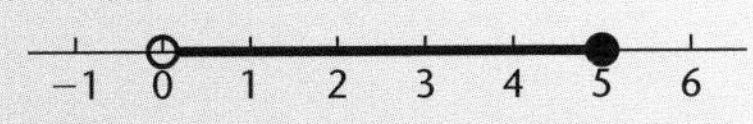

d 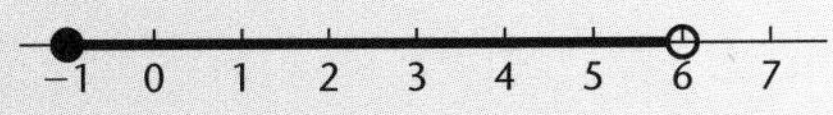

2 Solve these inequalities and show each solution on a number line.

a $4x < -8$ b $x + 3 \leqslant 9$ c $2x - 1 \geqslant 7$

3 Solve these inequalities.

a $2x < 8$	b $x + 1 < 6$	c $3x > 9$
d $x - 4 < 2$	e $x + 7 > 4$	f $2x > 5$
g $2x \geqslant 10$	h $x + 2 \geqslant 5$	i $x - 4 \leqslant 10$
j $3p < -9$	k $x - 3 > -1$	l $2s \geqslant -4$

4 Solve these inequalities.

a $2x + 3 < 9$
b $3x - 2 > 4$
c $6x < x + 10$
d $x - 2 \leqslant 6$
e $x + 4 > 3x$
f $2y + 5 > 9$
g $5a - 2 \geqslant 13$
h $2x - 3 \leqslant 7$
i $7x + 1 > x + 11$
j $2t + 4 < 18 - t$
k $3k - 1 \geqslant 2k + 6$
l $7y - 9 \leqslant 11 - 3y$
m $4 - 3s \geqslant 5 - 2s$
n $2 - 4x < 5x - 7$
p $5p + 6 \leqslant 2 - 3p$

In part c start by subtracting x.

5 Write down the integers that satisfy each inequality.

a $6 < x < 10$
b $-3 < x < 2$
c $4 \leqslant n < 7$
d $4 < 2x < 10$
e $-2 < 2n < 8$
f $-3 \leqslant 5n < 15$
g $4 < 4x \leqslant 14$
h $-6 \leqslant 2n \leqslant 2$
i $3 \leqslant 4n < 8$

Be careful. Look at the inequality signs.

UAM 6 Tim wrote $-3 < x$ so $x < -3$.

a Explain why Tim is wrong.
b What should Tim have written?

11.2 Inequalities in two unknowns

$y < x + 2$ is an inequality in two unknowns.

When $x = 2$, a value of y less than 4 gives a point below the line $y = x + 2$.

For any value of x, all values of y less than $x + 2$ give points below the line, so all points below the line $y = x + 2$ satisfy $y < x + 2$.

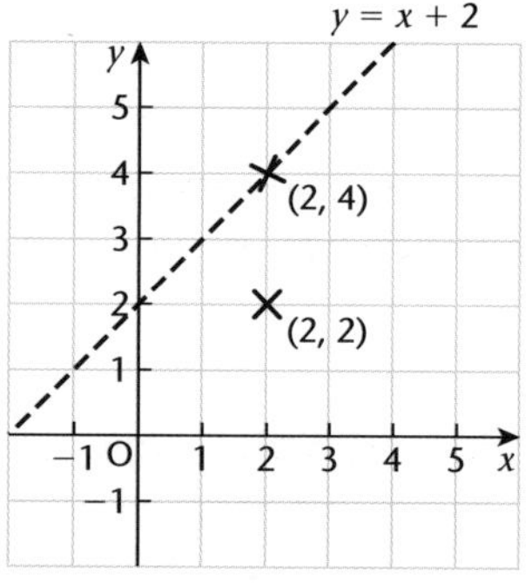

An inequality in two unknowns can be represented as a region on a set of x- and y-axes.

The line $y = mx + c$ divides the x-y plane into two regions.

The coordinates of all the points above the line satisfy the inequality $y > mx + c$.

The coordinates of all the points below the line satisfy the inequality $y < mx + c$.

The coordinates of all the points on the line satisfy the equation $y = mx + c$.

The shaded region, including its boundary line, is described by the inequality $y \geqslant mx + c$.

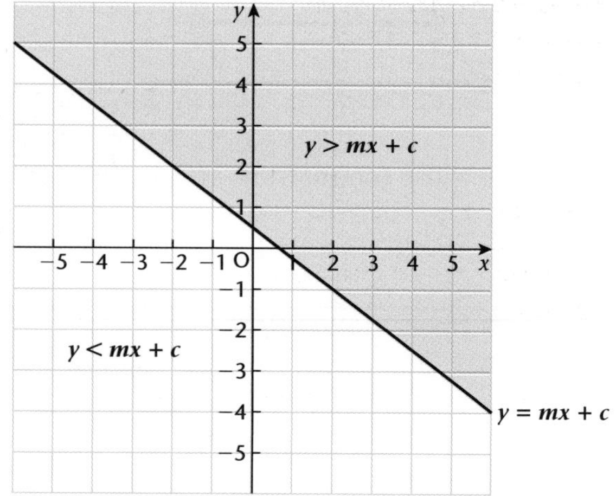

When the points on the boundary are included in the region, the line is shown as a solid line.

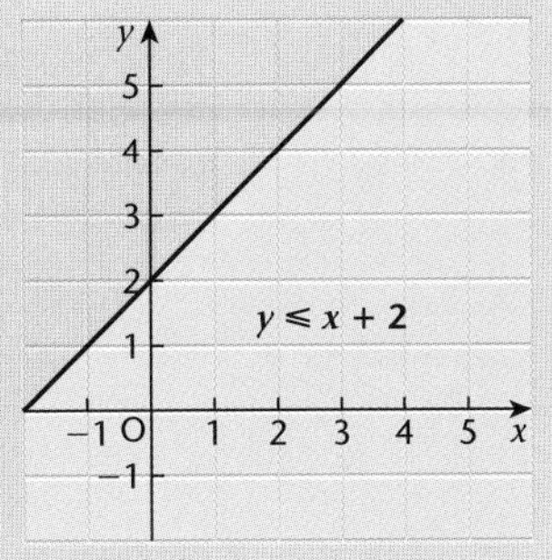

When the points on the boundary are not included in the region, the line is shown as a broken line.

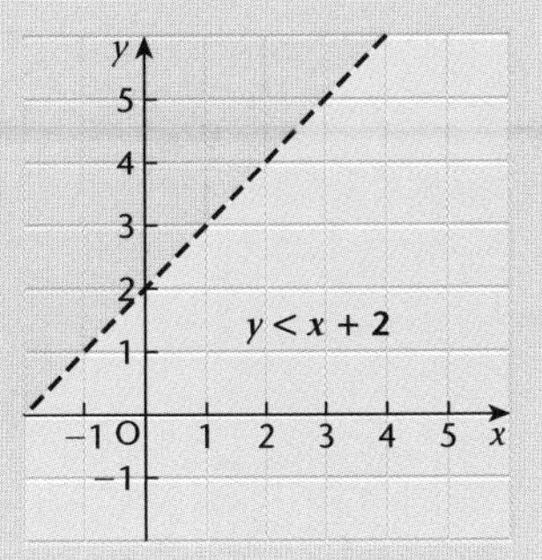

Example 3

Shade the region where $y - x \leqslant 1$.

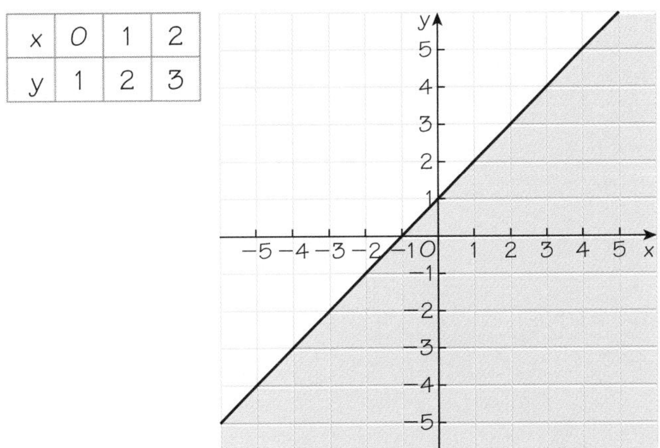

x	0	1	2
y	1	2	3

First draw the line $y - x = 1$. The inequality $y - x \leqslant 1$ includes the line so draw it as a solid line.

Rearrange $y - x \leqslant 1$ as $y \leqslant x + 1$ by adding x to both sides of the inequality. The region is below the line.

If you are not sure which region you want, try a point in one region: the origin is an easy point to use.
At (0, 0), $y - x = 0 - 0 = 0 \leqslant 1$, so (0, 0) is in the region you want.

You can use inequalities to describe a region. The region may be bounded by more than one line.

Example 4

Write down the inequalities that describe the shaded region.

First find the equations of the lines that define the region.

This is the line $x = -3$. It is solid so it is included. All the points in the region have an x-coordinate greater than or equal to -3.

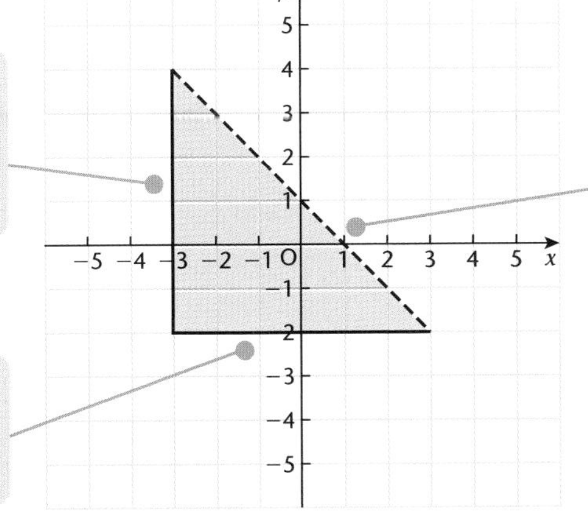

The gradient of this line is -1, and it cuts the y-axis at (0, 1). Its equation is $y = -x + 1$. The line is broken so the points on the line are not included. All the points in the shaded region are below this line, so their coordinates satisfy $y < -x + 1$.

This is the line $y = -2$. All the points in the region have a y-coordinate greater than or equal to -2.

$y < -x + 1$, $x \geqslant -3$ and $y \geqslant -2$

The points in the shaded region satisfy all three inequalities.

Exam practice 11B

Use copies of this grid for questions 1, 2, 3, 5 and 6.
Make sure you read the inequality sign and use the correct type of line.

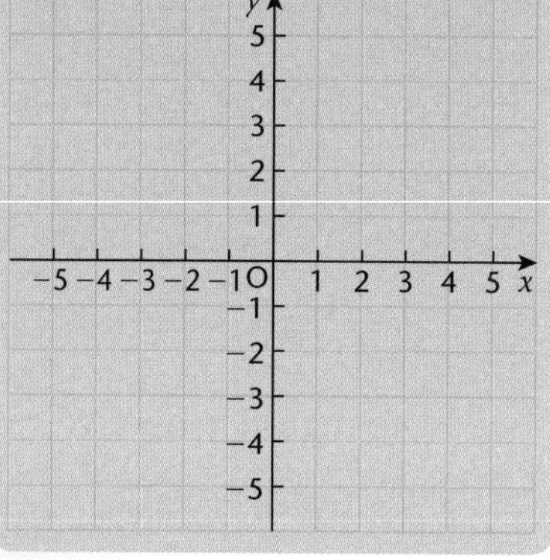

1 Shade the region where:

a $x > 5$ b $y < 2$

c $x \geqslant -3$ d $y \leqslant -1$

2 Shade the region where:

a $y \geqslant x - 1$ b $2x + 3y < 6$

c $2y + x \leqslant 3$ d $x + y \leqslant 5$

3 Shade the region where:

a $3 \leqslant x < 5$

b $-2 < y < 5$

c $-4 < x \leqslant 2$

4 Write down the inequalities that describe the shaded region.

a

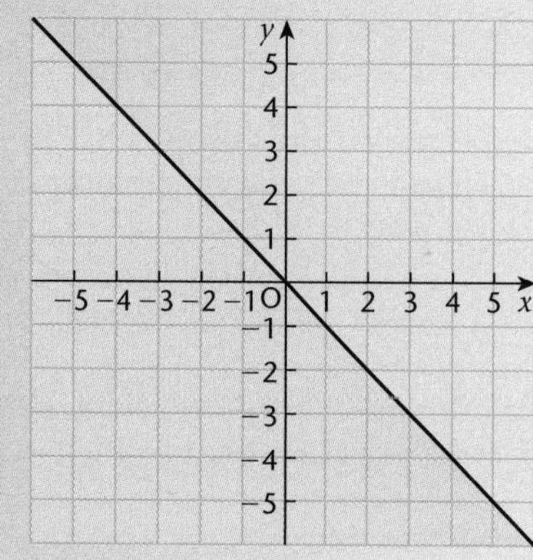

b

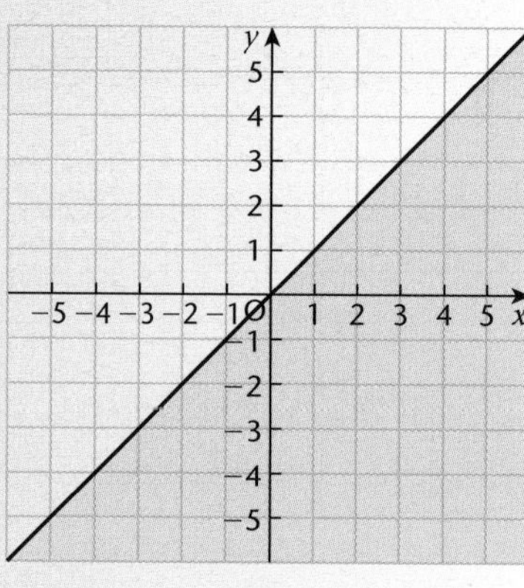

c

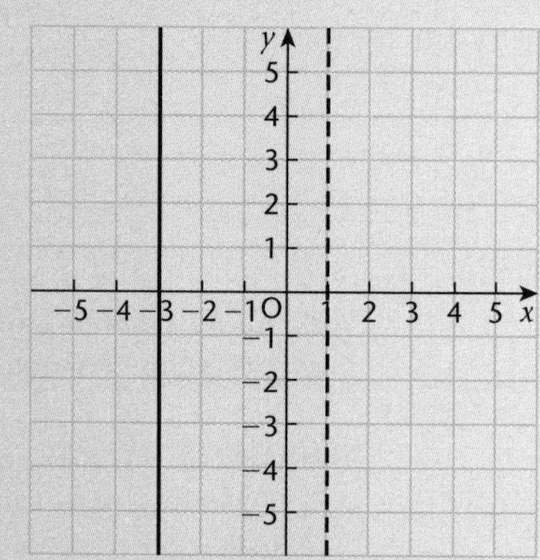

d

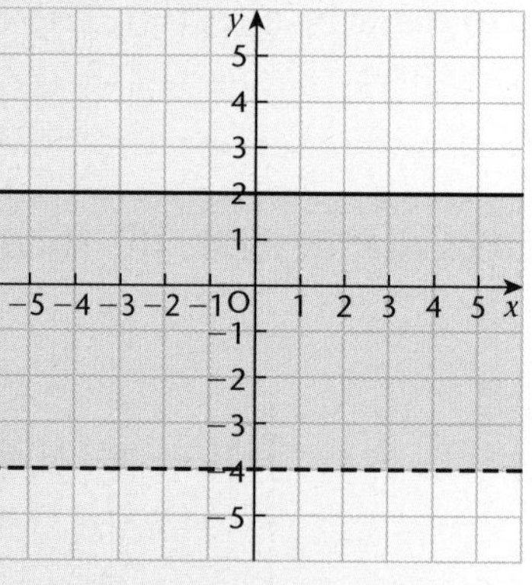

e

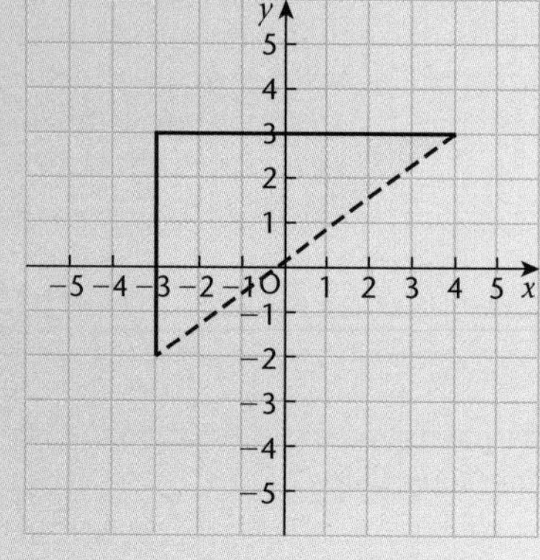

f

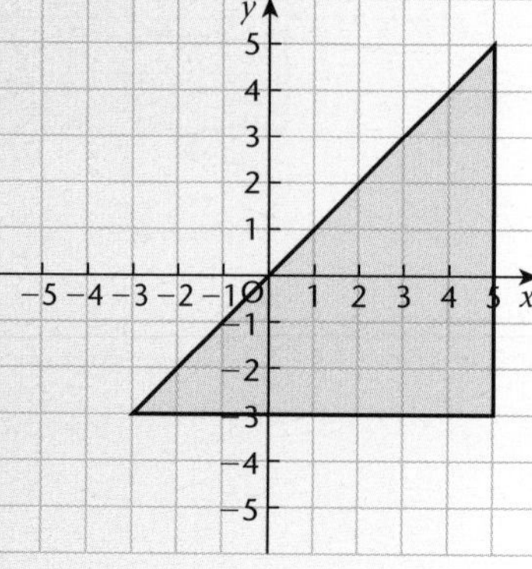

g

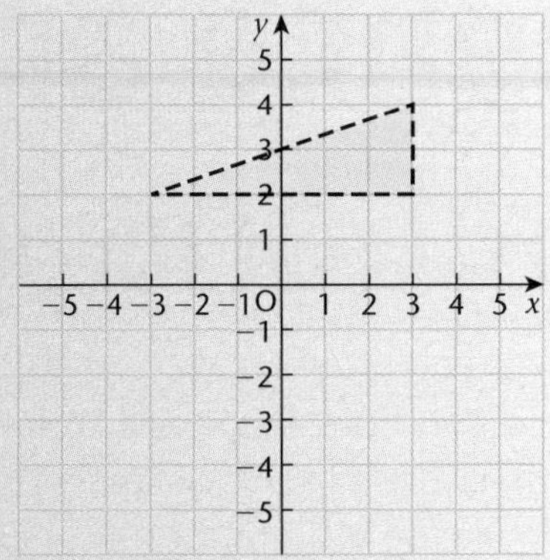

h

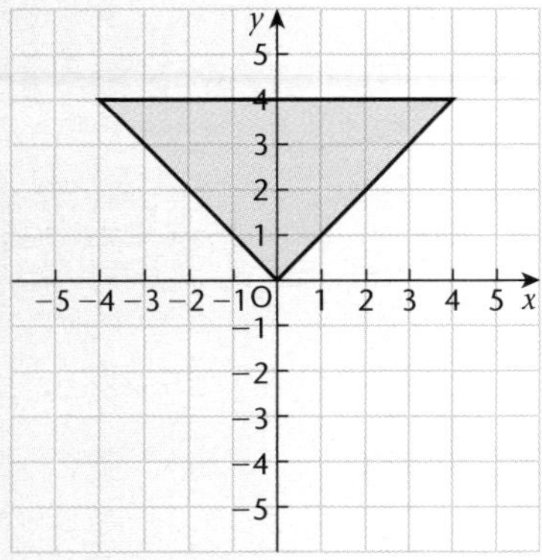

5 Shade the region where:

a $y \leqslant x + 2$ and $x > 1$

b $y \geqslant x - 3$ and $y \leqslant 0$

c $y < x$, $x < 4$ and $y > 0$

d $y + x \geqslant 0$, $x \leqslant 4$ and $y \leqslant 4$

6 a Shade the region where $y > 1$, $y < 3x$, $y < 5 - x$ and $x < 3$.

b Write down the coordinates of the points in the region whose coordinates are integers.

Draw all the boundary lines before deciding which region to shade.

Summary of key points

- You can add or subtract the same number on both sides of an inequality.
- You can multiply or divide both sides of an inequality by the same positive number.
- Use a solid circle on the number line when the point is included and an open circle when it is not.
- If you multiply or divide an inequality by a negative number you must change the direction of the inequality.
- Use a solid line when points on the line are included in a region and a broken line when points on the line are not included.

Most candidates who get GRADE C or above can:

- solve inequalities in one unknown and illustrate the solution on a number line.

Most candidates who get GRADE A or above can also:

- solve inequalities in two dimensions by drawing a region of the xy-plane.

Glossary

Inequality	two expressions related by an inequality sign

12 Congruence and constructions

This chapter will show you:

- ✓ how to decide whether or not two figures are congruent
- ✓ how to test pairs of triangles for congruency
- ✓ how to draw a triangle accurately
- ✓ how to bisect an angle using ruler and compasses only
- ✓ how to draw some angles using ruler and compasses only
- ✓ how to construct the perpendicular bisector of a line
- ✓ how to construct the perpendicular to a line at a point on the line
- ✓ how to construct the perpendicular from a point to a line
- ✓ how to draw a regular polygon
- ✓ how to draw parallel lines

Before you start you need to know:

- ✓ how to use a pair of compasses
- ✓ how to use a protractor
- ✓ the common units of length
- ✓ the properties of isosceles and equilateral triangles
- ✓ the properties of the special quadrilaterals
- ✓ the names and properties of polygons

12.1 Congruency

Two shapes are **congruent** if they are exactly the same shape and size.
Congruent shapes are alike in all respects.

Example 1

These two triangles are congruent.

Find **a** the length of AC
b the size of angle C.

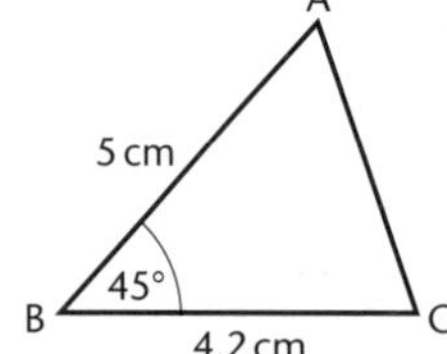

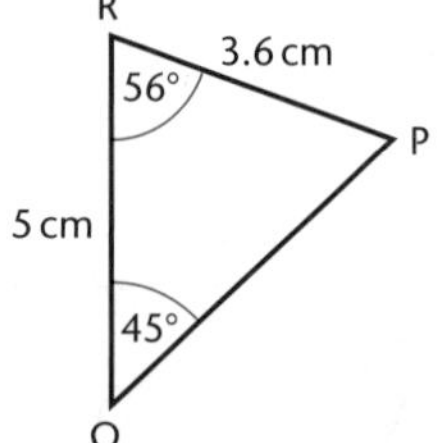

Sides or angles that are in the same position in both figures are called **corresponding** sides or angles. They are the same size.

a AC = 3.6 cm

Look for the side in triangle PQR that corresponds to AC. AC is opposite the angle 45°. PR is opposite the angle 45° so AC = PR.

b $\angle P = 180° - 101° = 79°$
$\angle C = 79°$.

$\angle C$ corresponds to $\angle P$. You can find $\angle P$ using the fact that the three angles in $\triangle PQR$ add up to 180°.

Exam practice 12A

1 Which shapes are congruent with A?

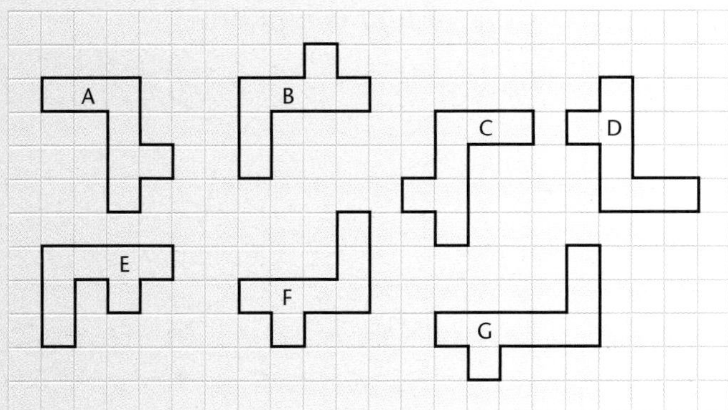

2

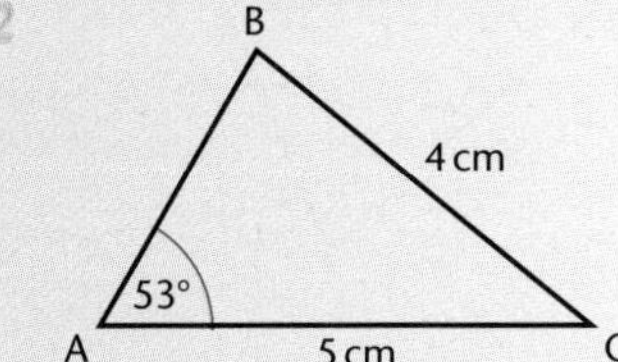

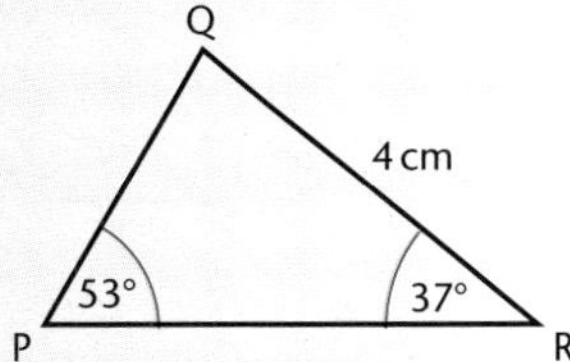

These two triangles are congruent.

a What is the size of ∠C?

b Write down the length of PR.

3

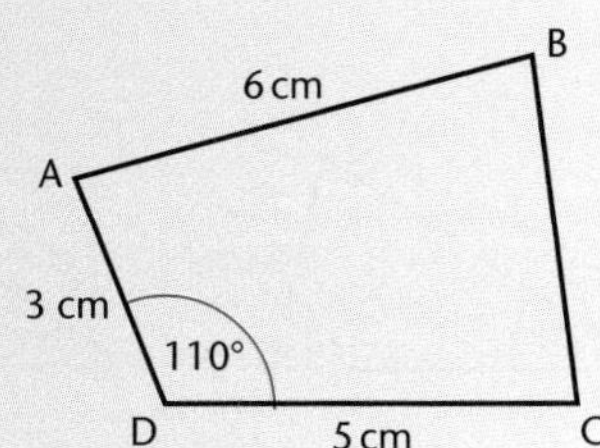

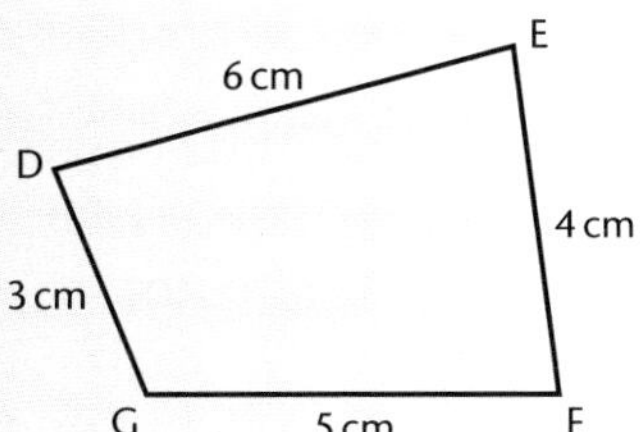

These two quadrilaterals are congruent.

a What is the size of ∠G?

b Write down the length of BC.

4

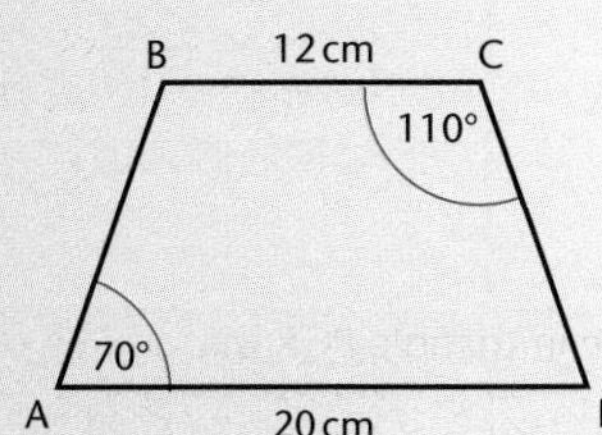

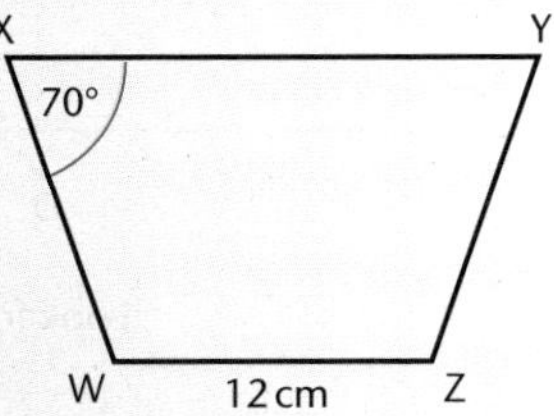

These two trapeziums are congruent.

a Write down the length of XY.

b What is the size of ∠WZY?

12.2 Congruent triangles

Two triangles are congruent if they satisfy any one of four conditions.

- The three sides of one triangle are equal to the three sides of the other triangle (SSS).
- Two sides and the included angle of one triangle are equal to two sides and the included angle of another triangle (SAS).
- Two angles and one side of one triangle are equal to two angles and the corresponding side of another triangle (AAS or ASA).
- Each triangle has a right angle and the hypotenuse and one side of one triangle are equal to the hypotenuse and one side of the other triangle (RHS).

Any one of the four conditions for congruences enables you to draw a unique triangle.

You need to be careful with the AAS property; the equal sides must be in corresponding positions. In this pair of triangles, two angles and a side are equal but the sides are not in coresponding positions (it is opposite the 40° angle in one triangle, but not the other), so the triangles are not congruent.

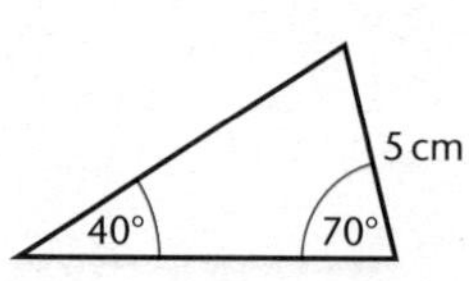

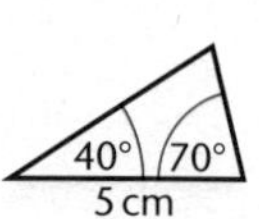

Example 2

Are these pairs of triangles congruent? Give a reason.

a

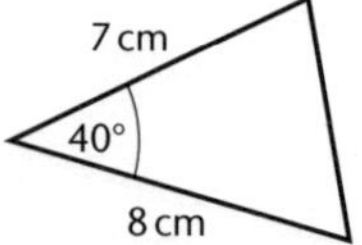

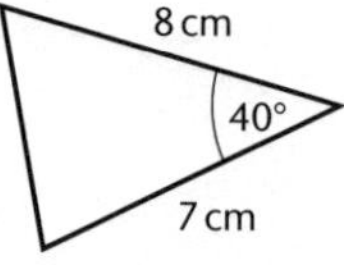

b

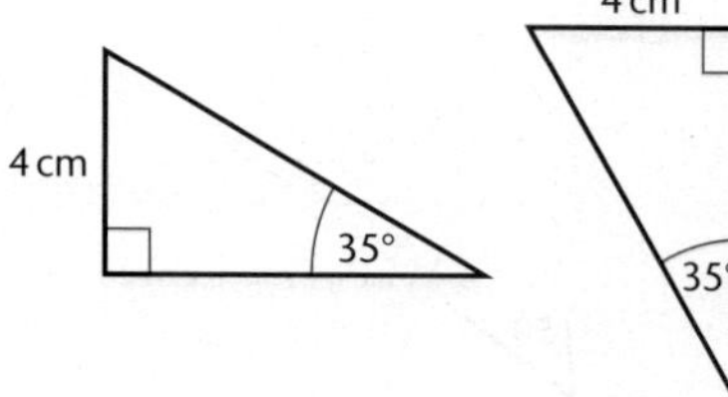

a Yes, two sides of one triangle are equal to two sides of the other triangle and the angle between them is 40°.

This is the SAS property.

b Yes, two angles in one triangle are equal to two angles in the other triangle and the side of length 4 cm is opposite 35° in both triangles.

This is the AAS property.

Example 3

This framework is made using four metal rods.
AB is equal and parallel to CD.

a Prove that △ABE is congruent with △CDE.

b Lee said that this means that E is the midpoint of AD and BC.
Is Lee right? Give a reasons for your answer.

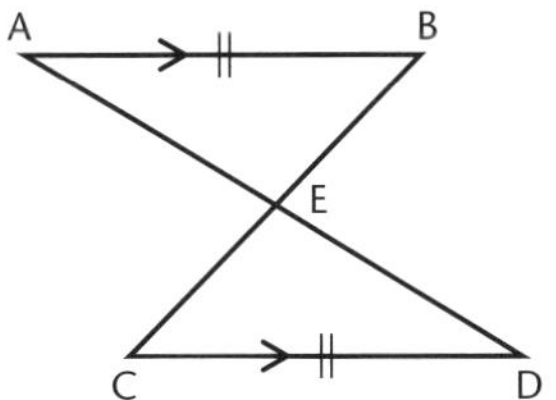

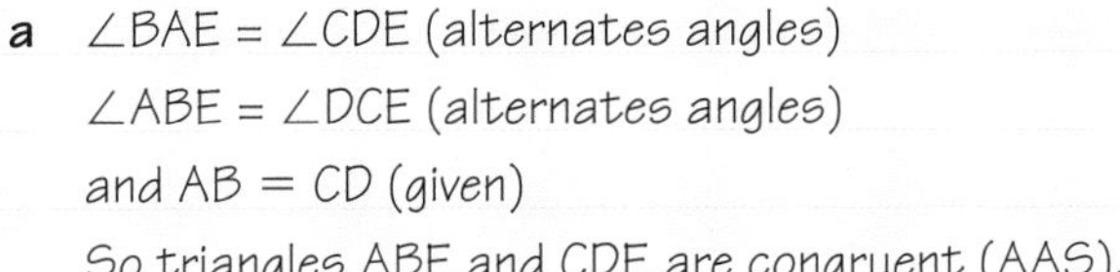

a ∠BAE = ∠CDE (alternates angles)
∠ABE = ∠DCE (alternates angles)
and AB = CD (given)
So triangles ABE and CDE are congruent (AAS).

When you are asked for a proof, you must give a reason for each step of your working.

b Yes, because triangles ABE and CDE are congruent.
AE = ED (sides opposite equal angles)
so E is the midpoint of AD.
BE = CE (sides opposite equal angles)
so E is the midpoint of BC.

This method can be used to prove that the diagonals of a parallelogram bisect each other.

Exam practice 12B

1 State whether or not each pair of triangles is congruent.
Say which of the four conditions is satisfied.

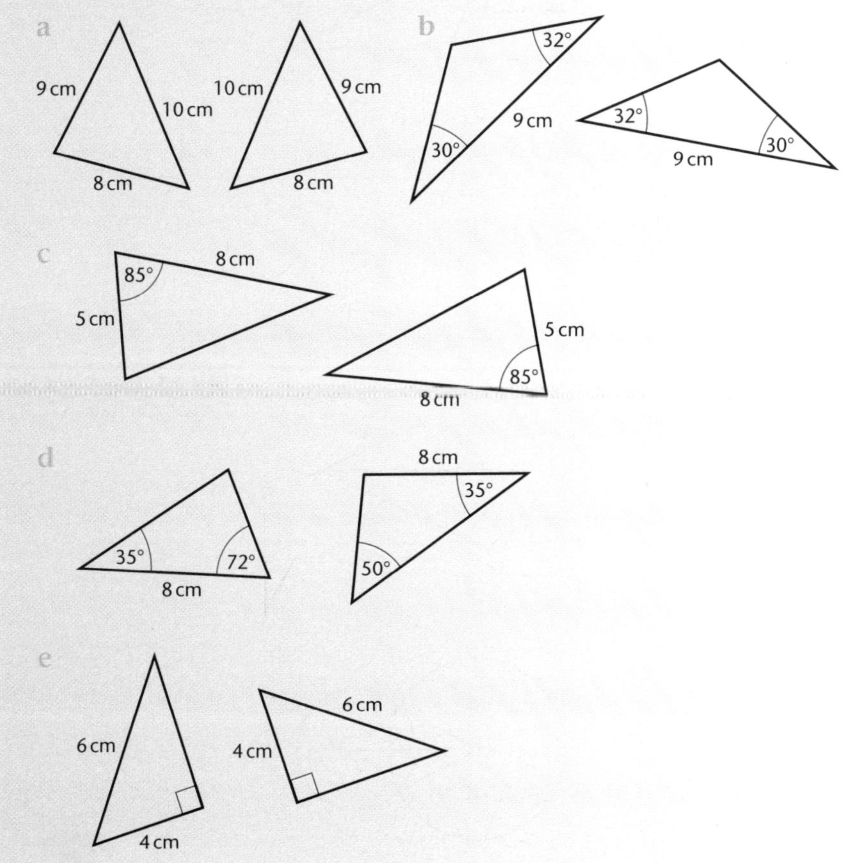

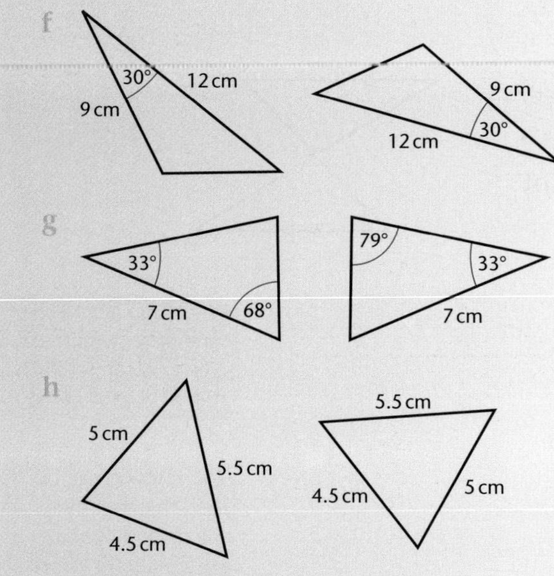

UAM

2 A rectangular wooden frame, ABCD, is kept square by a diagonal brace BD. Prove that triangles ABD and BCD are congruent.

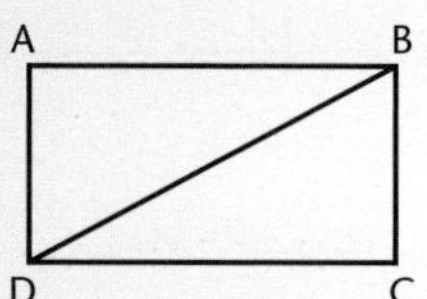

UAM

3 PQRS is a parallelogram. PR is a diagonal. Prove that triangles PQR and PSR are congruent.

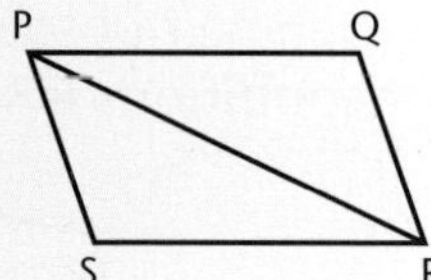

UAM

4 AB and CD are diameters in a circle, centre O. Prove that triangles OAC and OBD are congruent.

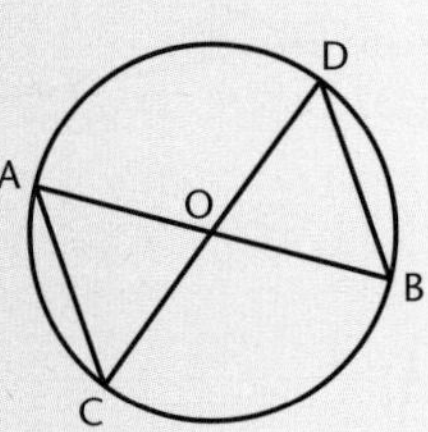

UAM

5 AC bisects ∠BAD. AB = AD.

a Prove that triangles ABC and ADC are congruent.

b Are CB and CD equal? Justify your answer.

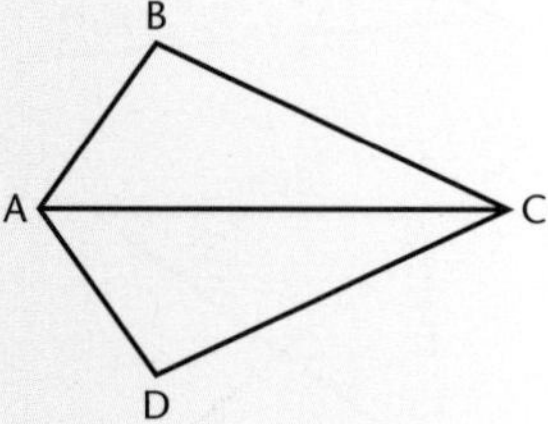

Bisect means 'cut exactly in half'.

UAM

6 Two circles, centres P and Q intersect at R and S.

a Prove that △PQR is congruent with △PQS.

b Name two acute angles in the diagram that are equal.

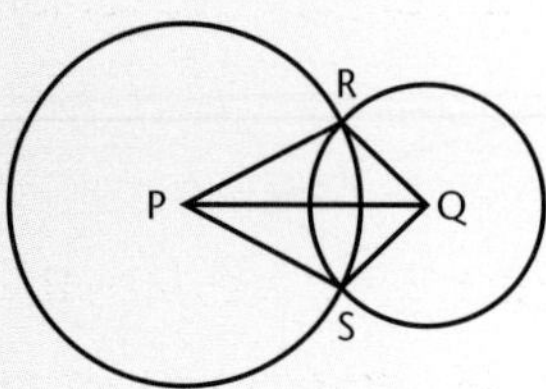

7 PQRS is a square.
PR and QS are diagonals of the square and intersect at T.
Prove that PR and QS bisect each other.

UAM

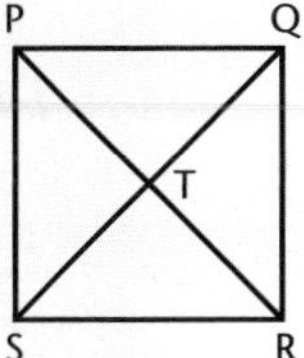

You need to prove that all triangles are congruent. Make sure that you choose the right two.

8 AD bisects ∠BAC.
DB is perpendicular to AB and DC is perpendicular to AC.
Prove that:

a AB = AC
b DB = DC.

UAM

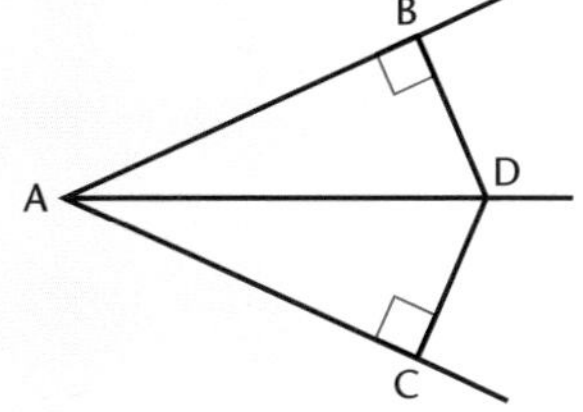

Take care that you choose the right condition to prove congruency.

12.3 Constructing triangles

A triangle has three angles and three sides.
You can use information about sides and angles to **construct** a triangle.

Construct means 'draw accurately'.

Example 4

This triangle is not drawn to scale.
Draw the triangle.

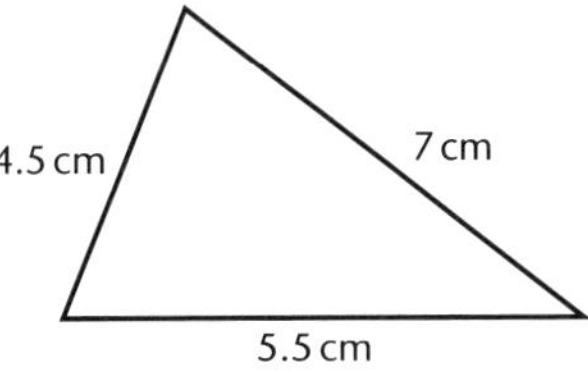

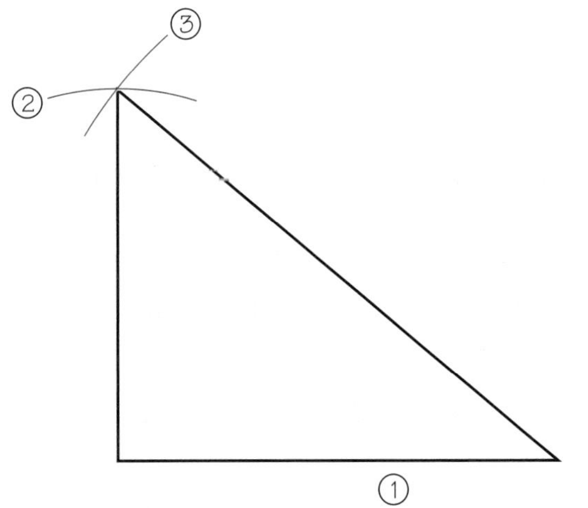

① Draw the side that is 5.5 cm long.
② Use a ruler to open your compasses to 4.5 cm (the length of another side). With the point of the compasses on one end of the first side draw an arc.
③ Open the compasses to 7 cm (the length of the third side).
With the point on the other end of the first side draw an arc to cut the first arc.
④ Join the point where the arcs cross to each end of the first line.

The triangle you draw when given the lengths of three sides is unique.

If you draw another triangle whose sides are the same three lengths, the two triangles are congruent.

This is the SSS property.

Example 5

This triangle is not drawn to scale.
Draw the triangle accurately.

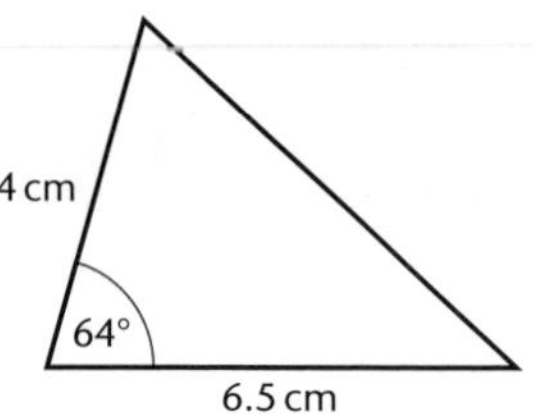

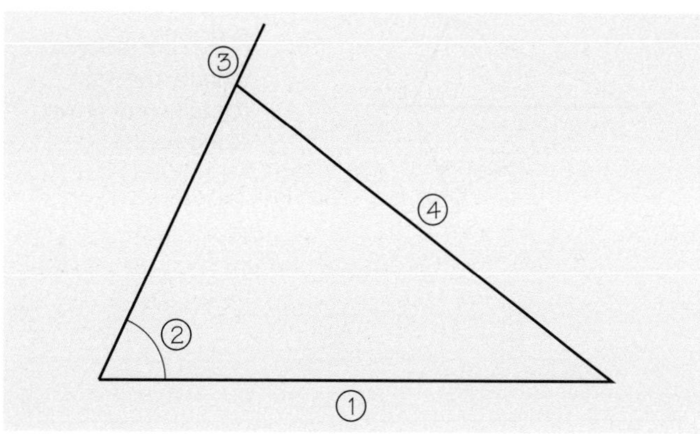

① Draw the side that is 6.5 cm long.

② Use a protractor to draw an angle of 64° at one end of the line. Make this arm quite long.

③ Use a ruler to mark a point on this arm 4 cm from the vertex of the angle.

④ Join this point to the other end of the first line.

The triangle you draw when given the lengths of two sides and the angle between them is unique.
If you draw another triangle whose sides are the same length with the same angle between them, the two triangles are congruent.

This is the SAS property.

Example 6

This triangle is not drawn to scale.
Draw the triangle accurately.

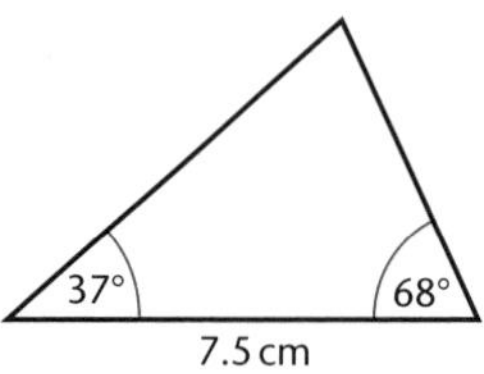

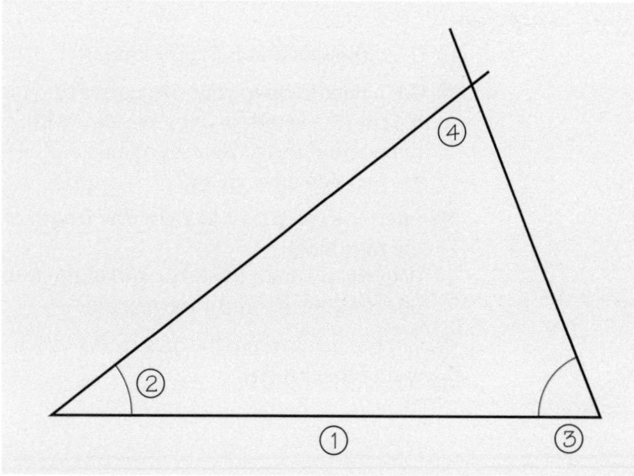

① Draw the side equal to 7.5 cm.

② Now use your protractor to draw angles of 37° at one end of the side and ③ 68° at the other end.

④ Extend the arms until they cross.

You can check your accuracy by measuring the third angle.

It should be $180° - 37° - 68° = 75°$.

The triangle you draw when given one side and two angles is unique.
If you draw another triangle with the same measurements it will be congruent with the first triangle.

This is the AAS property.

Example 7

This triangle is not drawn to scale.

a Draw the triangle accurately.

b Can you draw a different triangle with these measurements?

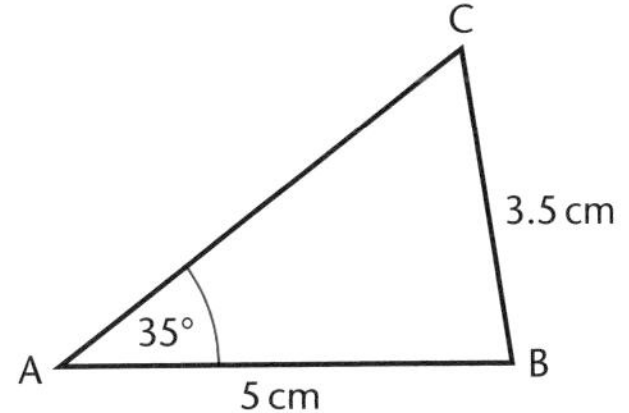

a

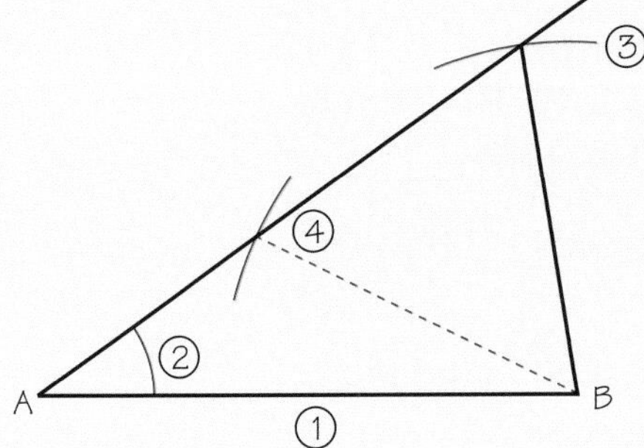

b Yes

① Draw and label the line AB.
② Construct an angle 35° at A.
③ With the point at B and your compasses opened to 4.3 cm, draw an arc to cut the arm of this angle. Join this point to B.
④ When you continue the arc it cuts the arm at a second point. When this is joined to B it makes a different triangle with the same measurements.

Exam practice 12C

You need a protractor, a ruler and a pair of compasses for these questions.

Make sure you have a *sharp* pencil.

1 These triangles are not drawn to scale.
Draw each triangle accurately and write down the measurement asked for.

a

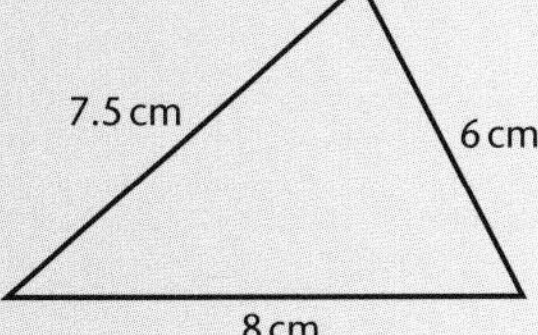

Measure the angle opposite the longest side.

b

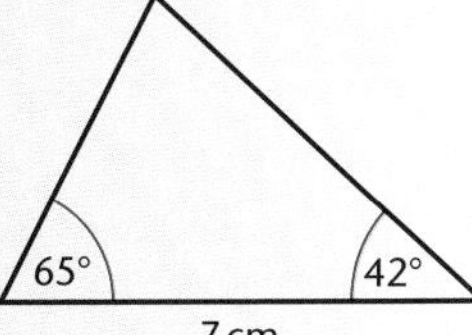

Measure the side opposite the angle of 65°.

c

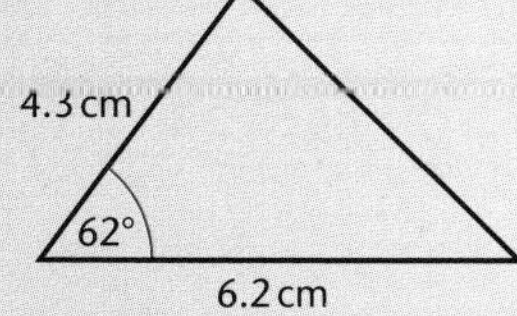

Measure the third side.

d

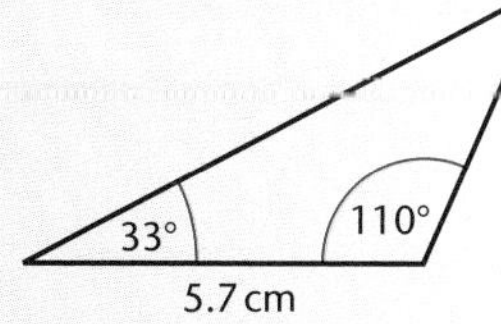

Measure the shortest side.

e

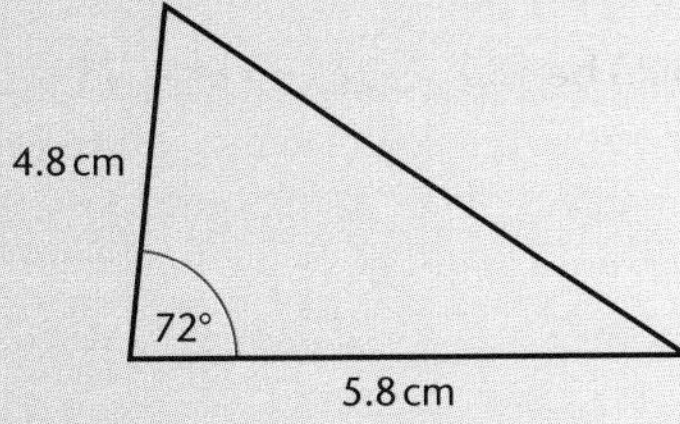

Measure the angle opposite the side of length 5.8 cm.

f

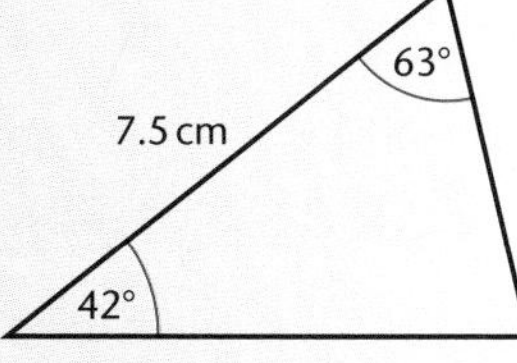

Measure the side opposite the angle of 63°.

g

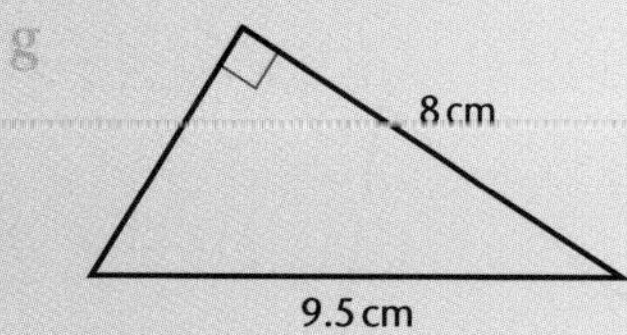

Measure the smallest angle.

h

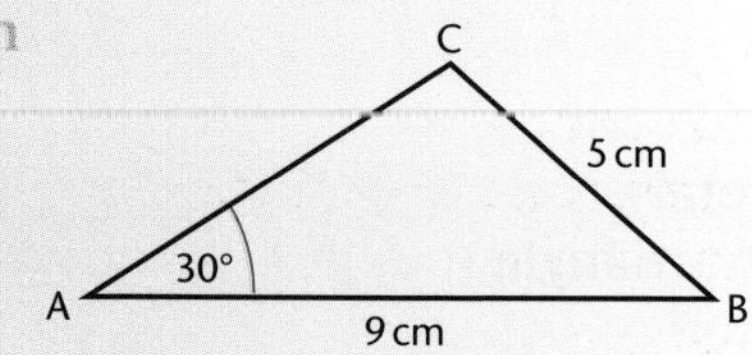

(i) Can you draw two different triangles with these measurements?

(ii) Now try it with BC = 4.5 cm. Explain your answer.

The triangle you draw when given a side, a right angle and the side opposite the right angle is unique.

2 Make an accurate drawing of an equilateral triangle whose sides are 8 cm long.

3 a Draw accurately an isosceles triangle with a base 7 cm long and base angles of 68°.
b How long are the equal sides?

4

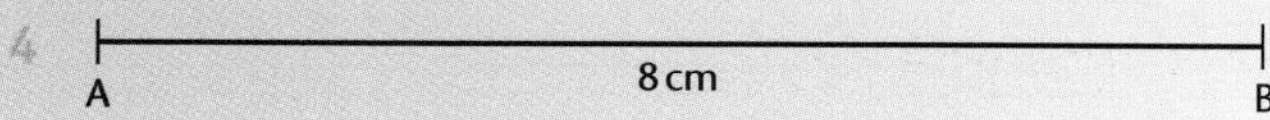

This line is a diagonal of a rhombus.
The sides of the rhombus are 7 cm long.
a Copy this line leaving at least 6 cm above and below it.
b Construct the rhombus.
c Measure the other diagonal.

12.4 Drawing regular polygons

You can use a circle to draw a regular polygon.
Divide the angle at the centre of the circle into the same number of equal parts as there are sides in the polygon.

Example 8

a Draw a hexagon using a circle with radius 6 cm.
b Measure the length of a side of the hexagon.

When you join each vertex of a **hexagon** to its centre, you get 6 congruent triangles: each angle at the centre is 360° ÷ 6 = 60°.

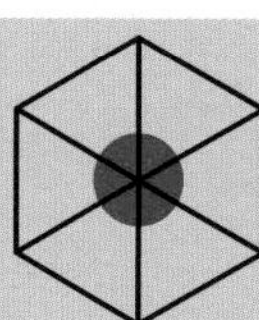

a

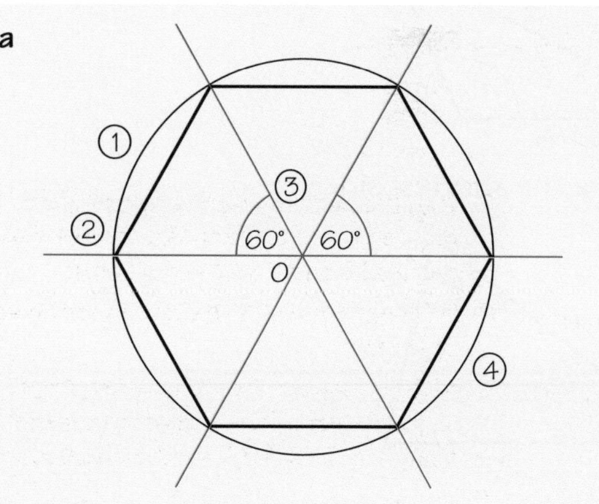

① Draw the circle.
② Draw a diameter.
③ Now draw two more diameters through O at 60° to the first diameter. (This gives you six angles of 60° at the centre.)
④ Join the points where the diameters cut the circle.

b The length of a side is 6 cm.

Exam practice 12D

1 a Draw a circle of radius 5 cm.
Use this circle to construct a regular octagon.
b Measure a side of the octagon.

2 a Draw a circle radius 6 cm.
Use the circle to construct a regular pentagon.
b Measure the length of a side.

3 a Use a circle with radius 7 cm to construct a regular polygon with twelve sides.
b Measure the length of a side of the polygon.

Use a protractor to measure the angles you need.

An octagon has 8 sides.

A pentagon has 5 sides.

12.5 Constructing angles without a protractor

Angles of 90°, 60°, 120°, 45° and 30° can be drawn without using a protractor.

When you use compasses for these constructions, open them to about 5 cm.

Example 9

Construct an angle of 60° at a point A on a line segment XY.

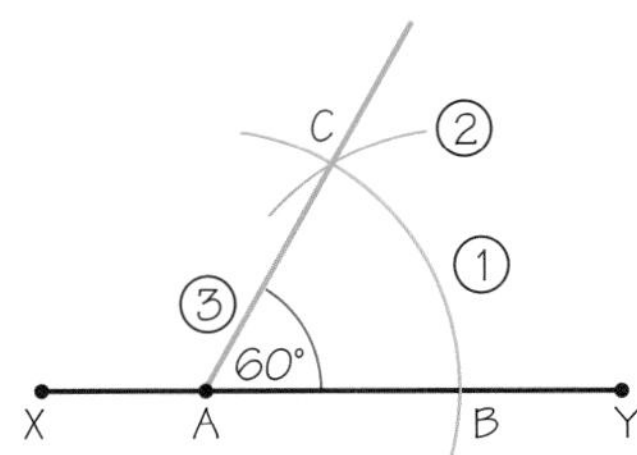

① With the point of the compasses on A draw an arc starting well above XY to cut XY. Label this point B.

② Move the compass point to B and draw an arc to cut the first arc at C. Do NOT change the radius.

③ Join AC. The angle at A is 60°. Label this angle.

∠A = 60° because the lengths AB, AC and BC are all equal.
This is also how to construct an equilateral triangle.

This construction also gives an angle of 120° at A.

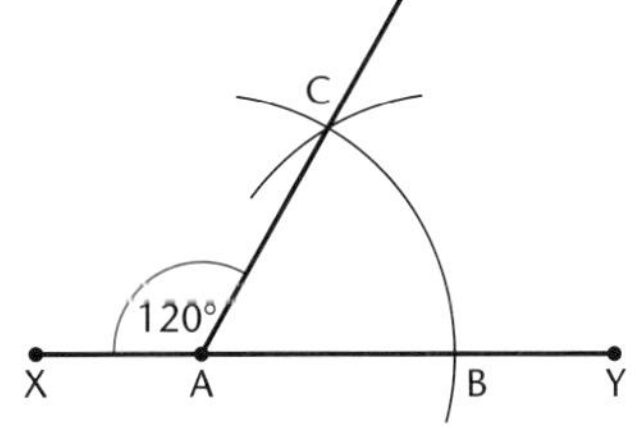

Example 10

Bisect angle A.

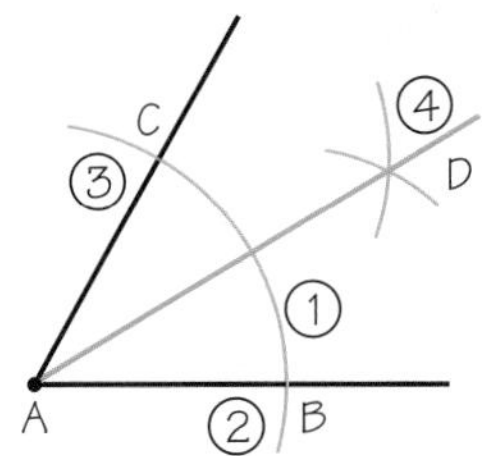

① With the point of your compasses on A, draw an arc to cut both the arms of ∠A (labelled B and C on the diagram).

② Put the point on B and draw an arc between the arms.

③ Next put the point on C and, keeping the radius the same, draw an arc to cut the other arc. (Labelled D on the diagram.)

④ Join AD.
AD bisects ∠A.

Example 11

Construct an angle of 30° at A.

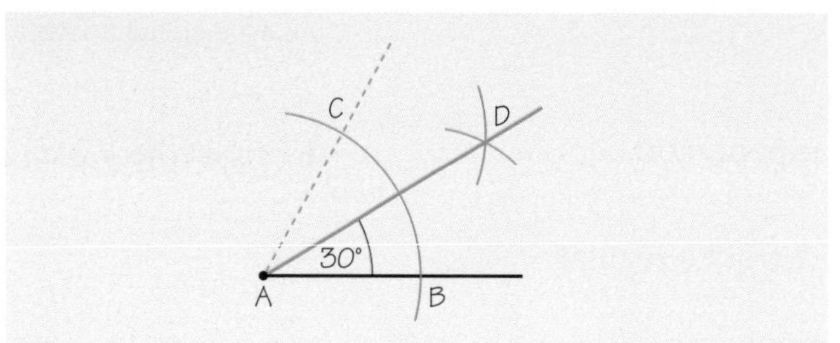

Start by constructing an angle of 60°. This is labelled ∠CAB on the diagram. Then bisect it.

Example 12

Construct the **perpendicular bisector** of the line segment PQ.

Perpendicular means 'at right angles'.

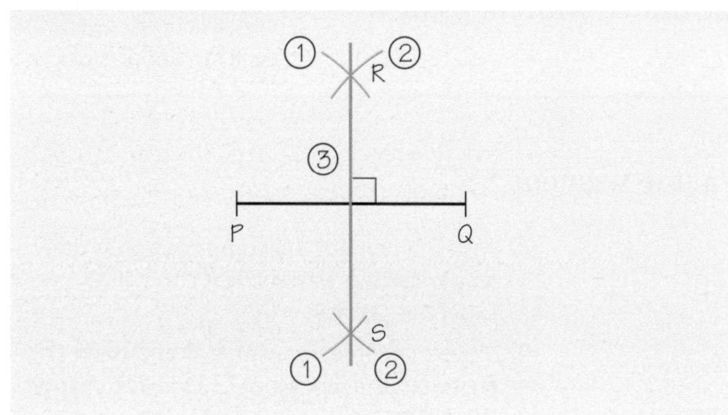

① Open your compasses to a radius more than half PQ. With the point of your compasses on P, draw arcs above and below PQ.

② Move the point to Q . With the same radius, draw arcs to cut the first arcs above and below the line, at R and S.

③ Join RS. This is the perpendicular bisector of the line segment PQ.

You can use this construction to find the midpoint of a line.

Example 13

Construct the line that is perpendicular to the line AB at the point P.

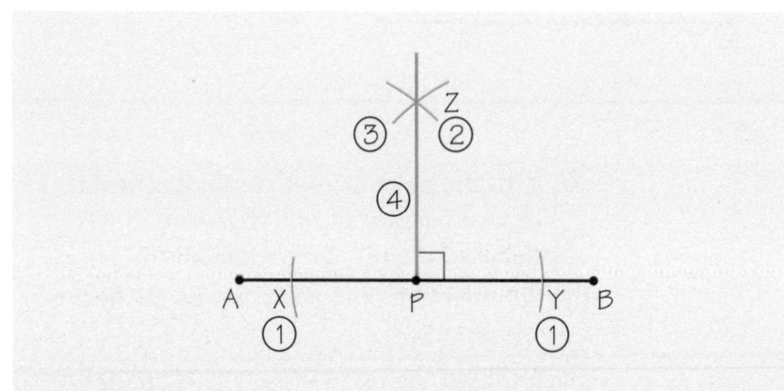

① Open your compasses to about 5 cm. Put the point on P. Draw an arc on each side of P to cut the line (labelled X and Y).

② Open your compasses a bit more then put the point on X. Draw an arc above the line.

③ Move the point to Y and, with the same radius, draw an arc to cut the first arc (labelled Z on the diagram).

④ Join PZ.
PZ is perpendicular to AB.

Example 13 can also be used to construct an angle of 90° at a point P on a line.

Example 14

Construct an angle of 45°.

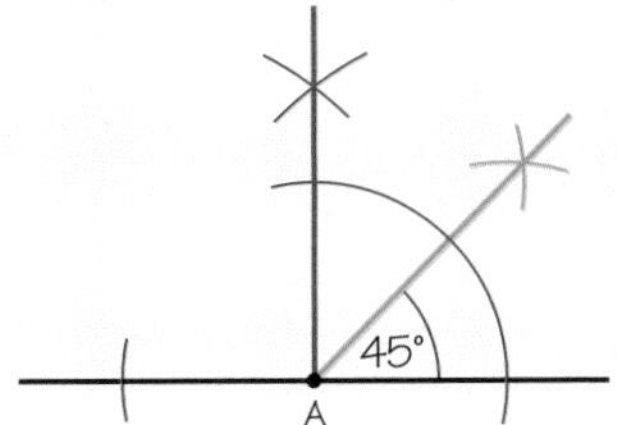

Draw a line and mark a point (A) on it.
Using the construction in Example 13, construct an angle of 90° at A.
Bisect this angle to give an angle of 45°.

Example 15

a Draw a perpendicular from the point A to the line BC.
b Explain why AZ is perpendicular to BC.

a

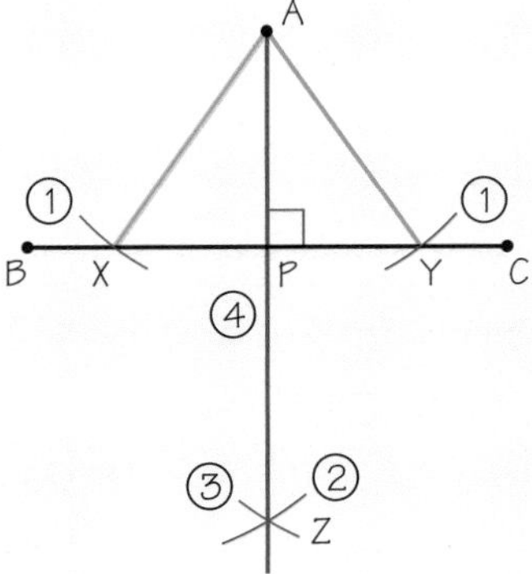

① Open your compasses to a radius more than the distance from A to the line BC. With the point on A draw arcs to cut the line BC (labelled X and Y on the diagram).
② Move the point to X and draw an arc below the line.
③ Move the point to Y and, with the same radius, draw an arc to cut the last arc (labelled Z on the diagram).
④ Join AZ.
AZ is perpendicular to BC.

b Triangles AXP and AYP are congruent (SAS)
So ∠APX = ∠APY.
But ∠APX + ∠APY = 180°
∴ ∠APX = ∠APY = 90°
i.e. AZ is perpendicular to BC.

AX = AY, ∠XAY is bisected by AZ, since △AXZ is congruent to △AYZ (SSS), so ∠XAP = ∠YAP and AP is a shared side.

Example 16

Draw a line through P parallel to the line AB.

Method 1

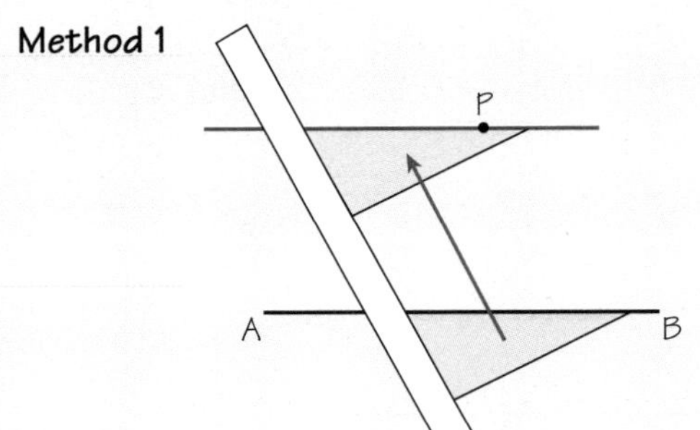

This method uses ruler and set square.
Put the long edge of the set square along AB.
Put the ruler against a short side of the set square.
Slide the set square along the ruler until the long edge passes through P.
Draw a line along this edge.
This line is parallel to AB.

Method 2

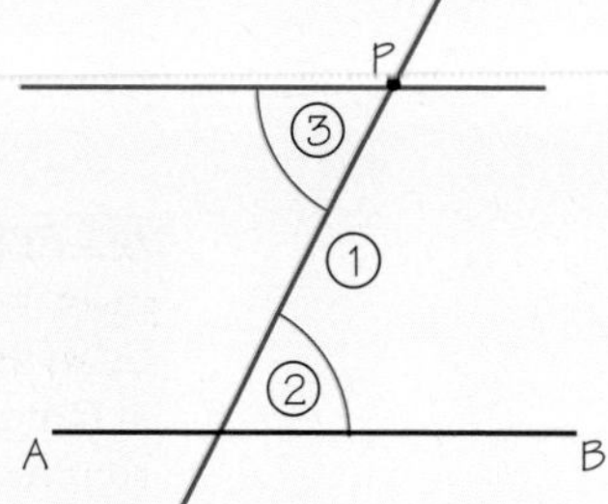

① Draw any line through P to cut the line AB.
② Measure the angle between your line and AB.
③ Use a protractor to draw an angle the same size at P.
The arm of this angle is parallel to AB, because you have drawn a pair of equal alternate angles.

Exam practice 12E

In this exercise only use a ruler and a pair of compasses.

Don't be tempted to use a protractor. If your construction lines can't be seen or are clearly wrong, you will not get all the marks in your examination.

1 a Copy this line.

b Draw an angle of 60° at P.
c Bisect your angle of 60°.
d What is the size of the two smaller angles at P?

2 a Copy this line.

b Draw an angle of 90° at C.
c Bisect your angle of 90°.
d What is the size of the two smaller angles at C?

3 This triangle is not drawn to scale.
a Construct this triangle accurately.
b Measure the length of the side opposite the angle of 60°.

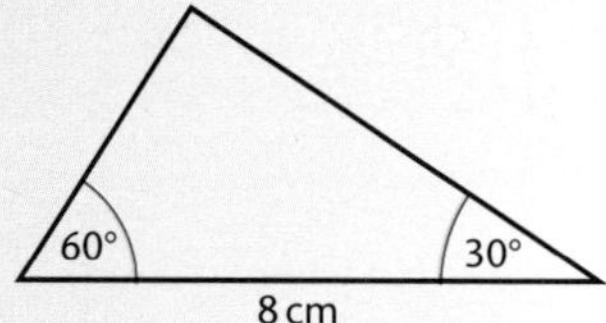

When you have done your construction, you can check the value of the third angle.
It should be 90°.

4 a Construct this triangle accurately.
b Measure the length of the side opposite the right angle.

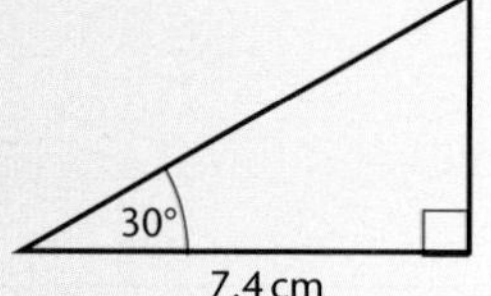

5 a Construct an equilateral triangle with side 7 cm.
b Construct the perpendicular from a vertex to the opposite side.
Measure and write down its length. Confirm your answer by calculation

6 a This triangle is not drawn to scale.
Construct this triangle accurately.
b Measure the length of the side opposite the angle of 45°.

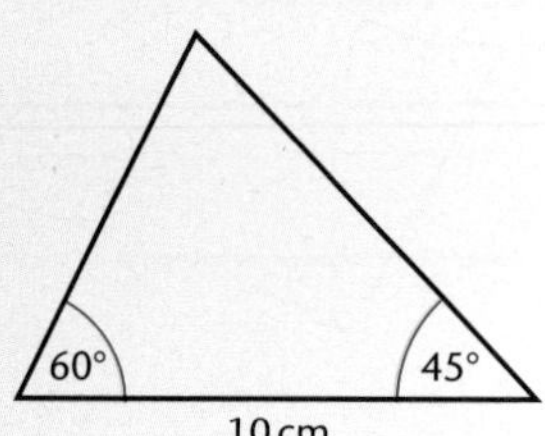

7 a Construct this triangle. Measure ∠XZY.
b Construct the perpendicular bisector of XY.
Mark the point M where the perpendicular bisector crosses XY.
c Draw a circle with centre M and radius 5 cm.

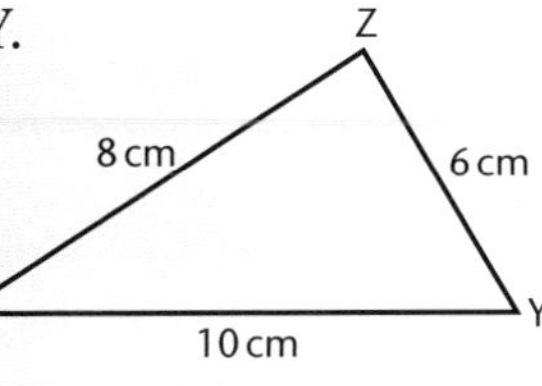

Your circle should pass through all three vertices of the triangle.

UAM 8 a Construct this isosceles triangle accurately.
b Construct the perpendicular bisector of the side of length 7.5 cm.
c Explain why this perpendicular bisector passes through the opposite vertex of the triangle.

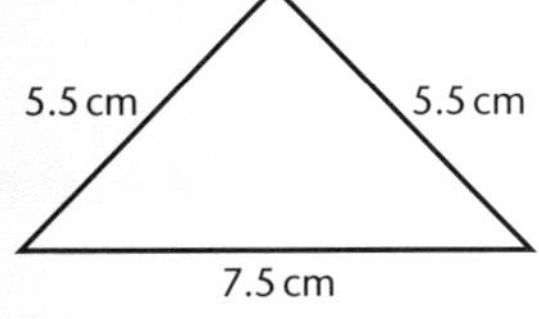

UAM 9 a Construct this isosceles triangle.
b Construct the perpendicular from P to the base of the triangle.
c Prove that the point where this perpendicular cuts the base is the midpoint of the base.

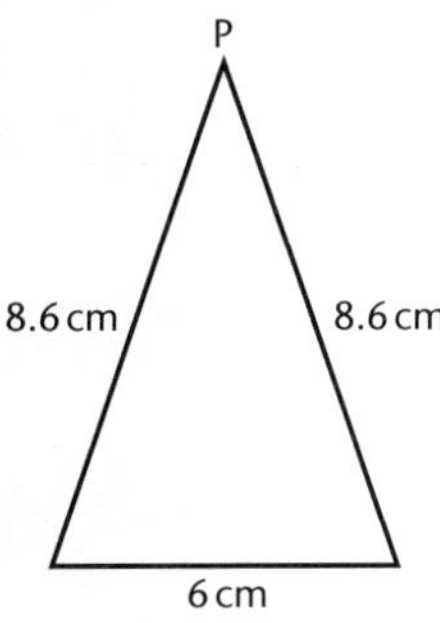

10 a Construct a triangle so that one side is 7.5 cm long and the angles at each end of this side are both 45°.
b Measure the third angle in the triangle. Confirm your answer by calculation.

11 Copy this diagram.
Draw a line through P that is parallel to AB.
Use either of the methods given in Example 16.

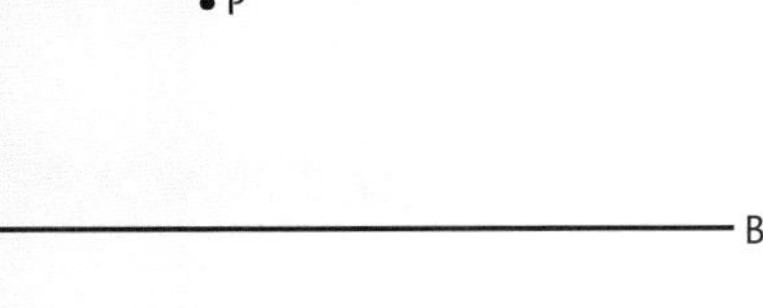

12 a Draw this rhombus accurately.
b Measure the longer diagonal.

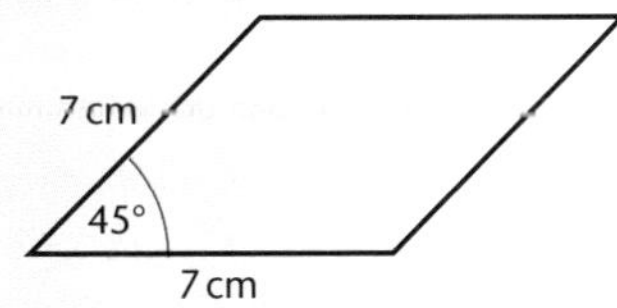

13 a Draw this kite accurately.
AC = 6 cm, BE = 2 cm and ED = 7 cm.
b Measure i AB ii CD.
Confirm your answer by calculation.

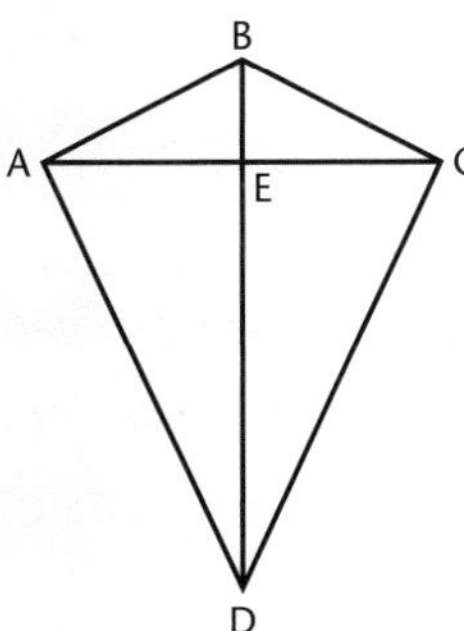

Summary of key points

- Congruent shapes are alike in every respect.
- If any one of the following four conditions is satisfied then two triangles are congruent:
  - the three sides of one triangle are equal to the three sides of the other triangle (SSS)
  - two sides and the included angle of one triangle are equal to two sides and the included angle of the other triangle (SAS)
  - two angles and one side of one triangle are equal to two angles and the corresponding side of the other triangle (AAS or ASA)
  - each triangle has a right angle, and the hypotenuse and one other side of one triangle are equal to the hypotenuse and the corresponding side of the other triangle (RHS)
- You can construct a unique triangle when you are given:
  - three sides
  - two sides and the included angle
  - two angles and one inclusive side
  - a side, a right angle and the side opposite the right angle
- To draw a regular polygon use a circle. Divide the angle at the centre of the circle into the same number of equal parts as there are sides to the polygon. The vertices of the polygon are where the arms of these angles cut the circle.

Most candidates who get GRADE C or above can:

- construct the perpendicular bisector of a given line and the bisector of a given angle.

Most candidates who get GRADE A or above can also:

- understand and use the conditions SSS, SAS, AAS and RHS to prove the congruence of triangles.

Glossary

Bisector a line that divides another line or an angle exactly in two
Congruent exactly the same size and shape
Construct draw accurately
Corresponding in the same position in two figures
Hexagon a polygon with six sides
Perpendicular at right angles

13 Transformations

This chapter will show you:

- ✓ how to draw the reflection of a shape in a mirror line
- ✓ how to recognise rotational symmetry and give the order
- ✓ how to draw the rotation of a shape by a given angle about a given point
- ✓ the meaning of a vector
- ✓ how to translate a shape from one position to another
- ✓ how to give a translation of a shape as a vector
- ✓ how to recognise transformations that are combinations of reflection, rotation and translation

Before you start you need to know:

- ✓ the meaning of **line symmetry**
- ✓ how to find the coordinates of a point
- ✓ how to plot a point given its coordinates
- ✓ how to find the equation of a straight line
- ✓ the names of special triangles and quadrilaterals
- ✓ how to use a protractor to measure angles

13.1 Reflection

This sketch shows a reflection of a triangle in a mirror.

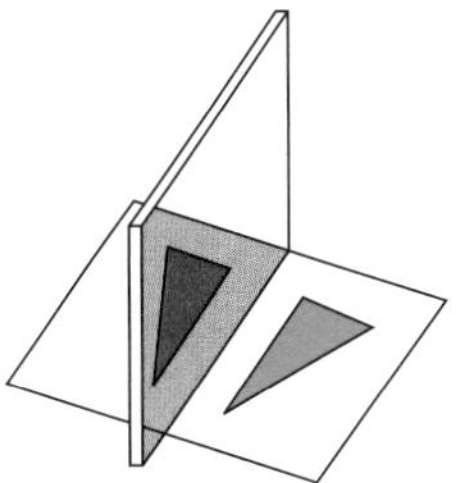

The triangle and its reflection are symmetrical about the **mirror line**.

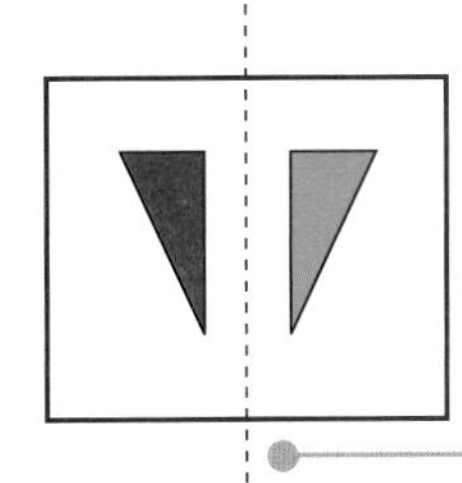

This line is called the mirror line.

Example 1

Draw the reflection of the red shape in the mirror line.

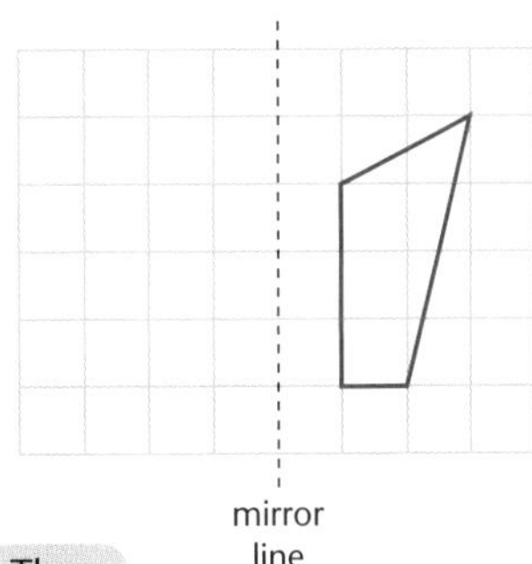

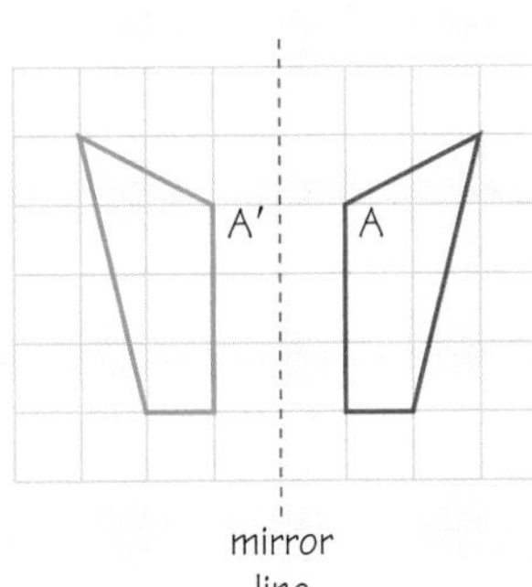

One vertex of the shape is marked A. The reflection of A in the mirror line is the point A'. A' is the same distance from the mirror line as A, but on the opposite side of it. The line AA' is perpendicular to the mirror line.

Example 2

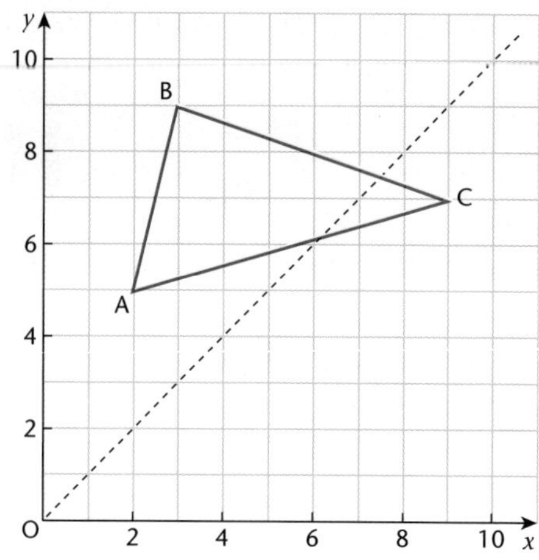

a Write down the coordinates of
i A **ii** B **iii** C.

b Draw the reflection of △ABC in the mirror line.

c Write down the coordinates of the reflection of
i A **ii** B.

a i (2, 5) ii (3, 9) iii (9, 7)

b

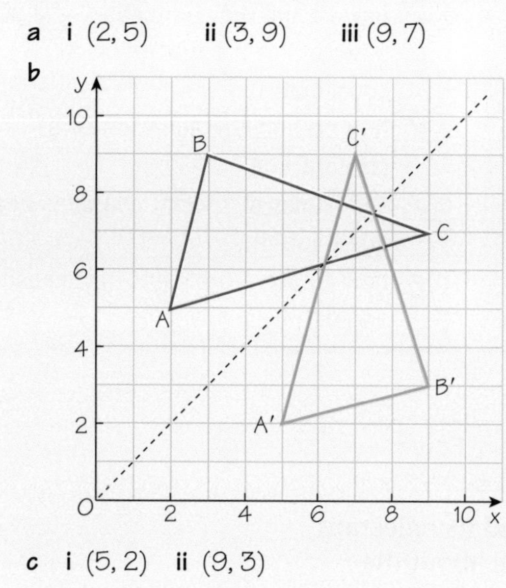

c i (5, 2) ii (9, 3)

Plot A′ such that the mirror line is the perpendicular bisector of AA′.
Do the same with B and C.

The combined shapes make a figure that is symmetrical about the mirror line.

Exam practice 13A

1 Use a copy of each diagram to draw the reflection of the shape in the mirror line.

The dotted lines are the mirror lines.

a
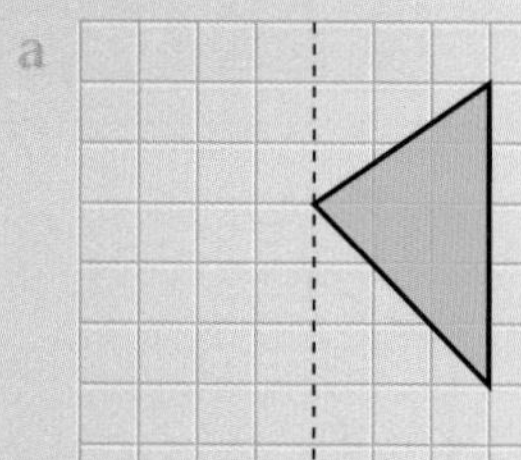

b
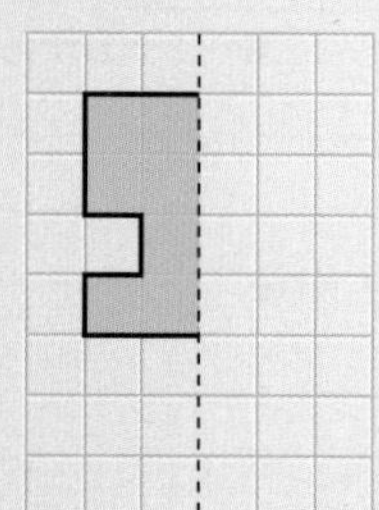

c
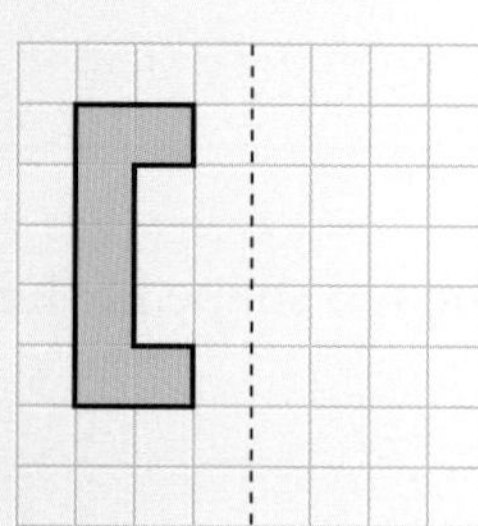

d
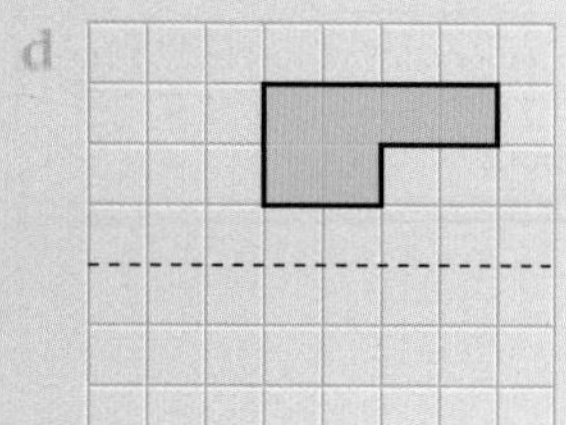

e
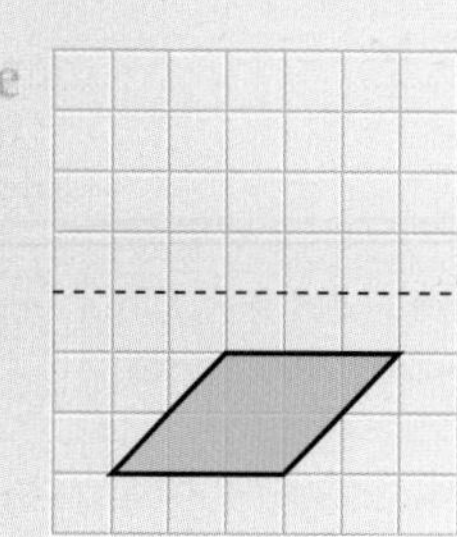

f
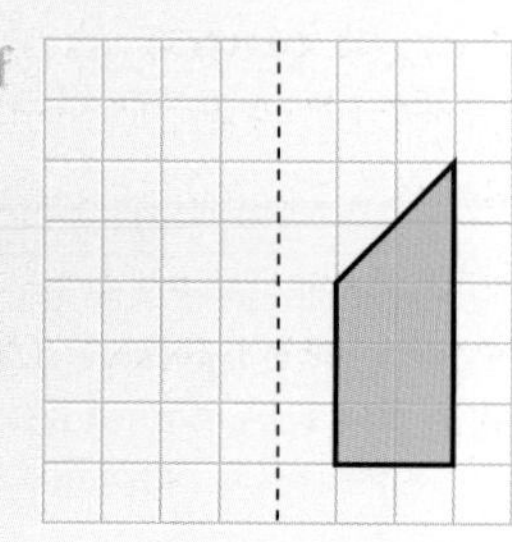

2 On a copy of the diagram draw the reflection of each shape in the mirror line.

a

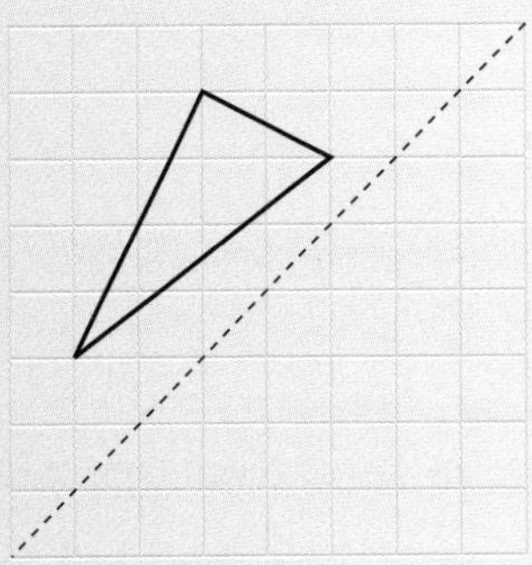

b

3 a What is the mathematical name of this shape?

b On a copy of this diagram draw the reflection of ABCD in the line PQ.

c What are the coordinates of the reflection of

i B ii D?

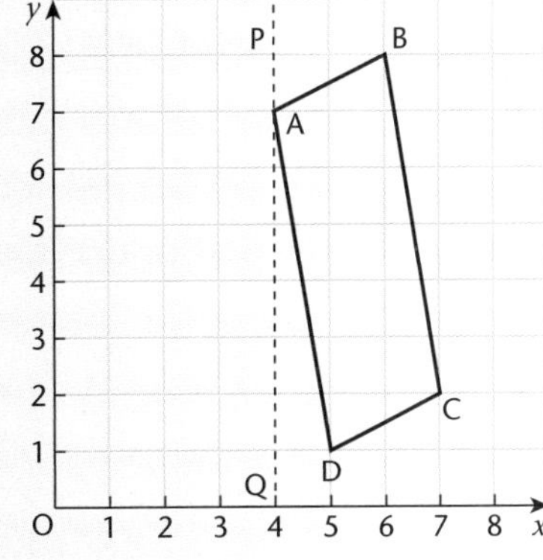

4 a On a copy of the diagram draw the reflection of $\triangle XYZ$ in the line PQ.

b What are the coordinates of the reflection of

i X ii Y?

c Write down the equation of the mirror line.

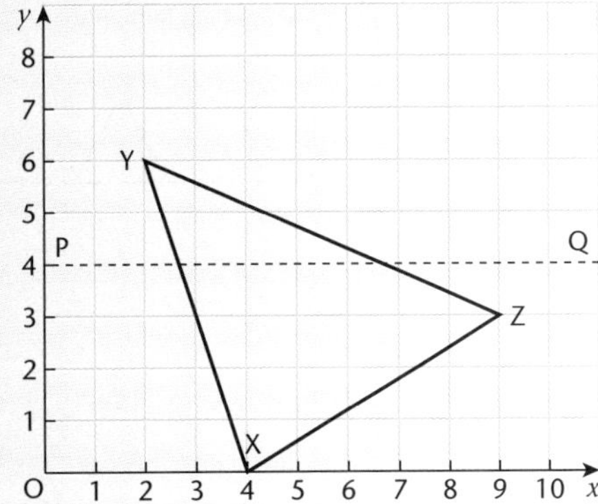

13.2 Transformations

A **transformation** moves (or **maps**) an object to another position. It may also change its shape.

A reflection is an example of a transformation.

To describe a reflection fully you need to give the mirror line, or if drawn with graph paper the equation of the mirror line.

This reflection changes the position of the red triangle to the position of the green triangle.

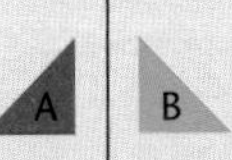

This is described as 'the reflection that maps A to B'.

Example 3

Describe fully the reflection that maps triangle ABC to triangle PQR.

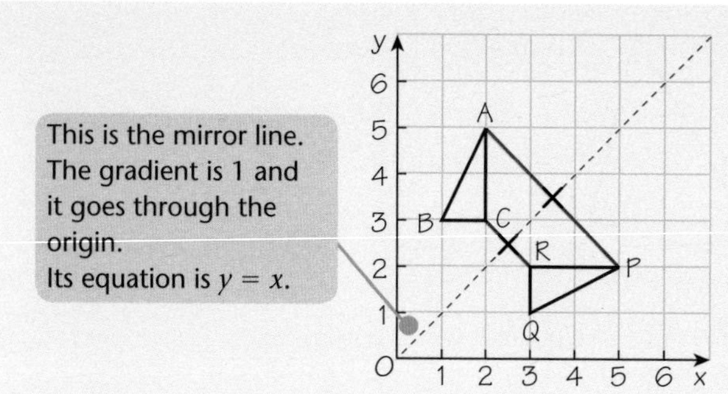

First you need to find the mirror line.
You can do this by joining two pairs of corresponding vertices. Then mark the midpoints of these lines.
The mirror line goes through these points.

The transformation is a reflection in the line $y = x$.

Exam practice 13B

1 Describe fully the transformation that maps triangle A to triangle B.

a

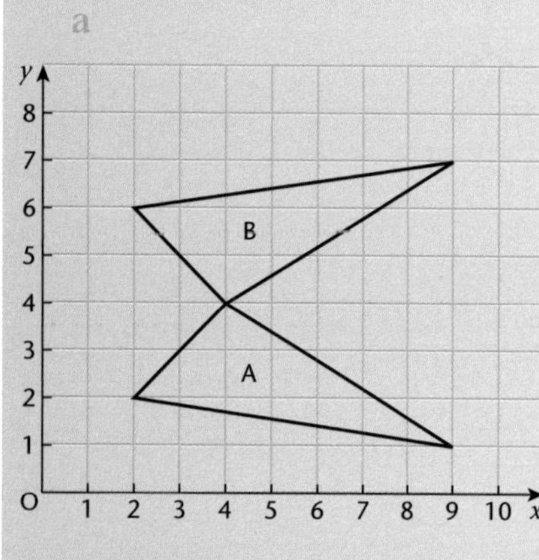

b

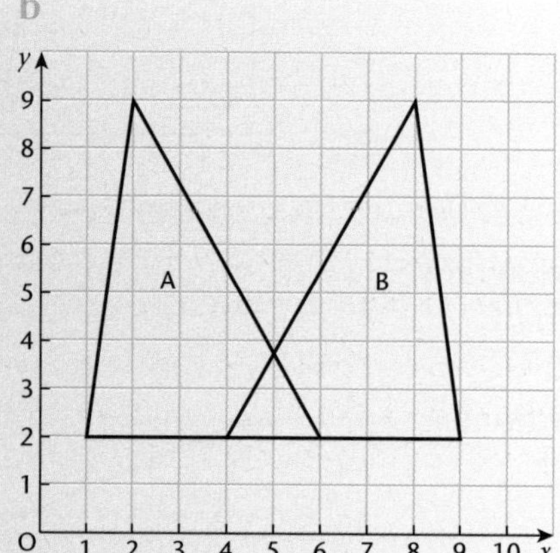

2 Describe fully the transformation that maps triangle A to triangle B.

a

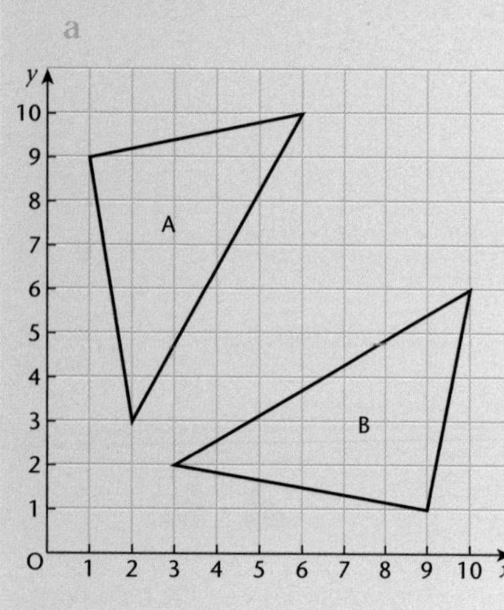

b

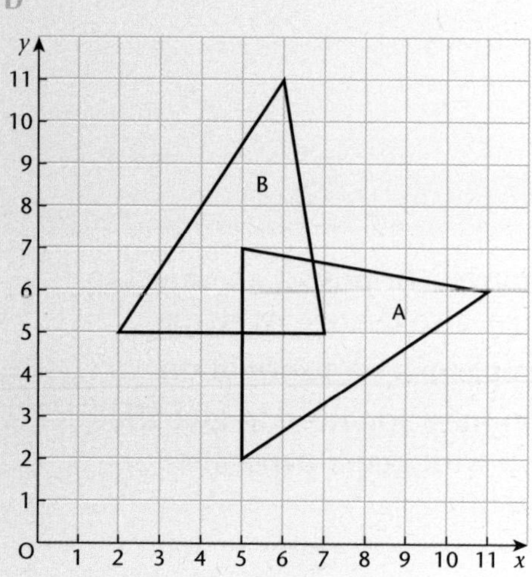

3 Copy this diagram and reflect shape A in the line $y = 4$.

4 Copy this diagram and reflect shape A in the line $x = 5$.

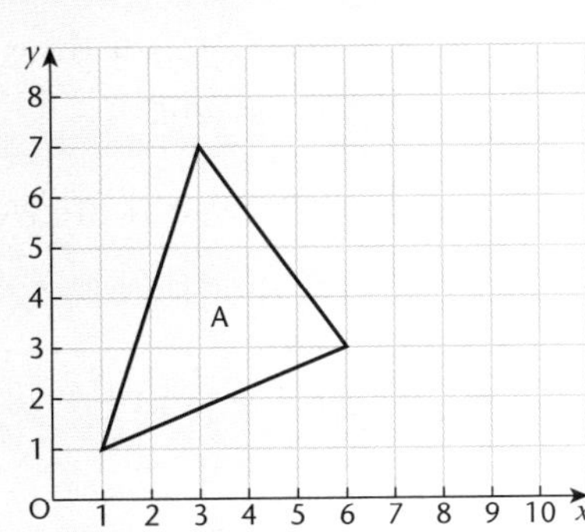

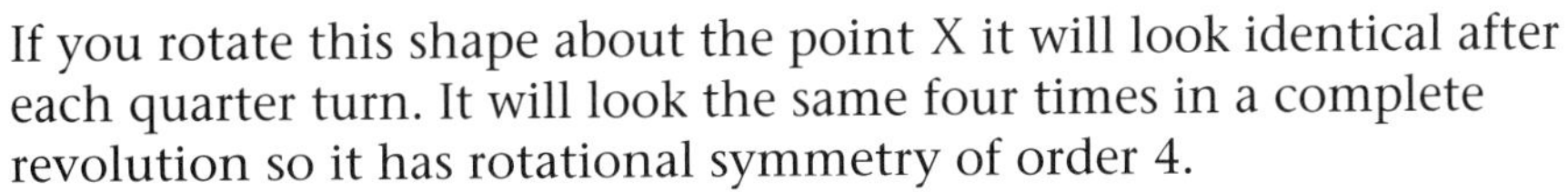

13.3 Rotational symmetry

Some shapes can be rotated about a point to a different position and still look the same. This is called **rotational symmetry**.
The **order of rotational symmetry** is the number of times the shape looks the same in one complete revolution.

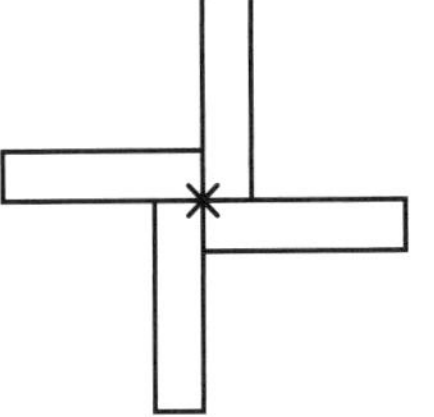

If you rotate this shape about the point X it will look identical after each quarter turn. It will look the same four times in a complete revolution so it has rotational symmetry of order 4.

Example 4

Write down the order of rotational symmetry of each shape.

a

This shape looks the same after a half-turn, then again after a full turn. It has rotational symmetry of order 2.

b

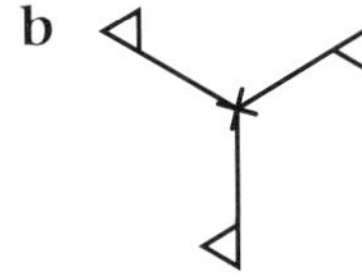

This shape looks the same after $\frac{1}{3}$ of a turn, $\frac{2}{3}$ of a turn and a full turn. It has rotational symmetry of order 3.

a 2 b 3

Some shapes have line symmetry and rotational symmetry.

Exam practice 13C

1 For each shape write down
i the order of rotational symmetry
ii the number of lines of symmetry.

a

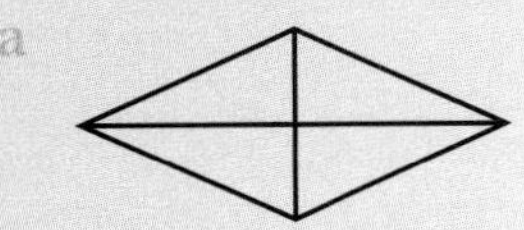

b

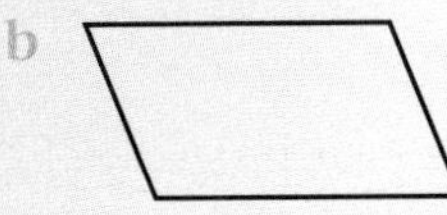

c

2 a 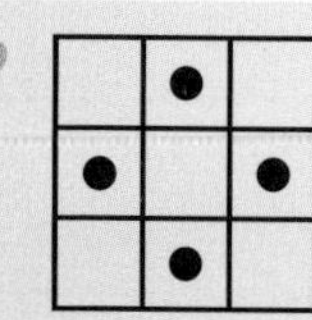 b 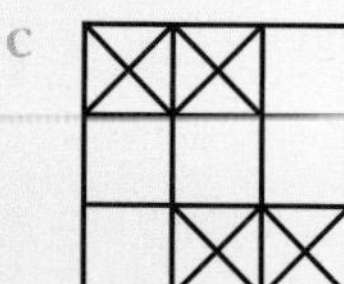 c

For each shape write down

i the number of lines of symmetry

ii the order of rotational symmetry.

3 a Kay says she can put spots in the centre of 4 squares so that the final shape has 4 lines of symmetry **and** rotational symmetry of order 4.
Is Kay correct? Give a reason for your answer.

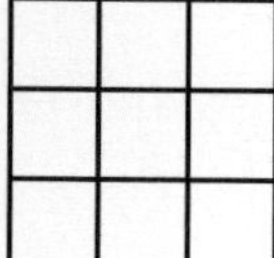

UAM

b Jim agrees with Kay but says that he can solve the problem in two completely different ways.
Is Jim correct? Give a reason for your answer.

UAM

Enrichment task

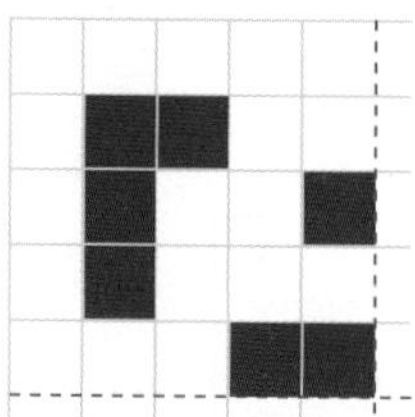

This diagram shows one-quarter of the blank grid for a 10 by 10 crossword.

The completed grid has rotational symmetry of order 4.

Copy the diagram and complete it.

13.4 Rotation

You can change the position of an object by rotating it about a point.
The amount it turns is the **angle of rotation**.

The point about which a shape turns is the **centre of rotation**.
This is often one of the **vertices** of the shape but can be any point.

The position of the yellow triangle is found by rotating the red triangle through a quarter turn (90°) anticlockwise about A.

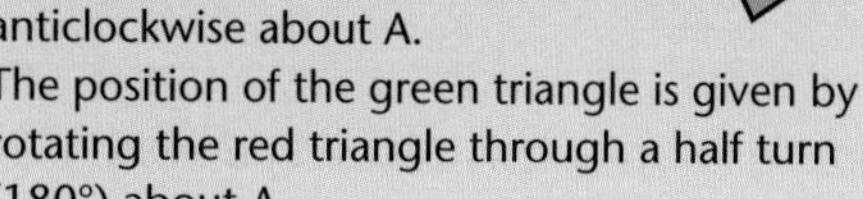

The position of the green triangle is given by rotating the red triangle through a half turn (180°) about A.

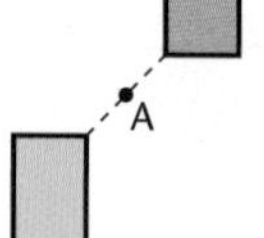

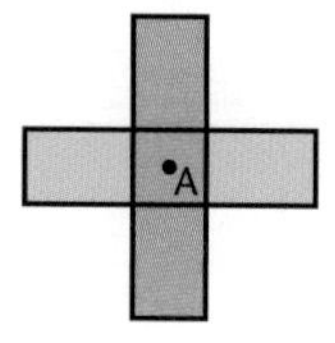

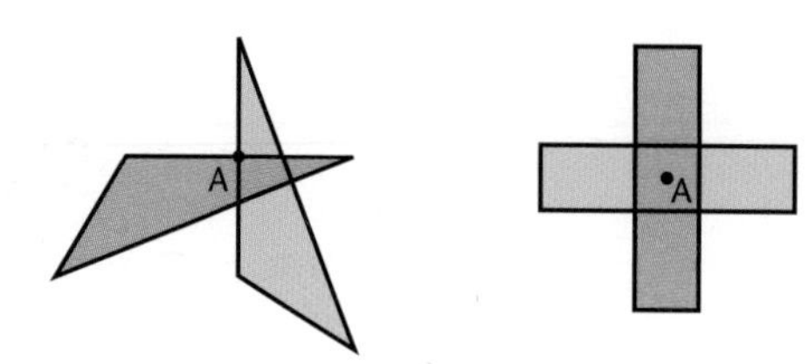

If no direction is given, the rotation is anticlockwise.

Example 5

A rotation maps the red triangle onto the green triangle.
Write down

a the angle and direction of rotation

b the letter that marks the centre of rotation.

Choose a pair of corresponding sides. You can see that C is the turning point and that the angle is 90°.

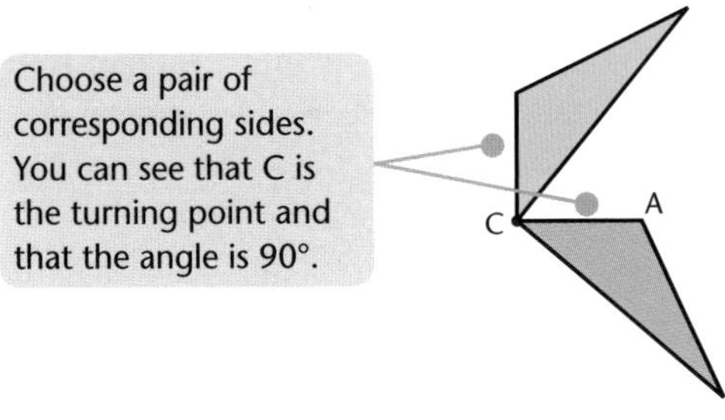

Anticlockwise means ' in the opposite direction to the direction in which the hands of a clock turn'.

Clockwise means 'in the same direction as the hands of a clock turn'.

For half a turn it doesn't matter whether the rotation is clockwise or anticlockwise.

a 90° anticlockwise.

b C

You need all of this information to describe the transformation fully.

Exam practice 13D

1 The red shape is rotated to the green shape.
Write down
i the angle and direction of rotation
ii the letter that marks the centre of rotation.

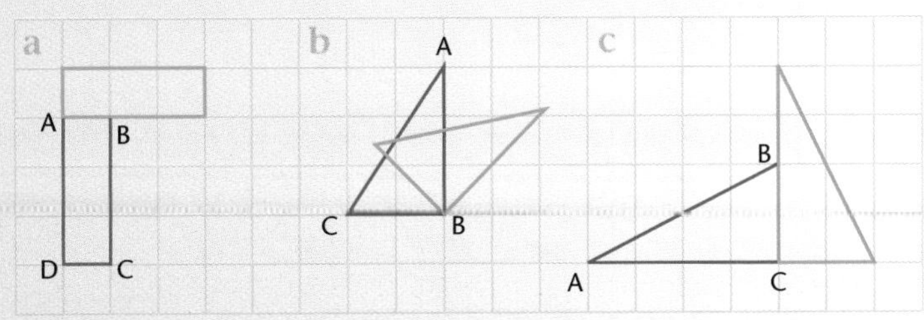

You can use tracing paper to help with these questions.

2 Use a copy of each diagram to sketch the shape that P is mapped to when it is rotated about A by the given angle.

a

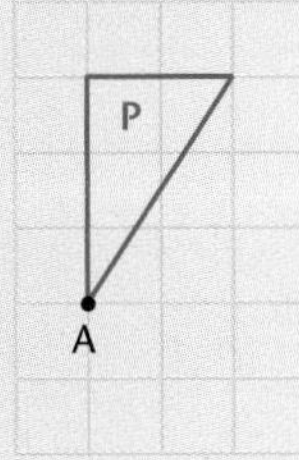

180°

b

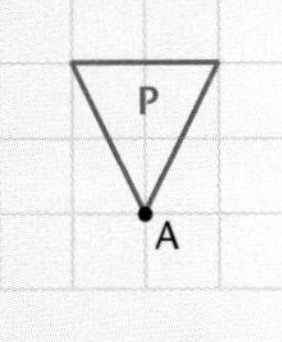

90° anticlockwise

c

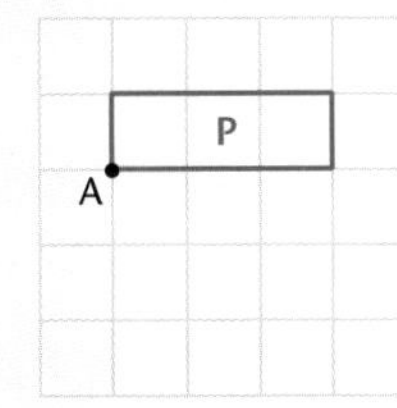

45° clockwise

Sketch means you do not have to draw the shape accurately.

3 Describe fully the rotation that maps the red shape to the green shape.

a
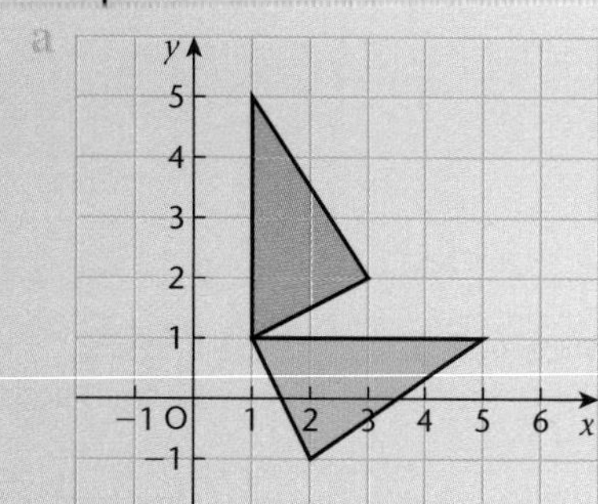

b
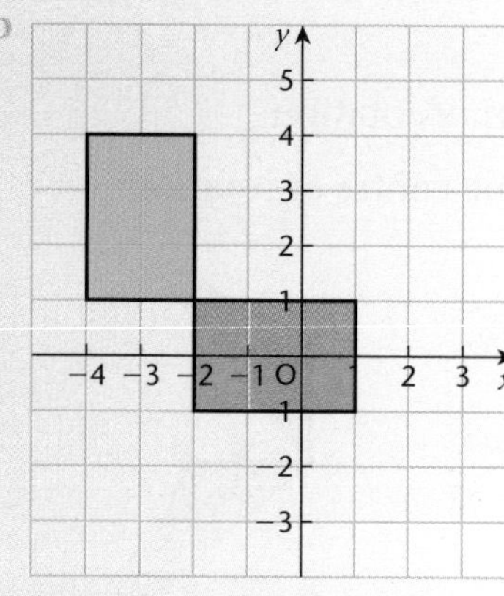

You need to give the coordinates of the centre of rotation and the angle through which the shape is turned. Don't forget to state the direction of turning.

c
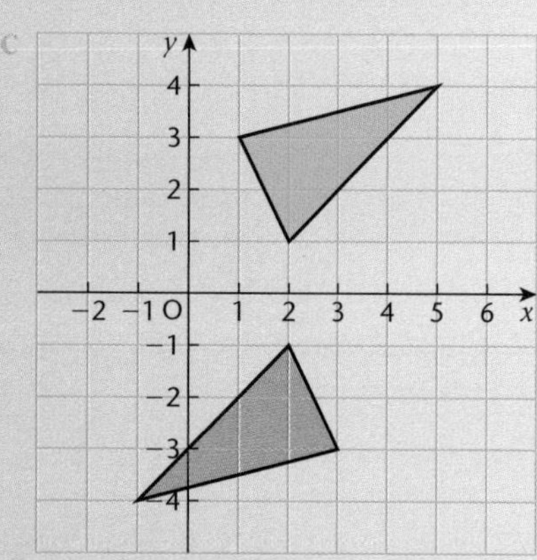

d
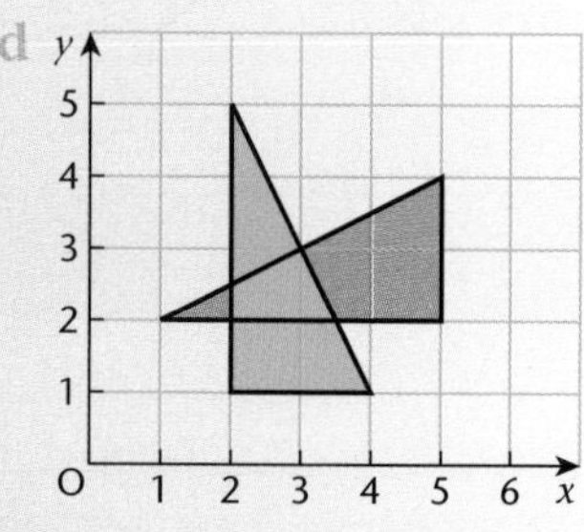

When you cannot 'see' the centre of rotation, you can find it by construction. Join two sets of corresponding points. Then find the point of intersection of the perpendicular bisectors of these lines.

www 4 Copy each diagram and transform shape A using the rotation given.
Label your transformed shape B.

a
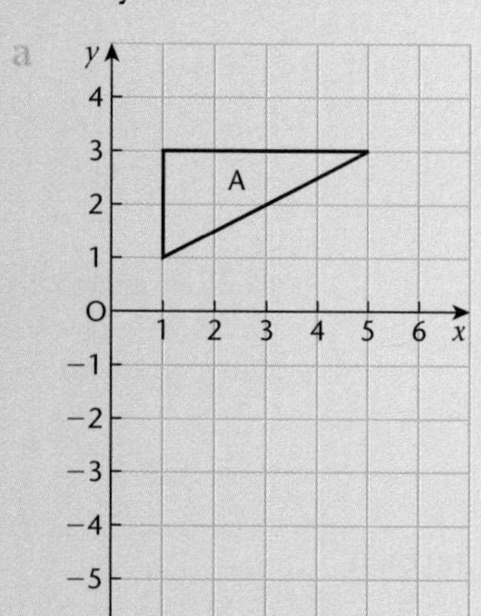

A rotation of 90° clockwise about the point (1, −1).

b
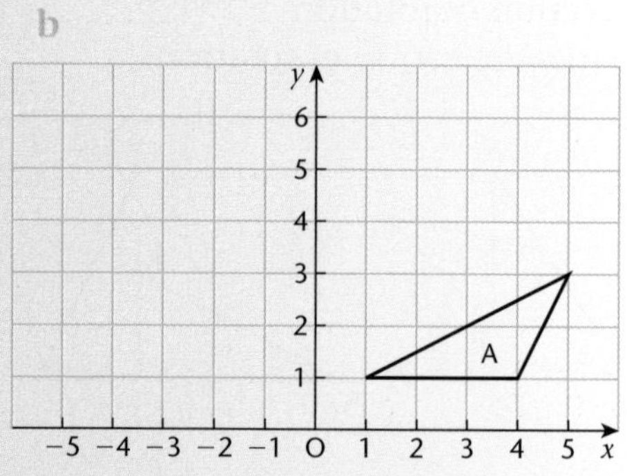

A rotation of 90° anticlockwise about the point (−1, 0).

5 Copy each diagram and transform triangle ABC using the rotation given. Label your transformed triangle A′B′C′.

a

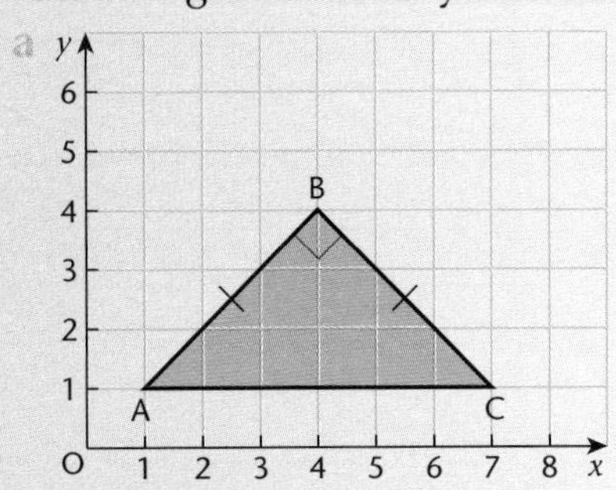

Rotation of 45° clockwise about the point (7, 1).

b

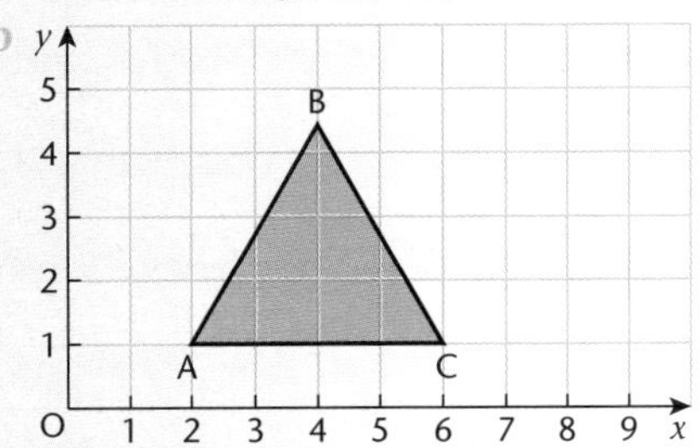

ABC is an equilateral triangle. Rotation of 60° clockwise about the point (6, 1).

In part a you will need to use a ruler to measure lengths.

13.5 Vectors

A **vector** has length and direction.

When vectors are drawn on squared paper you can show them by the number of squares you need to go across and the number you need to go up or down.

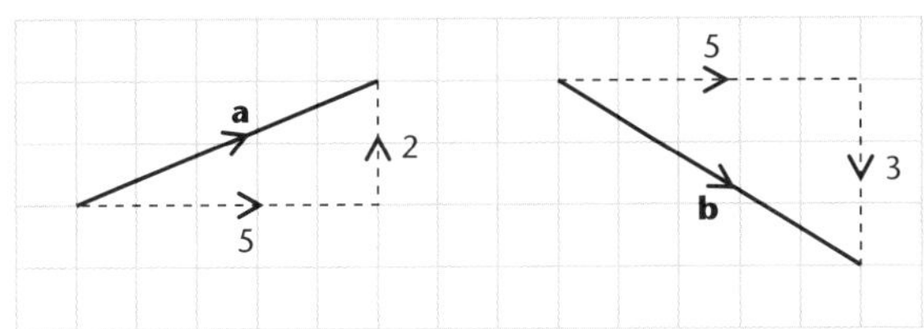

A vector always has a direction. This is marked with an arrow on the diagram.

The vector **a** shows a movement of 5 to the right and 2 up.

You write this as $\mathbf{a} = \begin{pmatrix} 5 \\ 2 \end{pmatrix}$.

The vector **b** shows a movement of 5 to the right and 3 down so $\mathbf{b} = \begin{pmatrix} 5 \\ -3 \end{pmatrix}$.

Positive numbers represent movement up or to the right. Negative numbers represent movement down or to the left.

Example 6

A (2, 1) is the starting point of the vector $\begin{pmatrix} 4 \\ 3 \end{pmatrix}$.

Draw this vector and mark it with an arrow.

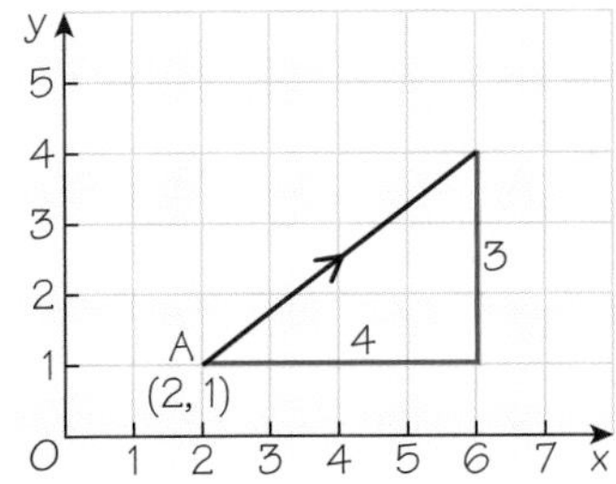

Plot the point A, then draw the vector. $\begin{pmatrix} 4 \\ 3 \end{pmatrix}$ means go 4 to the right then 3 up.

Exam practice 13E

1 Write the following vectors in the form $\begin{pmatrix} p \\ q \end{pmatrix}$.

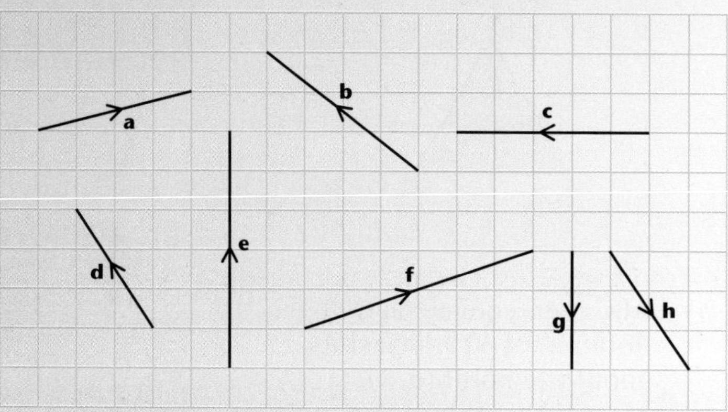

2 Draw these vectors on squared paper.
Label each vector with its letter and an arrow.

$\mathbf{a} = \begin{pmatrix} 5 \\ 2 \end{pmatrix}$ $\mathbf{b} = \begin{pmatrix} -3 \\ 2 \end{pmatrix}$ $\mathbf{c} = \begin{pmatrix} 4 \\ -3 \end{pmatrix}$ $\mathbf{d} = \begin{pmatrix} 10 \\ 4 \end{pmatrix}$

$\mathbf{e} = \begin{pmatrix} -7 \\ 0 \end{pmatrix}$ $\mathbf{f} = \begin{pmatrix} -3 \\ 3 \end{pmatrix}$ $\mathbf{g} = \begin{pmatrix} 1 \\ 2 \end{pmatrix}$ $\mathbf{h} = \begin{pmatrix} -3 \\ -3 \end{pmatrix}$

3 Look at your answers to question 2.
What do you notice about
i vectors **a** and **d** ii vectors **f** and **h**?

4 Plot the point, then draw the vector starting from that point.

a (1, 3), $\begin{pmatrix} 2 \\ 4 \end{pmatrix}$ b (−1, 4), $\begin{pmatrix} 2 \\ 3 \end{pmatrix}$

c (2, −2), $\begin{pmatrix} -3 \\ 4 \end{pmatrix}$ d (−2, 3), $\begin{pmatrix} -4 \\ -3 \end{pmatrix}$

e (−5, 0), $\begin{pmatrix} 5 \\ -3 \end{pmatrix}$ f (2, 1), $\begin{pmatrix} 4 \\ -2 \end{pmatrix}$

Use a grid like this.

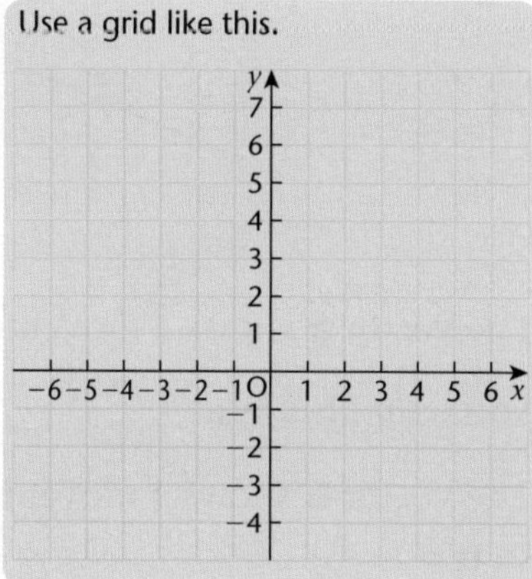

WWW

13.6 Translation

You can change the position of a shape by sliding it along a straight line.
This is called a **translation**.

The red triangle moves to the position of the green triangle by sliding 3 squares to the right.
This translation is described by the vector $\begin{pmatrix} 3 \\ 0 \end{pmatrix}$.

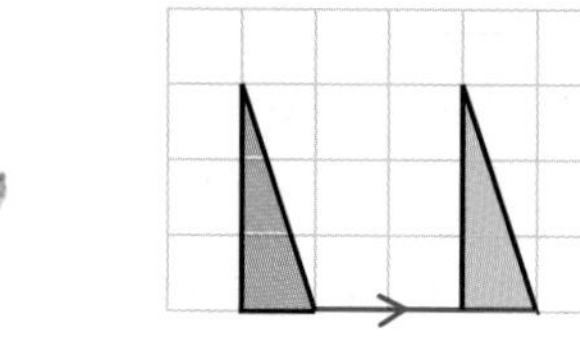

This translation moves a vertex 4 squares to the right and 1 up.
It is described by the vector $\begin{pmatrix}4\\1\end{pmatrix}$.

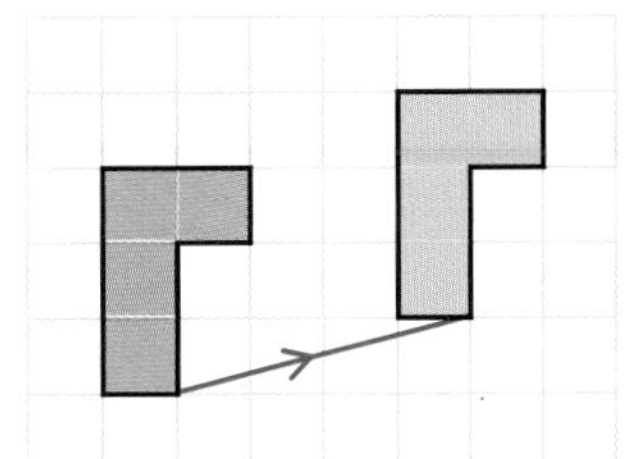

Exam practice 13F

You can describe a translation by either giving the number of squares moved left or right and up and down or by giving a vector.

1 Describe the translation that maps triangle A to triangle B.

a 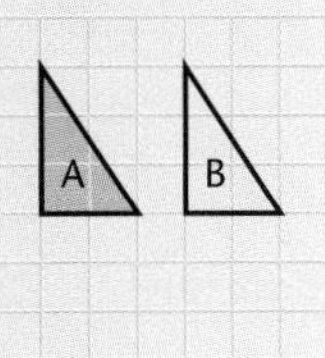

b 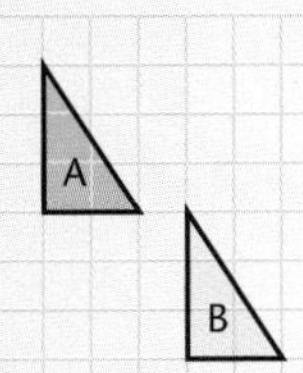

c 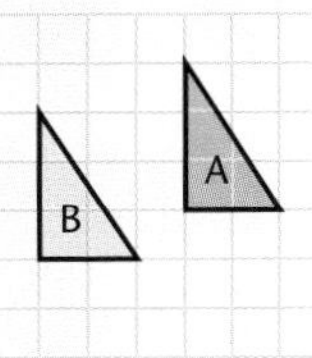

d 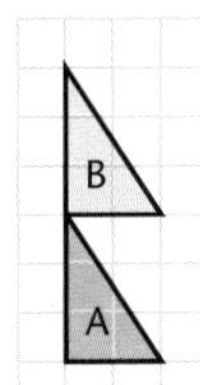

2 On a copy of each diagram draw the result of translating the given shape along the marked line by the number of squares given.

a 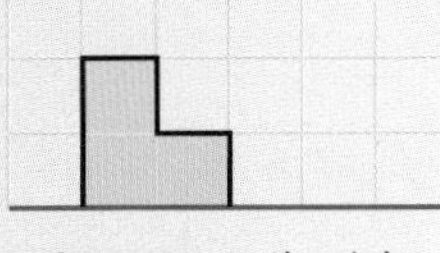
3 squares to the right

b 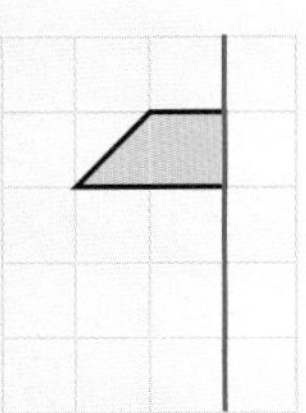
2 squares down

c 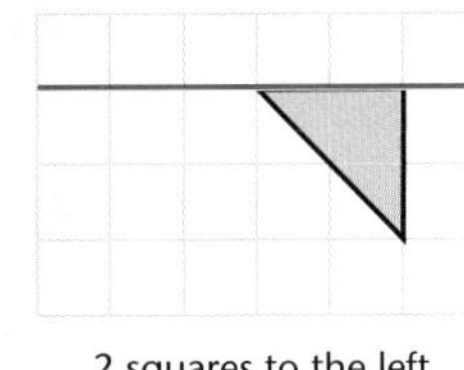
2 squares to the left

3 a What is the mathematical name of the shape ABCD?

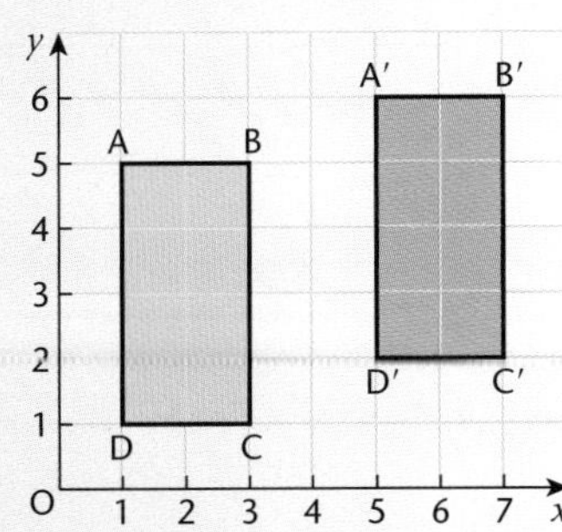

b Write down the coordinates of
i A ii C.

c The shape ABCD maps to A′B′C′D′.
Write down the vector that gives this translation.

d Write down the coordinates of
i A′ ii C′.

e Ceri said that the vector that translates A′B′C′D′ to ABCD is $\begin{pmatrix}-4\\-1\end{pmatrix}$.
Is Ceri correct? Give a reason for your answer.

UAM

UAM **4** Triangle ABC is translated so that A translates to A′.

a Write down the vector that gives this translation.

b On a copy of the diagram, draw the translation of △ABC using this vector. Label the transformed triangle A′B′C′.

c Write down the coordinates of **i** B′ **ii** C′.

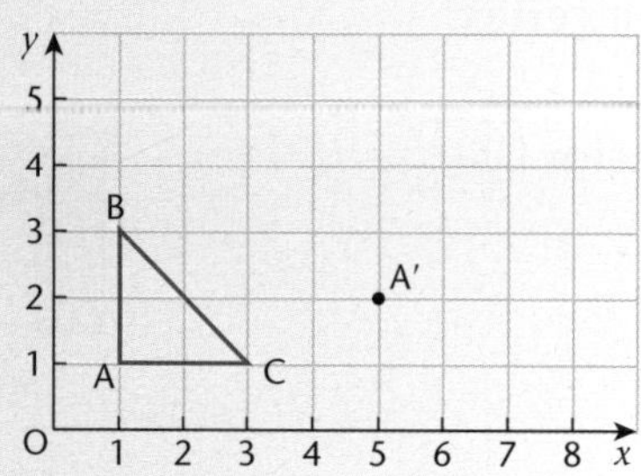

5 **a** Triangle ABC is translated so that A translates to A′. Write down the vector that gives this translation.

b Copy the diagram and draw the translation of △ABC using this vector. Label the transformed triangle A′B′C′.

c Write down the coordinates of **i** B′ **ii** C′.

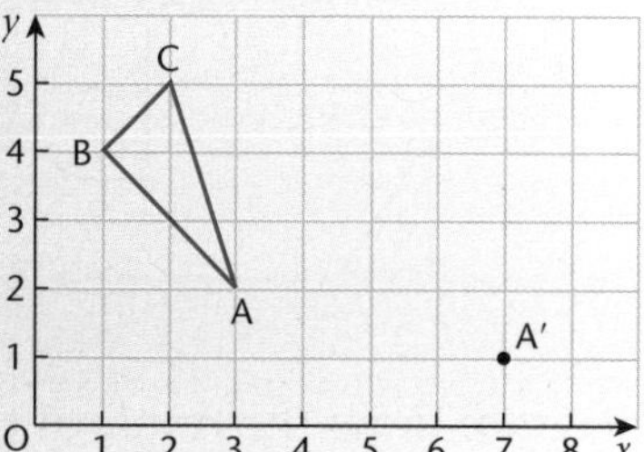

13.7 Combined and mixed transformations

Sometimes more than one transformation is needed to map one shape onto another.

Example 7

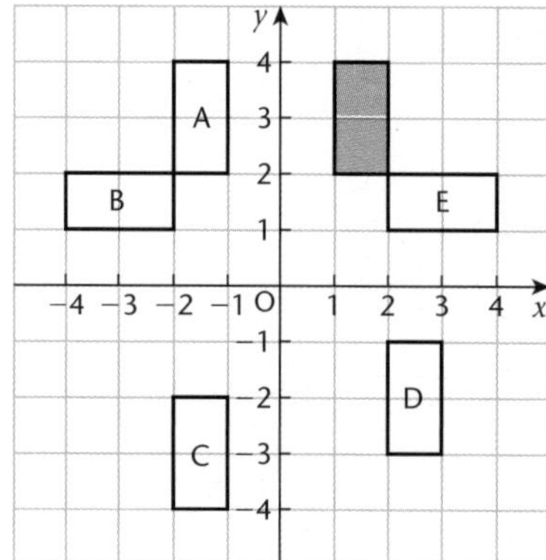

a Give the letter of the shape that the red rectangle is mapped to by each of the following transformations:

i translation of 1 square to the right and 5 squares down

ii rotated about O through 90° anticlockwise

iii reflected in the line $y = x$

b Draw the position of the red rectangle after a reflection in the y-axis followed by a reflection in the x-axis. Label the final image F.

a i D ii B iii E

Do the transformations even if you think you know the correct rectangle.
This will act as a check.

b

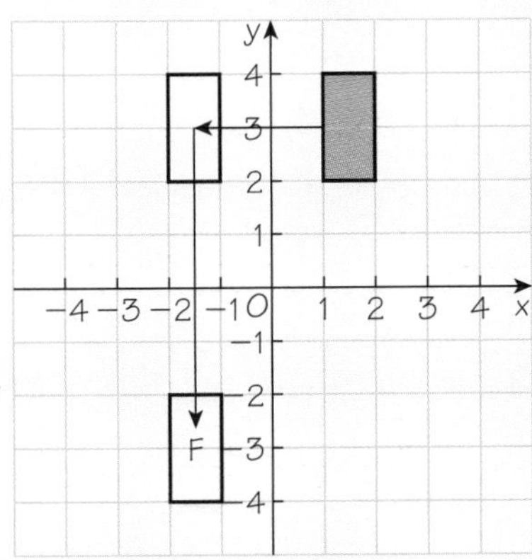

First reflect the rectangle in the y-axis, then reflect the result in the x-axis.

Exam practice 13G

1 Give the letter of the shape that the green triangle is mapped to by each of the following transformations:

a reflection in the y-axis
b reflection in the line $x = 3$
c translation by 2 squares to the right and 4 squares down
d rotation about O through 180°
e reflection in the line $x = 3$ then translation by 6 squares to the left

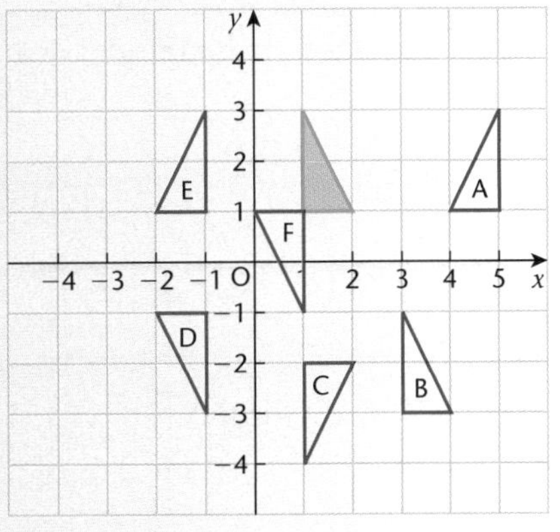

If you need to, use a copy of the diagram to do these transformations.
Not all the triangles are needed.

2

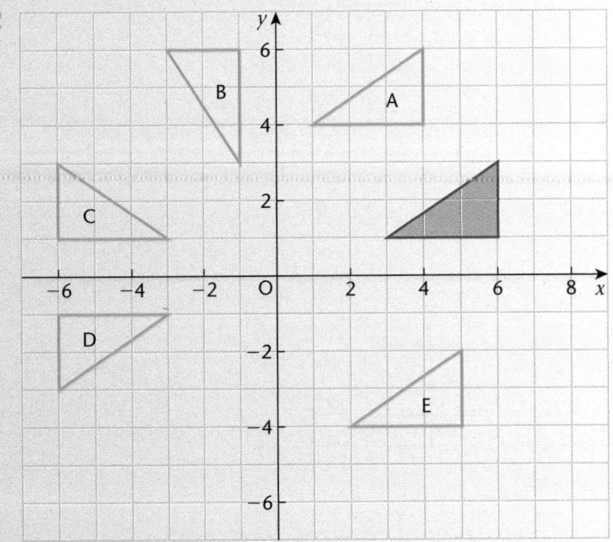

You need to give the name of the transformation as well as either a mirror line, a vector, or a centre and angle of rotation.

Describe fully the transformation that maps the red triangle onto:

a E b A c B d D e C

3

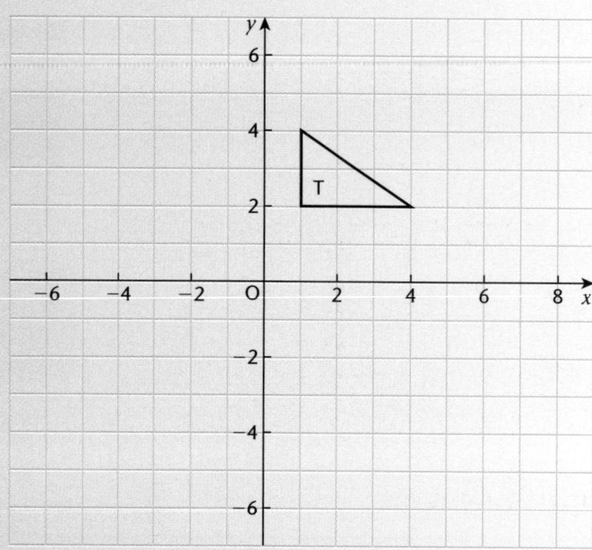

On a copy of this diagram draw the shape that T is mapped to when it is

a reflected in the line $y = x$. Label it A.
b reflected in the y-axis and then translated 3 squares down. Label it B.
c rotated by 180° about O. Label it C.
d reflected in the x-axis then rotated by 90° anticlockwise about (1, −2). Label it D.

4 The diagram shows two congruent shapes. Describe fully the single transformation which maps shape P onto shape Q.

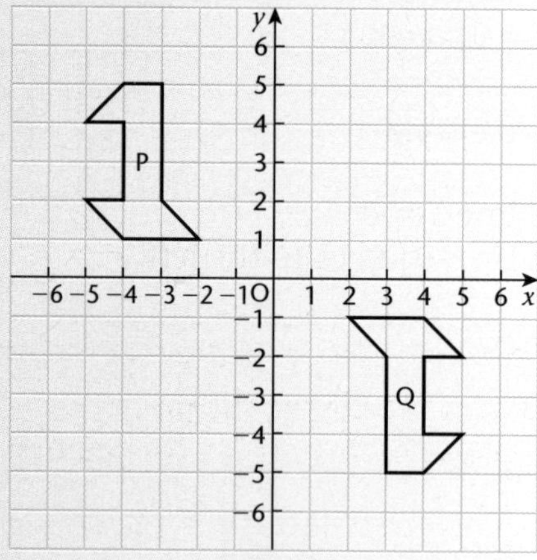

5 Triangle ABC is transformed by the translation $\begin{pmatrix} -2 \\ -6 \end{pmatrix}$ followed by reflection in the line $y = x$.
Draw its final position on a copy of this grid.
Label it A′B′C′.

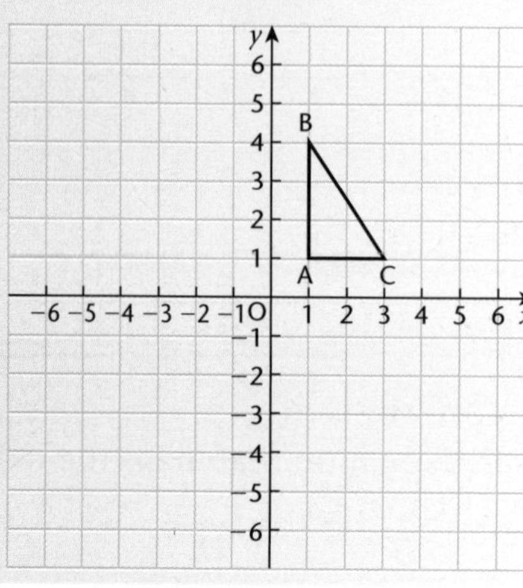

www

6 Rectangle ABCD is transformed by the translation $\begin{pmatrix} 4 \\ -5 \end{pmatrix}$ followed by reflection in the line $y = -x$
Draw the final position of the rectangle on a copy of this grid.

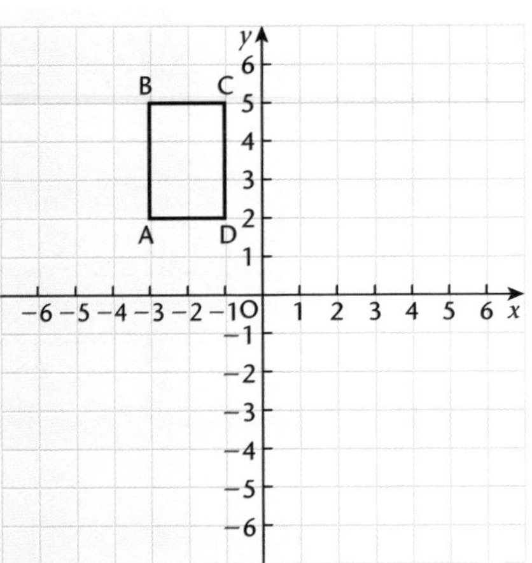

7 This diagram shows two triangles, A and B.

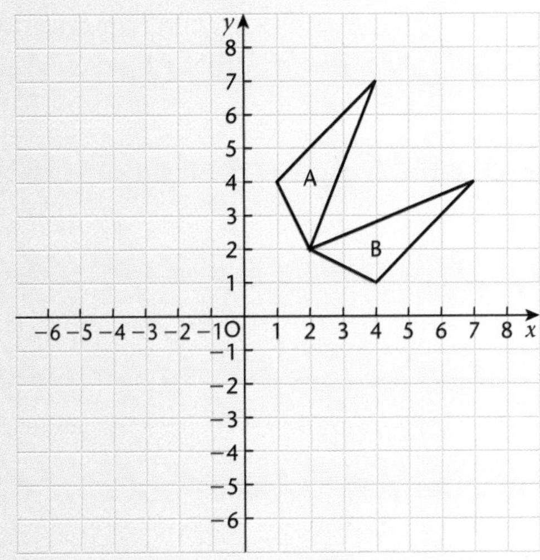

a Describe the single transformation that maps triangle A to triangle B.

b Triangle A is translated by the vector $\begin{pmatrix} -4 \\ -3 \end{pmatrix}$ and then rotated through 90° anticlockwise about the point (0, −2).
On a copy of the diagram draw the final position after these transformations.
Label it C.

8 Copy this diagram.

a Draw the reflection of P in the x-axis. Label it A.

b P is rotated through 180° about the origin to give B.
Draw B.

c P is reflected in the y-axis to give C. Draw C.

d Write down the transformation that maps B onto C.

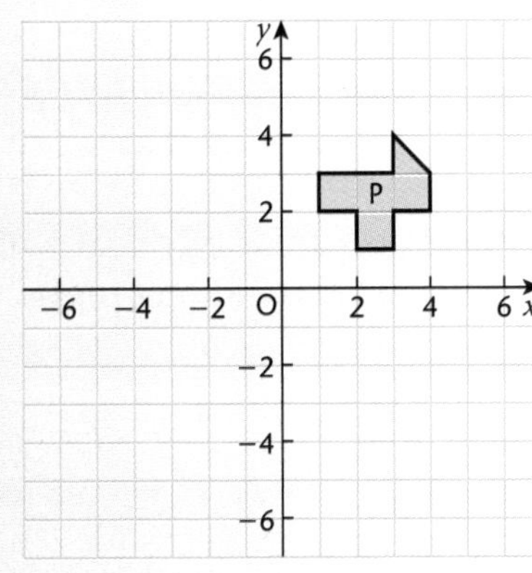

9 Copy this diagram.

a Draw the image of P after the following transformations

i Reflection in the y-axis. Label the result Q.

ii Rotation of 90° clockwise about O. Label the result R.

iii Reflection in the line $y = -x$. Label the result S.

b Describe fully the single transformation that maps:

i S onto R

ii S onto Q

iii R onto P.

WWW

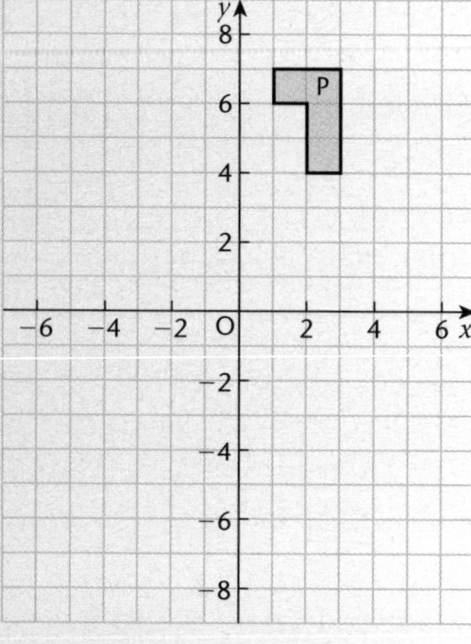

10

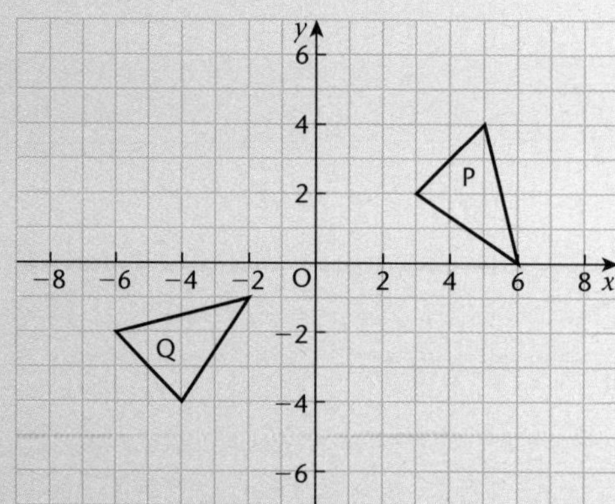

Triangle P is mapped onto triangle Q by an anticlockwise rotation about the origin followed by a translation.

a Write down the angle of rotation.

b Find the vector that describes the translation.

UAM 11 Describe two possible transformations that will transform triangle ABD to triangle BCD.

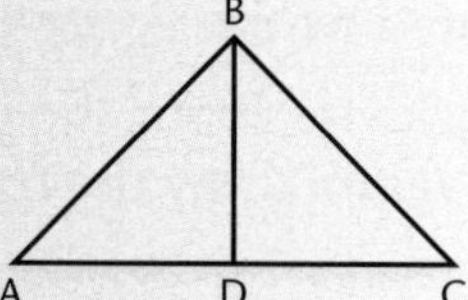

UAM 12

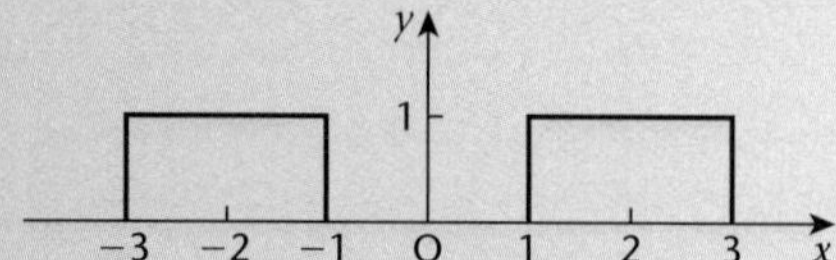

Describe three possible transformations that will transform the left hand rectangle to the right hand rectangle.

Summary of key points

- When a shape is reflected in a mirror line, the shape and its reflection are symmetrical about the mirror line.
- The mirror line is the perpendicular bisector of the line joining a point on the shape to the corresponding point on its reflection.
- A shape has rotational symmetry if it can be rotated about a point to a different position but still look the same.
- The order of rotational symmetry is the number of times, within one full revolution, the shape can be turned and still look the same before it returns to its original position.
- A translation moves a shape without reflecting or rotating it.
- A translation can be described by a vector.
- When you describe a transformation, you must give its name and:
  - to describe a reflection you must give the mirror line
  - to describe a rotation you must give the centre and angle of rotation and say whether it is clockwise or anticlockwise
  - to describe a translation you must give a vector, or the distance across and up or down.

Most candidates who get GRADE C or above can:

- describe a transformation fully.

Glossary

Angle of rotation the angle through which a shape is turned

Anticlockwise turning in the opposite direction to which the hands of a clock turn

Centre of rotation the point about which a shape turns

Clockwise turning in the same direction as the hands of a clock turn

Line symmetry describes a shape that can be folded so that one half fits exactly over the other

Maps moves a shape to a new position

Mirror line a line about which a shape and its reflection are symmetrical

Order of rotational symmetry the number of times a shape looks the same in one complete revolution

Rotation turns a shape through an angle about a fixed point

Rotational symmetry describes a shape that can be rotated about a point to a different position and still look the same.

Transformation an operation that moves a shape from one position to another

Translation changing the position of a shape by sliding it along straight lines

Vector a quantity that has magnitude and direction

Vertex (plural vertices) the corner of an object

14 Enlargement

This chapter will show you:

- ✓ how to enlarge a shape by a given scale factor
- ✓ what the centre of enlargement means
- ✓ the meaning of similar shapes
- ✓ how to make and read scale drawings
- ✓ what a locus is

Before you start you need to know:

- ✓ how to plot points and give the coordinates of a point
- ✓ the cubes and squares of the numbers 1 to 10
- ✓ how to transform a shape using reflection, rotation and translation
- ✓ what congruent means
- ✓ how to find the perimeter and area of a shape
- ✓ how to use Pythagoras' theorem
- ✓ the units of length, mass and capacity
- ✓ the relationships between angles on a straight line, round a point and with parallel lines
- ✓ how to draw parallel lines
- ✓ how to construct the perpendicular bisector of a line segment

14.1 Enlargement

An **enlargement** is a transformation that maps a shape to another shape by multiplying all the lengths by the same number.
This number is called the **scale factor**.

When the scale factor is larger than 1, the shape gets larger.

To enlarge a shape by a scale factor of 4 you have to make all the lengths 4 times longer.

When the scale factor is less than 1, the shape gets smaller.

To enlarge a shape by a scale factor of $\frac{1}{2}$, you have to make all the lengths half as long.

Square B is an enlargement of square A.

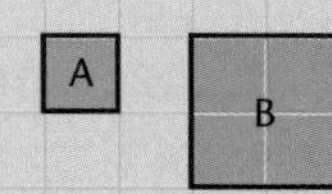

The sides of B are twice the length of the sides of square A. The scale factor is 2.

Example 1

In the diagram, rectangles B and C are enlargements of rectangle A.

a What is the scale factor of the enlargement that maps A to B?

b What is the scale factor of the enlargement that maps A to C?

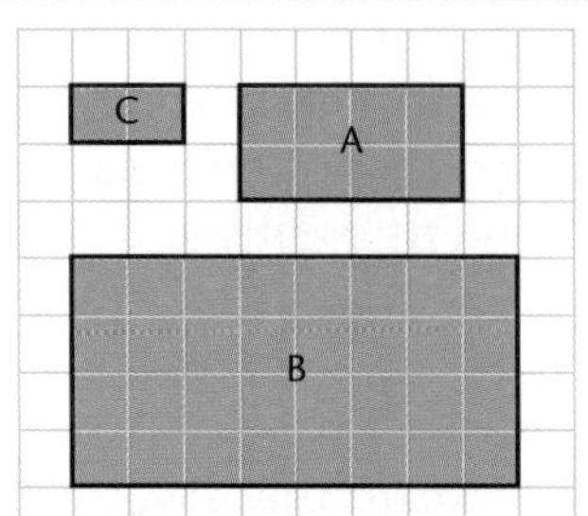

The word 'enlargement' is used for making a shape larger and for making it smaller.

a 2 — The sides of B are twice as long as the corresponding sides of A.

b $\frac{1}{2}$ — The sides of C are half the length of the corresponding sides of A.

You can also enlarge a solid.

Example 2

Draw an enlargement of the solid A with a scale factor of 2.

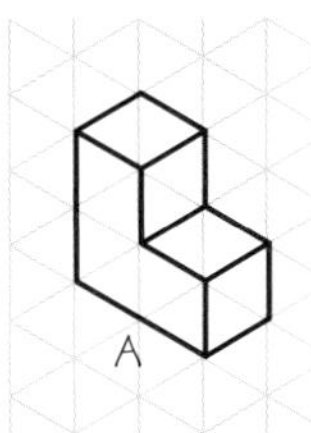

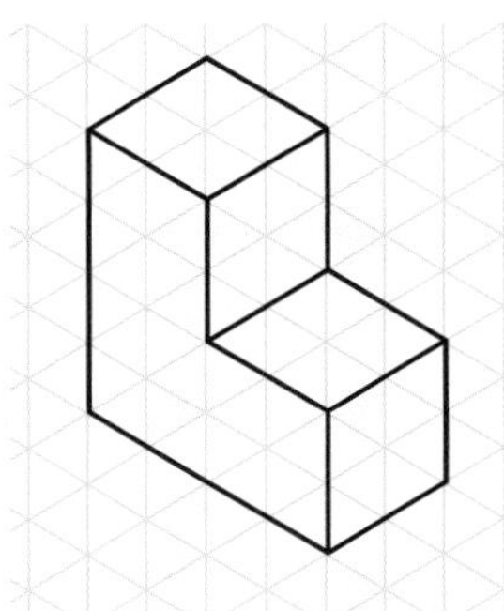

You need to draw your shape so that all its edges are twice as long as those of A.
It is drawn on isometric paper so every grid line is 5 mm long including the slanting ones.

Exam practice 14A

1 Give the scale factor for each of these enlargements.
The green shape is an enlargement of the blue shape.

a

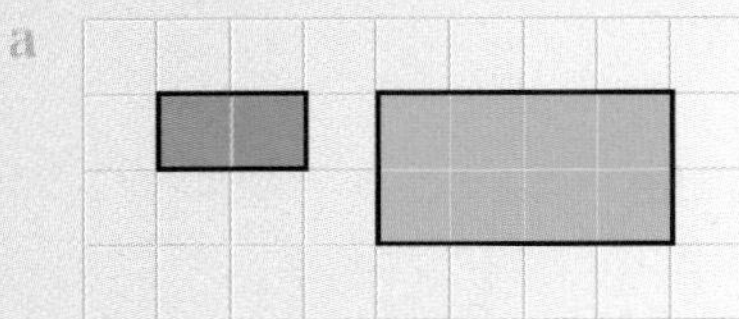

b

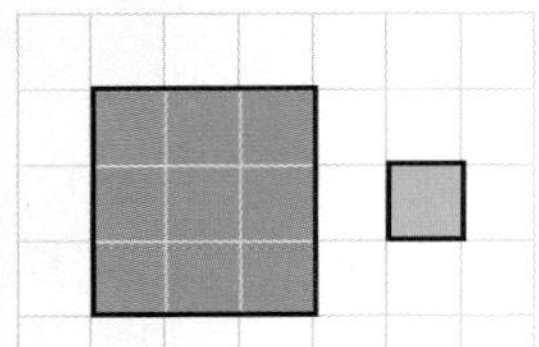

c

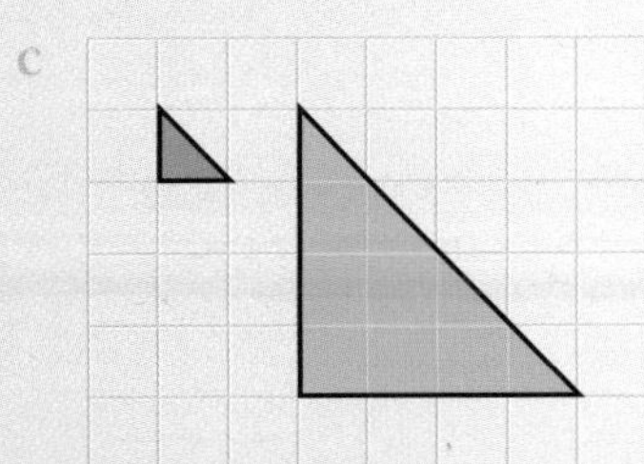

d

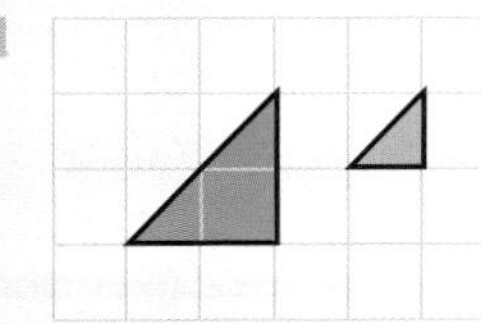

2 The green solid is an enlargement of the blue solid.
Give the scale factor for each enlargement.

a

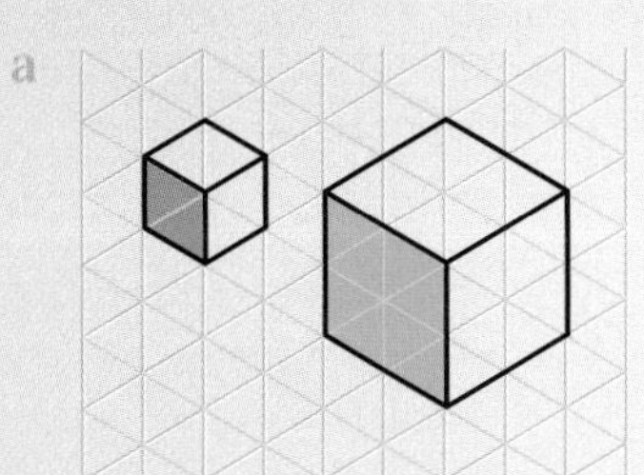

b

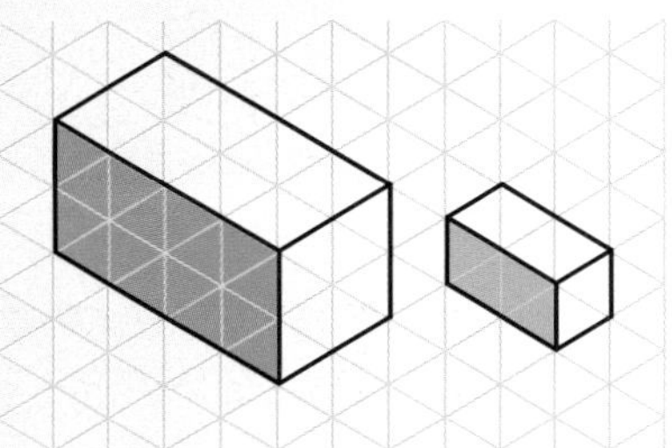

3 On a copy of each diagram, draw an enlargement of the shape by the scale factor given.

a Scale factor 3

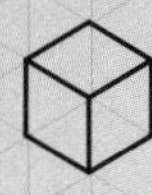

b Scale factor $\frac{1}{2}$

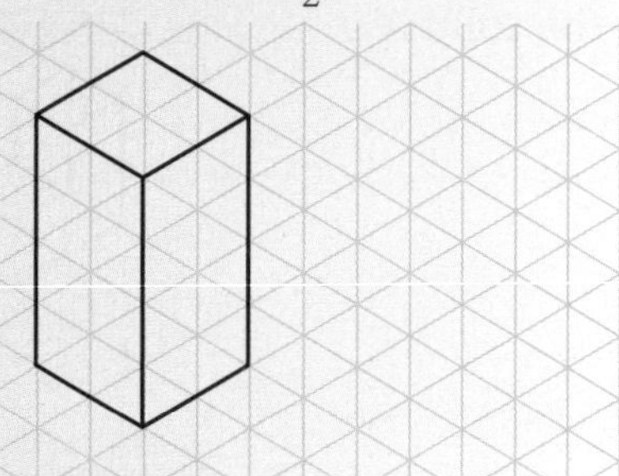

4 Kingston says 'the green rectangle is an enlargement of the red rectangle.'

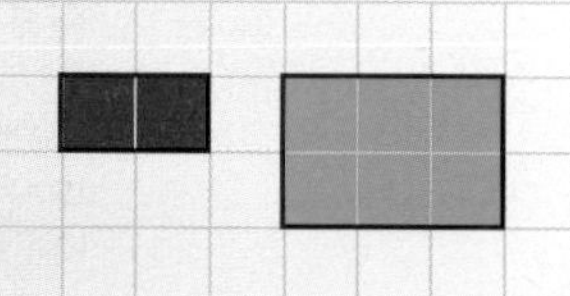

UAM Explain why Kingston is wrong.

14.2 Centre of enlargement

The **centre of enlargement** is a point. Lines are drawn from this point to each **vertex** of the shape and then lengthened to give the vertices of the enlarged shape.

$$\begin{pmatrix}\text{distance from the}\\ \text{centre of enlargement}\\ \text{to the vertices of the}\\ \text{enlarged shape}\end{pmatrix} = (\text{scale factor}) \times \begin{pmatrix}\text{distance from the}\\ \text{centre of enlargement}\\ \text{to the vertices of the}\\ \text{original shape}\end{pmatrix}$$

In this diagram the green triangle is an enlargement of the blue triangle. The scale factor is 3, and centre of enlargement is the point (0, 1).

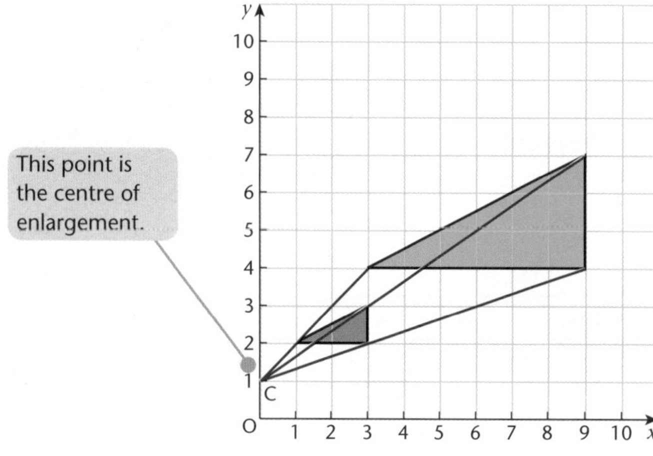

The red lines are drawn from C to the vertices of the blue triangle. They are then extended so that they are 3 times as long to give the vertices of the green triangle.

Example 3

Draw the enlargement of triangle ABC with centre (1, 2) and scale factor $\frac{2}{3}$.

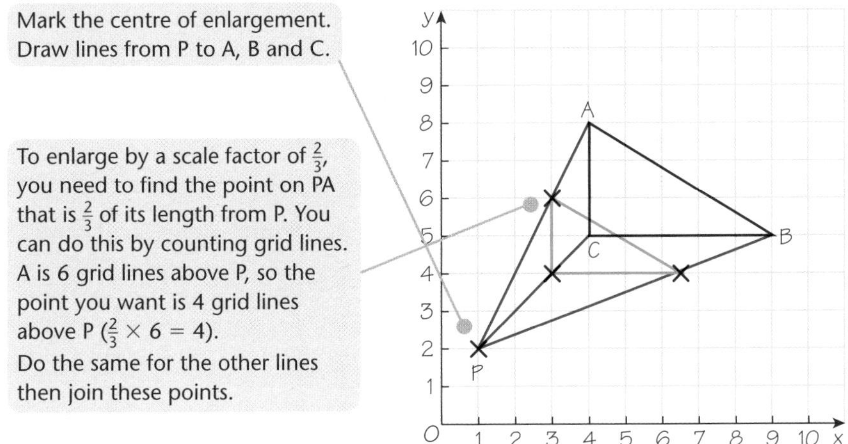

You can find the centre of enlargement by drawing lines through **corresponding** pairs of vertices.

Corresponding means in the same position in each shape.

Example 4

PQRS is an enlargement of ABCD.
Describe the enlargement.

To describe an enlargement, you must give the scale factor and the centre of enlargement.

You can find the centre of enlargement by joining the vertices of the enlarged rectangle to the corresponding vertices of the small rectangle and extending them until they meet. This point is the centre of enlargement.

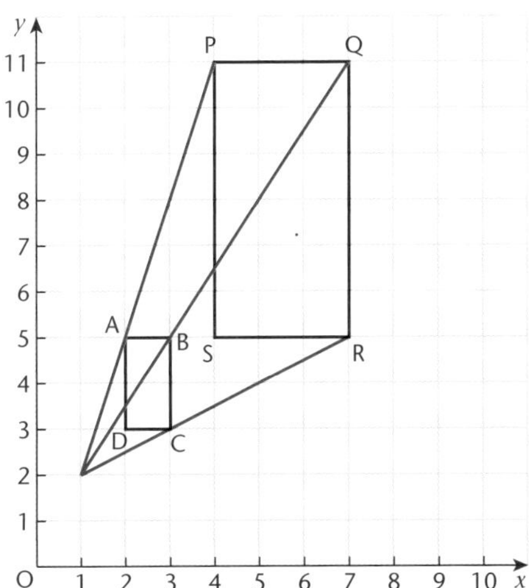

The scale factor is 3.

The centre of enlargement is the point (1, 2).

Exam practice 14B

1 On a copy of the diagram, draw the enlargement of each shape:

a centre (1, 1), scale factor 3

b centre (0, 2), scale factor $\frac{1}{2}$

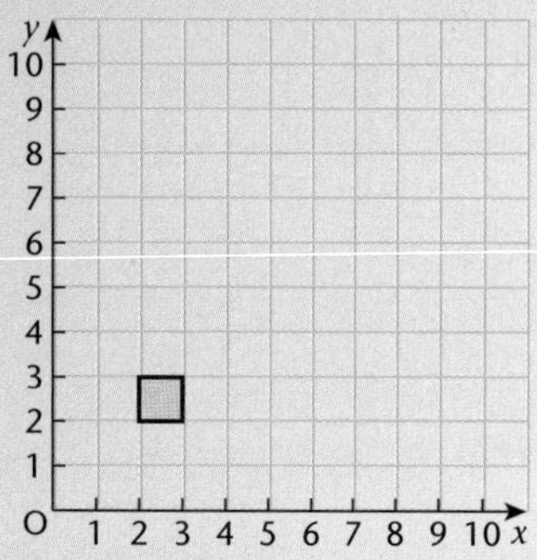

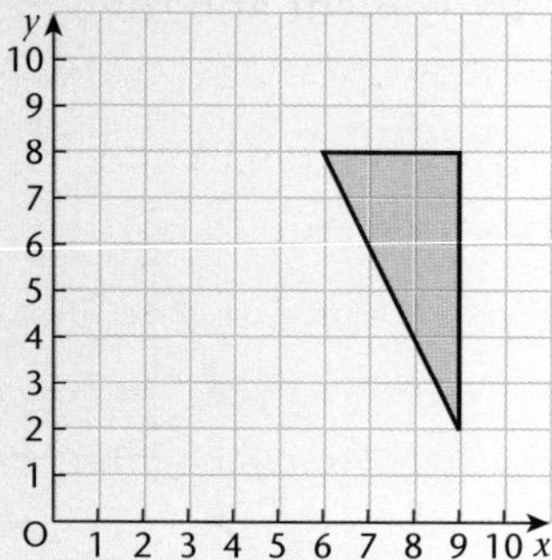

c centre (1, 1) scale factor $1\frac{1}{2}$

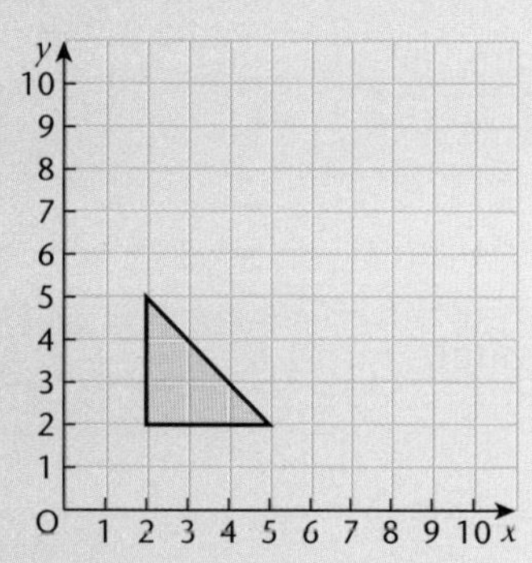

The enlarged triangle overlaps the grey triangle.

2 Describe the enlargement that maps A to B.

a

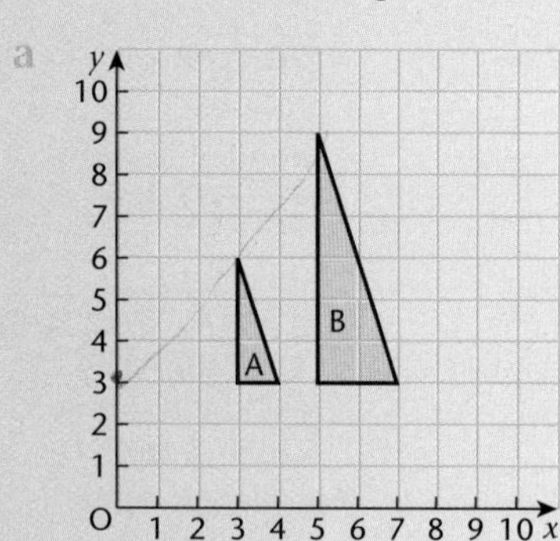

b

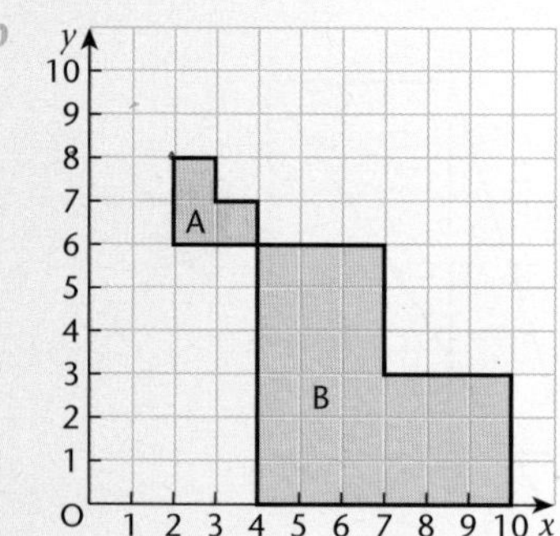

To describe an enlargement, you must give the scale factor and the centre of enlargement.

c

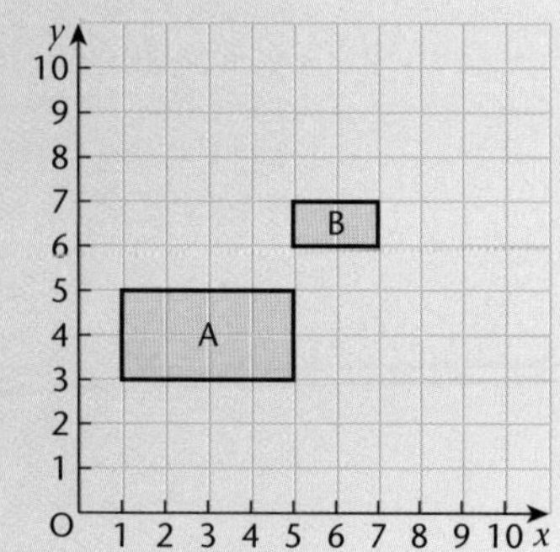

14.3 Negative scale factors

When the scale factor is negative, lines are drawn from each vertex of the shape to the centre of enlargement and then extended beyond the centre to give the vertices of the enlarged shape.

In this diagram, the green triangle is an enlargement of the blue triangle with scale factor -2 and centre (7, 6).

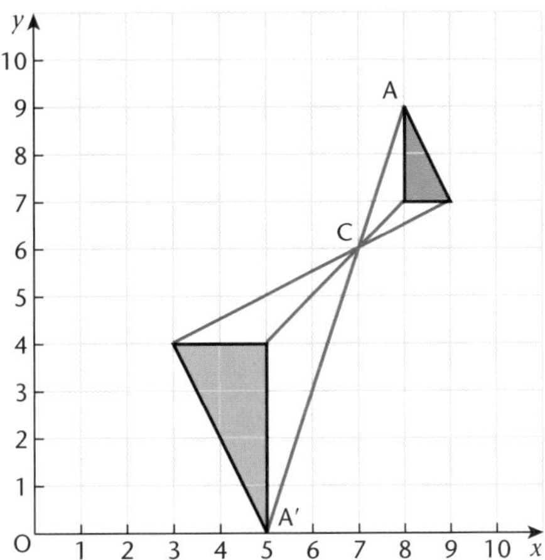

The red lines are drawn from the vertices of the blue triangle to the centre of enlargement and then continued. The scale factor is -2, so CA′ = 2CA.

Example 5

Draw the enlargement of triangle P with scale factor $-\frac{1}{3}$ and centre (0, 4).

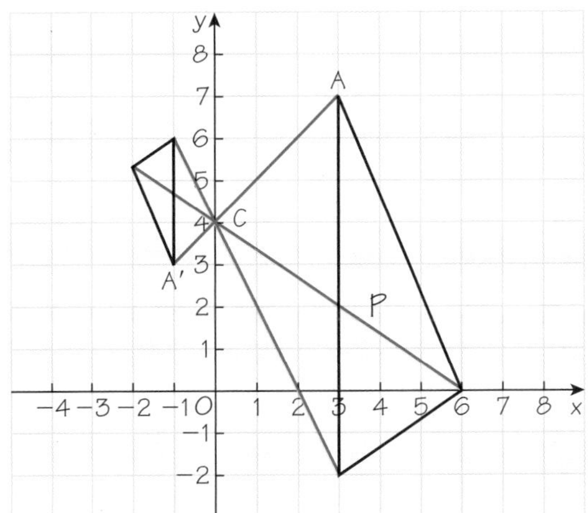

Mark the centre of enlargement, C. Draw a line from one vertex of P to C and extend it so that it is $\frac{1}{3}$ as long again. You can do this by counting grid lines. You go three squares across from A to C so continue the line so it is another 1 square across.
Do the same from the other two vertices of P.

Exam practice 14C

1 On a copy of the diagram, draw the enlargement of each shape:

a centre (2, 0), scale factor -2

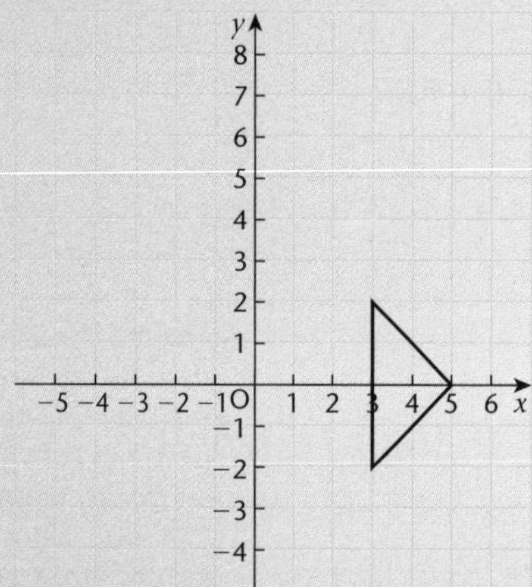

b centre (2, 2), scale factor -3

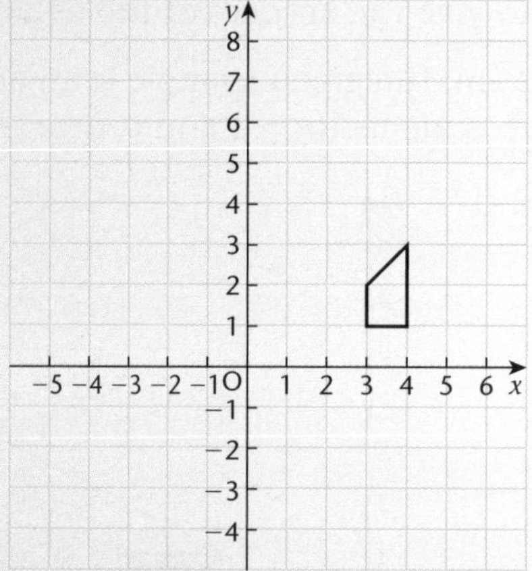

c centre (4, 3), scale factor $-\frac{1}{2}$

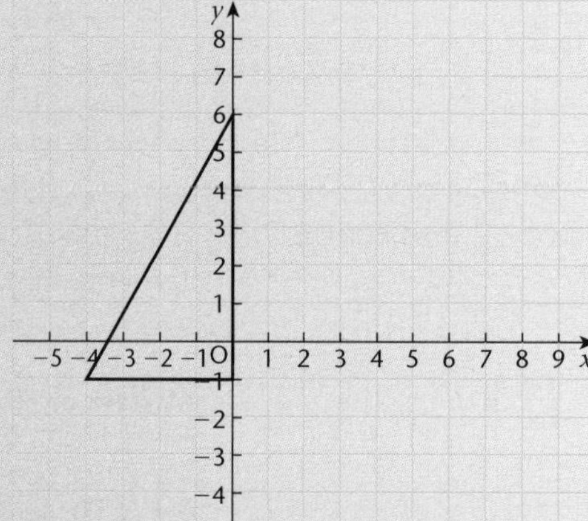

d centre (4, 5), scale factor $-\frac{1}{3}$

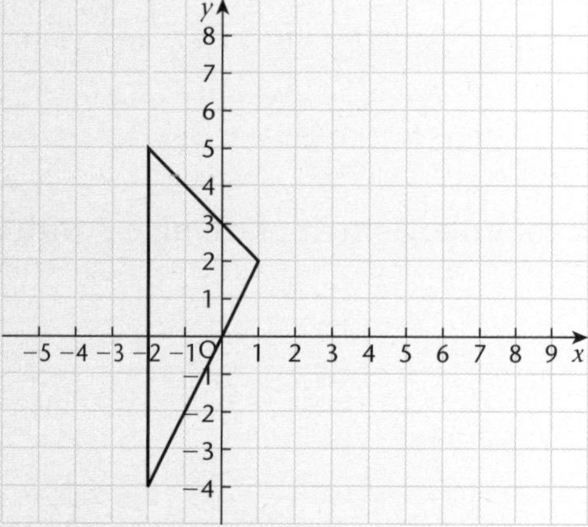

2 Describe the enlargement that maps A to B.

a

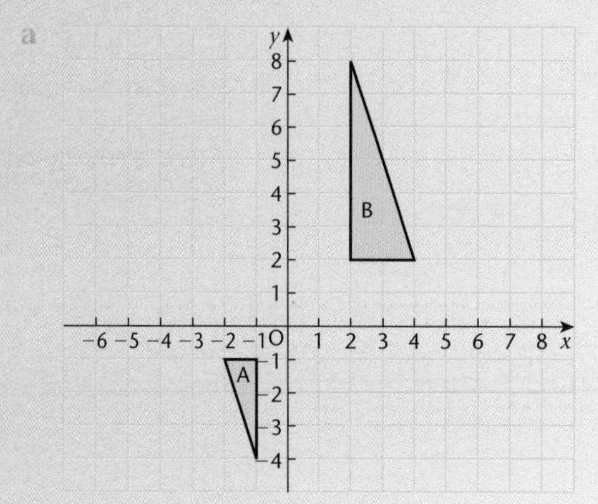

b

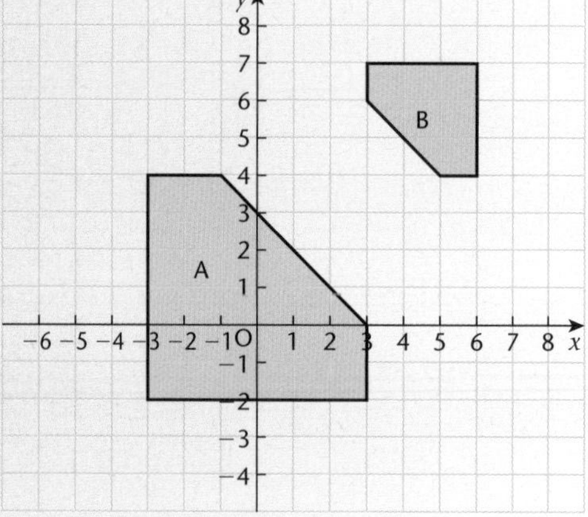

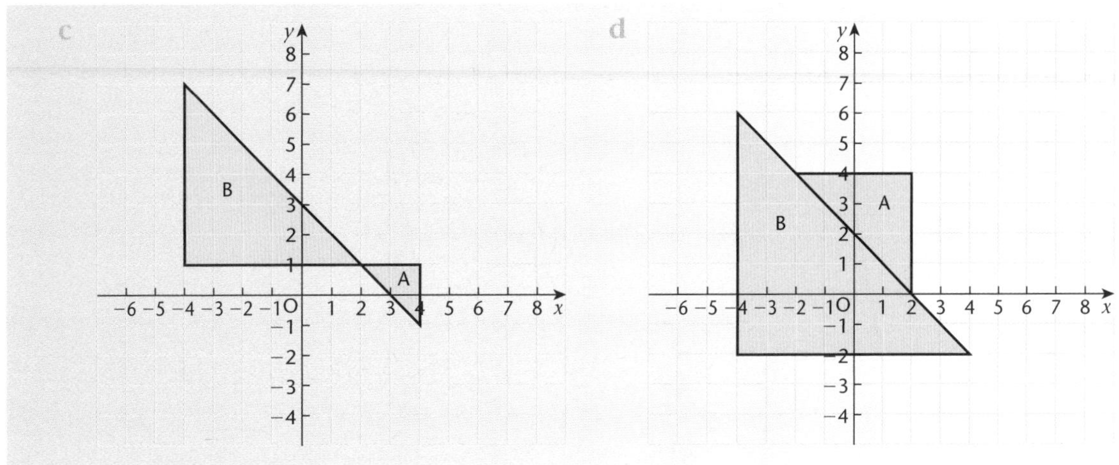

14.4 Describing a transformation

When you are asked to describe a transformation fully, you must give:

- the mathematical name
- the mirror line for a reflection
- the centre, angle of rotation and direction for a rotation
- the vector for a translation or a description of the movement
- the centre of enlargement and the scale factor for an enlargement.

Exam practice 14D

UAM Describe fully the transformation that maps A to B.

1

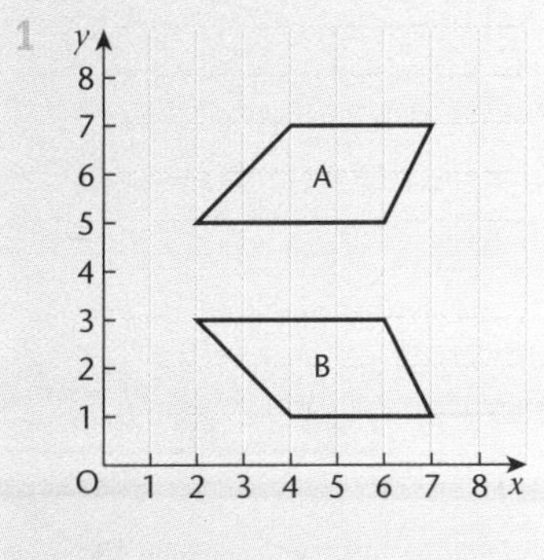

2

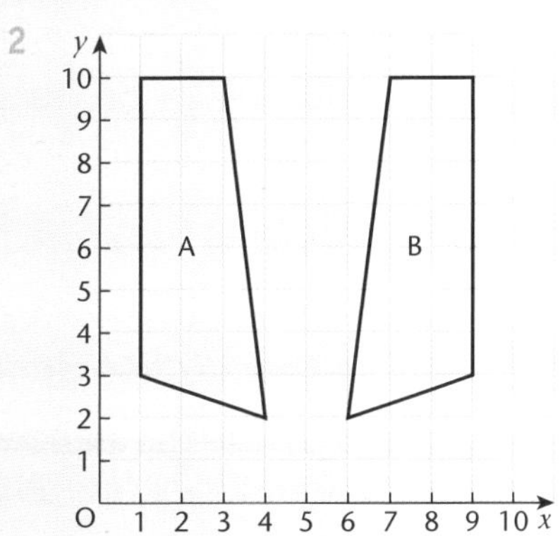

3

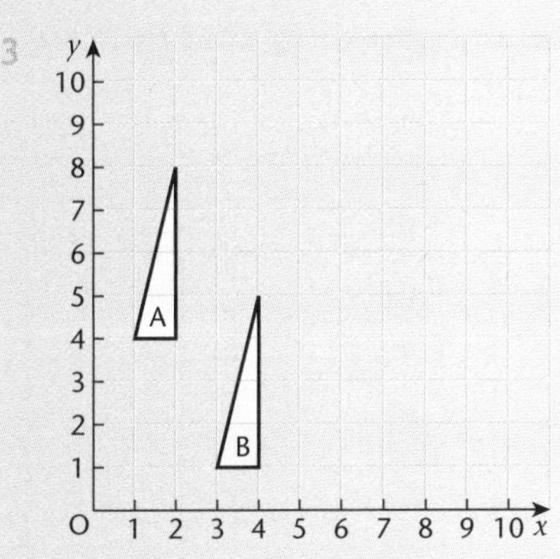

4

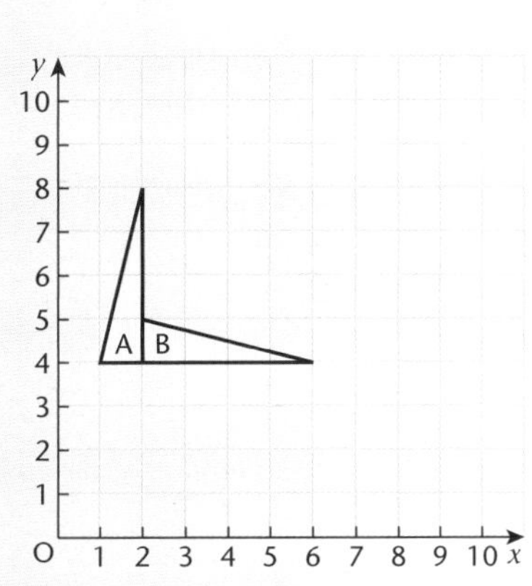

Class discussion

What is the mathematical name of this triangle?

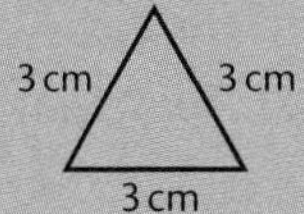

What are the properties of this triangle?
Which of these properties stay the same when the triangle is transformed

a by a reflection
b by a rotation
c by an enlargement
d by a translation?

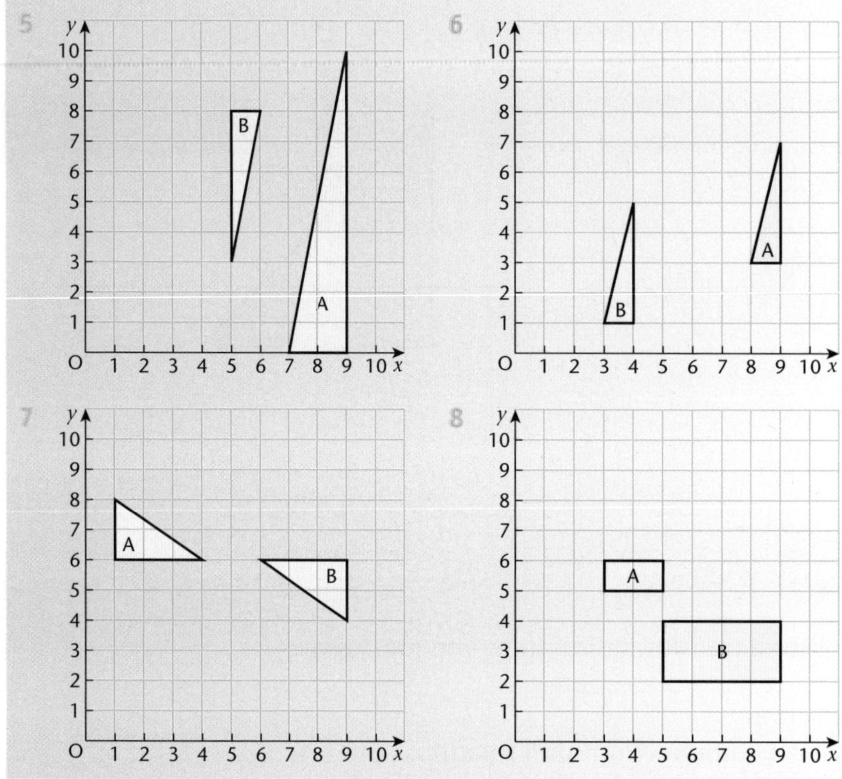

14.5 Similar shapes

Two shapes are **similar** when one is an enlargement of the other.
The enlarged shape may be reflected or rotated.
When two shapes are similar

- their corresponding angles are equal
- their corresponding lengths are in the same **ratio**.

When two quantities are in the same ratio, they behave in the same way.
If one quantity is doubled, so is the other, if one quantity is halved, so is the other, and so on.
Quantities that are related in this way are **proportional**.

To show that two triangles are similar all you need to do is to show that two angles of one triangle are equal to two angles of the other triangle.

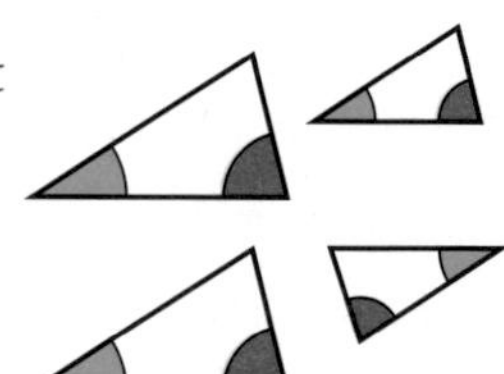

The third angles must then be equal, because the angle sum of each triangle is 180°. The triangles are the same shape, even if one is reflected and rotated.

To show that two shapes, other than triangles, are similar you need to show that they are equiangular and that their corresponding sides are proportional.

Example 6

Write down the letters of the rectangles that are similar. Explain your answer.

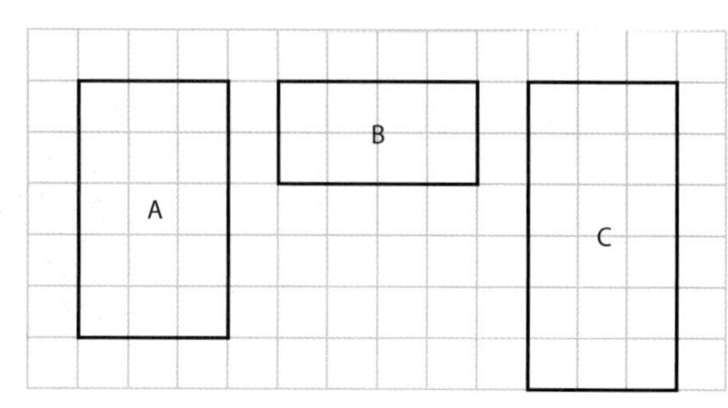

When correrspongding lengths are in the same ratio, if one side of the second shape is twice the corresponding side of the first shape, all sides of the second shape are twice the corresponding sides of the first shape.

B and C are similar because their angles are equal and their sides are proportional.
Length : width = 2 : 1 for both B and C.
A is not similar to B or C because the sides of A are not in the same proportion as the sides of B and C.

Compare the ratios of length to width.
For A, length : width = 5 : 3.
For B, length : width = 4 : 2 = 2 : 1.
For C, length : width = 6 : 3 = 2 : 1.

Length, area and volume

When two shapes A and B are similar and a is the scale factor that enlarges A to B.

length on B = a × (corresponding length on A)
area on B = a^2 × (corresponding area on A)
volume of B = a^3 × (volume of A)

The scale factor is 3:

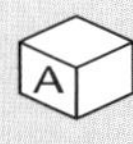

Perimeter of face B (12 cm) = 3 × perimeter of face A (4 cm).
Area of face B (9 cm^2) = 3^2 × area of face A (1 cm^2).
Volume of cube B (27 cm^3) = 3^3 × volume of cube A (1 cm^3).

Example 7

These two prisms are similar.

a Find the area of the cross-section of the smaller prism.

b The prisms are both made of the same material. The smaller prism weighs 30 g. Calculate the weight of the larger prism.

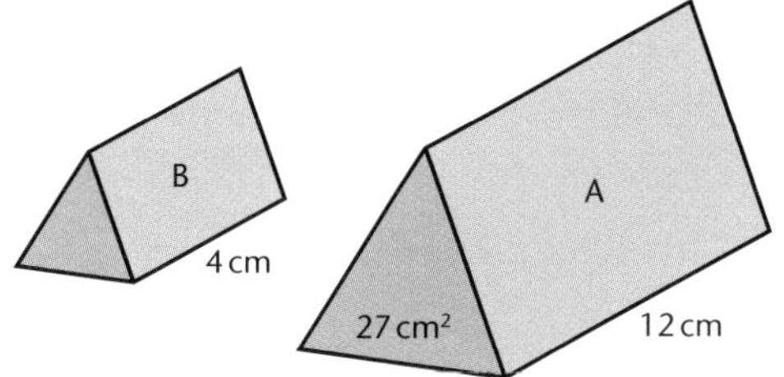

a The scale factor is 3.
Area of cross-section of smaller prism $= \frac{1}{9} \times 27\,cm^2$
$= 3\,cm^2$.

Length of A = 3 × length of B.
The prisms are similar so:
Area A = 3^2 × area B.
So 27 cm^2 = 9 × area of cross-section B.

b Weight of A $= 3^3 \times$ weight of B
$= 27 \times 30$ g
$= 810$ g.
The larger prism weighs 810 g.

Volume of A = 3^3 × volume of B.
The prisms are made of the same material so their weights are directly proportional to their volumes.

Example 8

Rectangles ABCD and ADEF are similar.
Calculate the length of AB.

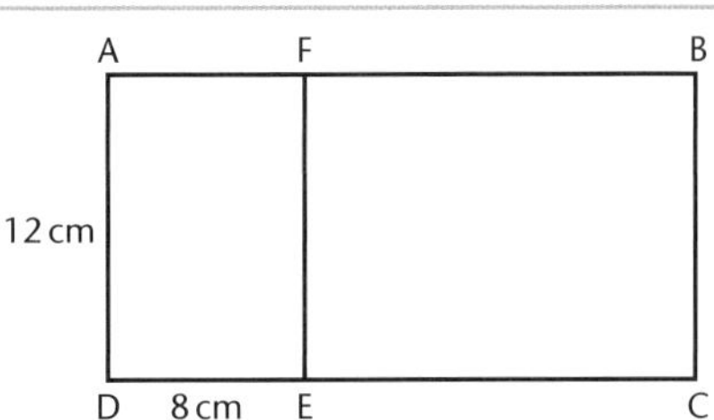

$\frac{AB}{12} = \frac{12}{8} = \frac{3}{2}$

$AB = \frac{3}{2} \times 12 = 18$

AB = 18 cm

The rectangles are similar so corresponding sides are in the same ratio.
Therefore, $\frac{\text{long side of ABCD}}{\text{long side of ADEF}} = \frac{\text{short side ABCD}}{\text{short side ADEF}}$

Exam practice 14E

1

Which two of these triangles are

a similar, but not congruent b congruent?

2 Write true or false for each statement.
Sketch an example to illustrate those that you think are false.

a All circles are similar.
b All rectangles are similar.
c All squares are similar.
d All equilateral triangles are similar.
e All right-angled triangles are similar.
f All regular hexagons are similar.
g All isosceles triangles are similar.

UAM

3 This diagram shows two rectangles.
Write true or false for each statement.

a A and B are congruent.
b A and B are similar.
c B is twice as long as A.
d The perimeter of B is four times the perimeter of A.
e The area of B is four times the area of A.

4 Triangles LMN and PQR are similar.

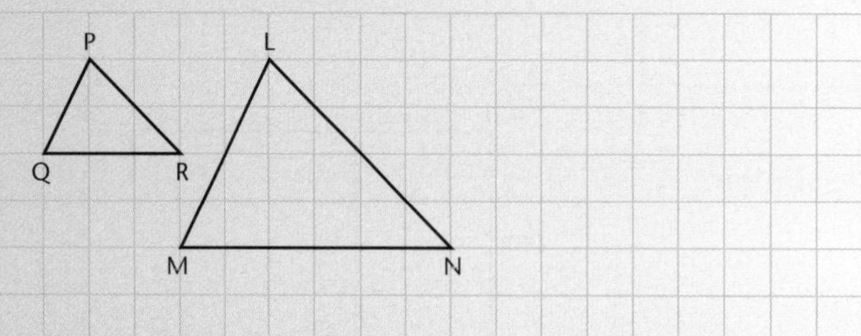

a Find the scale factor that enlarges triangle PQR to triangle LMN.
b The area of triangle PQR is $3\,\text{cm}^2$.
Work out the area of triangle LMN.

5 Parallelograms ABCD and WXYZ are similar.

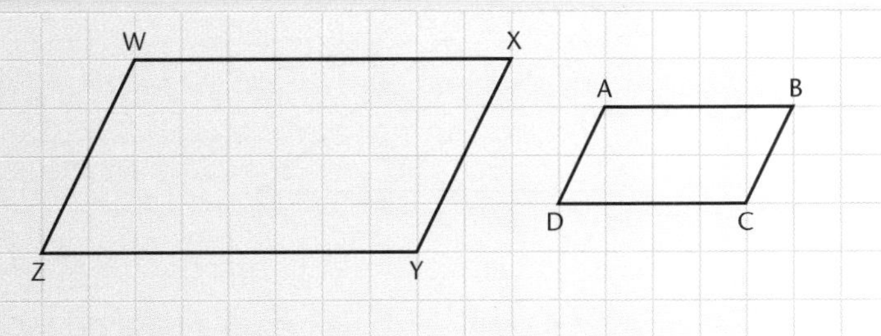

a Write down the scale factor that enlarges ABCD to WXYZ.

b Find the ratio:

i $\dfrac{\text{perimeter ABCD}}{\text{perimeter WXYZ}}$ ii $\dfrac{\text{area ABCD}}{\text{area WXYZ}}$

Be careful. Read the question carefully.

6 Solid B is an enlargement of solid A.

a Give the scale factor.

b The volume of A is 3 cm^3.
Work out the volume of B.

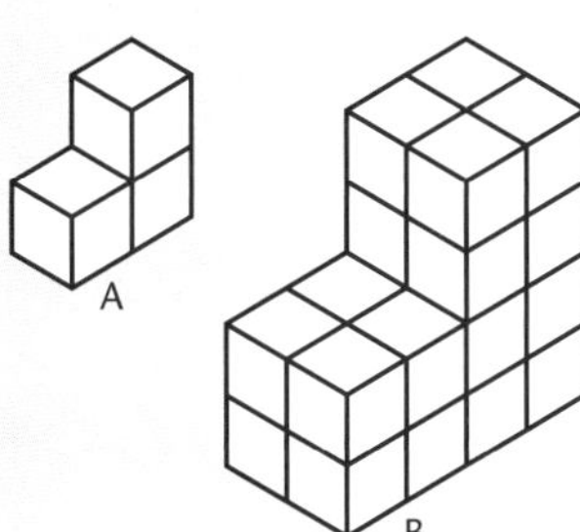

7 These two triangles are similar.
The area of the smaller triangle is 4.5 cm^2.
Calculate the area of the larger triangle.

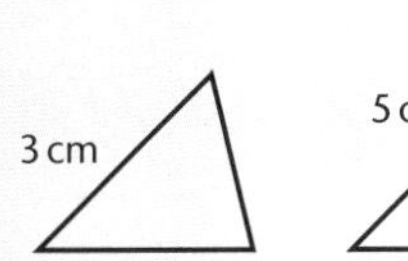

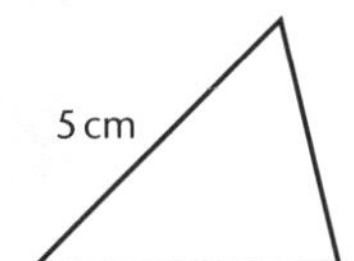

8 These two cans are similar.
The volume of the larger can is 36 cm^3.
Work out the volume of the smaller can.

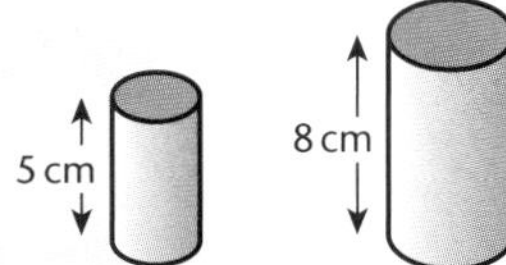

9 These two tanks are similar.
The smaller tank holds 800 litres.
What is the capacity of the larger tank?

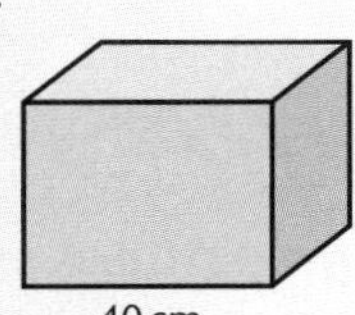

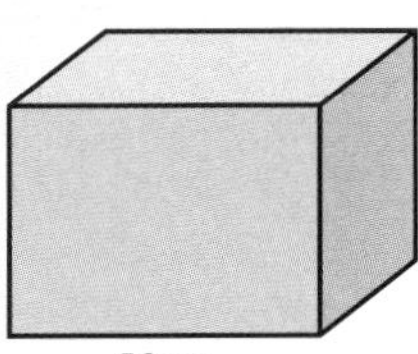

10 These two shapes are similar.
The height of the larger shape is 18 cm.
The area of the smaller shape is 36 cm^2 and the area of the larger shape is 81 cm^2.
Find the height of the smaller shape.

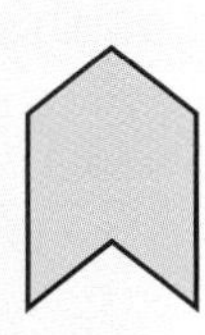

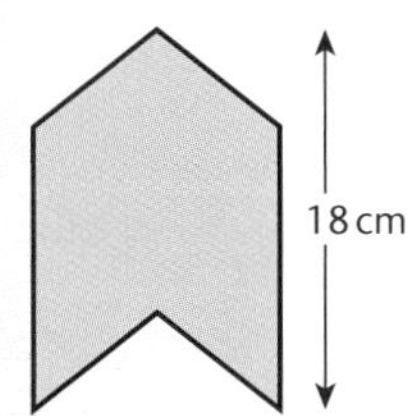

11 Triangles ABC and ADE are similar.
BC = 25 cm, AD = 12 cm and DB = 6 cm.

a Find the length of DE.
b Explain why DE is parallel to BC.

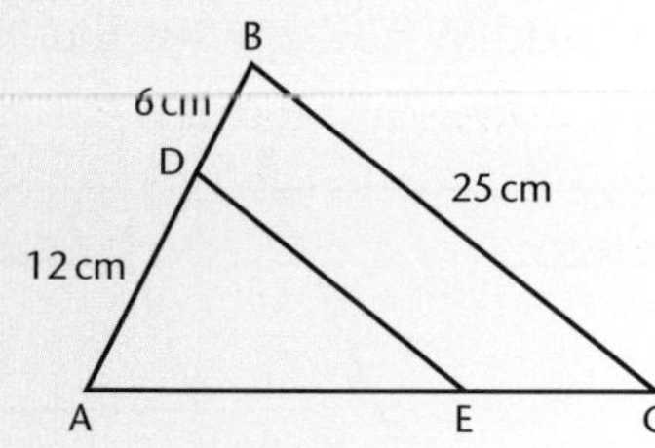

12 Triangles ABC and BDC are similar.
BC = 20 cm and DC = 16 cm.

a Find the length of AD.
b Which angle in triangle ABC is equal to angle BDC?

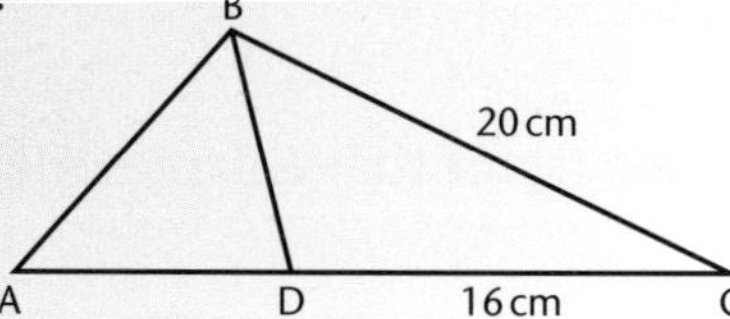

Call the length AD x cm. Write an equation in x and solve it.

13 Parallelograms ABCD and BCFE are similar.
EB = 4 cm and EF = 6 cm.
Calculate the length of AE.

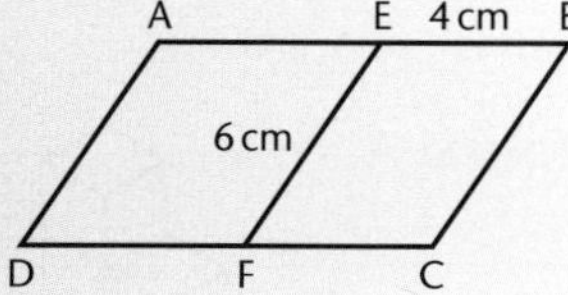

14 In this diagram, DE is parallel to BC.
AD = 6 cm and DB = 2 cm.

a Explain why triangles ABC and ADE are similar.
b Describe the transformation that maps triangle ADE to triangle ABC.

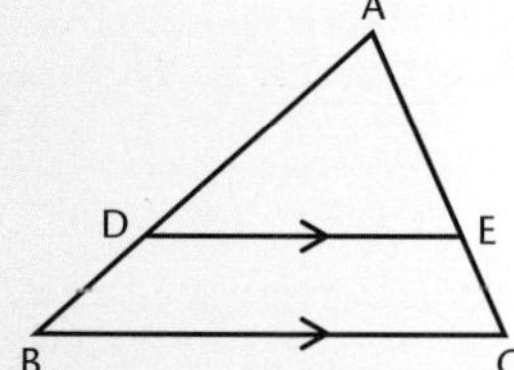

15 Rectangles ABCD and ADEF are similar.
AD = 8 cm and DE = 6 cm.
Calculate the area of rectangle BCEF.

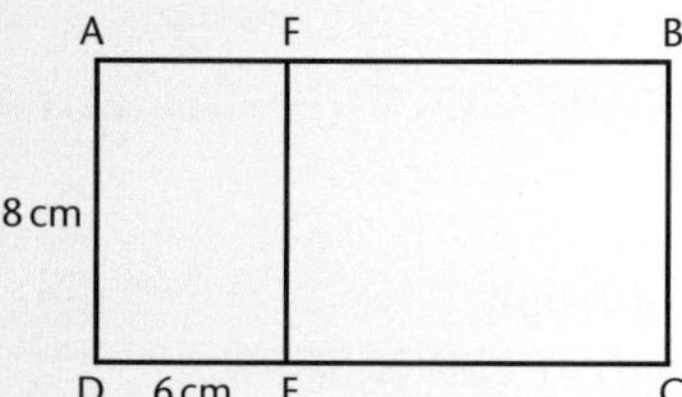

14.6 Scale drawings

A **scale drawing** is a drawing with the same proportions as the real thing but with a different size.
A scale drawing of a shape is similar to the real shape.

A scale drawing is an enlargement usually by a fractional scale factor.

A scale is given. This tells you what a length on the drawing represents on the real shape.

A scale where 1 cm represents 4 m is equivalent to a scale factor of $\frac{1}{400}$.

Example 9

This is a scale drawing of a house and garden.
It is drawn on a 1 cm grid.
Find the width of the garden.

Scale: 1 cm represents 8m.

Garden

House

The garden is 2 cm wide on the drawing.

The width of the garden is 2×8 m

$= 16$ m.

The scale tells you that 1 cm on the drawing is 8 m on the ground.
So 2 cm on the drawing is 2×8 m on the ground.

A map is a scale drawing.
The scale may be given the same way as a scale drawing or it may be given as a ratio.

A **map ratio** tells you the ratio of distances on the map to distances on the ground.

Example 10

A road on this map is 5 cm long.
How long is the road on the ground?

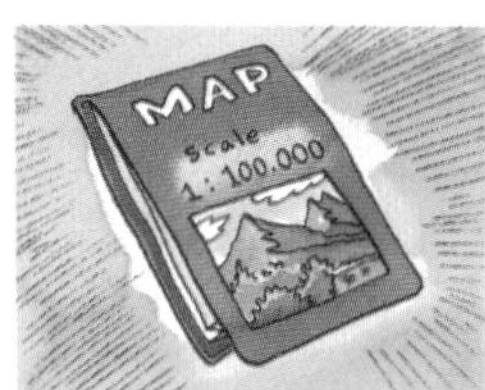

The road on the ground is $5 \times 100\,000$ cm long.

$5 \times 100\,000$ cm $= 500\,000$ cm

$= 5000$ m

$= 5$ km

So the road is 5 km long.

The scale on the map is 1 : 100 000.
This is the map ratio.
It means that a line on the map shows a line on the ground that is 100 000 times longer.

Exam practice 14F

1 Greg draws the floor plan of his kitchen on a 1 cm grid.

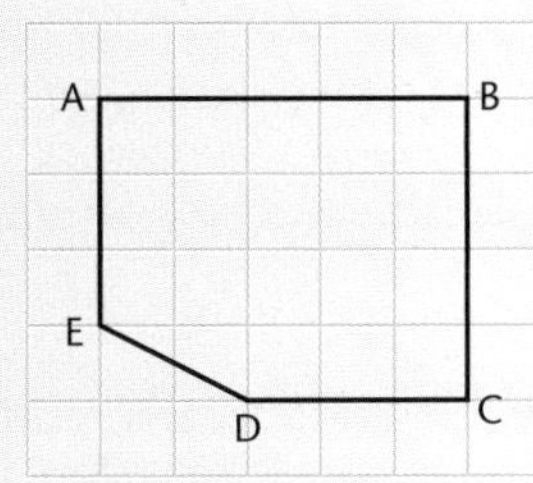

Scale: 1 cm represents 50 cm

a How long is the kitchen floor from A to B?
b Work out the floor area of Greg's kitchen.

2 This is a scale drawing of a village.

Scale: 1 cm represents 500 m

B
Church
Village Hall
Shop
A

a Measure the line AB.
b AB shows the road through the village.
How long is the road between A and B?
c Sally walks from the church to the shop.
How far does she walk?

3 This is part of a street map.
David walks from one end of Berry Road to the other.
How far does he walk?
Give your answer in metres.

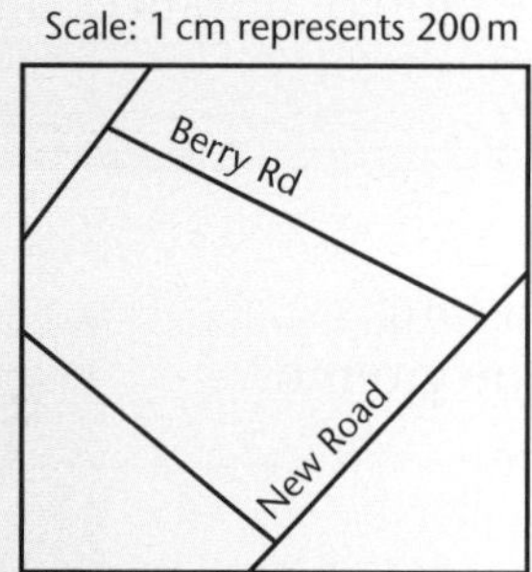

4 The map ratio of a map is 1 : 10 000.
The distance between two towns on the map is 25 cm.
How far apart are they? Give your answer in kilometres.

5 This is the floor plan of a flat.

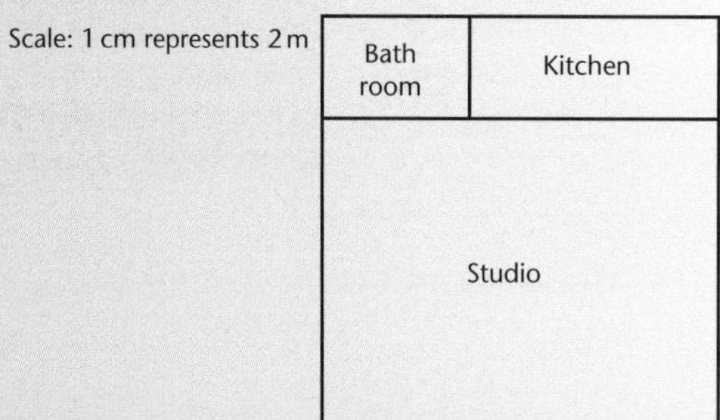

a Work out the width and length of the actual studio.
b Find the area of the actual kitchen.

6 Giles drew this sketch of a plot of land.
a A scale drawing is made using a scale of 1 cm to represent 1 m.
What is the length of AB on the scale drawing?
b Draw another sketch showing the measurements you need to use to make a scale drawing.
c Construct an accurate scale drawing of the plot.

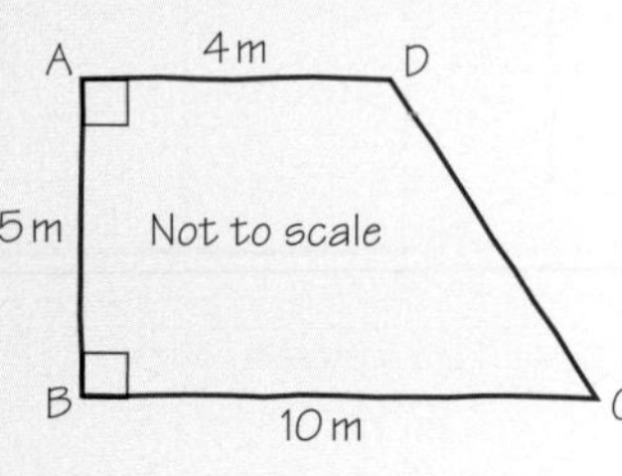

A sketch is not accurate. You cannot use a sketch to measure lengths or angles.

7 This sketch shows the cross-section of a roof.

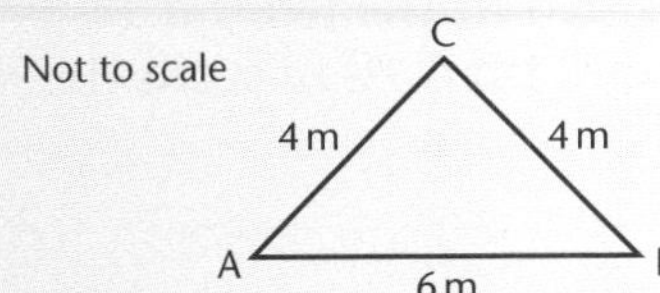

a Draw another sketch showing the measurements you need to use to make a scale drawing with a scale of 1 cm to represent 0.5 m.
b Construct an accurate scale drawing.
c What is the mathematical name for the shape of the cross-section?

8 This diagram shows a metal part in a sprayer with its real measurements.
It is a square with a circular hole in the centre.
Use a scale of 1 cm to represent 0.5 mm to make a scale drawing of this part.

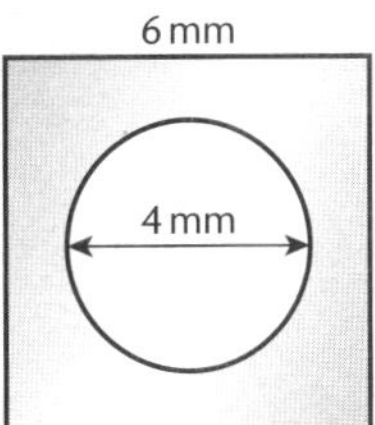

14.7 Loci

A **locus** (plural **loci**) is all the points that obey a rule.
A locus can be a straight line, a curve or an area.

Example 11

The seats on a roundabout are 3 metres from the centre, C.

a Draw the path that a seat follows as the roundabout turns.
b What is the mathematical name for the path that the seat follows?

a Scale: 1 cm represents 2 metres.

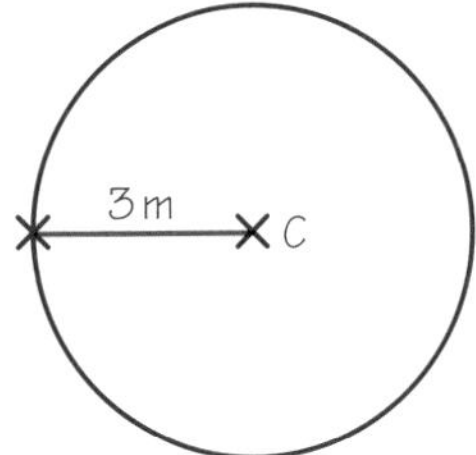

The seat must always be exactly 3 m from C. This means that the path it follows is a circle with radius 3 m.

The radius on the scale drawing is 1.5 cm.

b The path that the seat follows is a circle.

Example 12

T is a tree in a field ABCD. A cable has to be buried in the field. It must be more then 7.5 m from the tree and more than 10 m from the trees on the edge AB.
Shade the area where the cable can be buried.

Scale: 1 cm represents 5 m

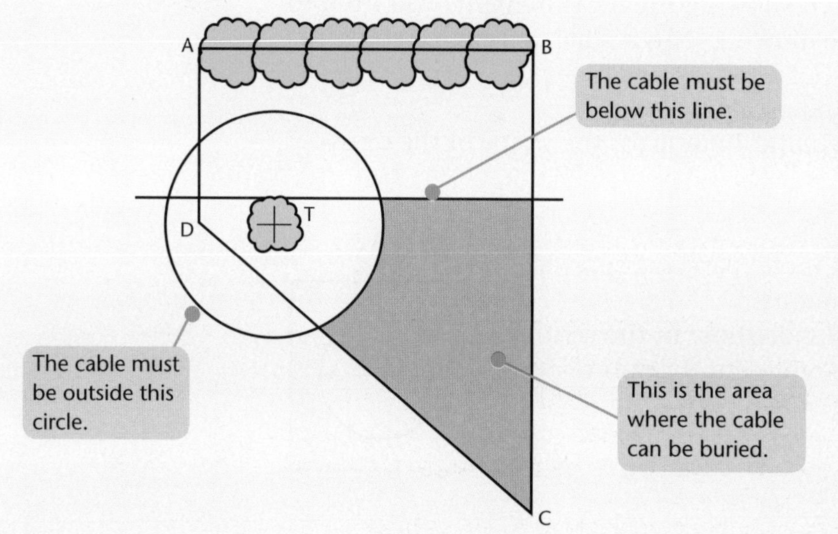

The points that are 7.5 m from T are on a circle, centre T, radius 7.5 m. Using the scale given, you need to draw a circle with radius 1.5 cm.

The points that are 10 m from AB are on a line parallel to AB at a distance of 10 m from AB. On the drawing, the line is 2 cm from AB.

Exam practice 14G

1 The diagram shows a goat tethered to a pole. The tether is 2 metres long.

On a copy of the diagram, shade the area that the goat can reach.

Scale: 1 cm represents 0.5 m

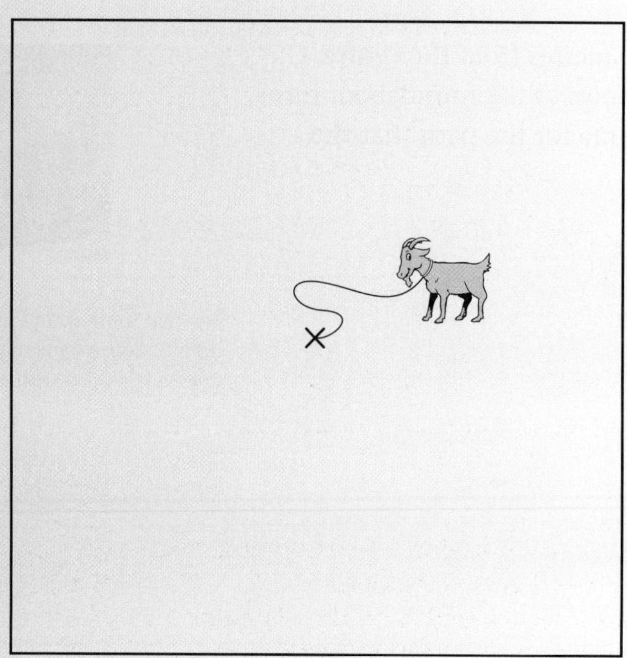

www

2 This diagram shows two towns, R and S.

a Find the actual distance between R and S.

b A road is to be built so that it is always equal distances from R and S.
Draw the path of the road on a copy of the diagram.

All the points on the perpendicular bisector of a line segment are the same distance from each end of the line segment.

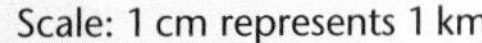

c The local council wants to build an estate.
This estate must be more than 3 km from S and less than 1 km from both sides of the new road.
Shade the area where they can build the new estate.

3 This is a scale drawing of the front garden of Kieran's house.
She wants to plant a tree.
The tree must be more than 3 m from the front of the house and it must be more than 1 metre from the path.
On a copy of the diagram shade the area where Kieran can plant the tree.

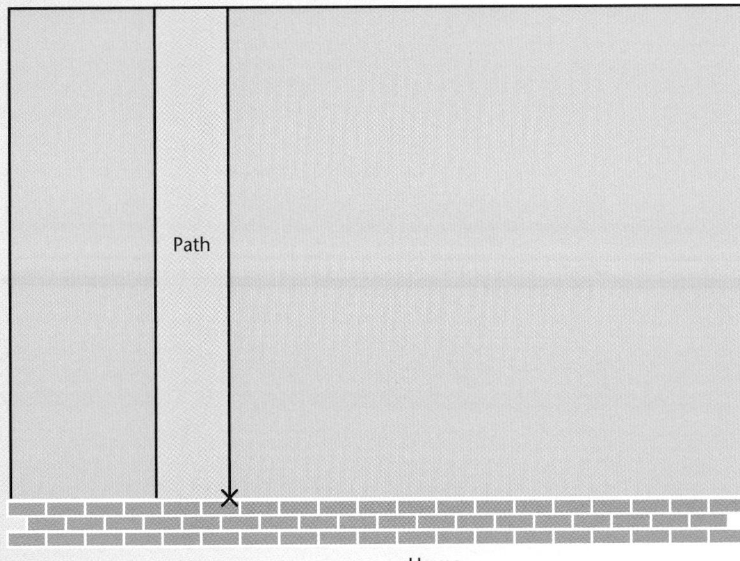

4 Use another copy of the diagram for question 3 for this question.
Kieran buys a lawn mower. It has a cable 6 m long.
He can plug the cable into a socket marked X on the diagram.
Shade the area that Kieran cannot reach with this lawn mower.

5 The diagram shows a circular flower bed and a single garden fence panel. Alec is sitting at a point A behind the fence. Beth is walking about on the other side of the fence in such a way that Alec cannot see her. Beth is also not allowed to walk on the flower bed.
Shade the locus of the point representing Beth.

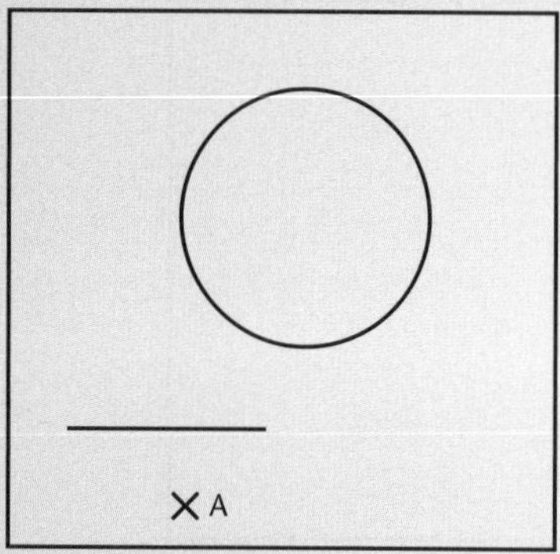

6 One end of a chain, 2 metres long, is attached to the collar of a guard dog. At the other end is a ring which can slide on a fixed wire 5 metres long. Assuming that the dog's collar is always the same distance above the ground, sketch the locus of the point of attachment on the collar.

Summary of key points

- You can simplify a ratio by leaving out the units (as long as both parts have the same units) and by dividing both parts by the same number.
- An enlargement with a scale factor greater than 1 makes a shape larger and an enlargement with a scale factor less than 1 makes a shape smaller.
- An enlargement with a negative scale factor rotates the shape by 180° about the centre of enlargement as well as changing its size.
- The relationships between length, area and volume of an enlargement and the original are:

$$\frac{\text{a length on the enlargement}}{\text{corresponding length on original}} = \text{scale factor},$$

$$\frac{\text{area of enlargement}}{\text{area of original}} = (\text{scale factor})^2,$$

$$\frac{\text{volume of enlargement}}{\text{volume of original}} = (\text{scale factor})^3$$

- To describe a transformation fully you must give:
  - the mathematical name
  - the mirror line for a reflection
  - the centre, direction and angle of rotation for a rotation
  - the vector for a translation
  - the centre of enlargement and the scale factor for an enlargement.
- Similar shapes have their corresponding angles equal and the lengths of their corresponding sides in the same ratio.

Most candidates who get GRADE C or above can:

- enlarge a shape by any positive scale factor from a given centre of enlargement
- describe a transformation fully.

Most candidates who get GRADE A or above can also:

- use the relationships between lengths, areas and volumes of similar objects.

Glossary

Centre of enlargement	the point from where lines drawn between corresponding vertices of the original shape and the enlarged shape meet
Corresponding	in the same position in each shape
Enlargement	a transformation that makes a shape larger or smaller
Locus (plural loci)	all the points that obey a rule
Map ratio	the scale of a map given as a ratio
Proportional	quantities that are in the same ratio
Ratio	a way of comparing quantities
Scale drawing	a different-sized drawing in the correct proportions
Scale factor	the number that tells you how much to enlarge a shape
Similar	two shapes are similar when one is an enlargement of the other
Vertex (plural vertices)	the corner of a shape

15 Circle geometry

This chapter will show you:
- ✓ the names of different parts of a circle
- ✓ the relationship between the angle subtended by an arc at the centre of a circle and an angle subtended by the same arc at a point on the circumference
- ✓ the relationship between different angles subtended by the same arc at the circumference
- ✓ what a cyclic quadrilateral is and its properties
- ✓ the size of an angle in a semicircle
- ✓ the properties of tangents to a circle
- ✓ what the alternate segment theorem is

Before you start you need to know:
- ✓ what acute, obtuse and reflex angles are
- ✓ what corresponding angles, alternate angles and vertically opposite angles are
- ✓ the angle sum of a triangle and the angle sum of a quadrilateral
- ✓ the properties of isosceles and equilateral triangles
- ✓ the properties of special quadrilaterals
- ✓ the meaning of an arc, radius and diameter of a circle
- ✓ how to use Pythagoras' theorem

15.1 The perpendicular bisector of a chord

A straight line joining two points on a circle is a **chord**.
A chord divides the region inside a circle into two parts.
The larger part is a **major segment** and the smaller part is a **minor segment**.

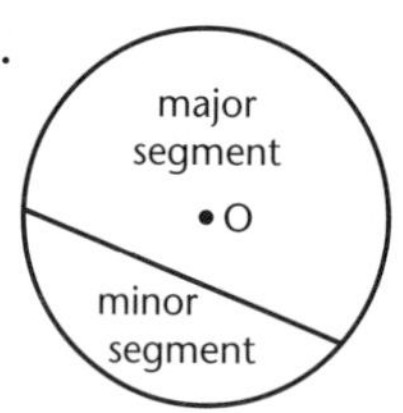

In the diagram the radius OC is perpendicular to the chord AB.

M is the foot of the perpendicular from O to AB.

Triangles OAM and OBM are congruent, because ∠OMA = ∠OMB = 90°, OA = OB (radii), and OM is common to both triangles.

So AM = MB.

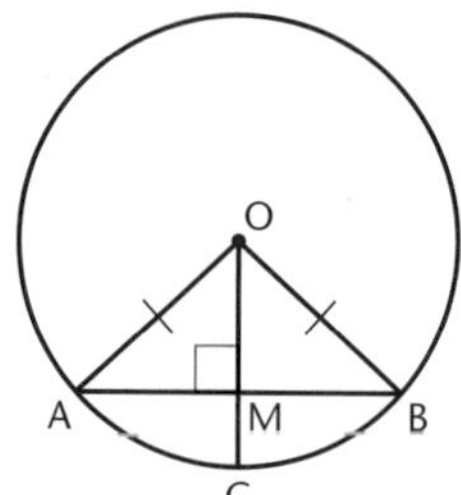

△OAM and △OBM are congruent by the RHS property.

> **The perpendicular from the centre of a circle to a chord bisects the chord.**

Conversely:

> **the radius that passes through the midpoint of a chord is perpendicular to the chord.**

Conversely means reasoning the opposite way round.
Can you prove the converse?
Be careful, do not assume the answer.

Example 1

In this diagram, O is the centre of a circle of radius 5 cm.
OM is perpendicular to AB and ON is perpendicular to CD.

a AB = 7 cm.
How far is AB from the centre of the circle?

b ON = 2 cm. Work out the length of CD.

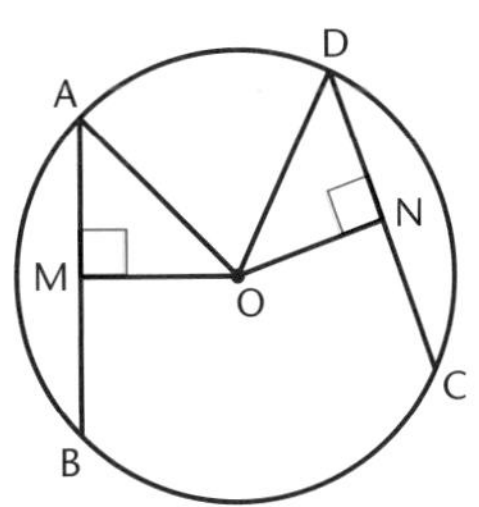

a AB = 7 cm so AM = 3.5 cm.

Then $AO^2 = AM^2 + OM^2$

$25 = 12.25 + OM^2$

$OM^2 = 12.75$

$OM = \sqrt{12.75} = 3.570\ldots$

OM = 3.57 cm to 3 s.f.

Perpendicular from centre to a chord bisects the chord.

AO = 5 cm as it is a radius. △AOM has a right angle at M so you can use Pythagoras' theorem.

b In △ODN $OD^2 = ON^2 + DN^2$

$DN^2 = 25 - 4$

$DN^2 = 21$

$DN = \sqrt{21} = 4.582\ldots$

DN = 4.582… cm

As N is the midpoint of CD, CD = 2DN = 9.17 cm to 3 s.f.

OD = 5 cm as it is a radius. △ODN is right angled so you can use Pythagoras' theorem.

Exam practice 15A

In this exercise O is used to mark the centre of the circle.

You need Pythagoras' theorem for these questions.

1 AO = 10 cm and AB = 16 cm.
How far is the chord from the centre of the circle?

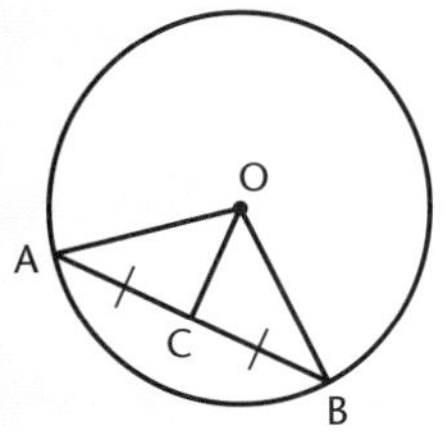

2 AO = 13 cm.
The chord AB is 5 cm from the centre of the circle.
Calculate the length of the chord.

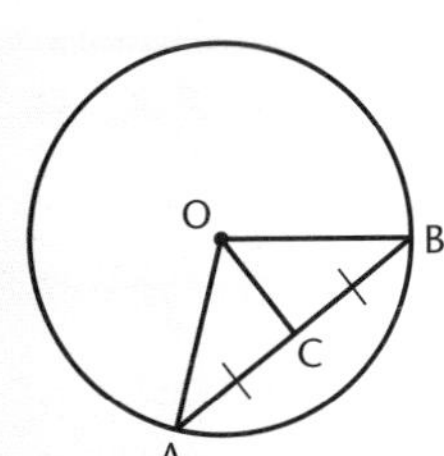

3 OR is perpendicular to the chord PQ.
The radius of the circle is 8 cm and the chord is 4.8 cm from the centre of the circle.
How long is the chord?

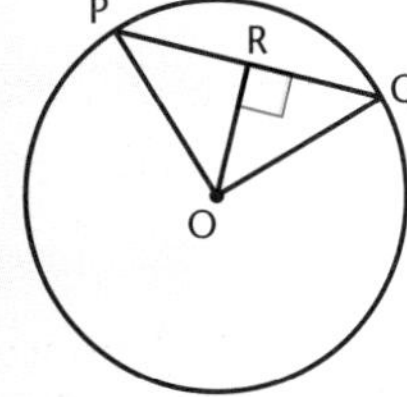

4 AB = 14.4 cm and ON = 9.6 cm.
What is the radius of the circle?

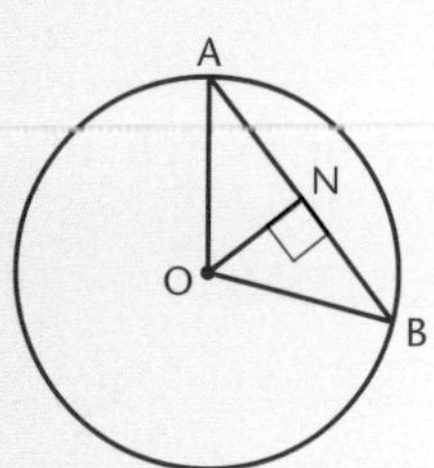

5 AB and CD are two chords in a circle of radius 8 cm.
AB = 7.5 cm and CD = 6.8 cm.
Which chord is nearer the centre of the circle?
Give a reason for your answer.

15.2 Angles in circles

Angle C is **subtended** by the chord (or arc) AB.
This means that angle C is opposite AB and the arms of angle C go to the ends of AB.

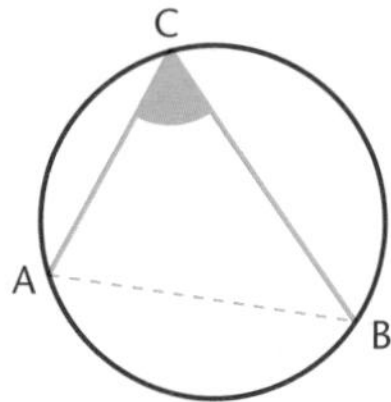

Class discussion

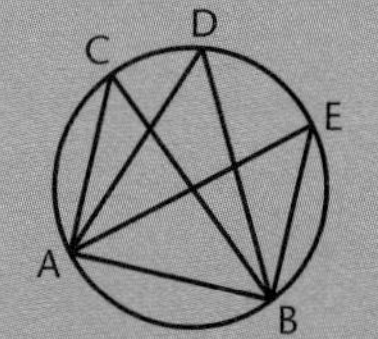

1 What other angles does the arc AB subtend at the circumference?
2 What other arcs subtend angles at the circumference? Name as many as you can.
3 Name chords that subtend angles at the circumference.

Angle at centre theorem

The angle subtended at the centre of a circle by an arc is twice the angle subtended at the circumference by the same arc.

In the diagram $\angle AOB = 2\angle ACB$.

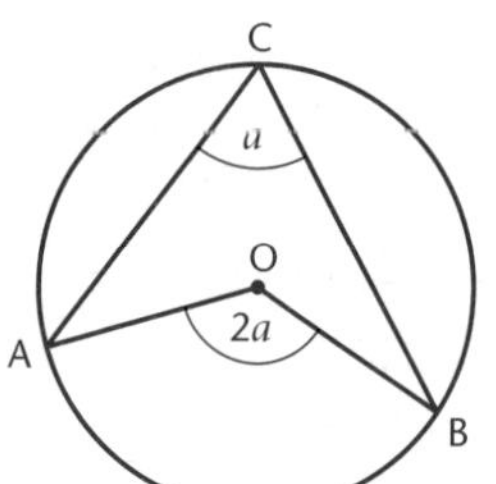

Proof

Join CO and extend it to N.

$\triangle$ ACO is isosceles because OC = OA (Both radii.)
so $\angle ACO = \angle CAO = x$.

$\triangle$OCB is also isosceles
so $\angle BCO = \angle CBO = y$.

Then $\angle AON = 2x$
and $\angle BON = 2y$.

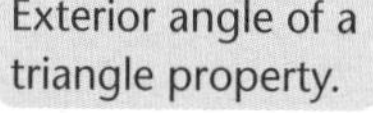
Exterior angle of a triangle property.

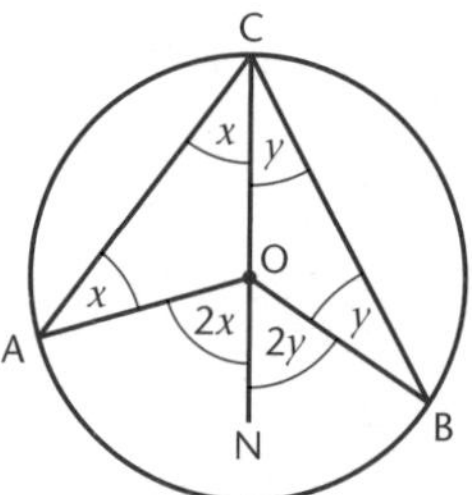

So $\angle AOB = 2x + 2y = 2(x + y) = 2\angle ACB$.

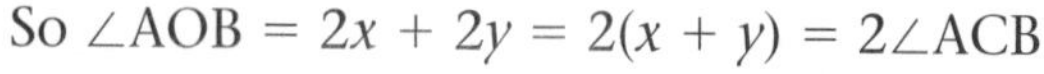
You can use this first result to prove the other results in this chapter.

Any angle in a semicircle is a right angle.

An angle in a semicircle is an angle subtended by a diameter.

Proof

$\angle AOB = 2\angle ACB$ (using the result above)
AOB is a straight line so $\angle AOB = 180°$
so $\angle ACB = \frac{1}{2}\angle AOB = \frac{1}{2} \times 180° = 90°$.

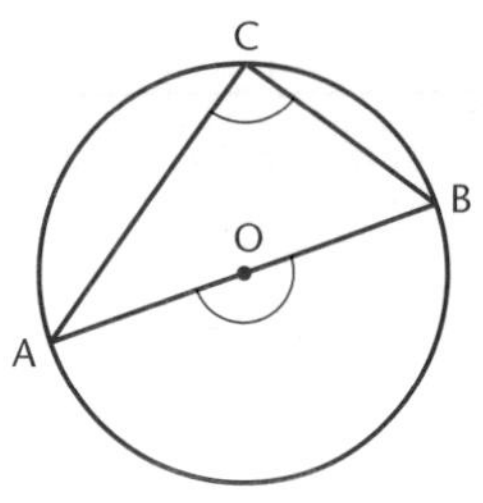

Example 2

AOB is a diameter and ∠AOC = 76°.
Find
a ∠ABC **b** ∠ACB.
Give a reason for each step of your working.

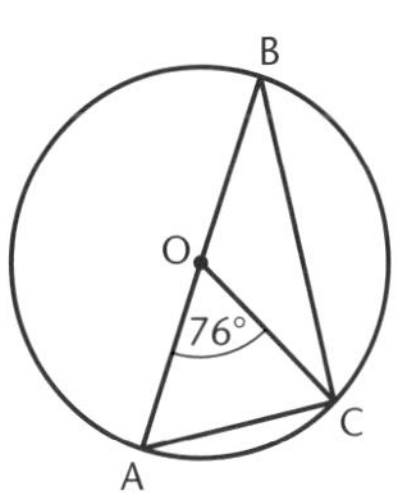

a ∠AOC = 2∠ABC

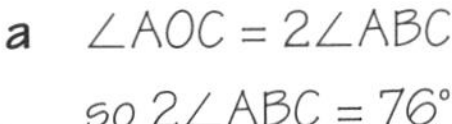

so 2∠ABC = 76°

because the angle at the centre is twice the angle at the circumference.

∠ABC = 38°

These angles are both subtended by the chord AC.

b ∠ACB = 90°

The angle in a semicircle is 90°.

Exam practice 15B

In this exercise, O is used to mark the centre of the circle.

1 a Which chord subtends
i ∠ACD ii ∠BAC?
b Name an angle subtended at the circumference by i AD ii AC.
c The chord BD divides the circle into two segments.
Name a point that lies
i in the major segment ii in the minor segment.
d Which arc subtends i ∠BAC ii ∠ADB?
e Name two angles that are subtended by the arc BC.

2 Write down the value of x.

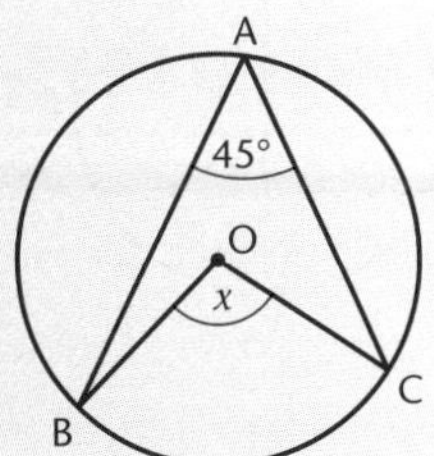

3 Write down the value of x.

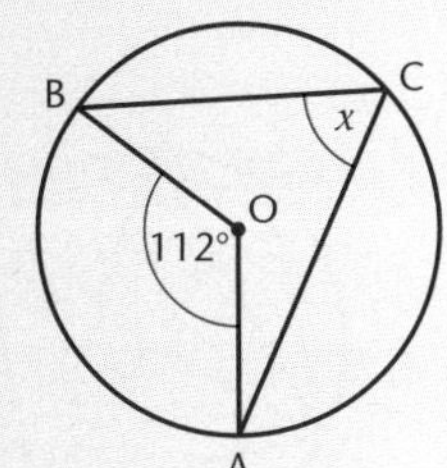

4 Write down the values of the angles marked with letters.
Give reasons for each step of your working.

a b 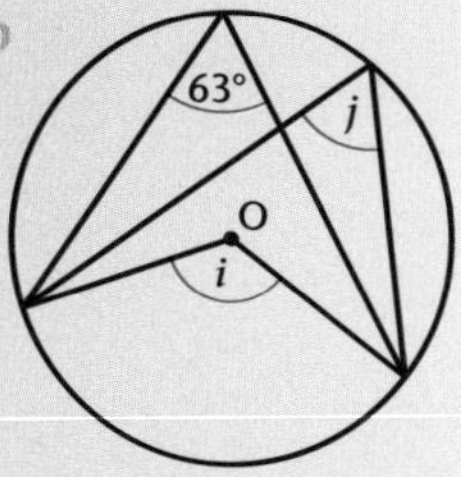 c

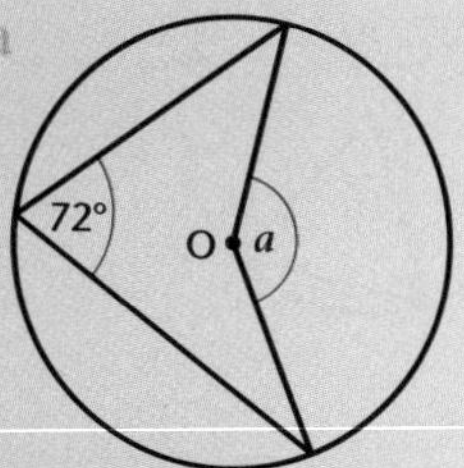

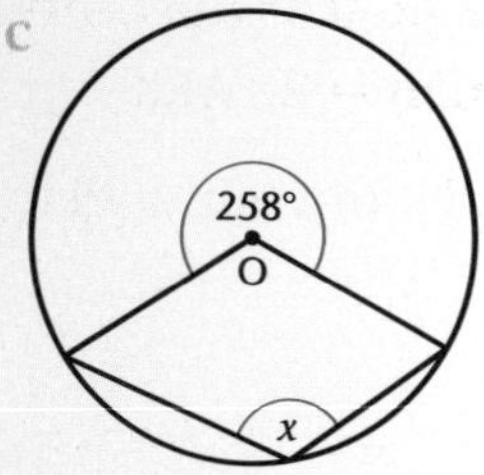

d e f

g h i

j k l

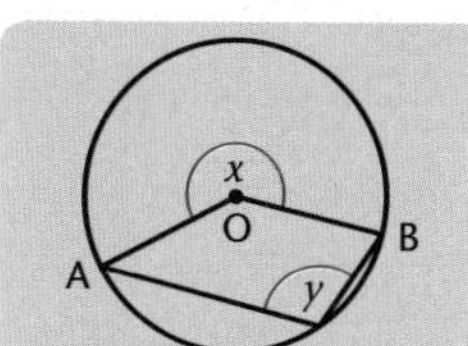

Angles x and y are both subtended by the major arc AB.

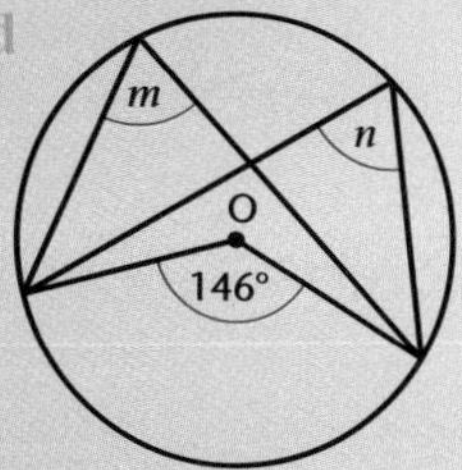

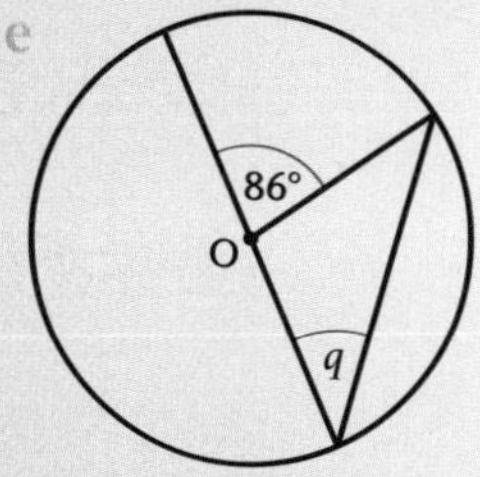

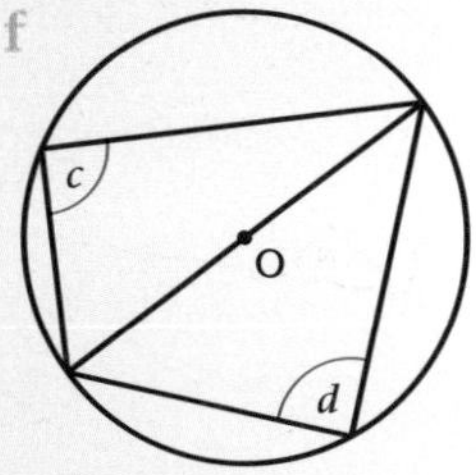

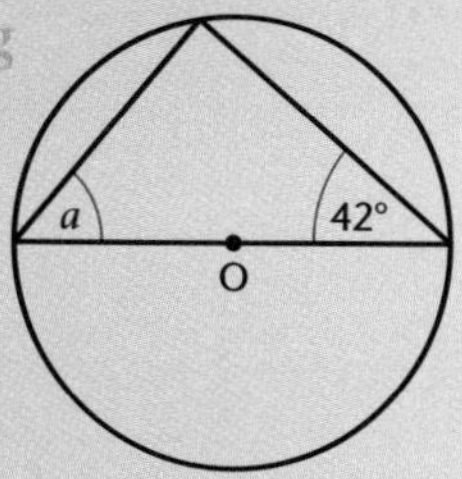

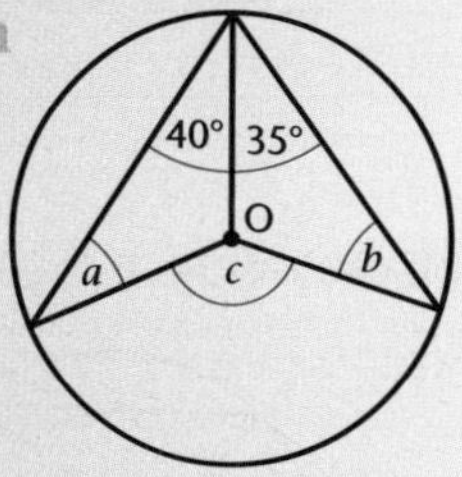

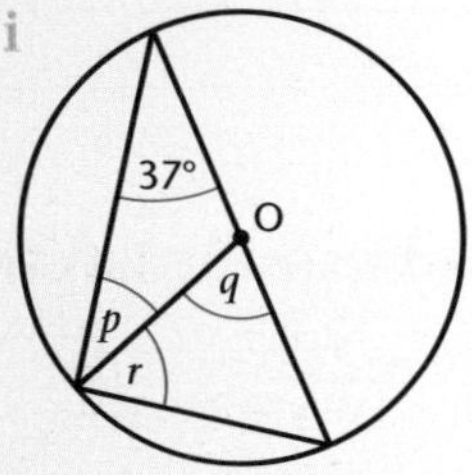

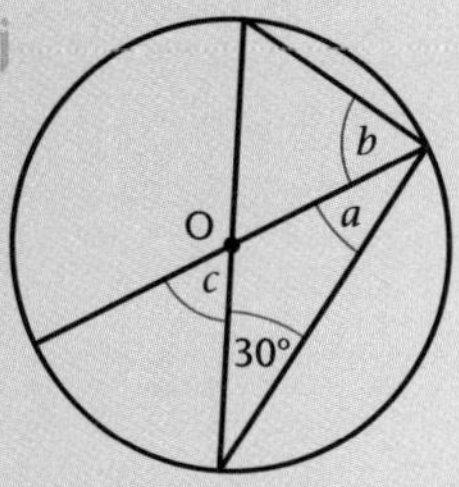

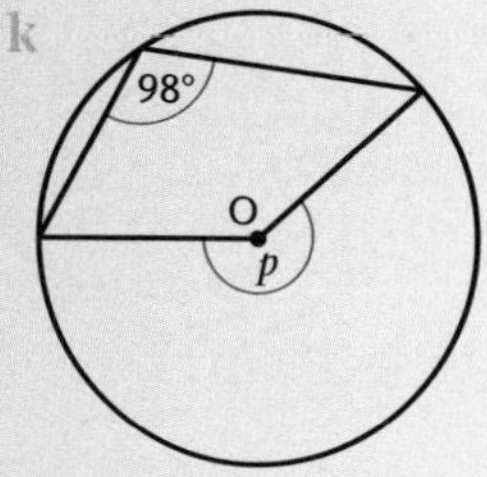

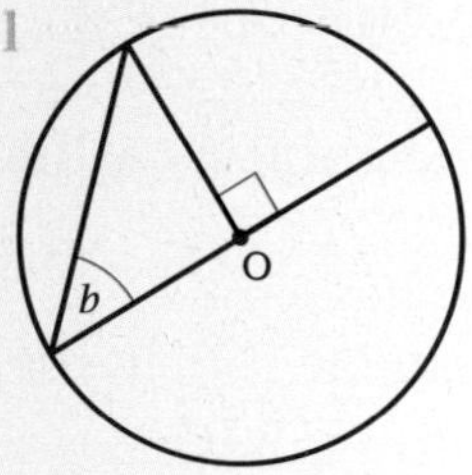

5 In this diagram, O is the centre of the circle and AB = BC.
Find the value of
a x b y.

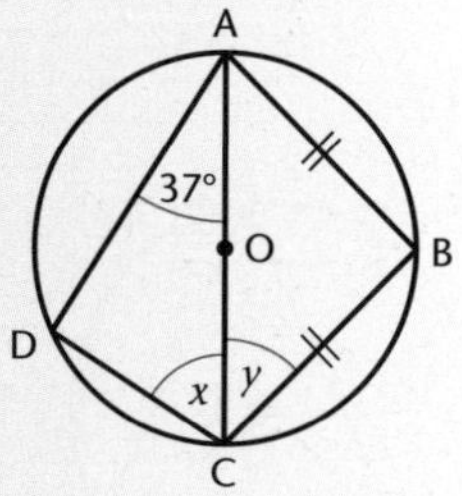

15.3 Angles in the same segment

The chord AB divides this circle into two segments.
Angles ACB, ADB and AEB are all subtended by this chord.
They are angles in the same segment.

Angles in the same segment of a circle are equal

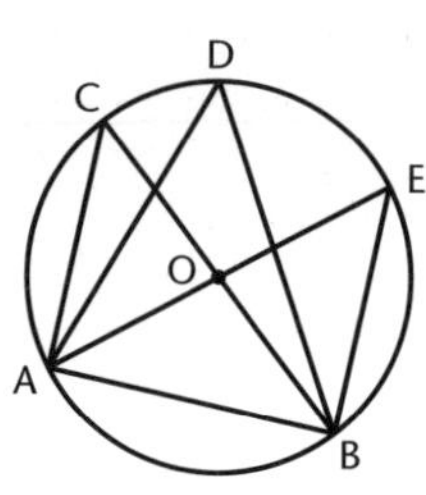

Proof

AB subtends angles ACB, ADB and AEB at the circumference and angle AOB at the centre so

$\angle AOB = 2\angle ACB = 2\angle ADB = 2\angle AEB$

so $\angle ACB = \angle ADB = \angle AEB$.

The theorem is also true for angles in the minor segment AB i.e. $\angle AEB = \angle AFB$.

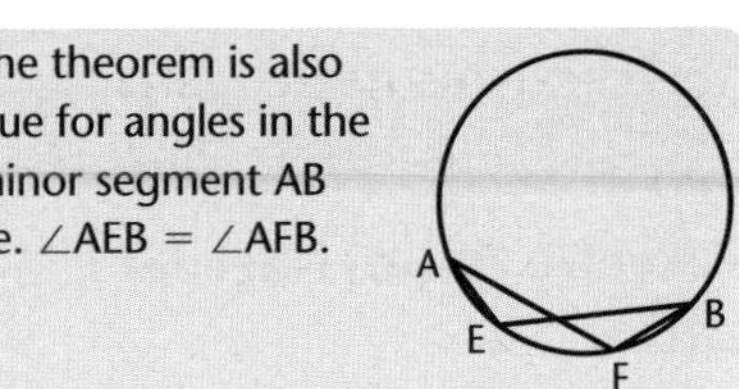

Example 3

Find the value of:

a x **b** y **c** z

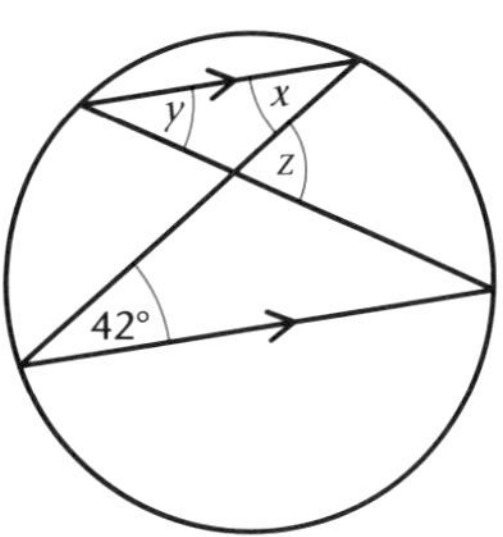

a $x = 42°$ — Alternate angles, parallel lines.

b $y = 42°$ — Angles in the same segment.

c $z = x + y$
$= 84°$ — Exterior angle of a triangle = sum of two interior opposite angles.

Exam practice 15C

In questions 1 to 9 write down the values of the angles marked with letters.

1

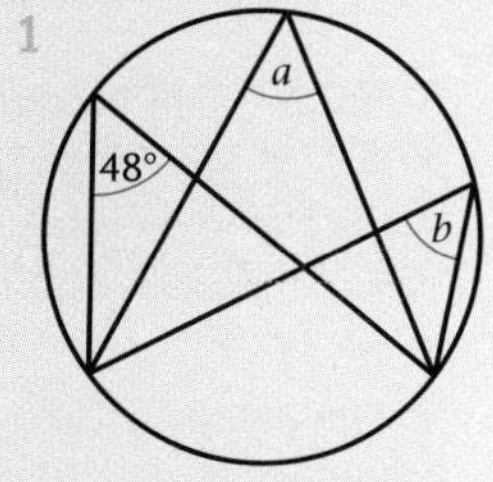

2

3

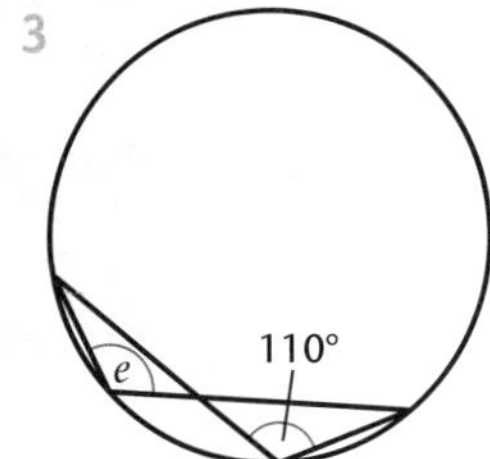

4

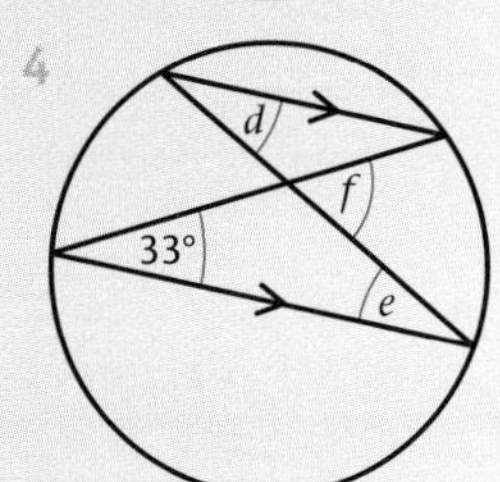

5

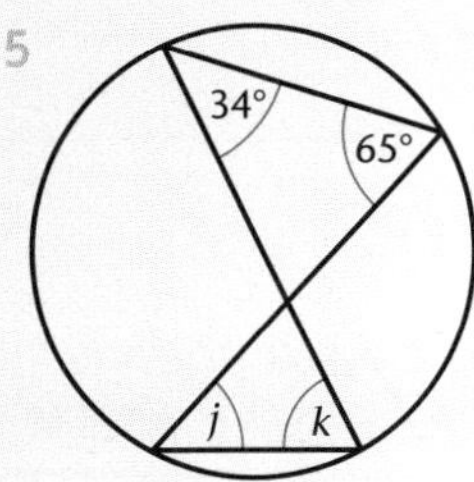

6

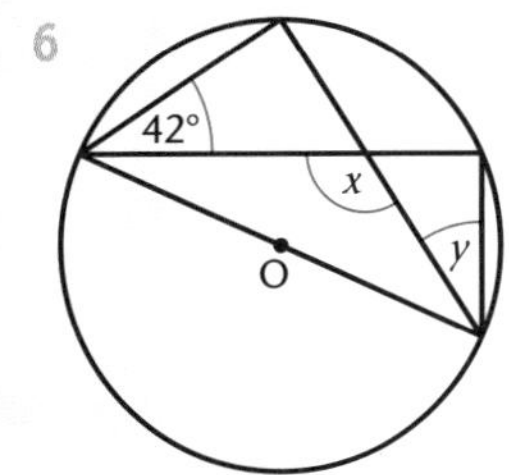

7

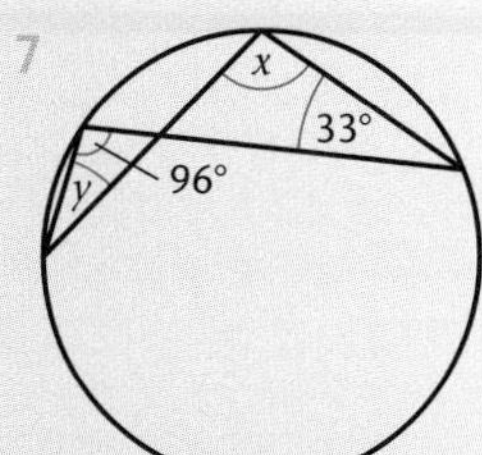

8

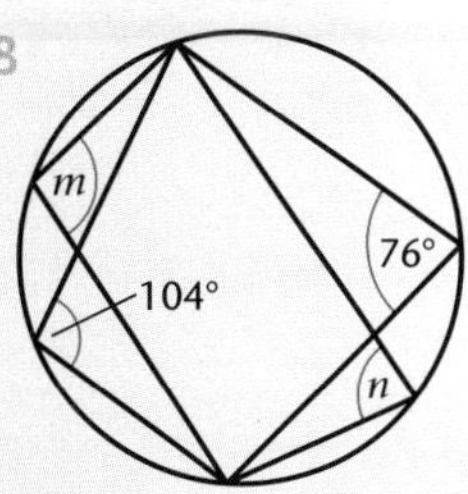

9

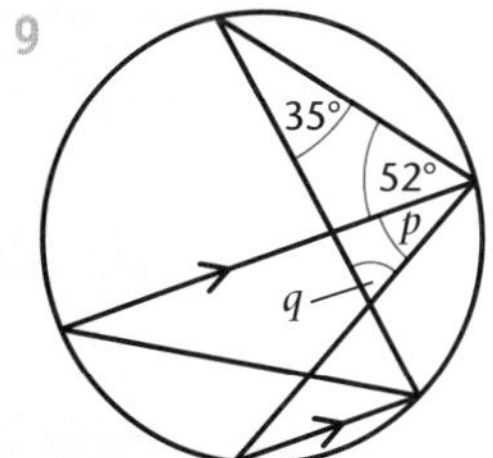

10 AC and BD are perpendicular and $\angle ACD = 62°$.
Calculate the value of p.
Give reasons for your answer.

UAM

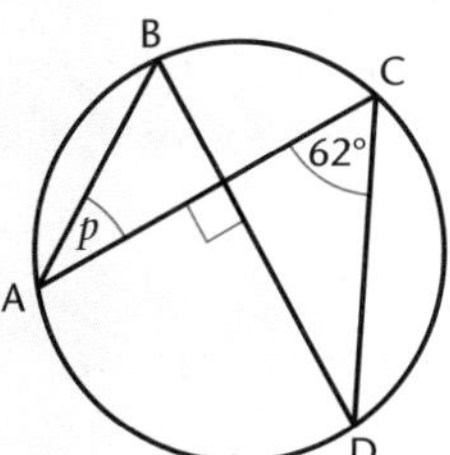

15.4 Cyclic quadrilaterals

A **cyclic quadrilateral** is a quadrilateral whose vertices lie on a circle.

> 'Supplementary' means that they add up to 180°.

The opposite angles of a cyclic quadrilateral are supplementary

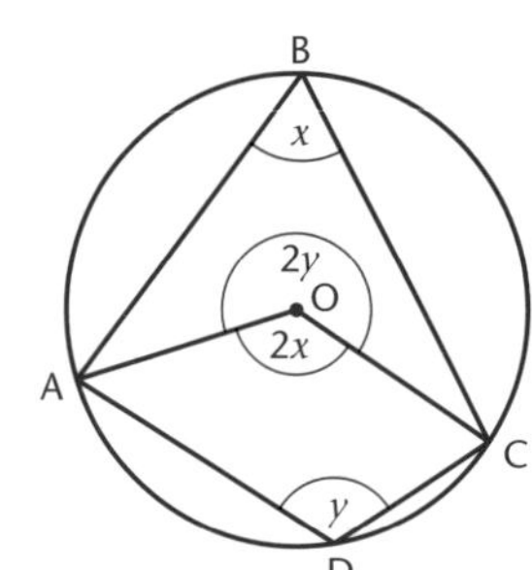

In the diagram, smaller angle AOC is $2x$ so $\angle ABC = x$.

> This uses the angle at the centre of a circle result.

Similarly, larger angle AOC is $2y$ so $\angle ADC = y$.

But the two angles at O make a full turn so $2x + 2y = 360°$
$x + y = 180°$.

> There are two angles at O. The smaller one is obtuse; the larger one reflex.

It follows that:

an exterior angle of a cyclic quadrilateral is equal to the opposite interior angle.

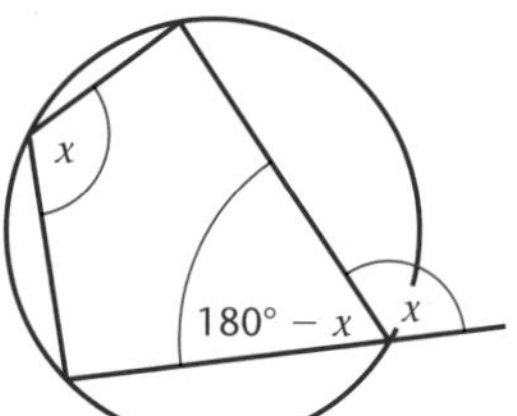

> The opposite angles of a cyclic quadrilateral add to 180° and angles on a straight line add up to 180°.

Example 4

Find the angles marked by letters.

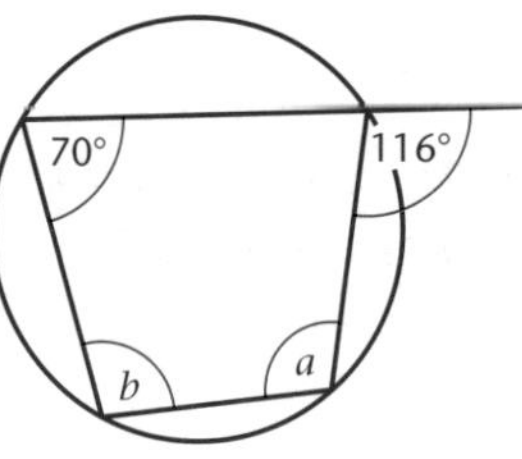

$a + 70° = 180°$
$a = 180° - 70°$
$a = 110°$
$b = 116°$

> a and 70° are opposite angles of a cyclic quadrilateral so they are supplementary.

> Exterior angle (116°) = opposite interior angle (b).

Exam practice 15D

In this exercise O is used to mark the centre of the circle.
Find the angles marked with letters.

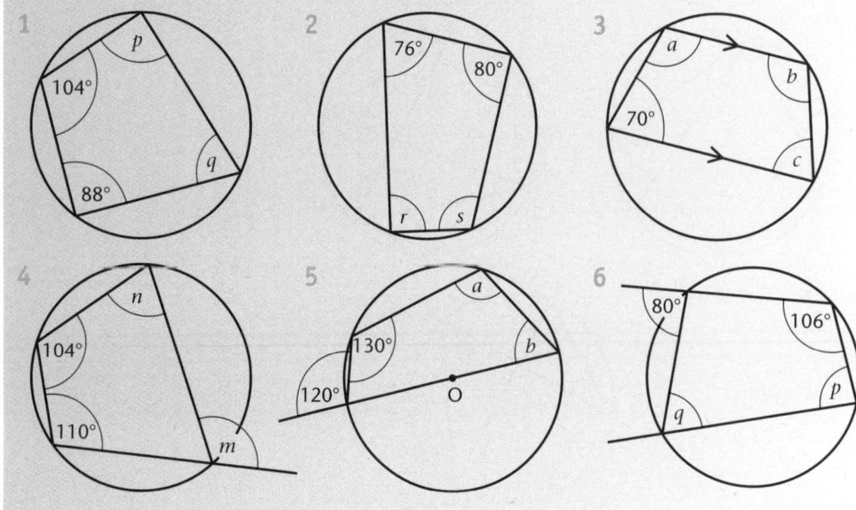

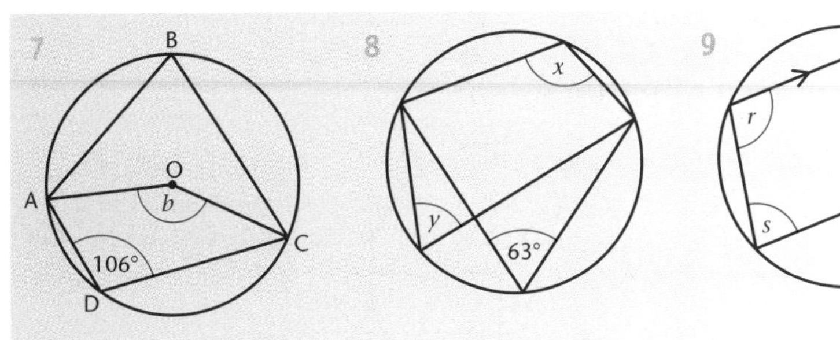

15.5 Tangents to a circle

A **secant** is a straight line that cuts a circle in two distinct points.

A **tangent** is a straight line that just touches a circle.

PAB and PCD are secants.
PT is a tangent.
A tangent just touches a circle.

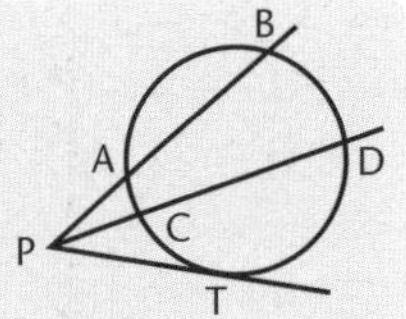

A tangent to a circle is perpendicular to the radius at the point of contact.

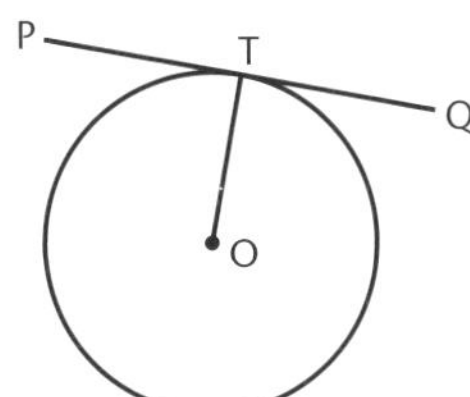

PTQ is a tangent.
OT is a radius.
∠OTP = 90°.

Two tangents drawn to a circle from the same point are equal in length.

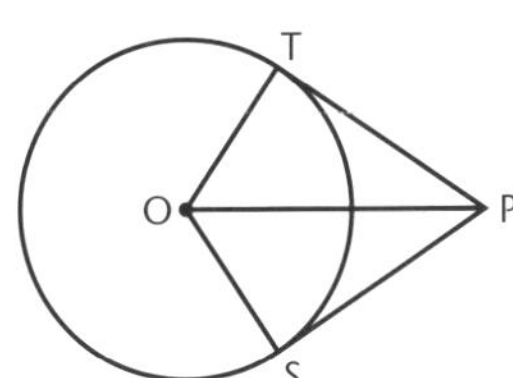

△OPT and △OPS are congruent (RHS) because OT = OS, OP is common, and △OTP = ∠OSP = 90°.

Example 5

In this diagram, O is the centre of the circle and PT and PS are tangents.

Work out **a** a **b** b.

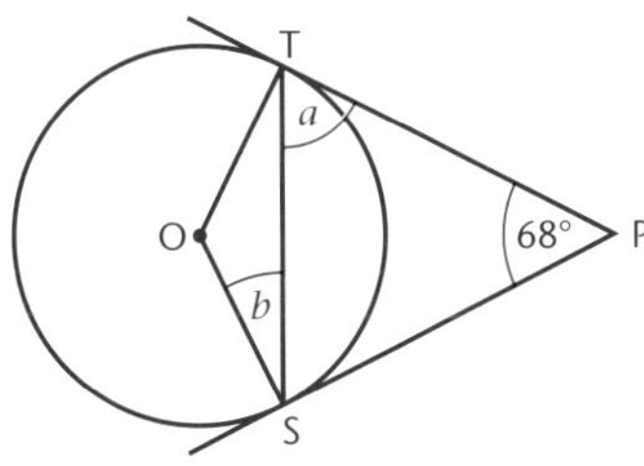

a $2a + 68° = 180°$
$2a = 112°$
$a = 56°$

As PT = PS, △PTS is isosceles.
So ∠PST = ∠PTS = a and the angles in △PTS add up to 180°.

b ∠OST + ∠PST = 90°
But ∠PST = a = 56°
so $b + 56° = 90°$
$b = 34°$

Angle between tangent and radius at point of contact is 90°.

Exam practice 15E

In questions 1 to 5, find the angles marked with letters.

Lines drawn from an external point to a circle are tangents. O is the centre of the circle.

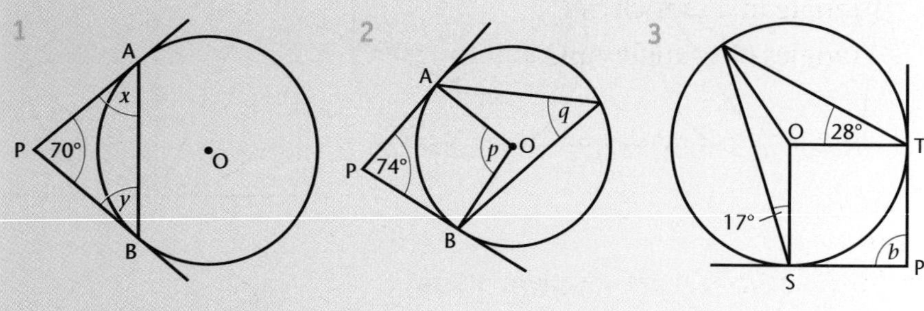

4

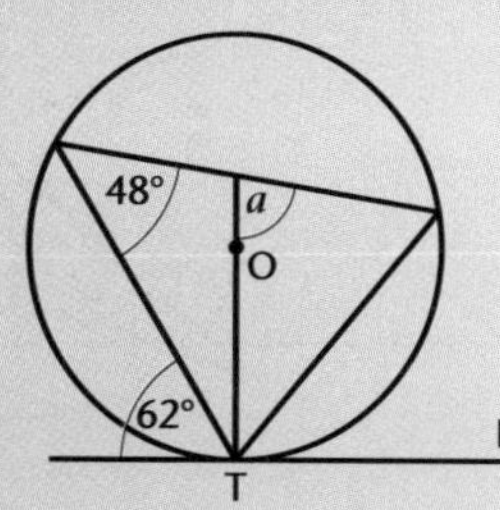

5

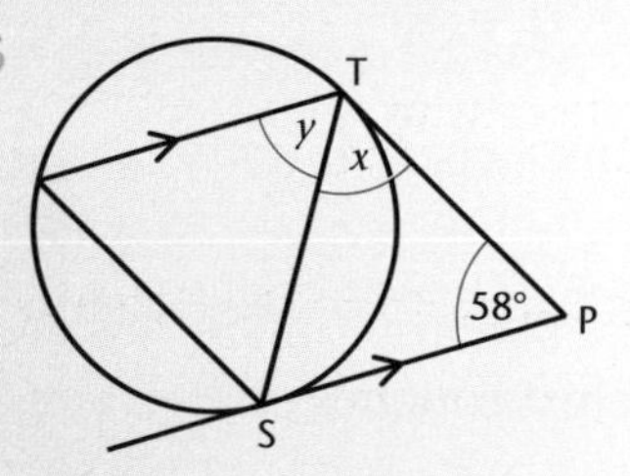

6 ABCD is a square drawn round a circle. AB, BC, CD and DA are tangents to the circle touching the circle at F, G, H and E. Show that EFGH is a square.

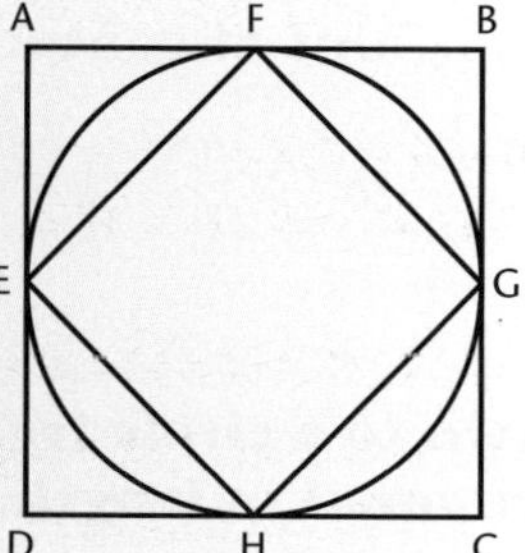

15.6 The alternate segment theorem

PQ is a tangent to the circle. TA is a chord. Angle ATQ is the angle between the tangent and the chord at the point of contact.

The segment that is shaded is called the **alternate segment** with respect to angle ATQ as it is on the side of the chord opposite, or alternate, to the angle.

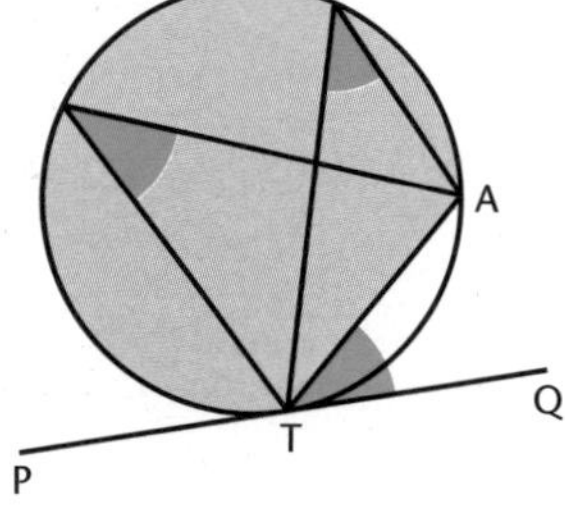

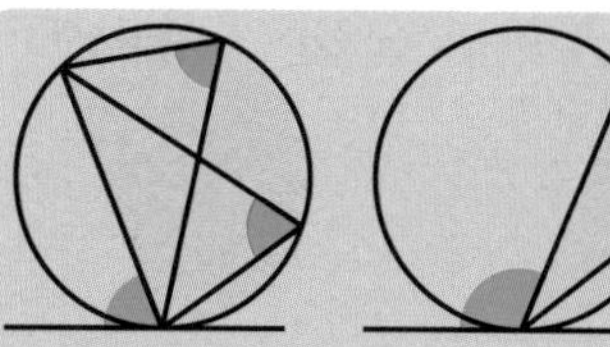

The angle between a tangent to a circle and a chord through the point of contact is equal to the angle subtended in the alternate segment.

Proof

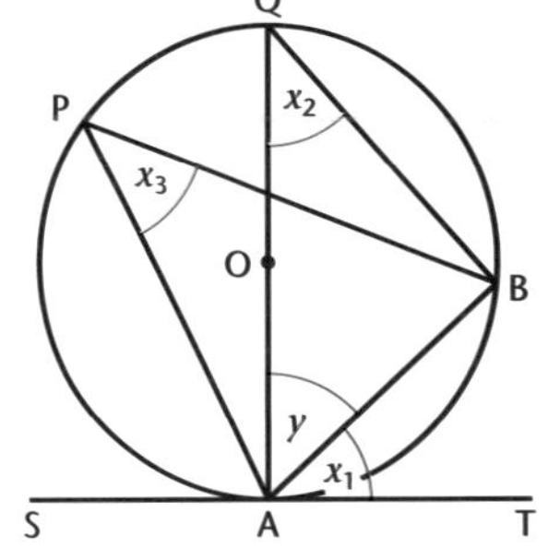

In the diagram $x_1 + y = 90°$ (angle between radius and tangent)
Also $\angle ABQ = 90°$ (angle in a semicircle)
so $x_2 + y = 90°$ (angles of triangle ABQ add to 180°)
$x_1 = x_2$.
But $x_2 = x_3$ (angles in the same segment are equal)
so $x_1 = x_3$.

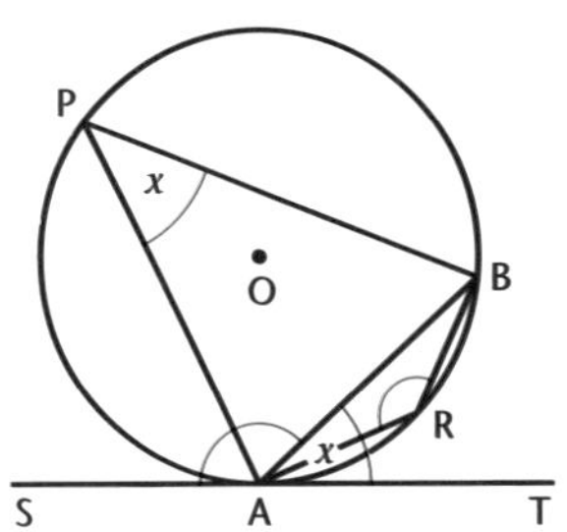

In quadrilateral APBR, $\angle ARB = 180° - x$
(opposite angles of the cyclic quadrilateral are supplementary)

and $\angle SAB = 180° - x$
(angles on a straight line are supplementary)

so $\angle SAB = \angle ARB$.

This proves the alternate segment theorem for both acute and obtuse angles.

Example 6

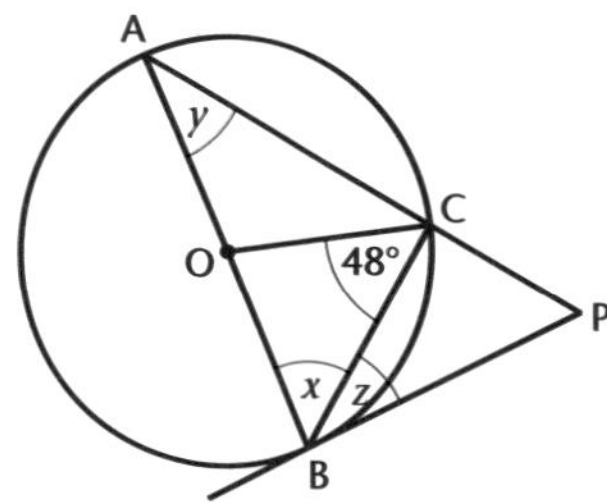

In the diagram, O is the centre of the circle and PB is a tangent.
Calculate the angles marked with letters.
Give a reason for each step of your working.

$x = 48°$ (OC = OB (both radii) and the base angles of an isosceles triangle are equal)

$x + z = 90°$ (angle between tangent and radius)

so $z = 90° - 48° = 42°$

$y = z$ (alternate segment theorem)

$\therefore y = 42°$

When working out angle problems such as this example, always mark the equal radii in the diagram. You will spot isosceles triangles more easily.

Exam practice 15F

1 In the diagram, PTQ is a tangent.
Calculate the value of
 a y
 b z.
Give a reason for each step of your working.

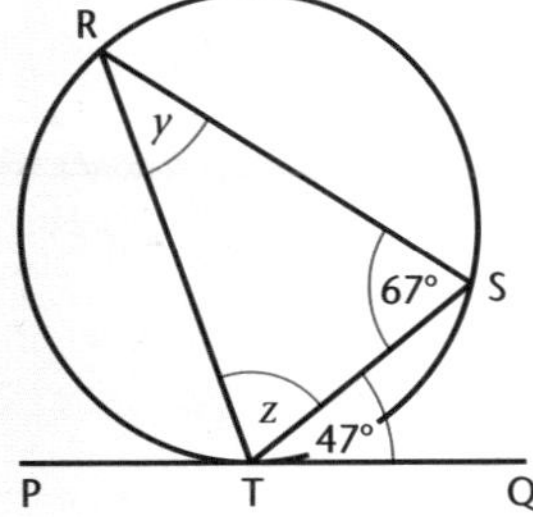

2 In the diagram, O is the centre of the circle and DCE is a tangent.
 a Work out the values of the angles x, y and z.
 b Explain why AB is parallel to DE.

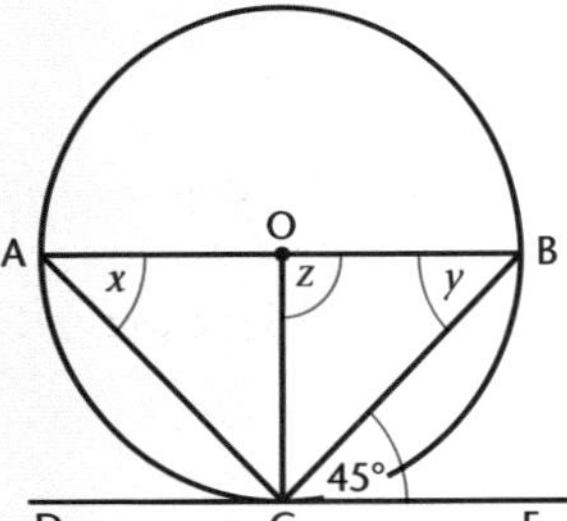

3 In the diagram, O is the centre of the circle and DCE is a tangent.
Write down the value of
a ∠BAC
b ∠ABC
c ∠BCA.

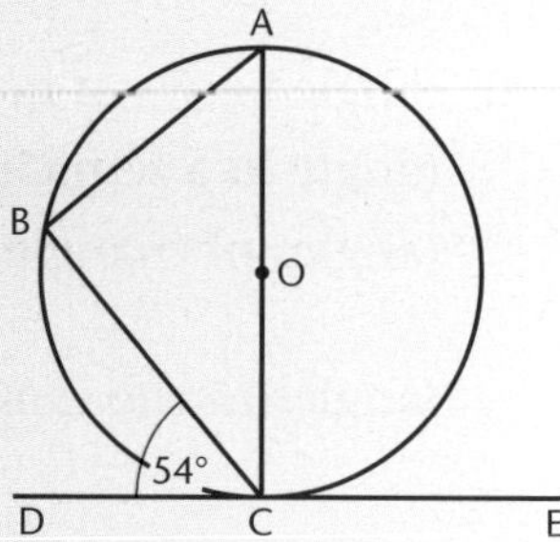

4 Find the angles marked with letters.

a
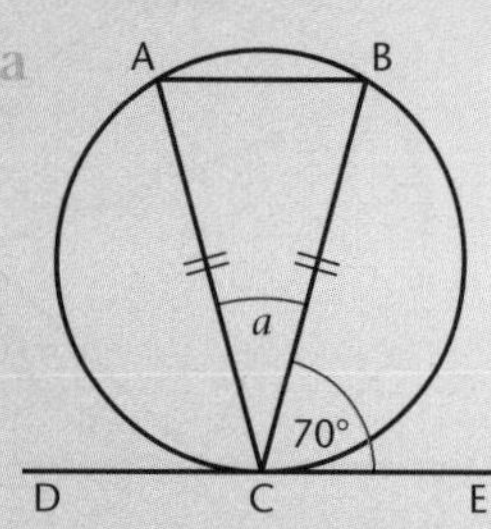

b
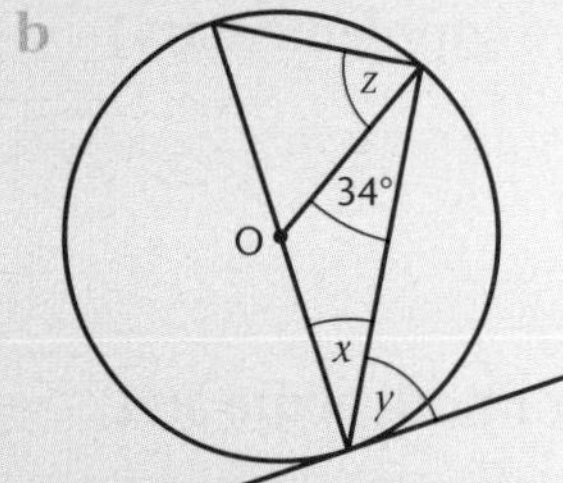

c
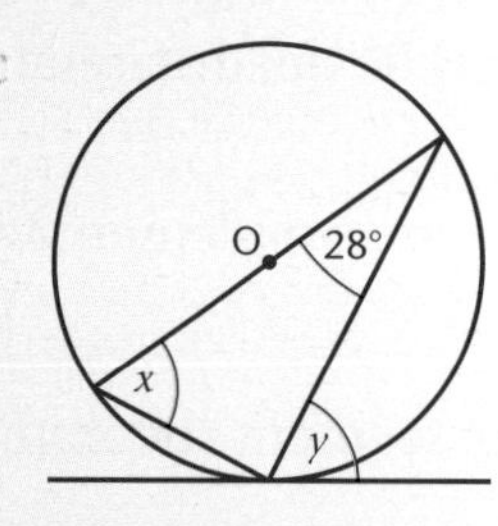

d
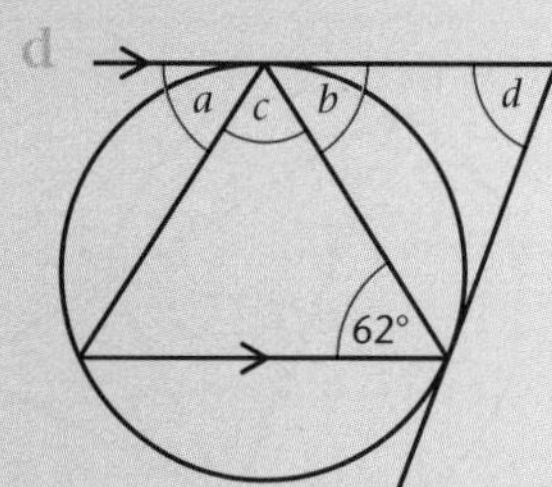

e
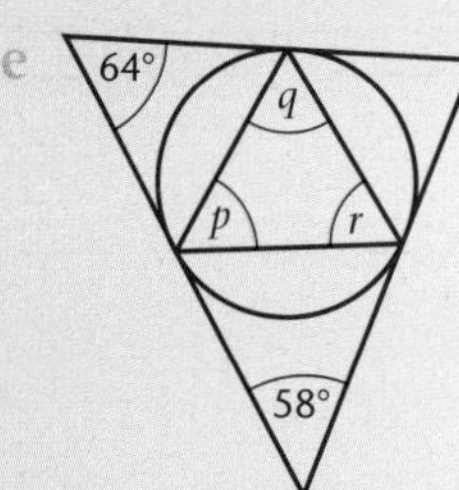

f
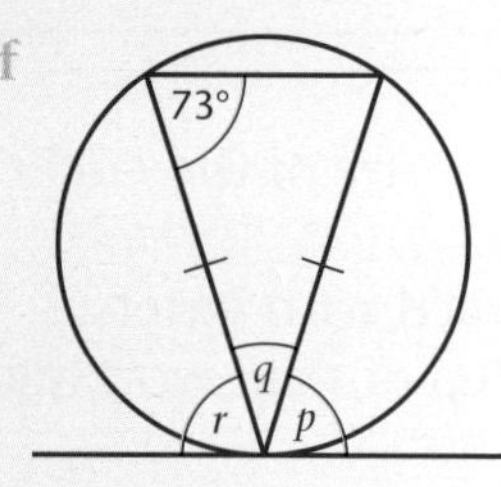

UAM 5 FDG is a tangent and AD is parallel to BC.
a Work out
i x ii y iii z.
b What kind of triangle is △BEC?

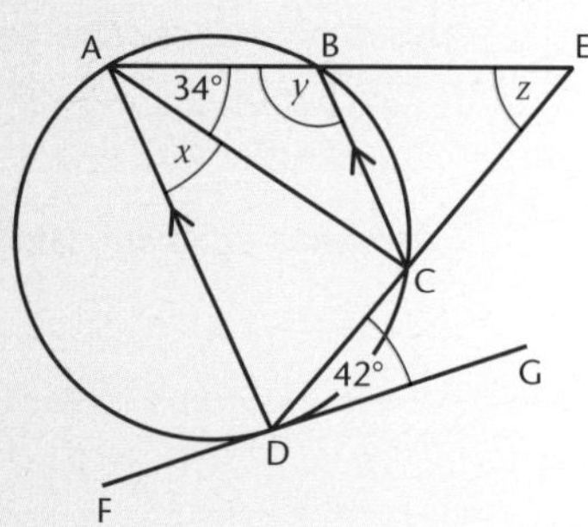

UAM 6 In the diagram, AD is parallel to BC.
Calculate the angles marked with letters.

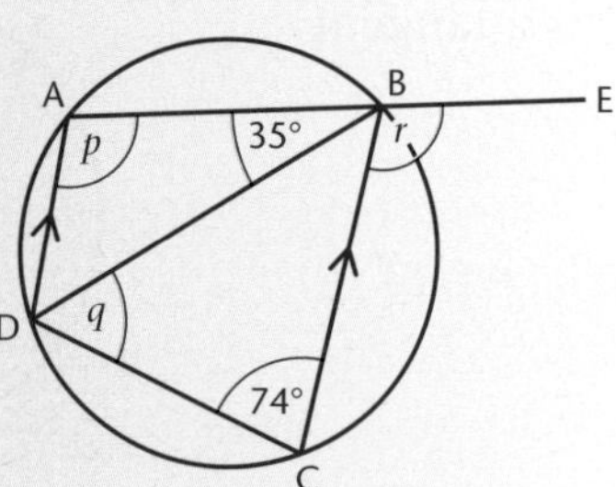

UAM 7 In the diagram, AB = BC and AC = AD.
Work out the angles marked with letters.

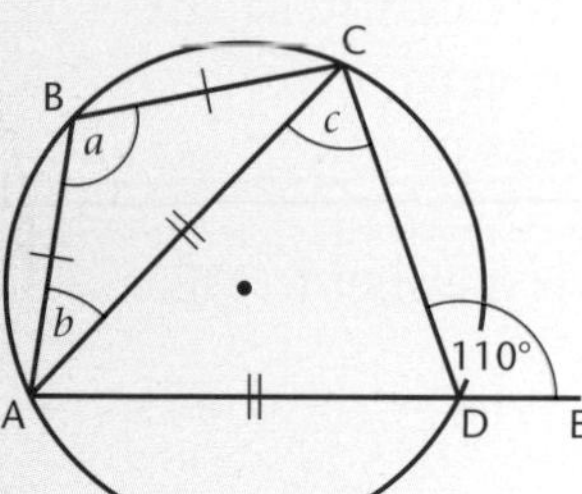

8 In the diagram, O is the centre of the circle, EAF is a tangent and AD = DC.
Work out the size of angle:
a x **b** y **c** z

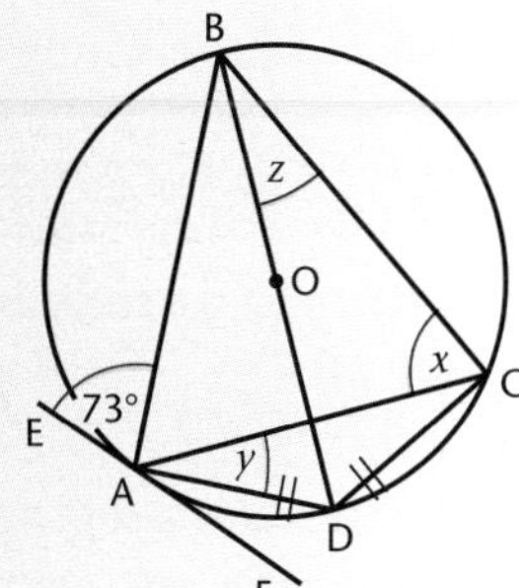

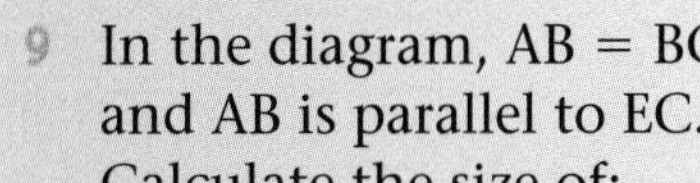

9 In the diagram, AB = BC and AB is parallel to EC.
Calculate the size of:
a p **b** q **c** r **d** s

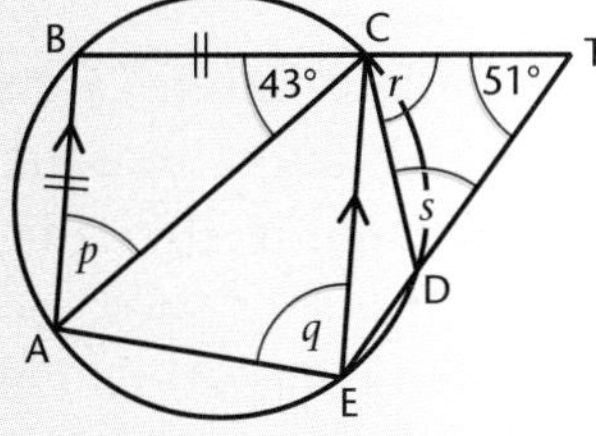

Summary of key points

- The angle subtended at the centre of a circle by an arc is twice the angle subtended at the circumference by the same arc.
- Any angle in a semicircle is a right angle.
- Angles subtended by an arc in the same segment of a circle are equal.
- The perpendicular from the centre of a circle to a chord bisects the chord, and the line drawn from the centre of a circle to the midpoint of a chord is perpendicular to the chord.
- The opposite angles of a cyclic quadrilateral are supplementary.
- An exterior angle of a cyclic quadrilateral is equal to the opposite interior angle.
- A tangent to a circle is perpendicular to the radius at the point of contact.
- Two tangents drawn to a circle from the same point are equal in length.
- The angle between a tangent to a circle and a chord through the point of contact is equal to the angle subtended in the alternate segment.

Most candidates who get GRADE A or above can:

- use the alternate segment theorem
- prove a result using theorems about angles in circles.

Glossary

Alternate segment	any chord drawn in a circle creates two segments and one is the alternate of the other
Chord	a straight line joining two points on a circle
Converse	the reverse of a statement
Cyclic quadrilateral	a quadrilateral whose four vertices lie on a circle
Major segment	the larger part of a circle that has been divided into two by a chord
Minor segment	the smaller part of a circle that has been divided into two by a chord
Secant	a straight line that cuts a circle in two distinct points
Subtended	if an angle is formed by joining a point on the circumference of a circle to the two ends of a chord or arc, then the angle is subtended by that chord or arc
Tangent	a straight line that touches a circle at a single point

16 Trigonometry

This chapter will show you:

✓ the meaning and use of the trigonometric ratios sine, cosine and tangent in right-angled triangles
✓ how to give and work with three-figure bearings
✓ how to find the sine, cosine and tangent of obtuse angles
✓ the sine rule and cosine rule and how to use them
✓ how to use trigonometry to find the area of a triangle
✓ how to find the angle between a line and a plane

Before you start you need to know:

✓ how to work with numbers including surds
✓ how to find a fraction of a quantity
✓ how to solve equations
✓ the properties of similar triangles
✓ how to use Pythagoras' theorem
✓ the properties of circles and chords, and isosceles triangles
✓ how to find the supplement of an angle

16.1 Trigonometry

Trigonometry deals with the relationships between sides and angles in triangles. It can be used to solve practical problems such as finding the height of a building or the distance between two places.

Right-angled triangles

In a right-angled triangle the side opposite the right angle is the longest side.

It is called the **hypotenuse**.

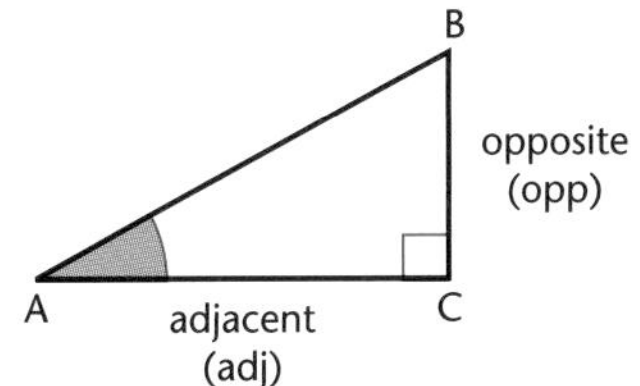

AB is the hypotenuse of this triangle.

BC is the side **opposite** angle A.

AC is the side **adjacent** to angle A.

The tangent of an angle

These right-angled triangles are similar.

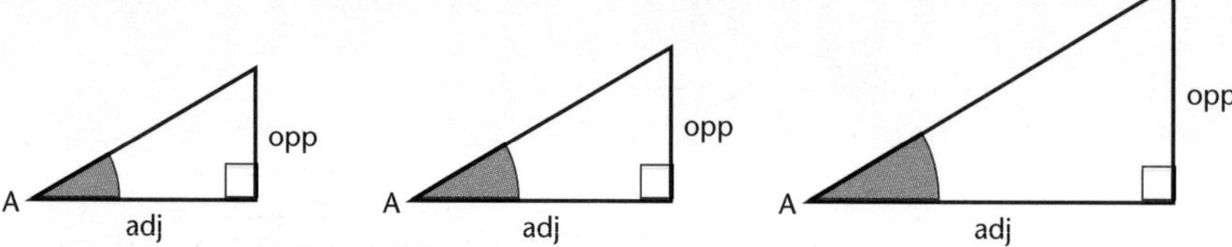

All have a right angle and another equal angle.
The ratio of corresponding sides is always the same.

In all three triangles the ratio $\frac{\text{opposite}}{\text{adjacent}}$ is the same.

This ratio is called the **tangent** of angle A.
It is written as tan A.

$$\tan A = \frac{\text{opp}}{\text{adj}}$$

The values of the tangents of all angles can be found using a scientific calculator.

You can use the tangent ratio to find an angle when the opposite and adjacent sides are given, or to find the opposite or adjacent side when the angle and the other side are given.

In this triangle:

$\tan A = \frac{BC}{AC}$

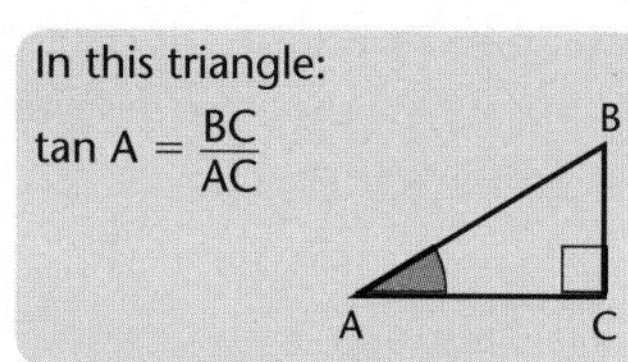

To find the tangent of 35° press
tan 3 5 =
The display shows 0.700207…
You write tan 35° = 0.7002 (4 s.f.).
Make sure your calculator is in 'deg' mode.

Example 1

Find angle A.

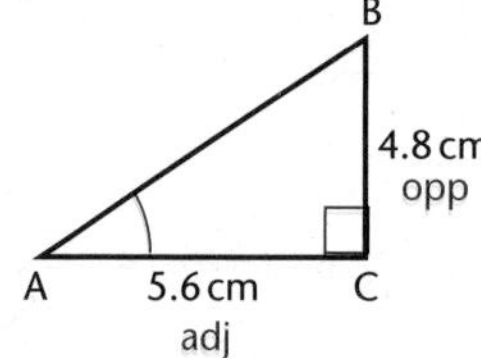

$\tan A = \frac{\text{opp}}{\text{adj}} = \frac{4.8}{5.6}$

$= 0.8571\ldots$

$\angle A = 40.6°$ (1 d.p.)

The side opposite A is BC.
The side adjacent to A is AC.
Label these sides on a sketch of the triangle.

Use $\tan^{-1}$ to find the angle when you know the tangent.

Example 2

Find the length of PQ.

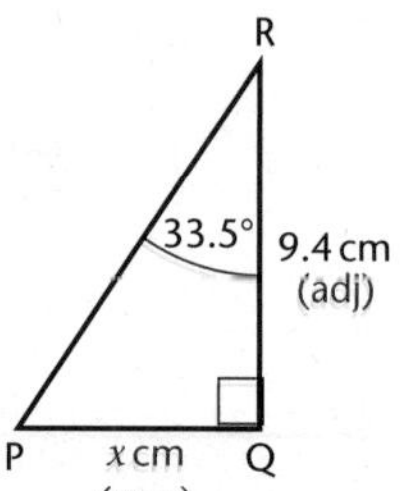

RQ is adjacent to the given angle and PQ is opposite. Label PQ as x cm.

$\tan 33.5° = \frac{\text{opp}}{\text{adj}} = \frac{x}{9.4}$

$9.4 \times \tan 33.5° = x$

$x = 6.2217\ldots$

PQ = 6.22 cm (3 s.f.)

Press 9 . 4 × tan 3 3 . 5 =

Example 3

In the diagram angle PRQ = 90°.
Find PR.

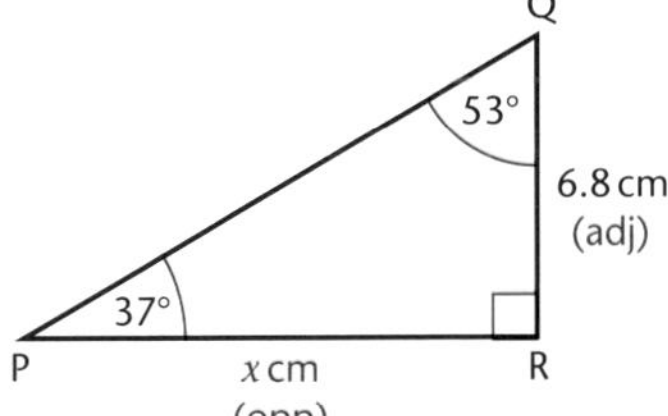

$\angle P = 37°$ so $\angle Q = 53°$

$\tan 53° = \frac{\text{opp}}{\text{adj}} = \frac{x}{6.8}$

$x = 6.8 \times \tan 53° = 9.023...$

PR = 9.02 cm (3 s.f.)

When the unknown side is adjacent to the given angle find the third angle of the triangle. The unknown side is then on the top of the ratio so it is easier to find.

Exam practice 16A

Give angles correct to 1 d.p. and lengths correct to 3 s.f.

1 a Find the tangent of the angle:
i 42° ii 74° iii 7.5° iv 24.7°.

b Find the angle whose tangent is
i 0.5 ii 1.67 iii 0.08 iv 0.678.

2 Find the marked angle in each triangle.

a
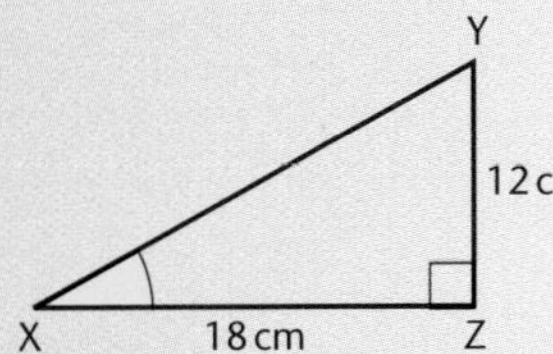

b
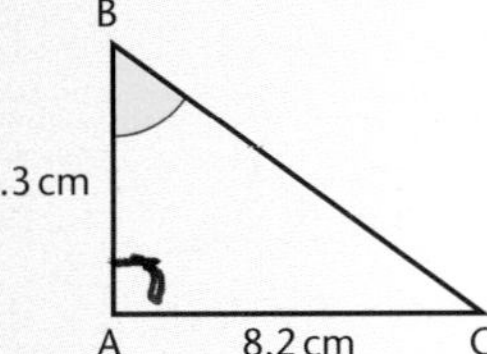

c
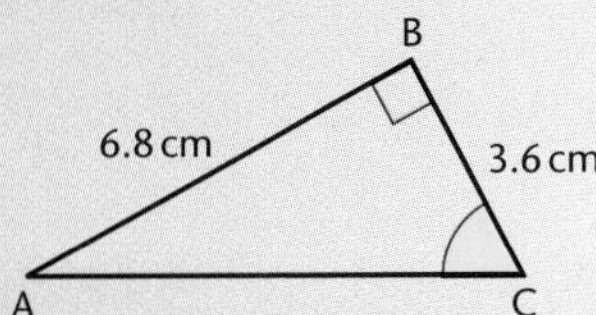

d
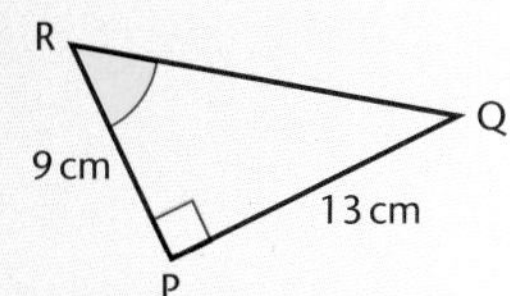

3 a Find angle A.

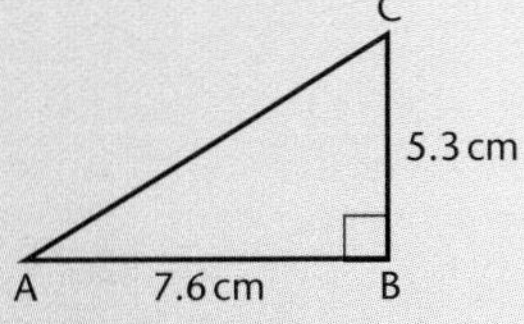

b Find angle X.

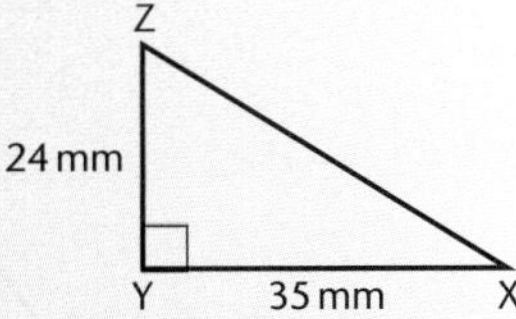

4 a Find angle R.

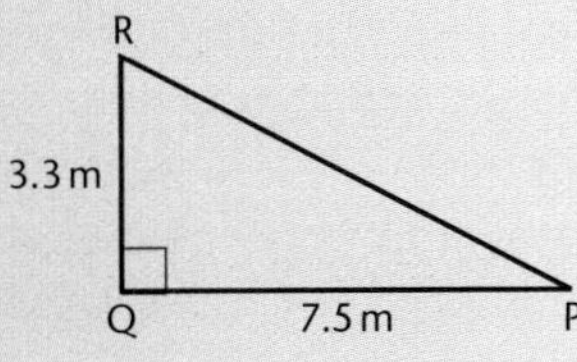

b Find angle E.

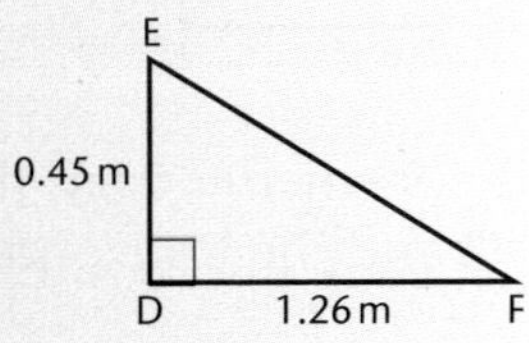

5 a Find AB. b Find DF. c Find XZ.

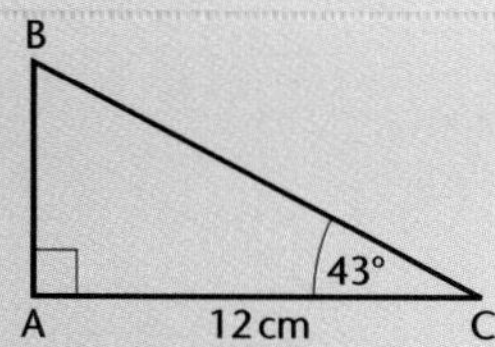

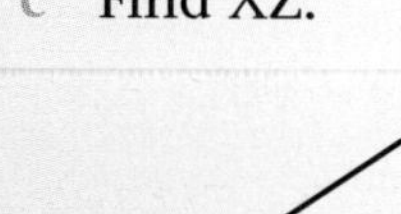

Y
53 mm
22°
Z
X

6 a Find AC. b Find XY. c Find DE.

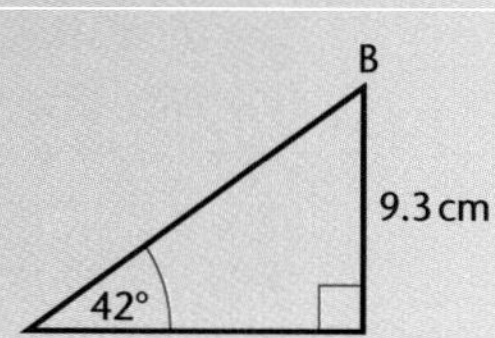

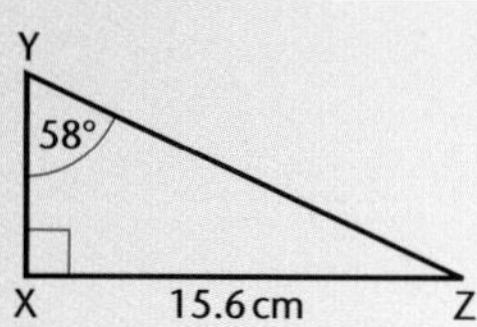

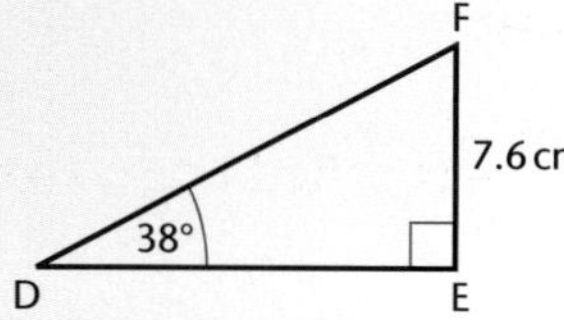

You need to find the third angle in the triangle first.

7 a Find BC. b Find DF.

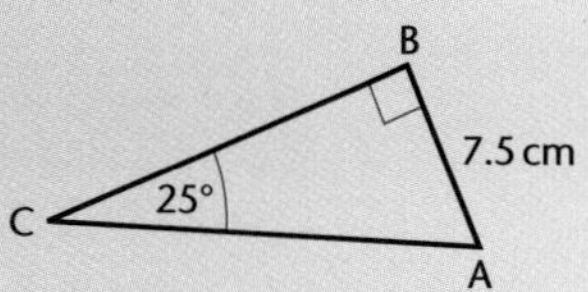

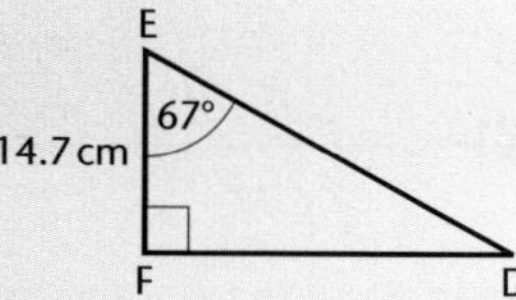

8 In the diagram AB = AC, BC = 10 cm and angle B = 70°.
 a Find the height of the triangle.
 b Hence find its area.

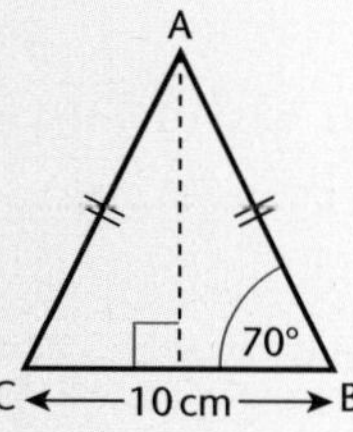

9 The coordinates of three points are A (2, 1), B (7, 1) and C (7, 5).
 a Find the lengths of the sides of △ABC.
 b Show that one of the angles of the triangle is 90°.
 c Find ∠A.

Plot the points on a grid.

10 O is the centre of the circle.
AB is 3 cm from the centre of the circle.
 a Find angle OAB.
 b Work out the radius of the circle.

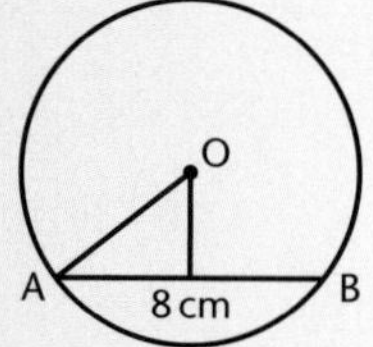

You need Pythagoras' theorem for part b.

UAM **11** AB represents a vertical television mast.

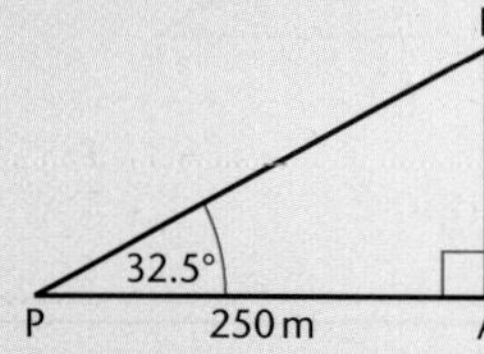

From a point P on the ground, 250 metres from the foot of the mast, the angle between PB and the horizontal ground is 32.5°. How high is the mast?

This angle is called an angle of elevation.

16.2 Sine and cosine

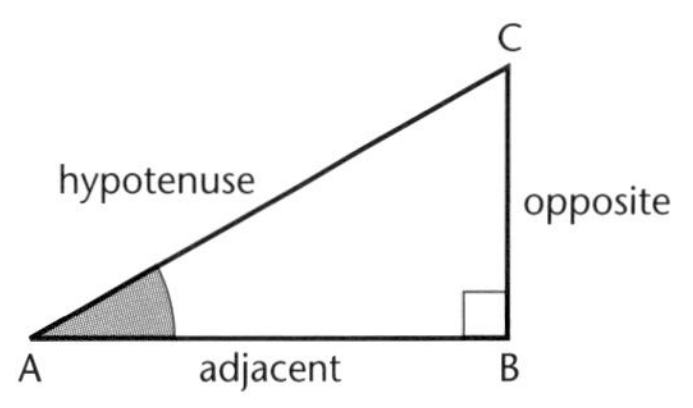

There are two other ratios in a right-angled triangle.

The ratio $\frac{\text{opposite}}{\text{hypotenuse}}$ is called the **sine** of angle A.

It is written as sin A.

$$\sin A = \frac{\text{opp}}{\text{hyp}} = \frac{BC}{AC}$$

The ratio $\frac{\text{adjacent}}{\text{hypotenuse}}$ is called the **cosine** of angle A.

It is written as cos A.

$$\cos A = \frac{\text{adj}}{\text{hyp}} = \frac{AB}{AC}$$

The word SOHCAHTOA may help you to remember these ratios. It is made from the initial letters taken in order.

$$\mathbf{\sin A = \frac{opp}{hyp}} \qquad \mathbf{\cos A = \frac{adj}{hyp}} \qquad \mathbf{\tan A = \frac{opp}{adj}}$$

Example 4

Find the length of AC.

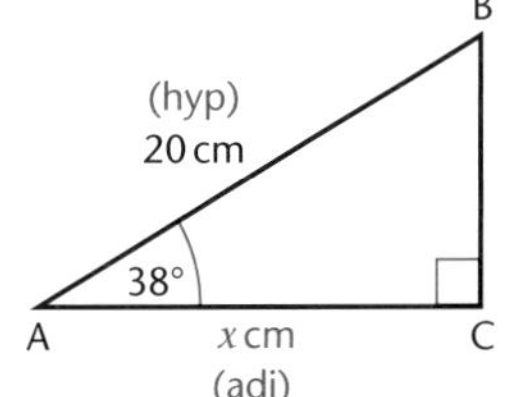

You know the hypotenuse and you need to find the adjacent side so use the cosine.

$\cos A = \frac{\text{adj}}{\text{hyp}} = \frac{x}{20}$

$x = 20 \times \cos 38° = 15.76\ldots$

AC = 15.8 cm (3 s.f.)

Press 2 0 × cos 3 8 =

Example 5

Find the length of PR.

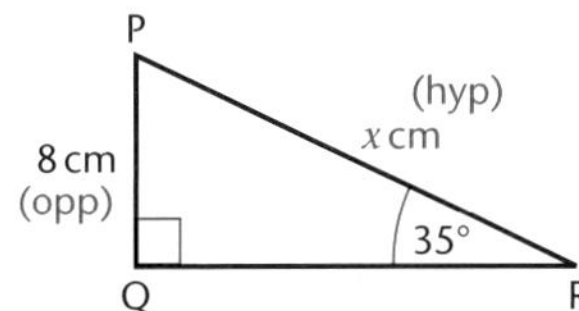

You know the opposite side and you need to find the hypotenuse so use sine.

$\sin 35° = \frac{\text{opp}}{\text{hyp}} = \frac{8}{x}$

$8 = x \times \sin 35°$

$x = \frac{8}{\sin 35°} = 13.94\ldots$

PR = 13.9 cm (3 s.f.)

Example 6

Find angle F.

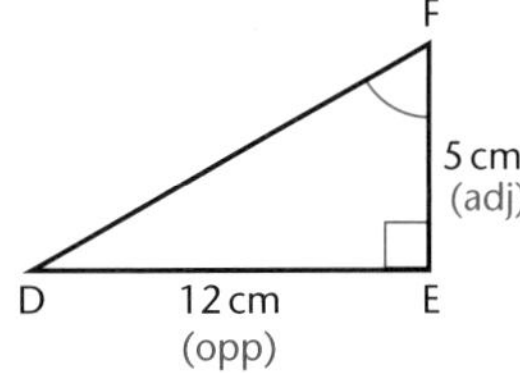

You know the side opposite F and the side adjacent to F so use tangent.

$\tan F = \frac{12}{5} = 2.4$

$\angle F = 67.4°$ (1 d.p.)

Exam practice 16B

For part **a** round your answers to 4 d.p. and for part **b** round your answers to 1 d.p.

1 a Find the sine of
i 52° ii 77° iii 9.5° iv 62.3°.

b Find the angle whose sine is
i 0.5 ii 0.67 iii 0.18 iv 0.774.

2 a Find the cosine of
i 45° ii 56° iii 32.5° iv 64.8°.

b Find the angle whose cosine is
i 0.8 ii 0.77 iii 0.12 iv 0.395.

3 Write down the exact value of
i sin A ii cos A iii tan A.

a

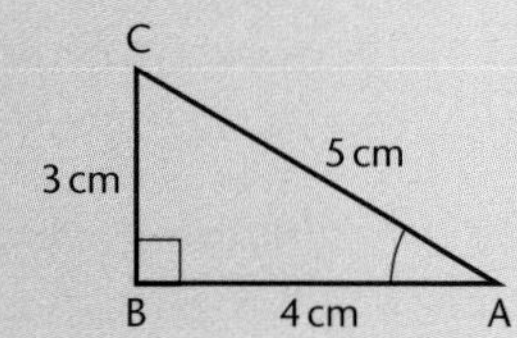

b

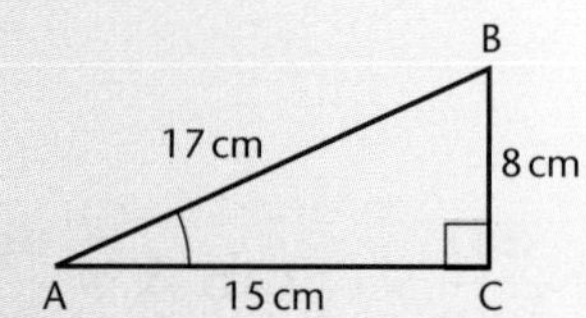

4 a Which ratio would you use to find the shaded angle?

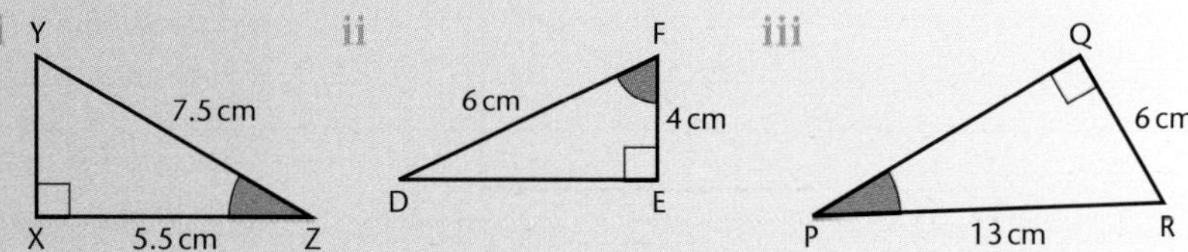

b Work out the size of the shaded angle in each triangle.

5 Work out the size of the shaded angle in each triangle.

a A, 5 cm, B, 8 cm, C

b Q, 13 cm, P, 15 cm, R

c Z, 24 mm, X, 19 mm, Y

6 a Find BC. **b** Find DE. **c** Find QR.

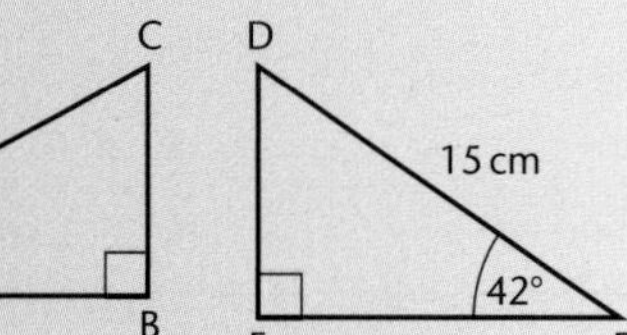

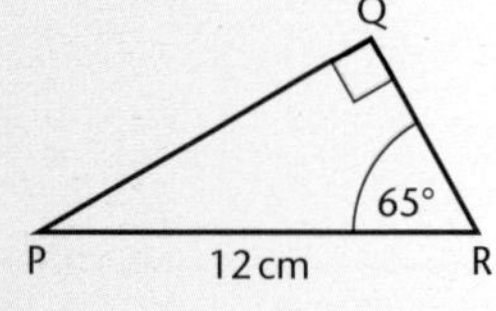

d Find XZ. **e** Find AC. **f** Find DE.

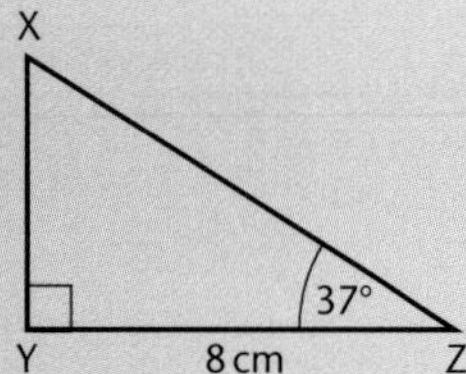

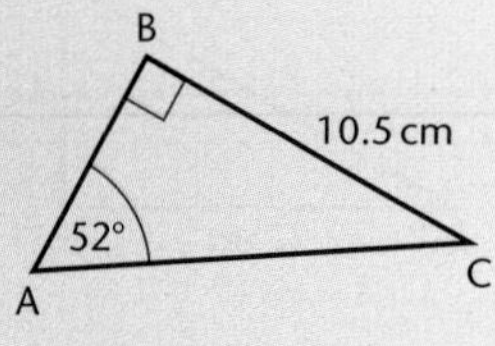

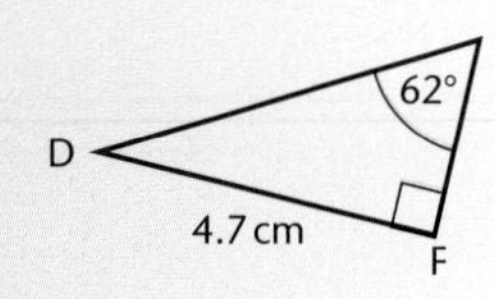

UAM

7 ABC is an equilateral triangle of side 2 cm.
M is the base of the perpendicular from A to BC.
Use the triangle to find the exact value of
a sin 30°, cos 30° and tan 30°
b sin 60°, cos 60° and tan 60°.

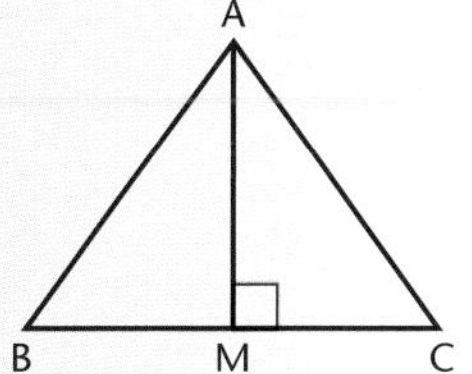

'Exact value' means that you do not find the square root of a quantity unless it is exact. Where appropriate leave square roots in your answer.

UAM

8 A ladder 4 m long rests against a vertical wall. The foot of the ladder is 1.5 m from the base of the wall.
a Find the angle between the ladder and the ground.
b How high up the wall does the ladder reach?

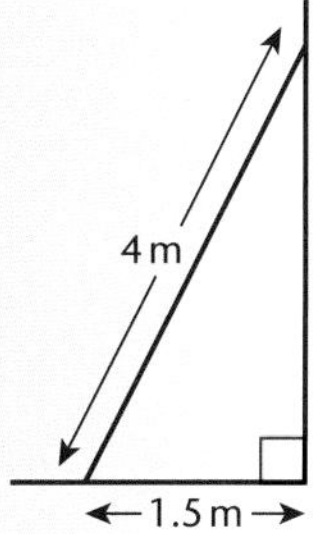

UAM

9 A picture is hanging horizontally from a hook by a cord 80 cm long. The cord is attached to the top of the picture at two points 50 cm apart. Work out the angle between the cord and the picture.

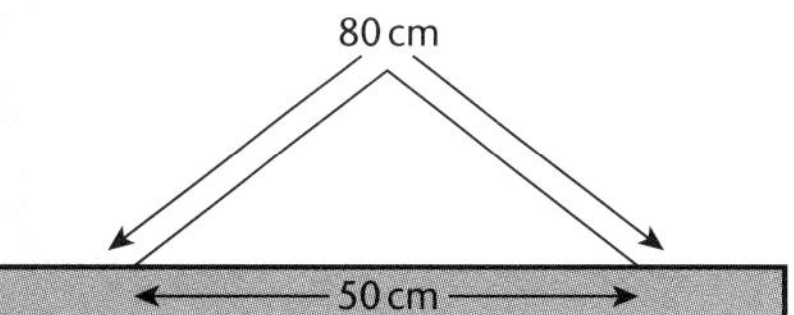

UAM

10 In the diagram, O is the centre of the circle. The diameter of the circle is 7.5 cm. Work out the angle subtended by the chord at a point on the circumference of the circle.

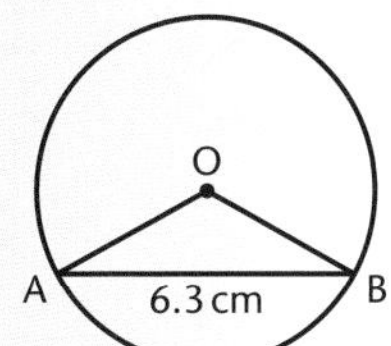

Copy the diagram and mark the lengths you know. You need to know the facts about angles in circles for this question.

16.3 Three-figure bearings

A **bearing** gives the direction from one place to another.
There are two ways of giving a bearing.

A **compass direction** gives the direction as a point on a compass.

The main compass points are north, south east and west.

A **three-figure bearing** gives the direction as an angle measured clockwise from north.

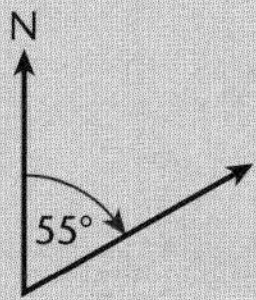

A three-figure bearing must have three digits. This bearing is 055°.

If the angle is less than 100° put 0 in front of it.

Example 7

This map shows three villages.

a Write down the bearing of Fordham from Denton.

b Work out the bearing of Denton from Fordham.

c Find the bearing of Fordham from Eastly.

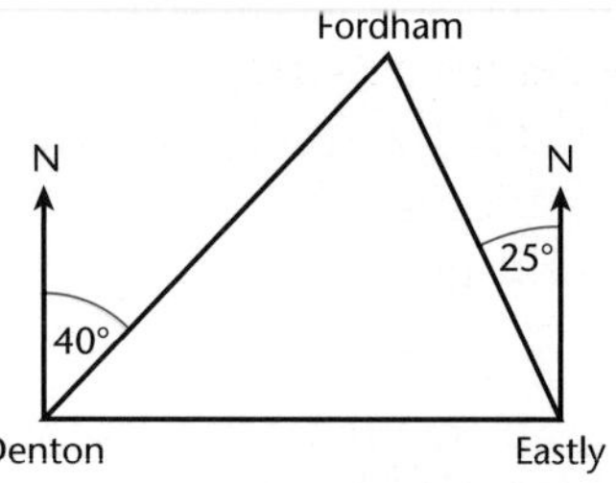

a 040°

The angle shown is 40°. You need to add a zero in front to give a three-figure bearing.

b 180° + 40° = 220°

You need to start at Fordham. Draw a north line here.
The angle you want is the clockwise angle from the north line to the line going to Denton. This is 180° + 40°.

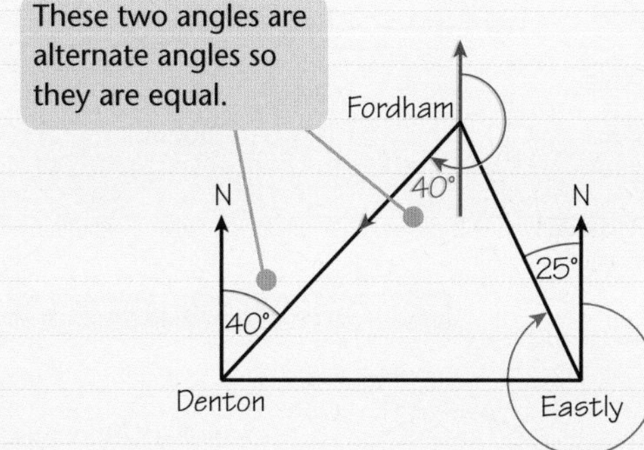

c 360° − 25° = 335°

You need to start at Eastly.
The angle you want is the clockwise angle from the north line to the line going to Fordham.
This is 360° − 25°.

Exam practice 16C

1 a Write down the three-figure bearing of A from B.

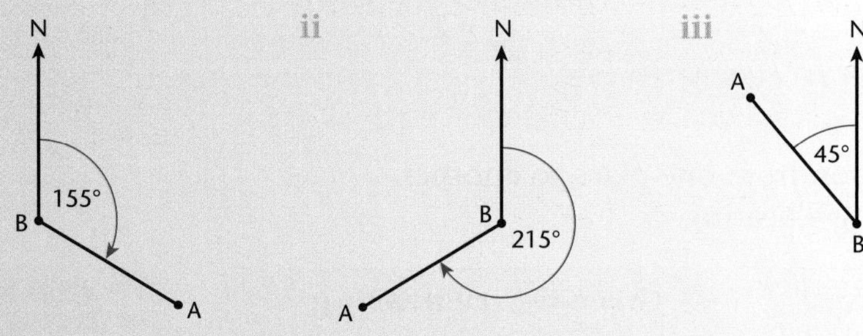

b Work out the three-figure bearing of L from M.

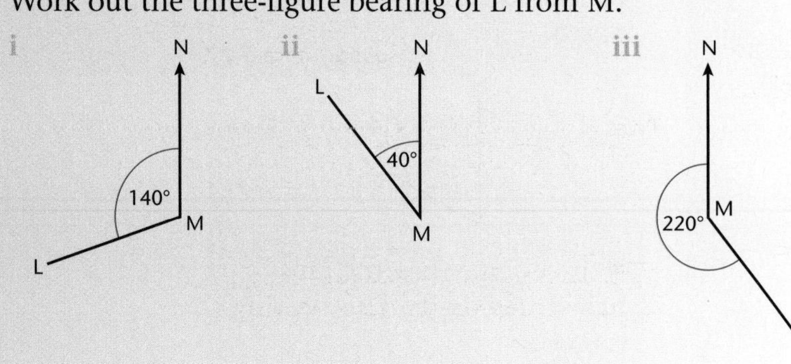

2 This map shows three villages, A, B and C.
B is due south of A.
Work out the three-figure bearing of
a A from C
b C from A
c B from C.

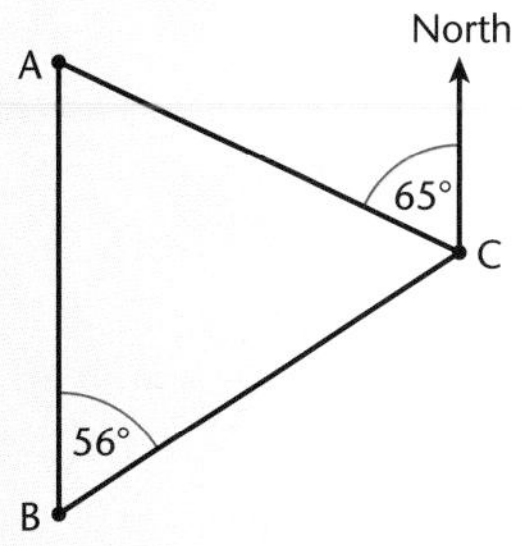

You need to add a 'north' line at the point you want the bearing from.

3 Draw a rough sketch to show
a an aeroplane, A, on a bearing of 123° from an airport P
b a church steeple, S, on a bearing of 280° from a farm F
c an oil tanker, T, on a bearing of 056° from a liner L
d a town, T, on a bearing of 175° from a village V.

Mark the angle on your sketch.

You must show all the points and any angle given. Always indicate north on your diagram.

4 Point C is 7 km from B on a bearing of 065°.
Write down the distance and bearing of
a B from A
b D from B
c A from B
d B from C
e B from D.

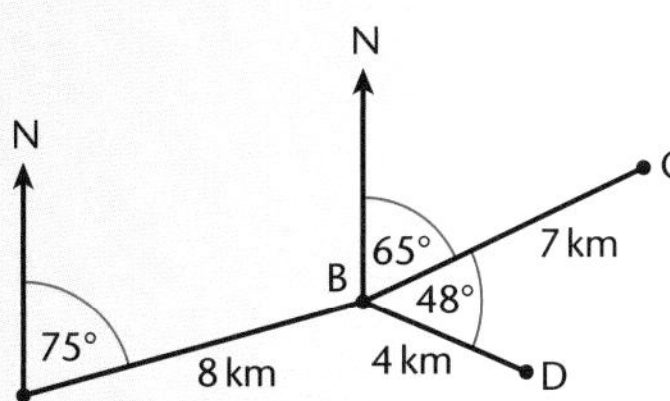

16.4 Trigonometric ratios for obtuse angles

The sine of an obtuse angle is the same as the sine of its supplement.

$\sin 120° = \sin 60°$ and $\sin 117.4° = \sin 62.6°$.

The cosine of an obtuse angle is minus the cosine of its supplement.

$\cos 130° = -\cos 50°$ and $\cos 96.7° = -\cos 83.3°$

The tangent of an obtuse angle is equal to minus the tangent of its supplement.

$\tan 140° = -\tan 40°$ and $\tan 107.3° = -\tan 72.7°$.

The supplement of an angle is the angle you get when you subtract the given angle from 180°.
The supplement of 76° is 180° − 76° = 104°.

Example 8

Find the obtuse angle for which **a** $\sin x = 0.6473$ **b** $\cos x = -0.4652$.

a $\sin x = 0.6473$

$x = 180° - 40.338°\ldots$

$= 139.66°\ldots$

$x = 139.7°$ to 1 d.p.

Find the acute angle whose sine is 0.6473 and subtract it from 180°.

Press
sin⁻¹ 0 . 6 4 7 3 =

b $\cos x = -0.4652$

$x = 117.72\ldots°$

$x = 117.7°$ to 1 d.p.

Press
cos⁻¹ +/− 0 . 4 6 5 2 =

Exam practice 16D

1 Find
  a $\cos 124°$ b $\sin 167°$ c $\tan 100°$
  d $\cos 96.5°$ e $\sin 167.3°$.

2 a $\sin 30° = 0.5$. Write down the value of $\sin 150°$.
  b $\cos 60° = 0.5$. Write down the value of $\cos 120°$.
  c $\sin 66° = 0.9135$. Write down the value of $\sin 114°$.
  d $\cos 47° = 0.6820$. Write down the value of $\cos 133°$.

3 Find the obtuse angle whose sine is
  a 0.866   b 0.6   c 0.4362.

4 Find the angle between 0° and 180° whose cosine is
  a 0.7   b −0.6   c − 0.77   d −0.6573   e 0.5688.

16.5 The sine rule

The sine rule gives a relationship between the sides and angles in any triangle.

The sine rule can be used in triangles that don't contain a right angle.

In △ABC *a, b* and *c* represent the lengths of the sides. *a* is opposite ∠A, *b* is opposite ∠B and *c* is opposite ∠C.

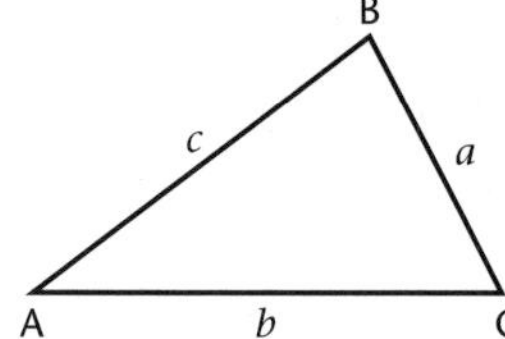

Using this notation the sine rule states that

$$\frac{a}{\sin A} = \frac{b}{\sin B} = \frac{c}{\sin C}$$

The sine rule is sometimes written as

$$\frac{\sin A}{a} = \frac{\sin B}{b} = \frac{\sin C}{c}$$

The derivation of the sine rule is on page 237.

Example 9

In △ABC, ∠B = 56°, ∠C = 42° and AC = 3.6 cm.
Find BC.

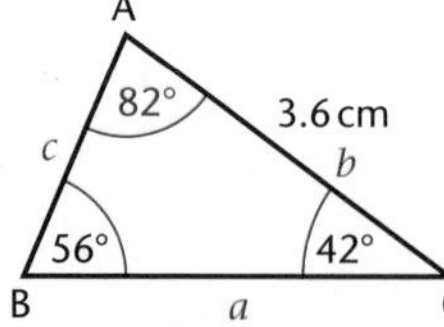

Mark the sides *a*, *b* and *c*. This will help you decide which pair of fractions to use.
You know *b* and ∠B and you want to find *a*, so use $\frac{a}{\sin A} = \frac{b}{\sin B}$.
You can find ∠A from the angle sum of the triangle.

$$\frac{a}{\sin 82°} = \frac{3.6}{\sin 56°}$$

$$a = \frac{3.6}{\sin 56°} \times \sin 82° = 4.3001\ldots$$

Press 3 . 6 × sin 8 2 ÷ sin 5 6 =

BC = 4.30 cm to 3 s.f.

Example 10

In $\triangle ABC$, $\angle A = 56°$, AC = 8.5 cm and BC = 9.4 cm.
Find $\angle B$.

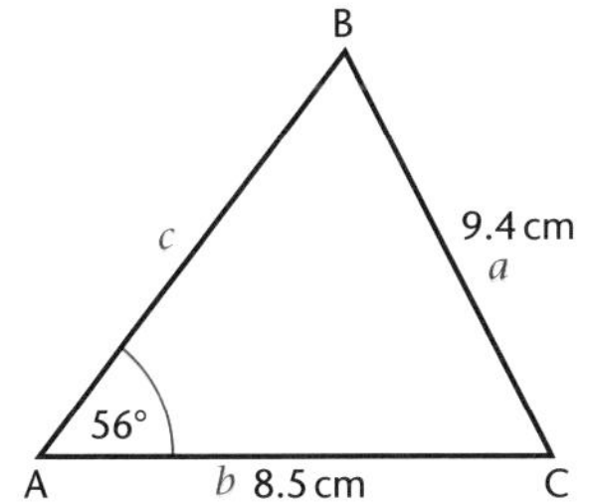

When you want to find an angle, it is easier to use the formula in the form $\frac{\sin A}{a} = \frac{\sin B}{b} = \frac{\sin C}{c}$
Mark the sides a, b and c. You know a, b and $\angle A$ so use $\frac{\sin A}{a} = \frac{\sin B}{b}$.

$$\frac{\sin 56°}{9.4} = \frac{\sin B}{8.5}$$

$$\sin B = 8.5 \times \frac{\sin 56°}{9.4} = 0.7496\ldots$$

$\angle B = 48.6°$ (1 d.p.)

You can find angle B in one step on your calculator.
sin⁻¹ (8 . 5 × sin 5 6 ÷ 9 . 4) =

Exam practice 16E

1 In $\triangle ABC$, $\angle B = 37°$, $\angle C = 54°$ and AC = 14 cm. Find AB.

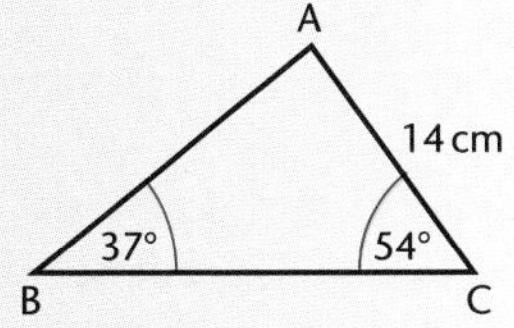

Use $\frac{b}{\sin B} = \frac{c}{\sin C}$.

2 In $\triangle DEF$, $\angle D = 74°$, $\angle F = 35°$ and EF = 16.5 cm. Find DE.

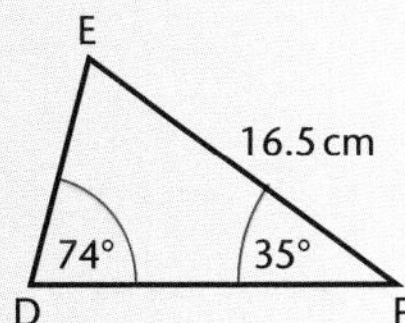

3 In $\triangle PQR$, $\angle P = 42°$, $\angle R = 68°$ and PR = 9.8 cm.
Find
a PQ b QR.

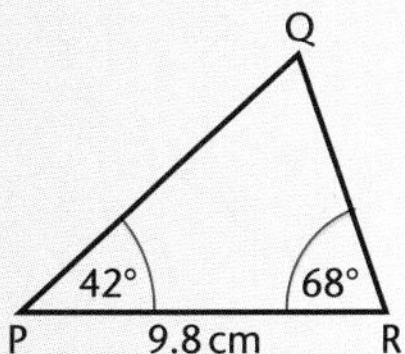

You need to find the third angle in the triangle first.

4 Find angles B and C.

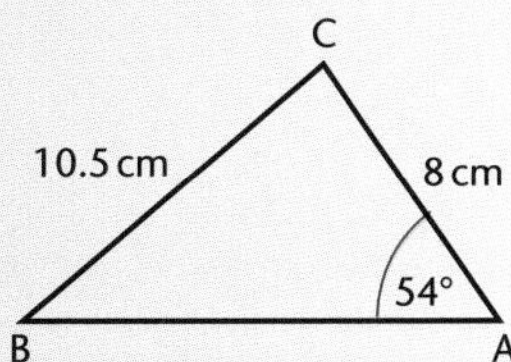

5 a Find DE and DF.

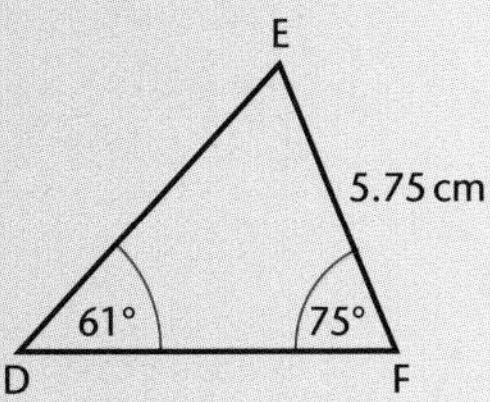

b Find PR and QR.

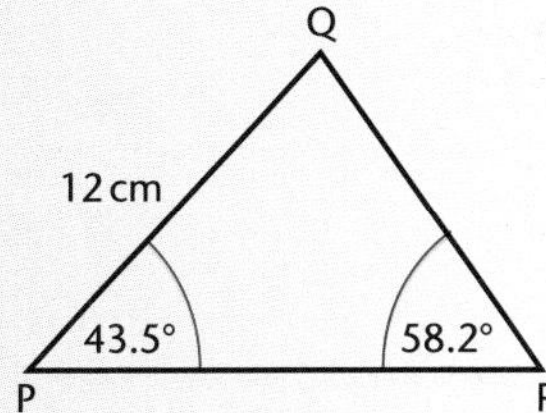

6 In $\triangle ABC$, AB = 9.4 cm, BC = 6 cm and $\angle A = 37°$.
Draw a sketch to show that there are two triangles that satisfy these dimensions.
a Find the two possible values of angle C.
b Hence calculate the two possible values of AC.

Sometimes only one angle is possible in a triangle for a given value of the sine. Here angle C can be acute or obtuse.

7 A golfer drives his ball 220 m from the tee but is short and 28° off the direct line from tee to hole.
His ball is now 140 m from the hole.
How far short would he have been if he had driven directly towards the hole?

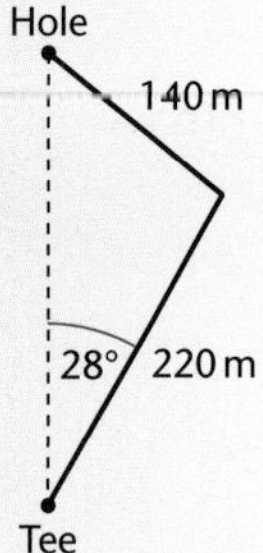

You need to find an angle first, then the length of a side.

8 A and B are two villages 4.3 km apart.
The bearing of B from A is 298°.
The bearing of an electricity pylon C from A is 214°.
The bearing of C from B is 152°.
Calculate the distance of the pylon from each village.

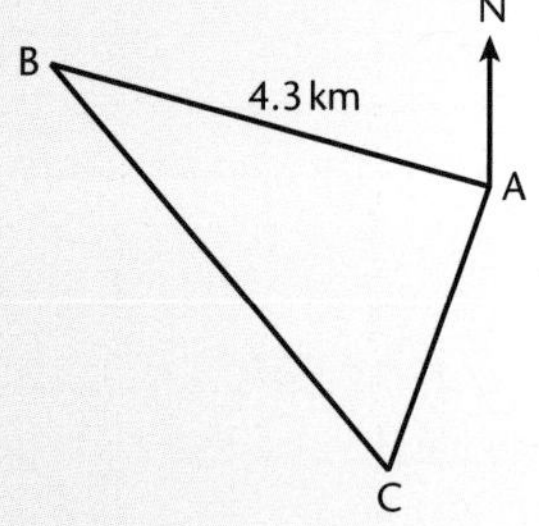

16.6 The cosine rule

In triangle ABC, a, b and c represent the lengths of the sides.

The cosine rule states that

$$a^2 = b^2 + c^2 - 2bc\cos A$$
$$b^2 = a^2 + c^2 - 2ac\cos B$$
$$c^2 = a^2 + b^2 - 2ab\cos C$$

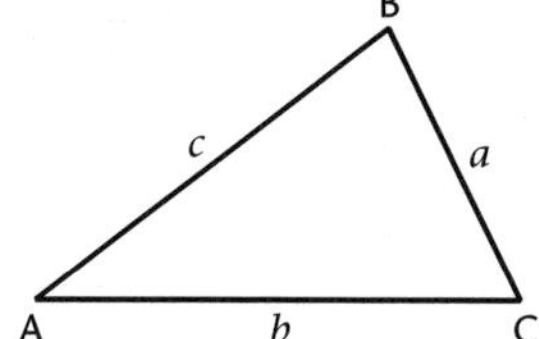

When three sides, or two sides of a triangle and the angle between them, are given you cannot use the sine rule.

The cosine rule can be used in any triangle.

The cosine rule can be used to find the third side when you know two sides and the angle between them or to find an angle when the three sides are given.

Make sure that you understand the pattern of the formula so that you can apply it to any triangle. The derivation of this rule is on page 237.

Example 11

In $\triangle$ABC, AB = 26 cm, AC = 23 cm and $\angle$A = 43°.
Calculate the length of BC.

Mark the sides with small letters the same as the opposite angles.

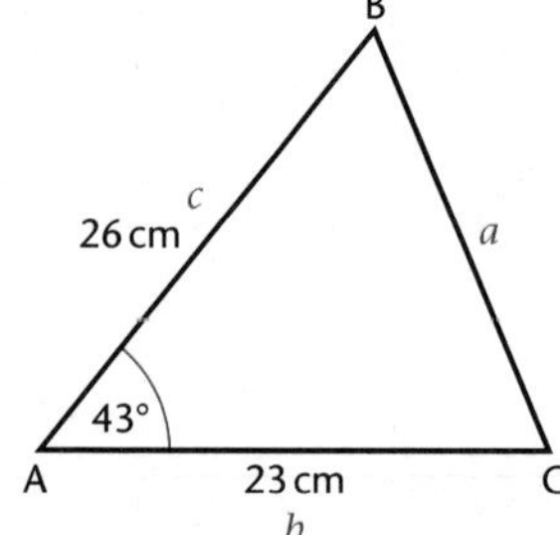

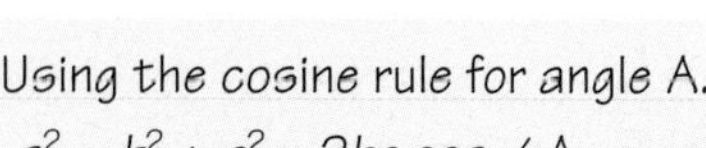
Using the cosine rule for angle A.

$a^2 = b^2 + c^2 - 2bc\cos\angle A$

$\quad = 26^2 + 23^2 - 2 \times 26 \times 23 \times \cos 43°$

$\quad = 330.30\ldots$

$a = \sqrt{330.30} = 18.174\ldots$

BC = 18.2 cm (3 s.f.)

Example 12

In △ABC, AB = 8 cm, BC = 7 cm and AC = 10 cm.
Find angle A.

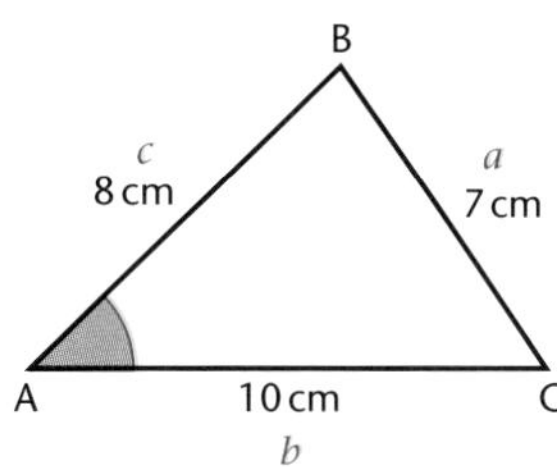

If three sides are given any angle can be found. For example, the formula involving cos A can be rearranged to give $\cos A = \dfrac{b^2 + c^2 - a^2}{2bc}$

$$\cos A = \frac{10^2 + 8^2 - 7^2}{2 \times 10 \times 8}$$

$$= 0.71875$$

$$\angle A = 44.0° \text{ (1 d.p.)}$$

Exam practice 16F

1 a Find BC.

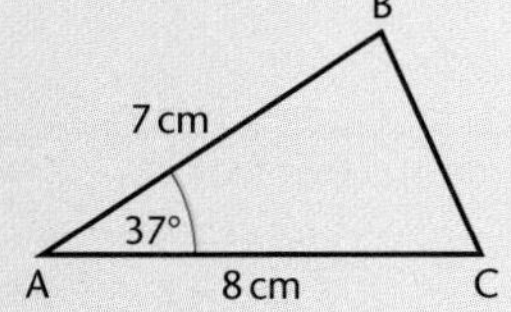

b Find DE.

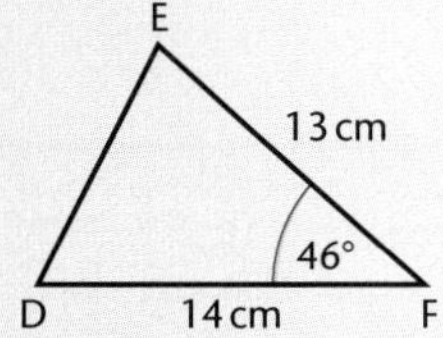

c Find PR.

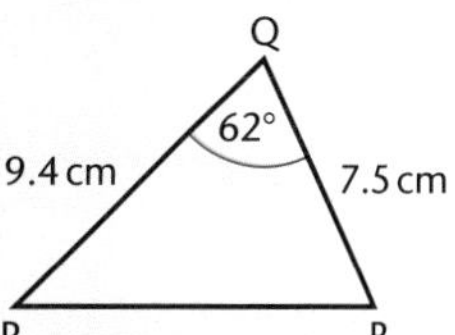

2 a Find YZ.

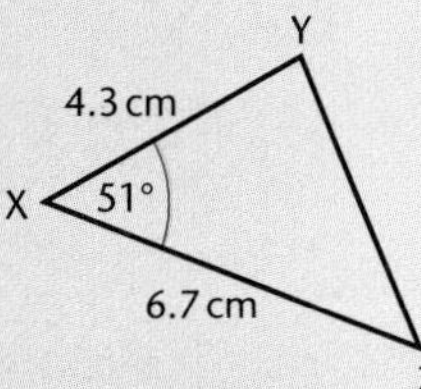

b Find AB

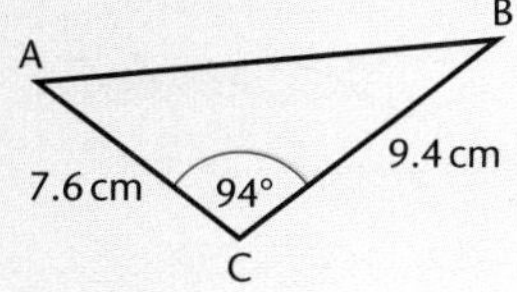

c Find DE

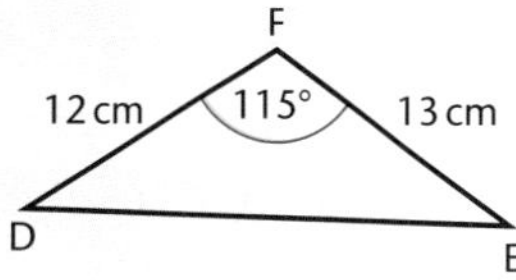

3 a Find angle R.

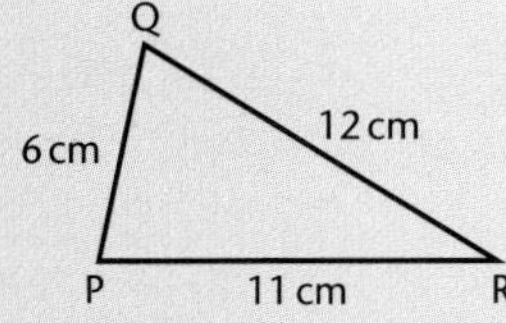

b Find angle E.

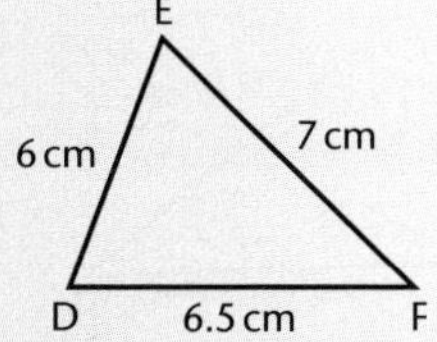

c Find angle B.

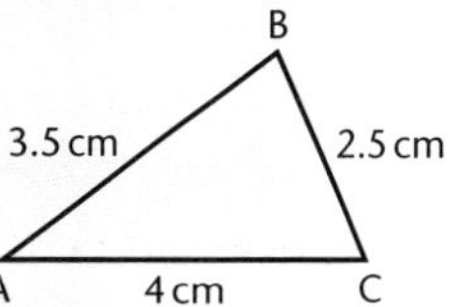

4 a Find angle X.

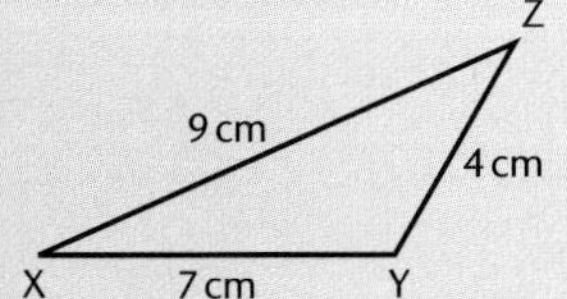

b Find angle C.

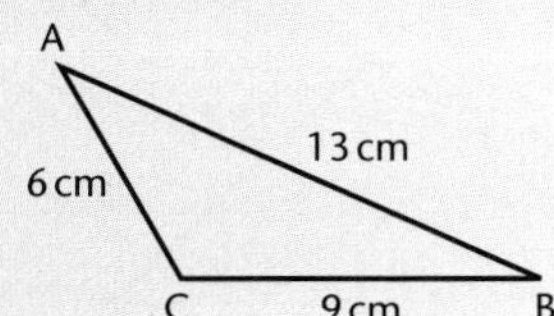

c Find angle E.

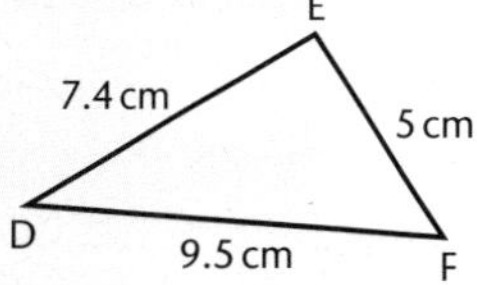

16.7 Problems

The sine rule is easier to use than the cosine rule, so use the sine rule whenever you can. In some problems you may have to start with the cosine rule but you can continue using the sine rule.

Example 13

Calculate **a** the length of AC
b angle A.

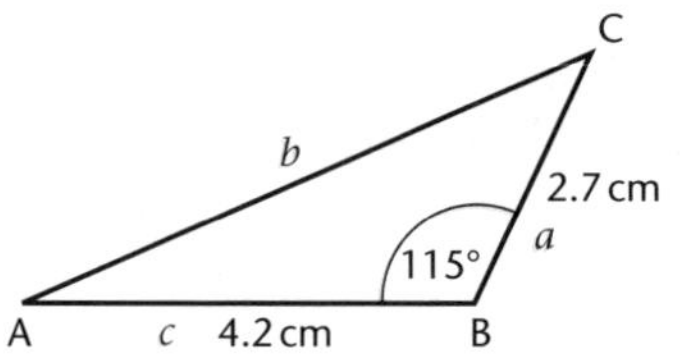

First mark the sides using small letters. You are given two sides and the angle between them. The only way to find AC is to use the cosine rule.

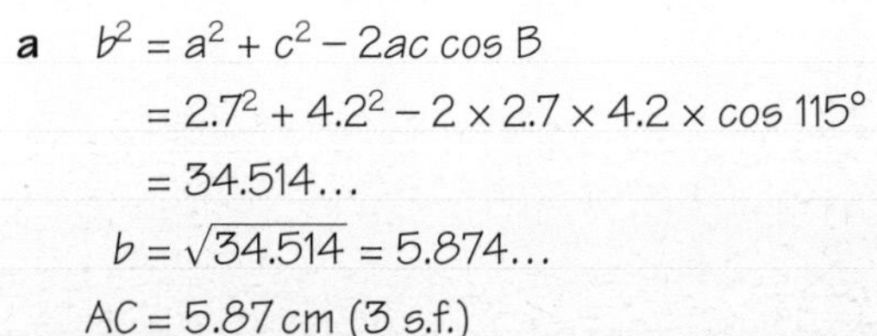

a $b^2 = a^2 + c^2 - 2ac \cos B$

$= 2.7^2 + 4.2^2 - 2 \times 2.7 \times 4.2 \times \cos 115°$

$= 34.514...$

$b = \sqrt{34.514} = 5.874...$

AC = 5.87 cm (3 s.f.)

Now you know all three sides and one angle. You can use the sine rule to find angle A.

b $\frac{\sin A}{2.7} = \frac{\sin 115°}{5.874...}$

Use the unrounded value of *b* from part **a**.

$\sin A = \frac{2.7 \times \sin 115°}{5.874}... = 0.41658...$

$\angle A = 24.6°$ to 1 d.p.

Exam practice 16G

You may need to use the sine rule or cosine rule or both.

In part b the angle you use in the cosine rule is obtuse. Remember that the cosine of an obtuse angle is negative.

1 a Find i BC ii angle B. b Find i PQ ii angle P.

B, 4.8 cm, 67°, A, 5.7 cm, C

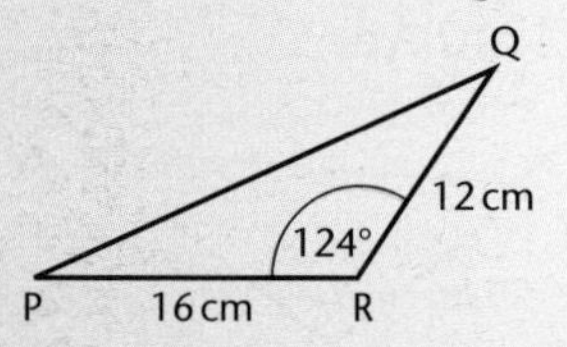

2 a Find the length of i AC ii BC. b Find i angle D ii the length DE.

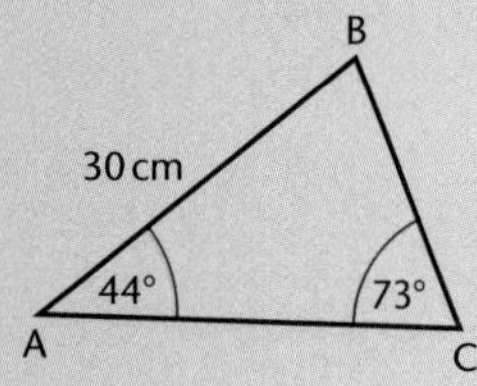

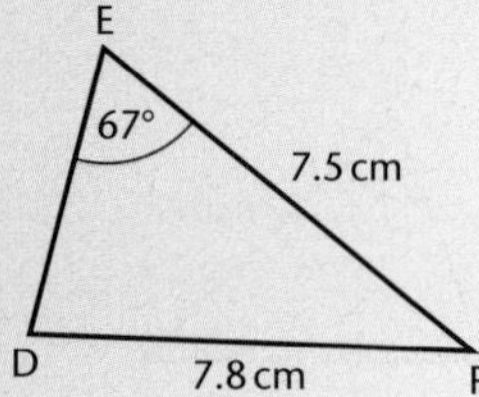

3 a Find i AB ii angle B. b Find i PQ ii angle P.

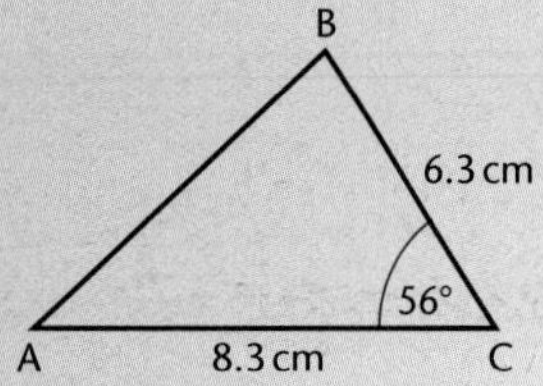

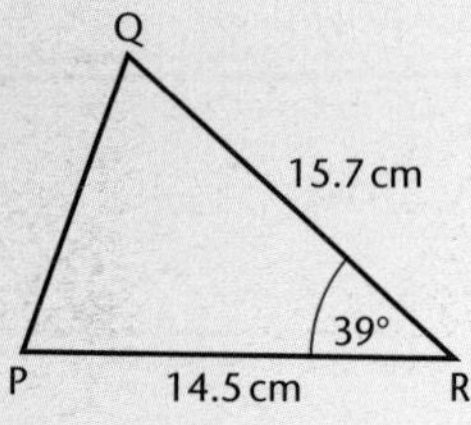

4 Find a the length of PQ
b angle Q.

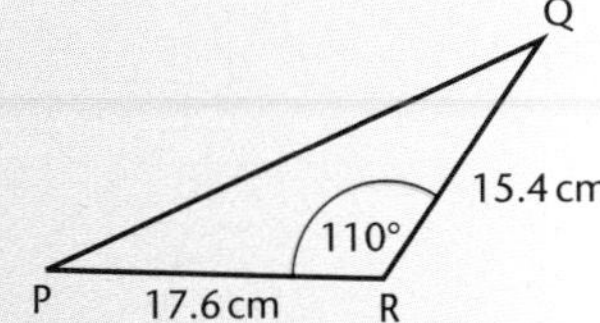

5 Find the three angles in each triangle.

a

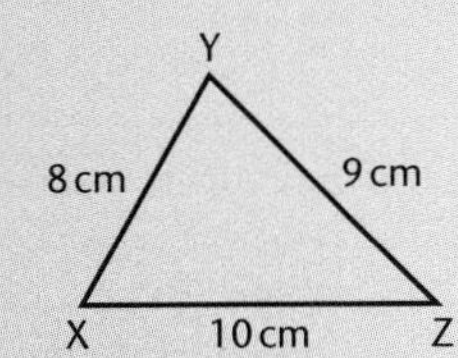

b

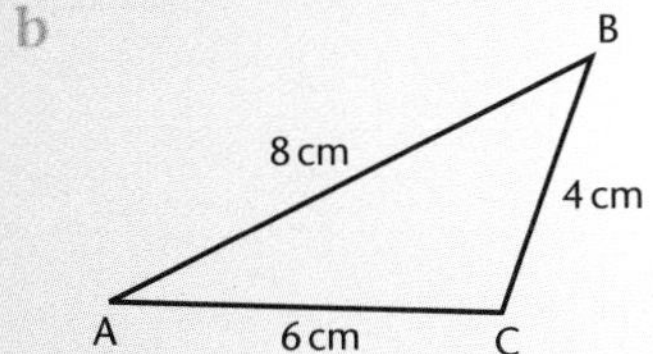

Remember that if the cosine of an angle is negative the angle is obtuse.

UAM 6 The sketch shows the position of a tanker T and a yacht Y in relation to a lighthouse L.

a Write down the three-figure bearing of
i T from L ii Y from L.

b Work out the distance between the tanker and the yacht.

n.m. stands for nautical mile.
1 international nautical mile or air mile = 1852 m (6076 feet).

UAM 7 The position of a ship, S, is 3 nautical miles from a port, P, on a bearing of 047°.
Another ship T is 5 nautical miles from P on a bearing of 136°.
Work out the distance and bearing of S from T.

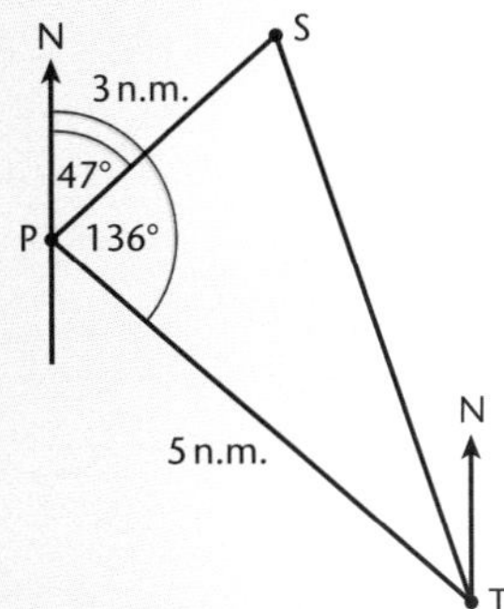

You will need to find ∠STP.

UAM 8 Find the angle between the hands of a clock at 12.30.
If the hour hand is 6 cm long and the minute hand is 8 cm long, how far apart are the tips of the hands at this time?

UAM 9 In a factory complex the main office is 270 metres from the entrance on a bearing of 308°, and the canteen is 130 metres on a bearing of 241°.
Find the distance and direction of the office from the canteen.

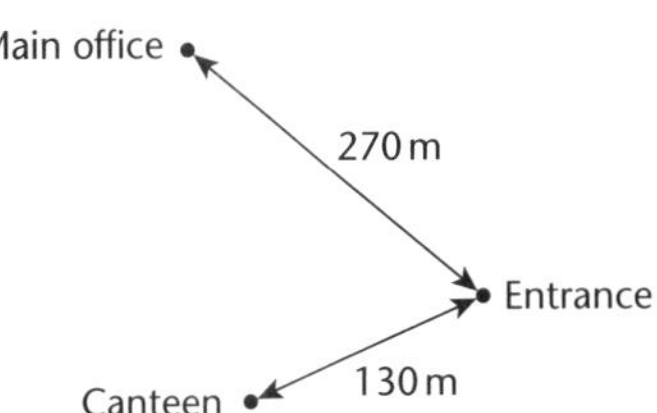

UAM 10 Two ships, A and B leave a port, P, at 1500 hours.
Ship A travels at a constant speed of 20 km per hour on a bearing of 065°.
Ship B travels at a constant speed of 27 km per hour on a bearing of 127°,
Work out the distance between the ships at 1600 hours.

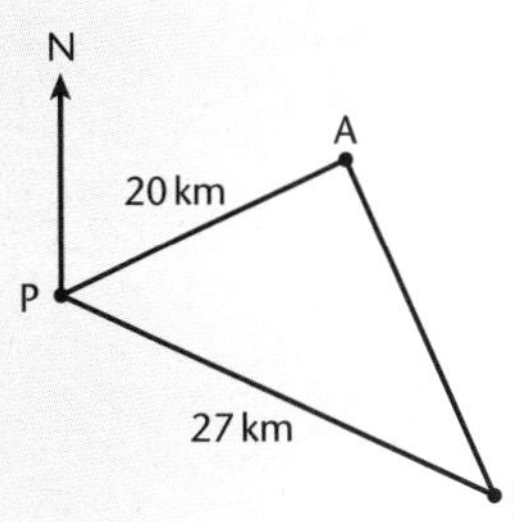

11 The diagram shows the plan of a garden.
∠BAD is obtuse.
Work out angle BAD.

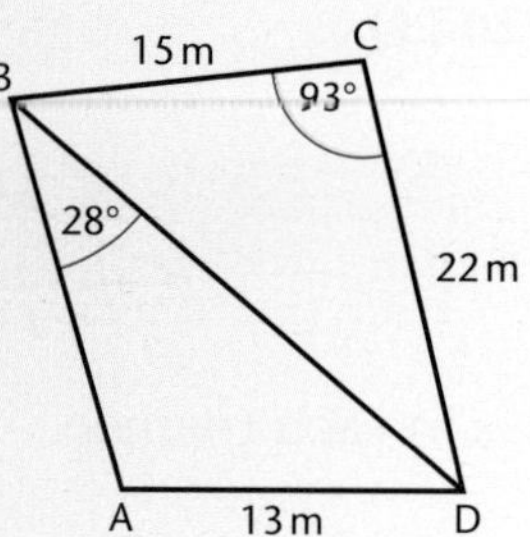

16.8 Area of a triangle

The area of a triangle is half the product of any two sides multiplied by the sine of the angle between them.

Area $= \frac{1}{2}bc \sin A$

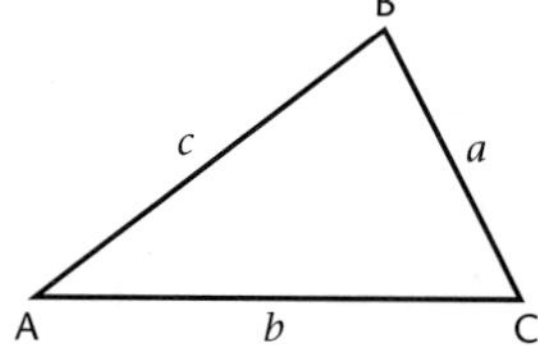

Try to remember the formula in words. For this triangle the area is also $\frac{1}{2}ac \sin B$ and $\frac{1}{2}ab \sin C$. The derivation of this formula is on page 237.

Example 14

Find the area of this triangle.

$$\text{Area} = \frac{1}{2}bc \sin A$$
$$= \frac{1}{2} \times 4.9 \times 5.6 \times \sin 55^\circ \text{ cm}^2$$
$$= 11.238\ldots \text{ cm}^2 = 11.2 \text{ cm}^2 \text{ (3 s.f.)}$$

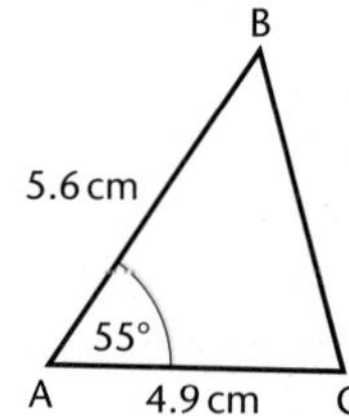

Exam practice 16H

1 Find the area of each triangle.

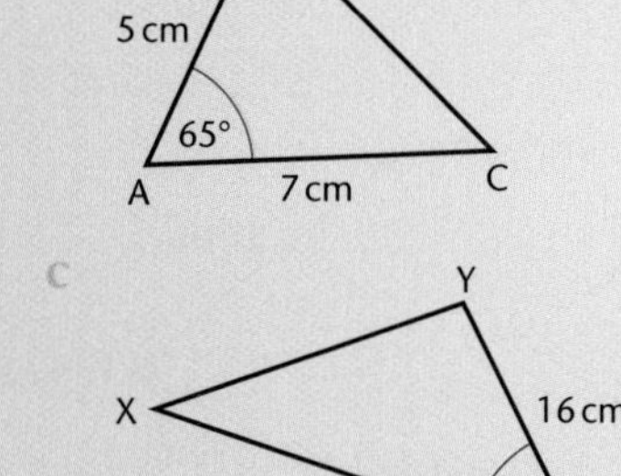

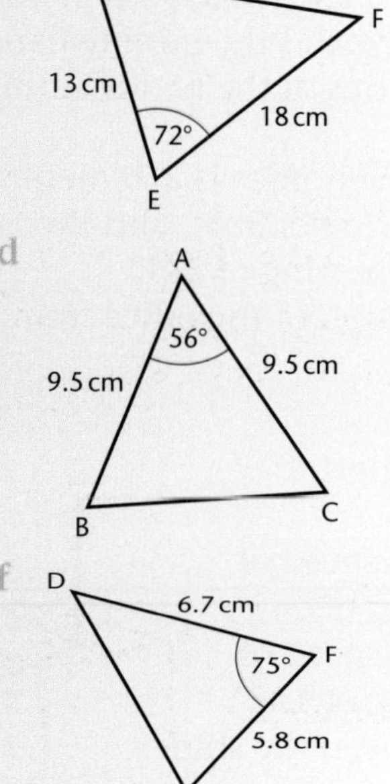

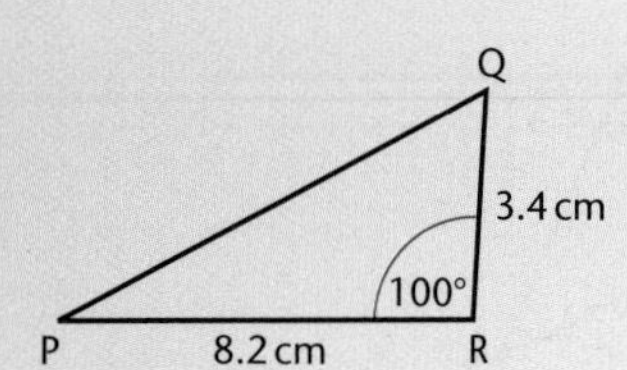

2 Find
   a the length of
      i DE   ii EF
   b the area of the triangle.

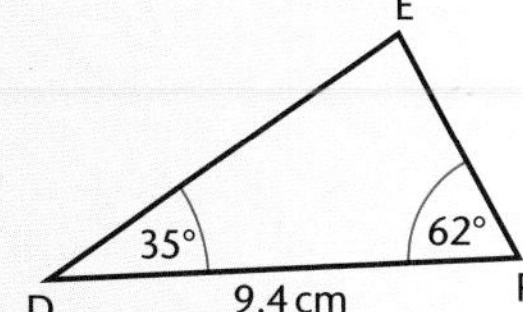

3 Calculate
   a the length of PQ
   b angle Q
   c the area of the triangle.

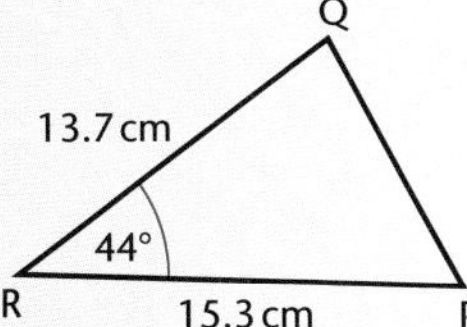

You need to use the sine rule and the cosine rule in this question.

4 Calculate
   a the length of YZ
   b angle Y
   c the area of the triangle.

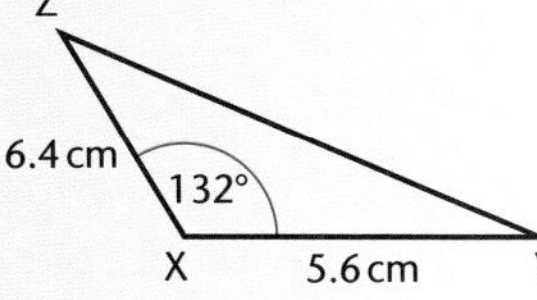

5 ABCD is a quadrilateral.
   a Find the length of AC.
   b Work out the area of the quadrilateral.

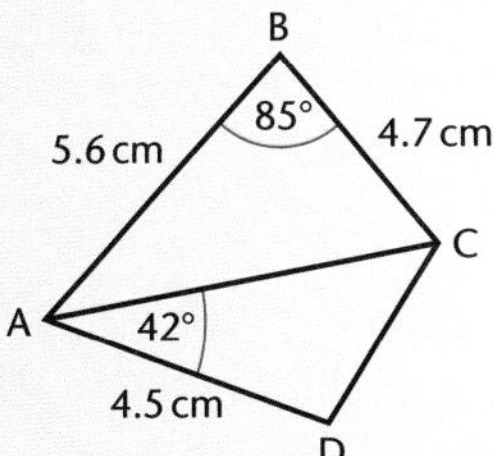

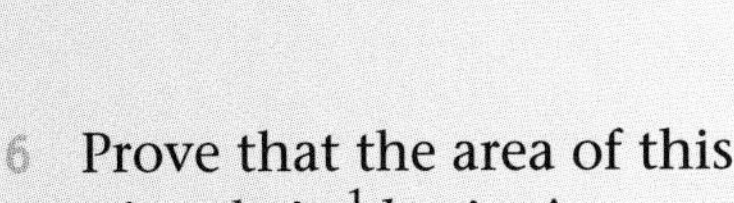

UAM 6 Prove that the area of this triangle is $\frac{1}{2}bc \sin A$.

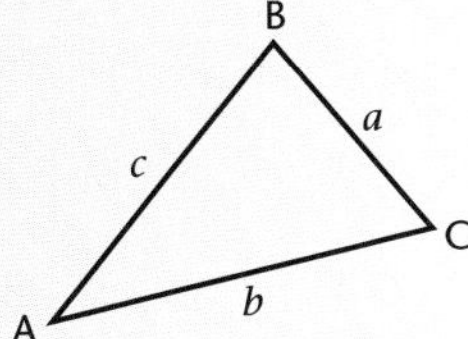

Draw the perpendicular from B to AC.

16.9 Angle between a line and a plane

In the drawing, N is the foot of the perpendicular from P to the plane ABCD. AN is called the projection of AP on the plane.

The angle between the line AP and the plane ABCD is the angle between AP and its projection on the plane. This is angle PAN.

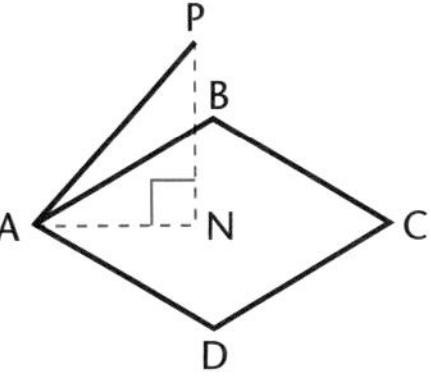

Example 15

This cuboid, which is 9 cm long, has square ends of side 6 cm.

Find the angle between the diagonal AG and the base EFGH.

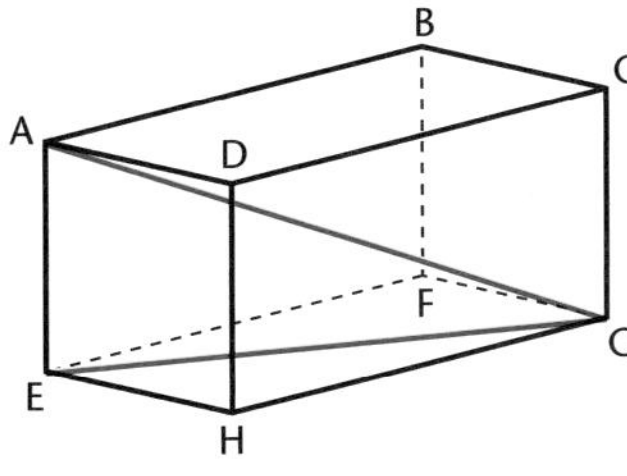

In $\triangle EHG$,

$EG^2 = EH^2 + HG^2$ Pythagoras' theorem

$= 6^2 + 9^2$

$= 36 + 81$

$= 117$ cm

$EG = \sqrt{117}$ cm

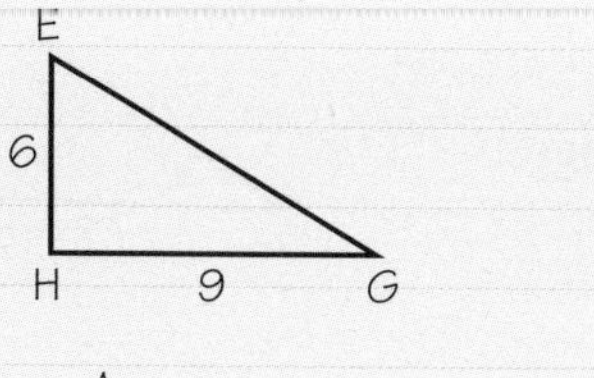

$\tan \angle G = \frac{\text{opp}}{\text{adj}} = \frac{AE}{EG} = \frac{6}{\sqrt{117}} = 0.5547\ldots$

$\angle G = 29.0°$ (3 s.f.)

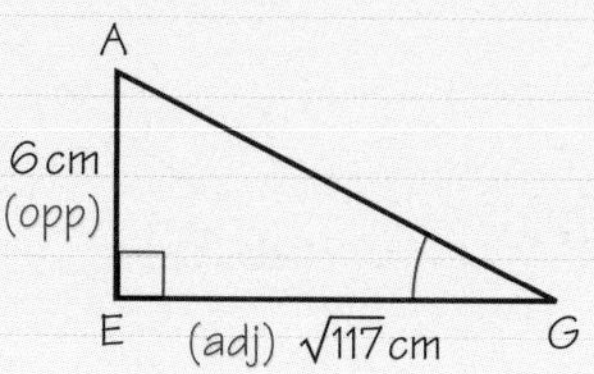

E is vertically below A so E is the base of the perpendicular from A to the plane. You need to find ∠AGE, so draw right-angled triangle AGE. To find ∠AGE you need the lengths of two sides in the triangle. AE is given but you must calculate the length of EG. Put any information you know on the diagram.

Exam practice 16I

1 The drawing shows a cuboid.
DC = 5 cm, CG = 8 cm and FG = 3 cm.

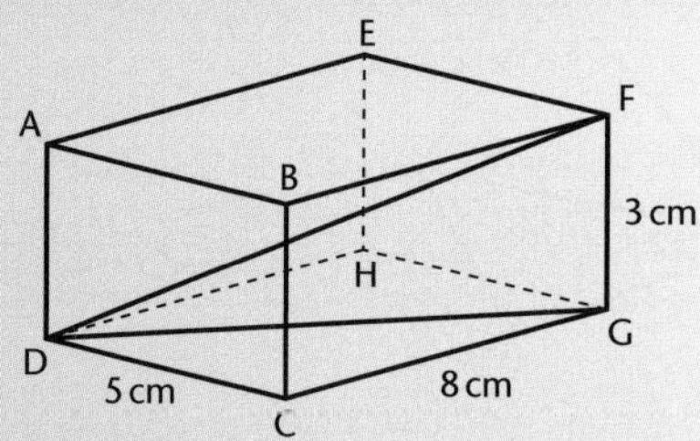

a Calculate the length of i DG ii DF.
b Work out the angle between DF and the base DCGH.

UAM 2 The sketch shows a cuboid.
AE = 4 cm, EH = 6 cm and HG = 10 cm.
Work out the angle between BH and the base EFGH.

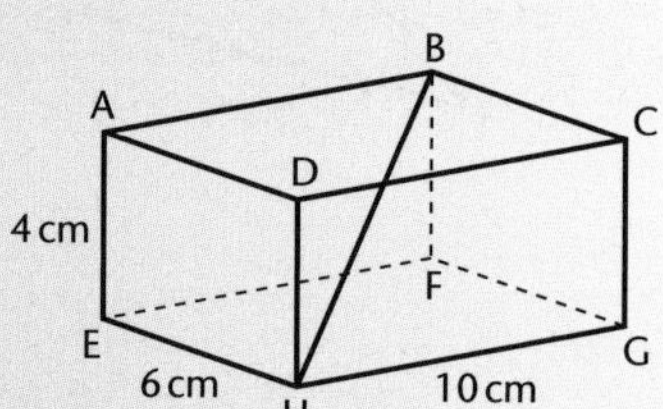

3 The diagram shows a cube of side 5 cm.
Calculate
a the length of EC
b the angle between EC and the base DCGH.

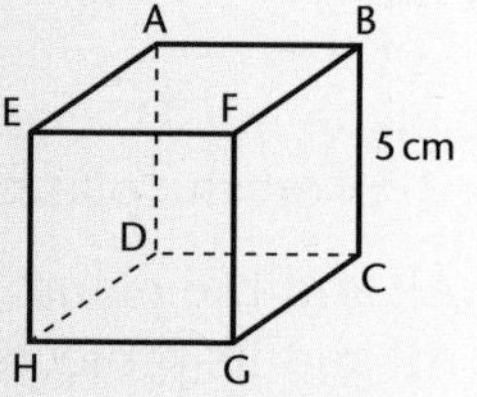

UAM 4 The drawing shows a right pyramid on a square base.
E is vertically above the centre of the square.
Calculate
a the length of AC
b the height of E above the base
c the angle the edge AE makes with the base ABCD.

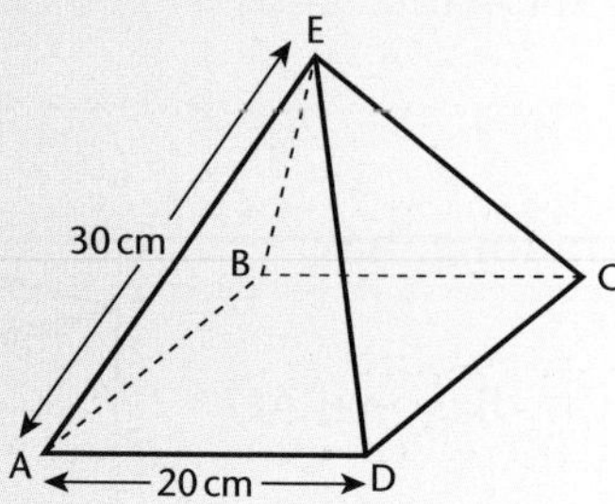

5 VABCD is a right pyramid on a rectangular base.
VA = VB = VC = VD = 14 cm.
Find the angle between VC and the base ABCD.

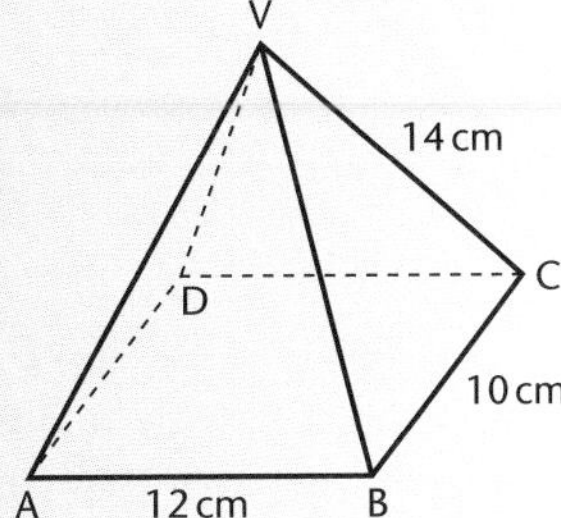

6 ABC is an equilateral triangle with side 10 cm and is the base of a tetrahedron VABC.
N is the point in the triangle ABC directly below V.
E is the midpoint of BC.
NE = $\frac{1}{3}$AE and VA = VB = VC = 12 cm.
Calculate

a the length of VE

b the angle between VE and the base.

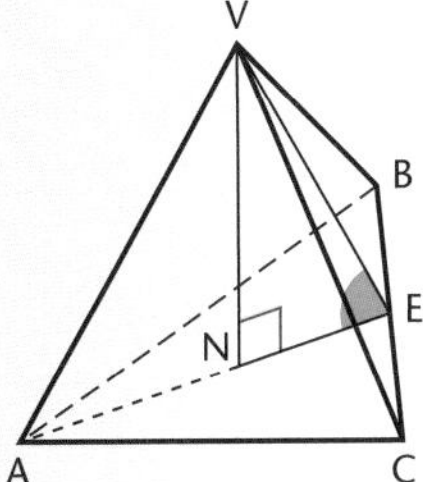

Derivation of the sine rule

In the diagram,

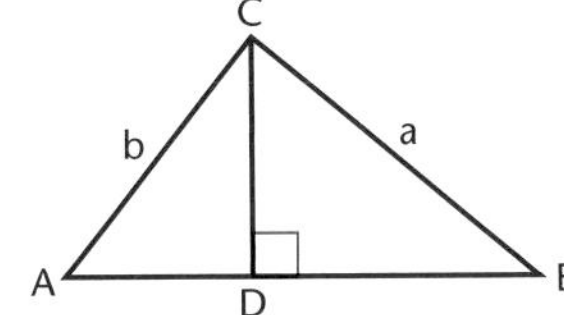

$\sin B = \frac{CD}{a}$ so $CD = a \sin B$

$\sin A = \frac{CD}{b}$ so $CD = b \sin A$

hence $a \sin B = b \sin A$ which can be rearranged to $\frac{a}{\sin A} = \frac{b}{\sin B}$

If a line from B is drawn to AC and perpendicular to AC, the result is

$$\frac{a}{\sin A} = \frac{c}{\sin C}$$

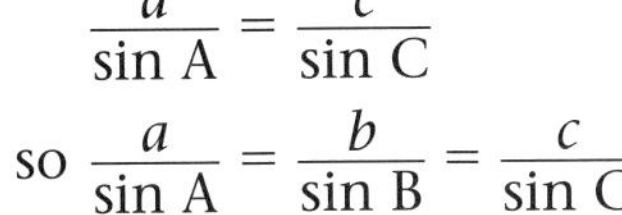

so $\frac{a}{\sin A} = \frac{b}{\sin B} = \frac{c}{\sin C}$

Derivation of the cosine rule

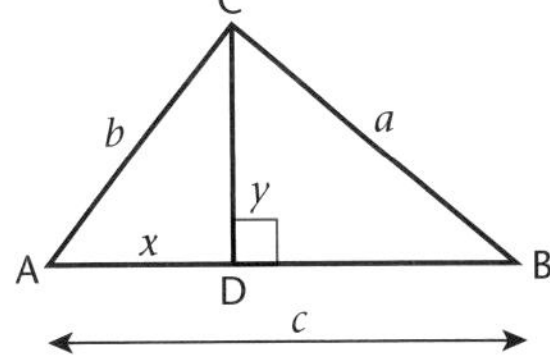

In triangle ACD, $\cos A = \frac{x}{b}$ so $x = b \cos A$. [1]

Using Pythagoras' theorem in triangle ACD and triangle BCD

gives $b^2 = x^2 + y^2$ [2]

and $a^2 = (c - x)^2 + y^2$ [3]

[3] − [2] gives $a^2 - b^2 = (c - x)^2 - x^2$

$$a^2 - b^2 = c^2 - 2cx + x^2 - x^2$$

$$a^2 = b^2 + c^2 - 2cx$$

Using [1] to substitute for x gives $a^2 = b^2 + c^2 - 2bc \cos A$

Derivation of the area formula

Area of triangle ABC $= \frac{1}{2}AB \times CD = \frac{1}{2}c \times (b \sin A)$

so area of triangle ABC $= \frac{1}{2}bc \sin A$

Summary of key points

- In a right-angled triangle $\sin = \frac{\text{opp}}{\text{hyp}}$, $\cos = \frac{\text{adj}}{\text{hyp}}$, $\tan = \frac{\text{opp}}{\text{adj}}$.
- The three-figure bearing of a point Q from a point P is the clockwise angle, in degrees, between the north direction at P and the line PQ.
- For an obtuse angle A:
  - $\sin A = \sin(180° - A)$ e.g. $\sin 120° = \sin 60°$
  - $\cos A = -\cos(180° - A)$ e.g. $\cos 130° = -\cos 50°$
  - $\tan A = -\tan(180° - A)$ e.g. $\tan 140° = -\tan 40°$
- In any triangle ABC, where a, b and c are the sides opposite the angles A, B and C respectively.

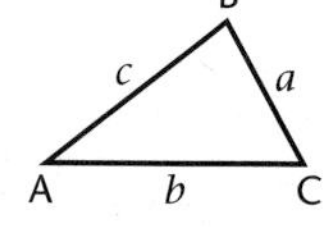

  - the sine rule gives $\frac{a}{\sin A} = \frac{b}{\sin B} = \frac{c}{\sin C}$
  - the cosine rule gives $a^2 = b^2 + c^2 - 2bc \cos A$
    $b^2 = a^2 + c^2 - 2ac \cos B$
    $c^2 = a^2 + b^2 - 2ab \cos C$
  - the area of the triangle is $\frac{1}{2}bc \sin A = \frac{1}{2}ab \sin C = \frac{1}{2}ac \sin B$
- The angle between the line AP and the plane is the angle between the line AP and the line AN where N is the foot of the perpendicular from P to the plane. AN is called the projection of AP on the plane

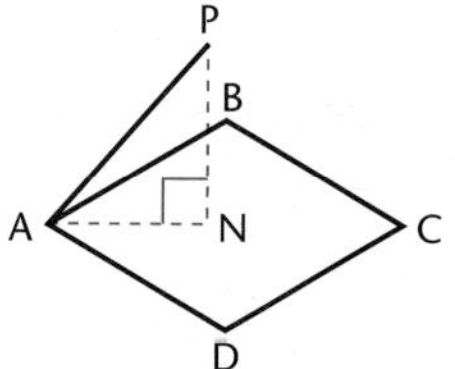

Most candidates who get GRADE A or above can:

- use the sine rule and cosine rule to solve problems.

Glossary

All these terms refer to right-angled triangles.

Adjacent side — the side, other than the hypotenuse, adjacent to the angle being considered

Cosine of an angle — the ratio $\frac{\text{adjacent side}}{\text{hypotenuse}}$

Hypotenuse — the side opposite the right angle

Opposite side — the side opposite the angle being considered

Sine of an angle — the ratio $\frac{\text{opposite side}}{\text{hypotenuse}}$

Tangent of an angle — the ratio $\frac{\text{opposite side}}{\text{adjacent side}}$

Also

Bearing — the direction of one place from another

Compass direction — the direction as a point on a compass

Three-figure bearing — the direction of one place from another as a 3-figure angle measured clockwise from north

17 Graphs

This chapter will show you:

- ✓ what the equation of a circle with its centre at the origin looks like
- ✓ how to use graphs to solve simultaneous equations when one equation is linear and the other equation is $x^2 + y^2 = r^2$
- ✓ the characteristic shapes of the graphs of the following equations $y = ax^2 - bx + c$, $y = ax^3 + bx^2 + cx + d$, $y = k^x$, $y = \frac{1}{x}$, $y = \sin x$, $y = \cos x$
- ✓ transformations that change a graph and how these change the corresponding equations

Before you start you need to know:

- ✓ the meaning of indices
- ✓ how to substitute positive and negative numbers into an expression
- ✓ how to make a table of values and plot points to draw a graph
- ✓ what the equation of a straight line looks like
- ✓ that the coordinates of the points where two graphs cross give the solution to the simultaneous equations of these graphs
- ✓ how to multiply out brackets
- ✓ how to factorise quadratic expressions
- ✓ how to complete the square
- ✓ the meaning of sine and cosine
- ✓ how to transform a shape by a reflection, a translation, and a stretch

17.1 The equation of a circle

This diagram shows a circle with centre O and radius r.

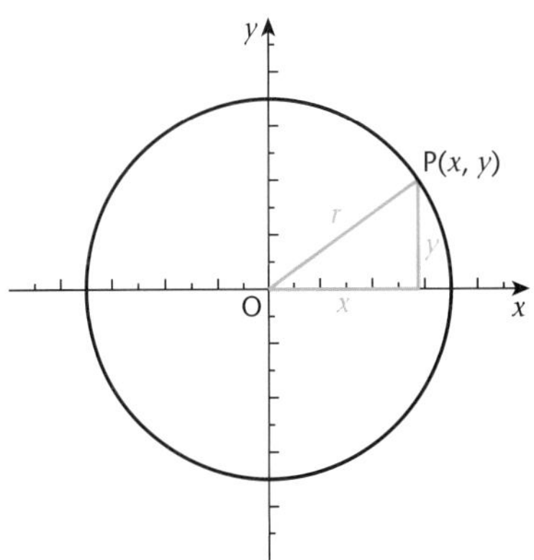

The length of the line from any point on this circle to O is equal to the radius.
For a point P(x, y) to lie on the circle, OP must be equal to r.
Using Pythagoras' theorem on the green triangle gives $x^2 + y^2 = r^2$.

The coordinates of any point on this circle must satisfy the equation

$$x^2 + y^2 = r^2.$$

This is the equation of the circle.

You can draw graphs to find a solution to a pair of simultaneous equations where one equation is linear and the other is of the form $x^2 + y^2 = r^2$.

$x^2 + y^2 = 4$ is the equation of a circle with centre O and radius 2.

Example 1

Draw the graphs of $x^2 + y^2 = 9$ and $3y + x = 3$ on the same set of axes.
Use your graphs to find the solutions to the simultaneous equations $x^2 + y^2 = 9$ and $3y + x = 3$.

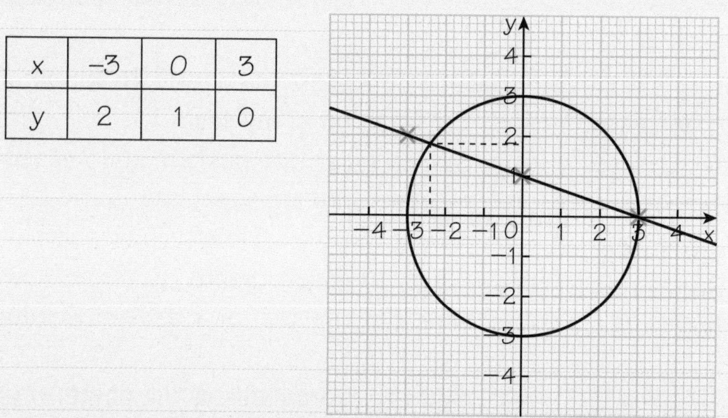

x	−3	0	3
y	2	1	0

You need to recognise that $x^2 + y^2 = 9$ is the equation of a circle. Its centre is O and its radius is 3 ($r^2 = 9$ so $r = 3$). You do not need to make a table of values. You can use compasses to draw the circle but you must have the same scale on both axes.

Make a table of values to draw the line.
The solutions are where the graphs cross.

$x = -2.4$, $y = 1.8$ and $x = 3$, $y = 0$

Exam practice 17A

1 Write down the equation of each circle.

a

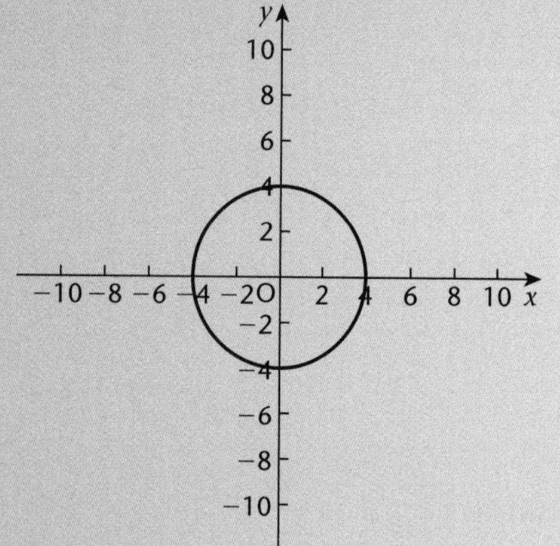

b

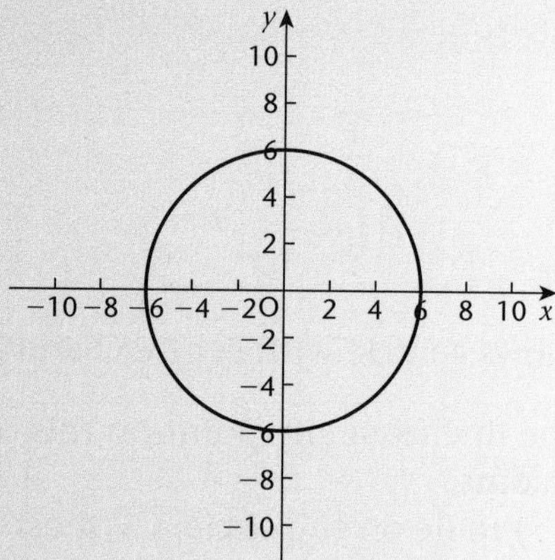

2 Draw the graphs of $x^2 + y^2 = 49$ and $y = 2x - 4$ on a grid like this.
Use your graphs to find the solutions to the simultaneous equations $x^2 + y^2 = 49$ and $y = 2x - 4$.

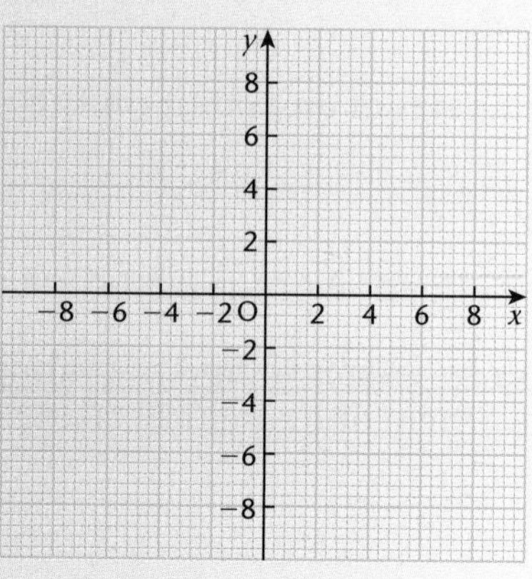

3 These are the graphs of $y^2 + x^2 = 25$ and $y = 3x - 5$.
Show that the x-coordinates of the points of intersection satisfy the equation $x^2 - 3x = 0$.
Calculate the coordinates of their points of intersection.

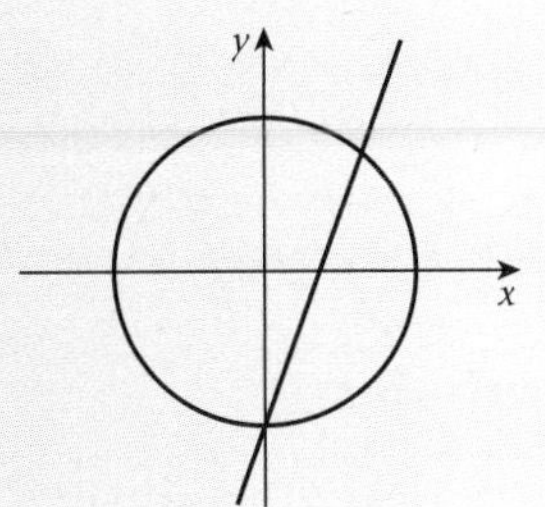

Give exact answers.

17.2 Graphs of quadratic functions

The equation of any curve has the form y = (a function of x) which is shortened to $y = f(x)$. You say 'f of x'.
You can think of a function like a number machine. x is the input and $f(x)$ is the output. For $f(x) = x^2 + 2x$, $f(1) = 3$, $f(-2) = 0$ and $f(3) = 15$.
The quadratic function is $ax^2 + bx + c$.
Graphs of the form $y = ax^2 + bx + c$, where a, b and c are constants and a is not zero, give a parabolic curve.

A function of x can be any expression in x that gives one value of y when you substitute a value for x.

You can draw the graph of a quadratic by making a table of values.

Example 2

a Draw the graph of $y = 2x^2 - 2x + 3$ for values of x from -2 to 3.
b Use your graph to solve the equation $2x^2 - 2x + 3 = 8$.
c Explain why the graph shows that the equation $2x^2 - 2x + 3 = 0$ has no solution.

Make a table of values. Choose integer values of x. You will need extra values near the point where the graph turns.
You may find it helps to add extra rows to the table.

a

x	-2	-1	0	$\frac{1}{2}$	1	2	3
$2x^2$	8	2	0	$\frac{1}{2}$	2	8	18
$-2x$	4	2	0	-1	-2	-4	-6
$y = 2x^2 - 2x + 3$	15	7	3	2.5	3	7	15

Plot the points and draw a smooth curve through them.

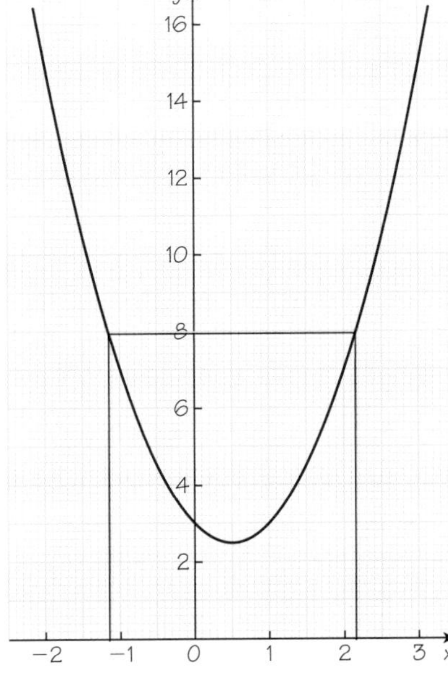

b $x = -1.15$ and 2.15

c When $y = 0$, $2x^2 - 2x + 3 = 0$
The curve does not cross the x-axis so there are no values of x for which $y = 0$.

Compare $2x^2 - 2x + 3 = 8$ with $y = 2x^2 - 2x + 3$.
The solutions are the values of x when $y = 8$. You can see these by drawing a horizontal line at $y = 8$ then reading the values of x where this line cuts the curve. These values are approximate because you cannot always read values accurately from a graph.

17.3 Minimum and maximum values

All quadratic graphs look like $\cup$ or $\cap$

These curves are called **parabolas**.

They have a line of symmetry that goes through the point where the curve turns.
y has either a maximum value or a minimum value at this point.

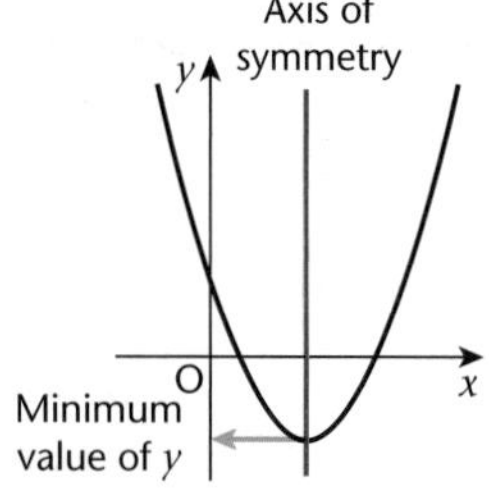

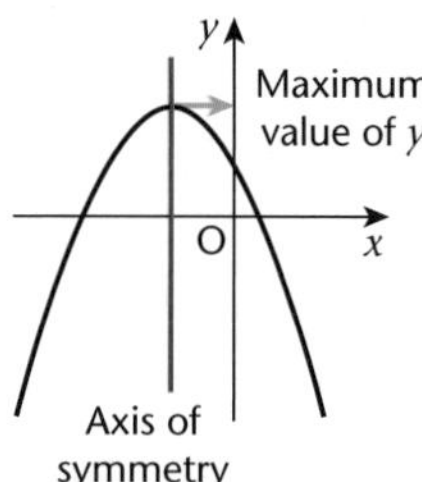

You can find the maximum or minimum value of y without drawing an accurate graph.
If the quadratic function factorises, you can find the value of x for the line of symmetry from a sketch of the graph. Then find y for this value of x.

Example 3

This diagram shows the graph of $y = x^2 - 5x - 6$.

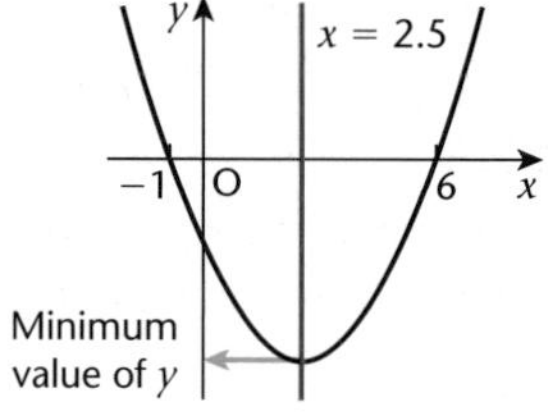

a Factorise $x^2 - 5x - 6$

b Find the minimum value of $x^2 - 5x - 6$.

a $x^2 - 5x - 6 = (x - 6)(x + 1)$

b When $(x - 6)(x + 1) = 0$, $x = 6$ or -1.
The value halfway between 6 and -1 is 2.5.
The equation of the line of symmetry is $x = 2.5$.

The minimum value of y is $(2.5 - 6)(2.5 + 1)$
$= -3.5 \times 3.5 = -12.25$.

The line of symmetry is halfway between the points where the curve cuts the x-axis. The values of x where the curve cuts the x-axis are the solutions of $x^2 - 5x - 6 = 0$.

You find the minimum value of $x^2 - 5x - 6$ by substituting $x = 2.5$ into the expression.

You can also find the maximum or minimum value by 'completing the square'.

The above example gives $y = (x - 2.5)^2 - 2.5^2 - 6$
$y = (x - 2.5)^2 - 12.25$

Since $(x - 2.5)^2 \geqslant 0$, the minimum value of y occurs when $x = 2.5$ and the minimum value is -12.25.

Example 4

a Find the values of a and b for which $x^2 - 7x + 2 = (x - a)^2 + b$.

b Hence find the minimum value of $x^2 - 7x + 2$.

a $x^2 - 7x + 2 = (x - a)^2 + b$

$x^2 - 7x + 2 = x^2 - 2ax + a^2 + b$

So $-7 = -2a$

$a = 3.5$

and $2 = a^2 + b$

$2 = (3.5)^2 + b$

$b = 2 - (3.5)^2 = -10.25$

Alternatively:
$x^2 - 7x + 2 = x^2 - 7x + \left(\frac{7}{2}\right)^2 + 2 - \left(\frac{7}{2}\right)^2$
$= (x - \frac{7}{2})^2 - \frac{41}{4}$

b $x^2 - 7x + 2 = (x - 3.5)^2 - 10.25$

The minimum value of $(x - 3.5)^2$ is 0,

so the minimum value of $x^2 - 7x + 2$ is -10.25.

'Hence' means use the result from part **a**.

$(x - 3.5)^2 \geqslant 0$ whatever the value of x because when you square a number the result is always positive.

Exam practice 17B

1 a Copy and complete this table of values for the equation $y = x^2 + 6x - 1$.

x	-7	-5	-4	-3	-2	-1	0	1
y	6	-6	-9	-10			-1	6

b Use the values in your table to draw the graph of $y = x^2 + 6x - 1$.
Use a grid like this.

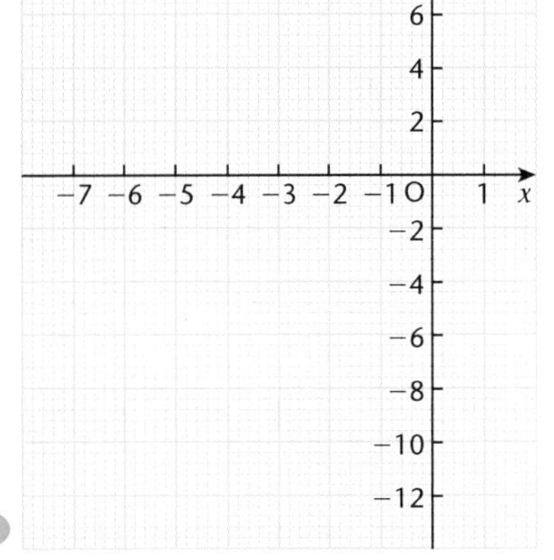

c i Write down the values of x when $y = 0$.

ii Write down the equation that has these values as its roots.

d What is the least value of y?

WWW

2 a Copy and complete this table of values for the equation $y = 3 - x - 2x^2$.

x	-3	-2	-1.5	-1	0	1	2
y		-3	0		3		-7

b Draw the graph of $y = 3 - x - 2x^2$ for these values of x.

c Write down the values of x when $y = -1$.

d What is the highest value of y?

3 a Draw the graph of $y = x^2 - 5x + 3$ for values of x from -1 to 6.

b Write down the least value of y.

Start by finding values of y for integer values of x. This will show you roughly where the graph turns. Add more values of x close to this point.

4 a Draw the graph of $y = 7 - 2x - x^2$ for values of x from -5 to 3.

b Write down the equation of the line of symmetry of your graph.

5 a Factorise $x^2 - 5x - 36$.
b This diagram shows the graph of $y = x^2 - 5x - 36$.
Find the equation of the line of symmetry.
c Hence find the minimum value of $x^2 - 5x - 36$.

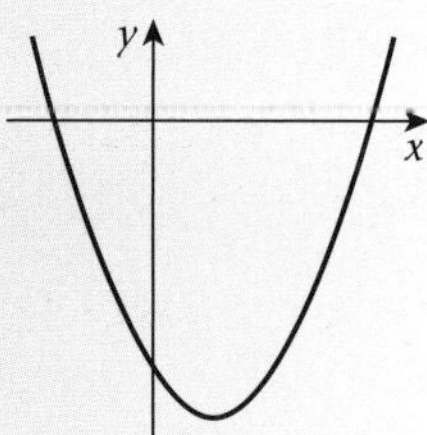

6 a Factorise $6 - x - x^2$.
b This diagram shows the graph of $y = 6 - x - x^2$.
Find the equation of the line of symmetry.

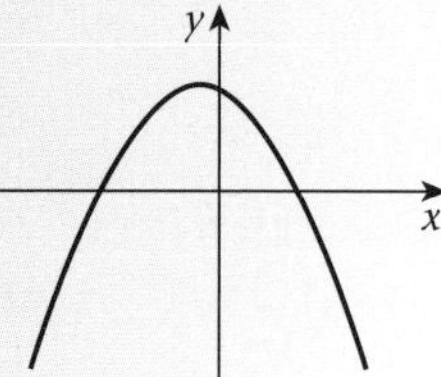

7 a Find the values of a and b for which $x^2 - 4x + 5 = (x - a)^2 + b$.
b Hence find the minimum value of $x^2 - 4x + 5$.

8 a Find the values of a and b for which $x^2 - 3x - 2 = (x - a)^2 + b$.
b Hence find the minimum value of $x^2 - 3x - 2$.

9 a Find the values of a and b for which $3 + 4x - x^2 = b - (x - a)^2$.
b Hence find the maximum value of $3 + 4x - x^2$.

17.4 Graphs of other functions

You can draw the graph of $y =$ (any function of x) by making a table of values.
Different types of function give graphs with a characteristic shape.

Cubic graphs

Functions of the form $y = ax^3 + bx^2 + cx + d$, where a, b, c and d are constants and a is not zero, are called **cubic functions**.

When you plot the graph of a cubic function, the shape of the curve will look like one of these graphs.

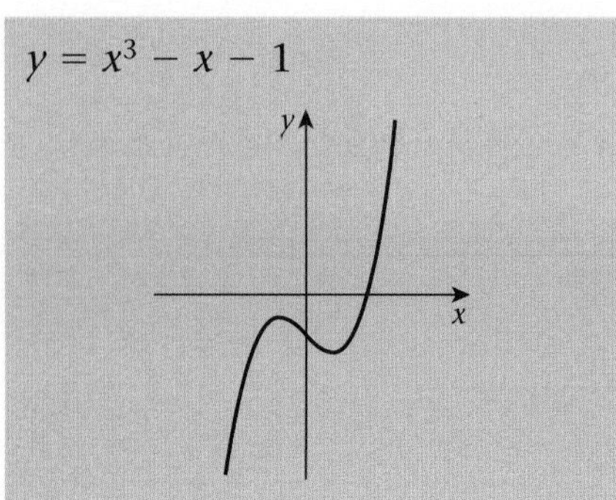

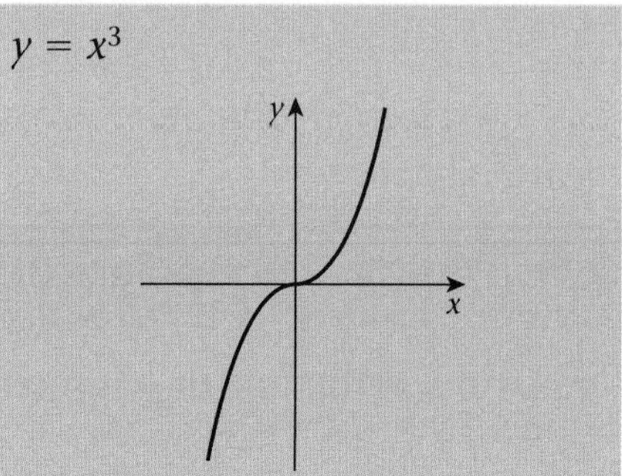

If $a < 0$, the curves will be reflected to look like

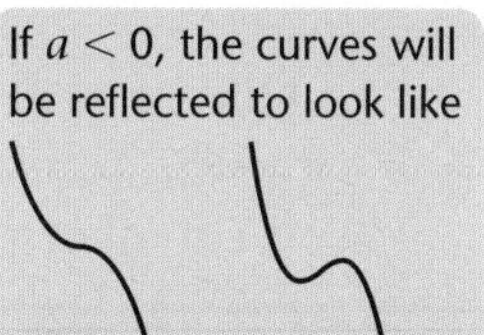

Exponential functions

Exponential functions have x as a power, so they are of the form $y = k^x$ where k is a constant.

The graph of $y = k^x$ where k is a positive integer looks like this.

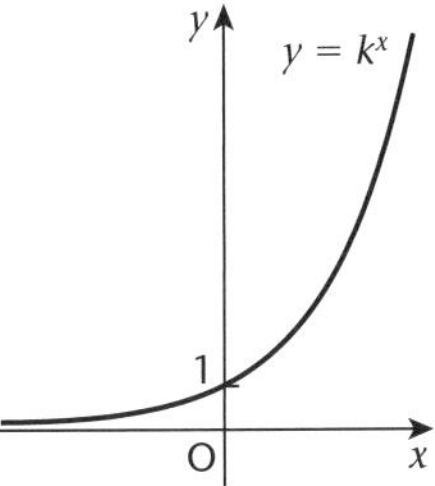

It always cuts the y-axis at (0, 1).
It gets closer to the x-axis as the values of x get lower but never crosses it.

Exponent is another word for power or index.

When $x = 0$, $y = k^0$ and any number to the power 0 is equal to 1.

The reciprocal function

The function $y = \frac{1}{x}$ is called the reciprocal function.

The graph of $y = \frac{1}{x}$ looks like this.

It has two parts but neither part cuts either axis.

You can use these graphs to solve equations.

It is called this because $\frac{1}{x}$ is the **reciprocal** of x.

When two quantities, x and y, are inversely proportional, they are related by the equation $y = \frac{k}{x}$ where k is a constant. The graph will have a similar shape to that of $y = \frac{1}{x}$.

Example 5

This is the graph of $y = x^3 - 3x^2 + 2$.

a Use the graph to solve the equation $x^3 - 3x^2 + 2 = 0$.

b Write down the equation of the straight line that you need to draw to solve the equation $x^3 - 3x^2 + x + 1 = 0$.

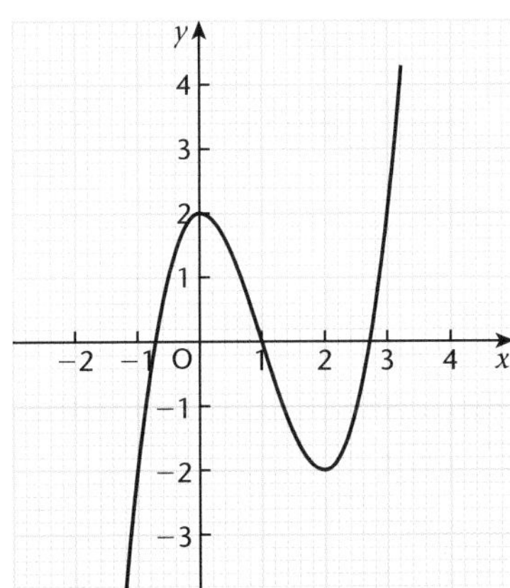

a $x = -0.7$, 1 and 2.7

The solutions of the equation $x^3 - 3x^2 + 2 = 0$ are the values of x where $y = 0$.

b $x^3 - 3x^2 + x + 1 = 0$

so $x^3 - 3x^2 + 2 = -x + 1$

Rearrange $x^3 - 3x^2 + x + 1 = 0$ so that the left-hand side is equal to $x^3 - 3x^2 + 2$. You can do this by subtracting x from both sides and adding 1 to both sides.

The line is $y = -x + 1$.

The solutions of $x^3 - 3x^2 + x + 1 = 0$ are the points where the curve $y = x^3 - 3x^2 + 2$ and the line $y = -x + 1$ intersect.

Exam practice 17C

1 a Copy and complete this table of values for the function $y = x^3 - 1$.

x	−2	−1	−0.5	0	0.5	1	2
y	−9		−1.125	−1		0	7

b Use the values in your table to draw the graph of $y = x^3 - 1$.
Use a grid like this.

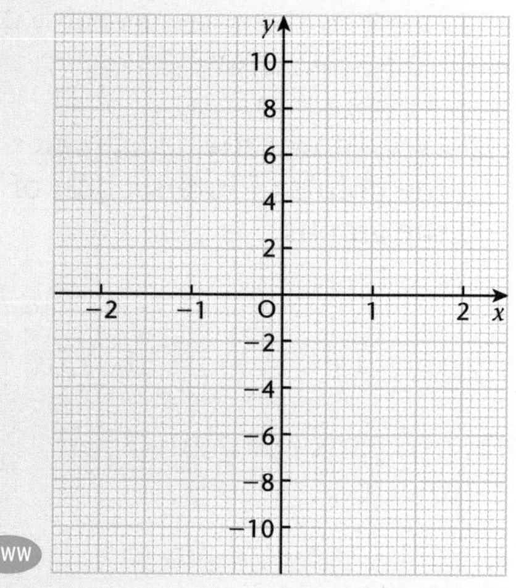

c i Write down the values of x when $y = 0$.
ii Write down the equation that has these values for its roots.

d Use your graph to find the solutions of the function $x^3 - 2 = 0$.

WWW

2 a Copy and complete this table of values for the function $y = x^3 - 3x - 1$.

x	−3	−2	−1	0	1	2	3
y	−19	−3		−1	−3		17

b Use the values in your table to draw the graph of $y = x^3 - 3x - 1$.
Use a grid like this.

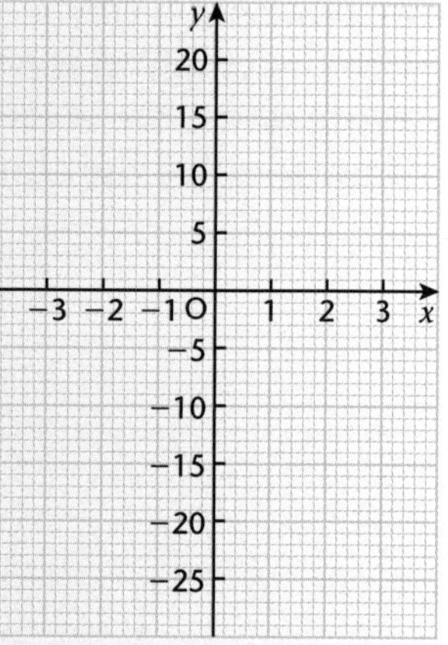

c i Write down the values of x when $y = 0$.
ii Write down the equation that has these values for its roots.

d Use your graph to find the solutions of the equation $x^3 - 3x + 2 = 0$.

e Write down the equation of the line you would need to draw to solve the equation $x^3 - 2x + 5 = 0$.

WWW

3 a Copy and complete this table of values for the function $y = 2^x$.

x	−3	−2	−1	0	1	2	3
y	0.13			1	2	4	

b Use the values in your table to draw the graph of $y = 2^x$.
Use a grid like this.

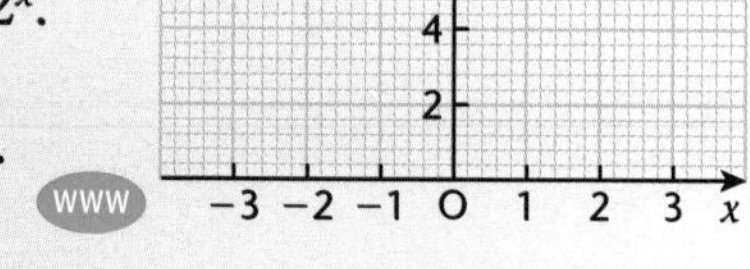

c Use your graph to find the value of x for which $2^x = 3$.

d Make a table of values for $y = 3^x$ for values of x from −3 to 3.
Give the values of y to 2 decimal places.
On the same set of axes, draw the graph of $y = 3^x$.

WWW

4 a Copy and complete this table of values for the function $y = \frac{1}{x}$.

x	−3	−2	−1	−0.5	0.5	1	2	3
y	−0.33		−1		2	1	0.5	

b Use the values in your table to draw the graph of $y = \frac{1}{x}$. Use a grid like this.

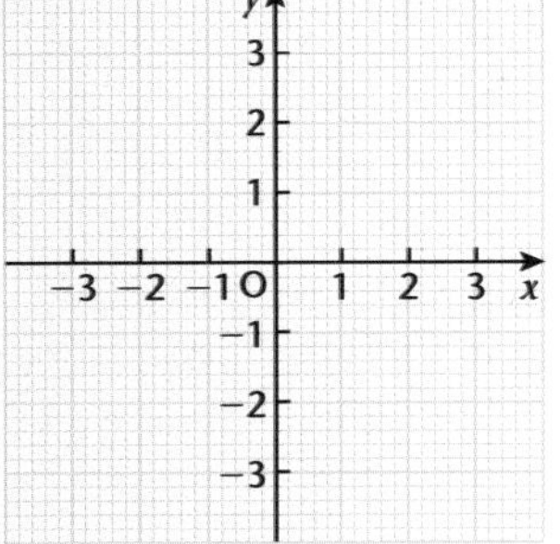

UAM

c Explain why $x = 0$ is not included in the table.

d Draw the graph of $3y - 2x = 1$ on the same axes.

Remember that this curve has two parts.

e Write down the coordinates of the points of intersection of the graphs.

5 Which of these functions could give each graph?

$y = x^2$, $y = x^3$, $y = 4^x$, $y = \frac{1}{x}$, $y = x$

a
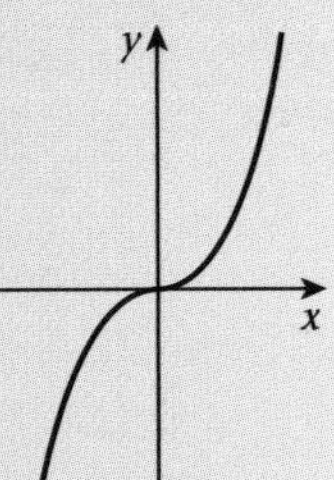

b
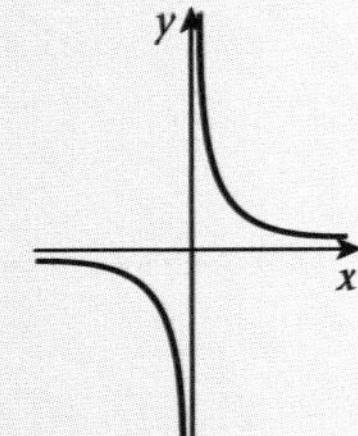

c
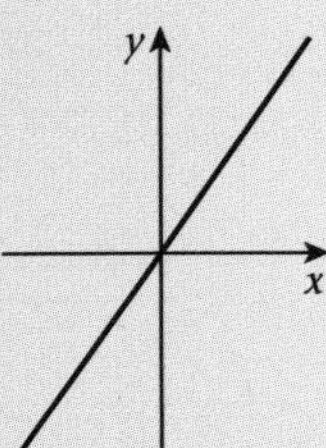

d
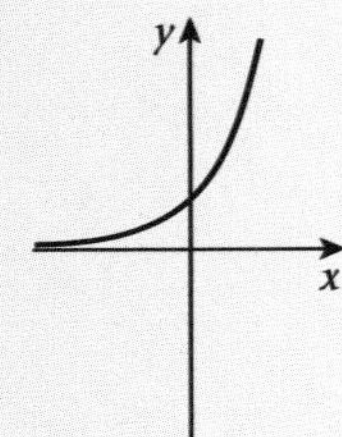

6 Which of these graphs could have the equation $y = 2x^2 - 5x + 1$?

A
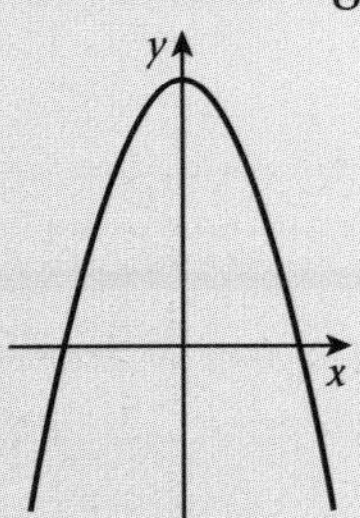

B
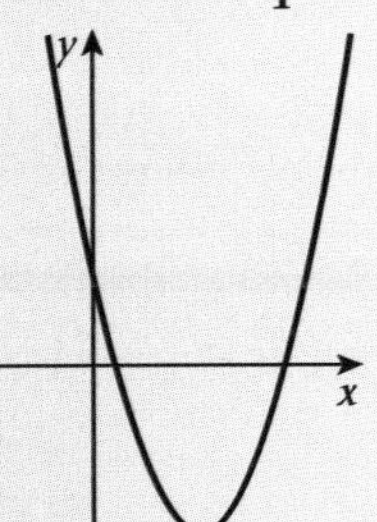

C
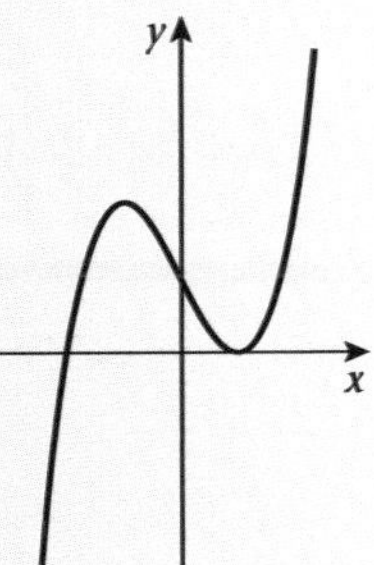

17.5 Graphs of $y = \sin x$ and $y = \cos x$

You can use a calculator to find the value of sin x for any value of x. This means you can use a table to plot the graph of $y = \sin x$.

You can do the same for $y = \cos x$.

The graph of $y = \sin x$

This is the graph of $y = \sin x$ for values of x from $-180°$ to $720°$.

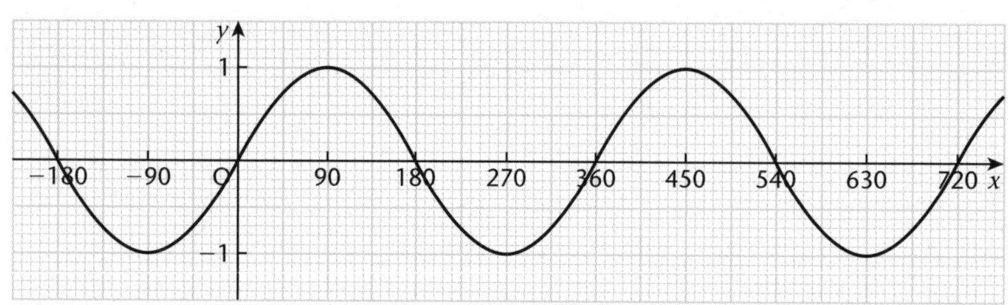

The shape of this curve is sometimes called a sine wave.
The curve repeats every 360°.
It shows that $y = \sin x$ has a maximum value of 1 and a minimum value of -1.
This means that $-1 \leqslant \sin x \leqslant 1$ for all values of x. The graph also has rotational symmetry of order 2 about O.

The graph of $y = \cos x$

This is the graph of $y = \cos x$ for values of x from $-180°$ to $720°$.

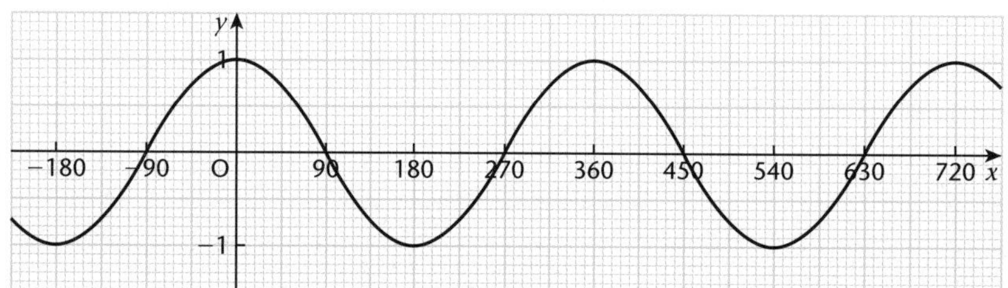

It is the same shape as the sine wave so it has the same properties.
It is in a different position from the curve $y = \sin x$.
It is a translation of the curve $y = \sin x$ by 90° to the left.

Example 6

a This is the graph of $y = \cos x$ for values of x from 0° to 360°.

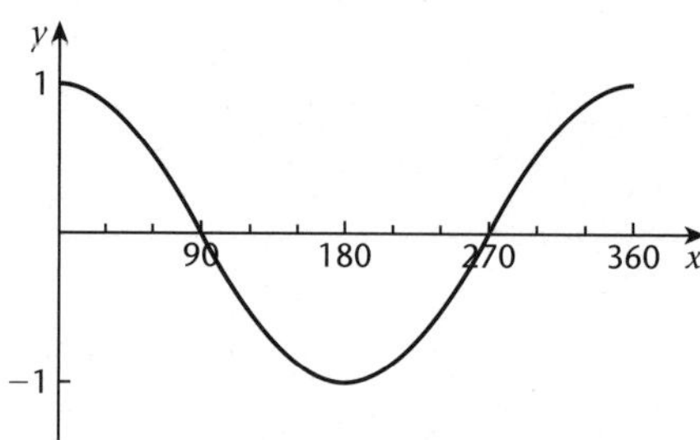

Use the graph to solve the equation $\cos x = 0$ for values of x from 0° to 360°.

b Solve the equation $\sin x = -0.4$ for values of x from 0° to 360°.

a $x = 90°$ or $270°$.

$\cos x = 0$ where $y = 0$. This is where the graph crosses the x-axis.

b $\sin x = -0.4$

Press (sin⁻¹) (+/−) (0) (.) (4) (=). This gives one value of x.

$x = -23.6°$ to 1 d.p.

This is the solution given by the calculator.

The graph of $y = \sin x$ shows that there is more than one value of x for which $\sin x = -0.4$. (There are an infinite number.) This is why you will always be asked to find solutions for a range of values of x. To make sure you find these values, draw a sketch of $y = \sin x$ covering the given range and the calculator solution.

y
1
−1
−90
0
90
180
270
360
x

You can see that $y = -0.4$ cuts the curve twice between $x = 0$ and $x = 360$. Mark the solution given by the calculator. You can then use the symmetries of the curve to find the solutions between 0° and 360°.

$x = 180° + 23.6°$ and $360° - 23.6°$

$x = 203.6°$ and $336.4°$.

Exam practice 17D

1 Sketch these graphs for values of x from 0° to 360°.

a $y = \sin x$ b $y = \cos x$

> Do not draw an accurate graph. Draw the curve freehand but label the x-axis every 90° and the y-axis with the maximum and minimum values.

2 Use your answer to question 1 to write down the values of x from 0° to 360° when

a $\cos x = -1$ b $\sin x = 0$ c $\cos x = 1$.

3 This is the graph of $y = \cos x$.

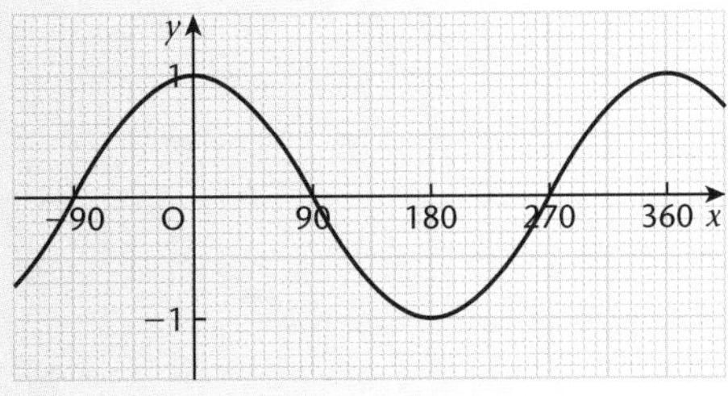

Write down the values of x between 0° and 360° when

a $\cos x = 0.5$ b $\cos x = -0.5$ c $\cos x = 0.7$

d $4 \cos x = 3$ e $5 \cos x = 2$ f $3 \cos x - 1 = 0$.

4 This is the graph of $y = \sin x$.

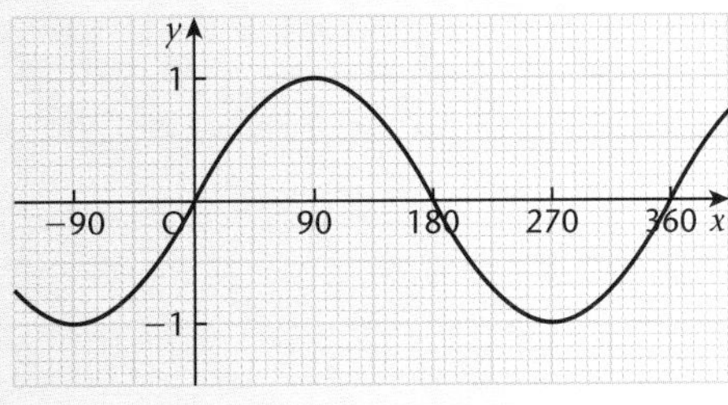

Use the graph to solve these equations for values of x between 0° and 360°.

a $\sin x = 0.25$ b $\sin x = -0.7$ c $6 \sin x = 2$

ICT task

You can use a spreadsheet program to do the calculations for a table of values and you can use a chart to draw the graph. You can make a table of values for $y = \sin x$ and draw its graph like this.

	A	B	C	D	E	F	G
1	x	0	10	20	30	40	50
2	y	0	0.1736	0.3420	0.5	0.6428	0.7660
3							
7							
8							
9							

Enter the formula B1+10 in this cell. Then use the fill function to fill in the row up to a value of 360.

Enter the formula for sin B1. Then use the fill function to complete the row.

1.20, 0.80, 0.40, 0.00, −0.40, −0.80, −1.20; 0, 50, 100, 150, 200, 250, 300, 350, 400

Choose insert chart and then choose type scatter graph.

You need to make sure your spreadsheet can calculate angles in degrees. Many spreadsheets use another unit for measuring angles called **radians**. To find sin x when the spreadsheet measures angles using radians you may need to enter sin (degrees (B1)).

Use a spreadsheet to draw the graphs of

a $y = \cos x$ for $0° \leqslant x \leqslant 360°$ **b** $y = x^3 + 2x^2 - 5x - 10$.

17.6 Transformations of graphs

Any curve can be transformed in the same way that you can transform any other object such as a triangle.

There is a relationship between the equation of a curve and the equation of its transformation.

A transformation of an object changes its position and it may also change its shape.

Reflection in the x-axis When a curve $y = f(x)$ is reflected in the x-axis, the equation of the reflected curve is $y = -f(x)$.	y, x, O P(s, t) $y = f(x)$ $y = -f(x)$ P$'(s, -t)$	When the point P(s, t) is reflected in the x-axis, it maps to the point P$'(s, -t)$. So the y-coordinate of a point on the reflected curve is minus the y-coordinate of the corresponding point on the original curve.
Reflection in the y-axis When a curve $y = f(x)$ is reflected in the y-axis, the equation of the reflected curve is $y = f(-x)$.	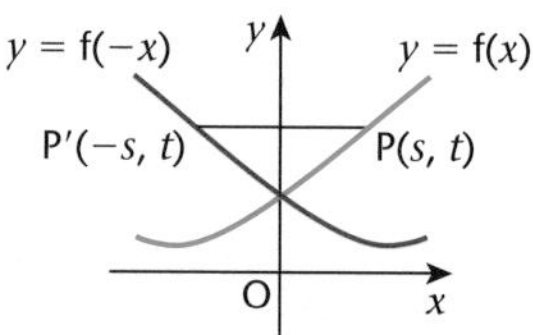	When the point P(s, t) is reflected in the y-axis it maps to the point P$'(-s, t)$. So the x-coordinate of a point on the reflected curve is minus the x-coordinate of the corresponding point on the original curve.
Translation parallel to the y-axis When a curve $y = f(x)$ is translated by a units parallel to the y-axis, the equation of the translated curve is $y = f(x) + a$. When a is positive, the curve moves up the y-axis. When a is negative it moves down.	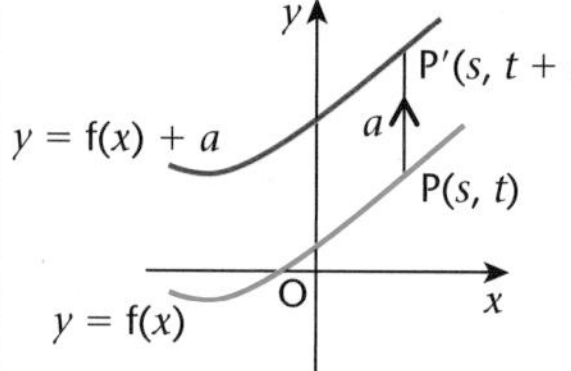	When the point P(s, t) is translated by a units up the y-axis it maps to the point P$'(s, t + a)$. So the y-coordinate of a point on the translated curve is a units greater than the y-coordinate of the corresponding point on the original curve.
Translation parallel to the x-axis When a curve $y = f(x)$ is translated by a units parallel to the x-axis, the equation of the translated curve is $y = f(x - a)$. When a is positive, the curve moves to the right. When a is negative it moves to the left.	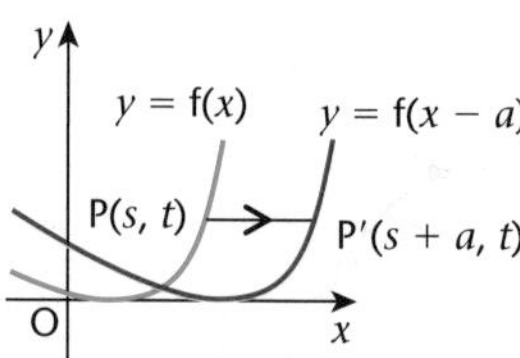	When the point P(s, t) is translated by a units to the right it maps to the point P$'(s + a, t)$. So the x-coordinate of a point on the translated curve is a units greater than the x-coordinate of the corresponding point on the original curve. The y-coordinates are the same. To get the same value of y you need to subtract a from the x-coordinate of P$'$.

Stretch by a factor *a* parallel to the *y*-axis When a curve $y = f(x)$ is stretched one-way by a factor a parallel to the y-axis, the equation of the stretched curve is $y = af(x)$.	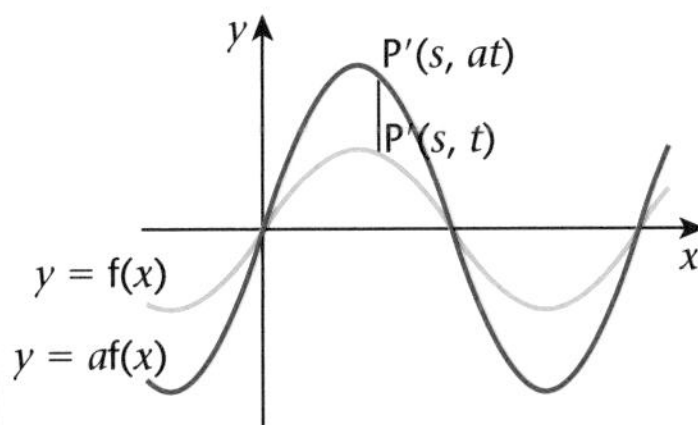	When the curve $y = f(x)$ is stretched by a factor of a units parallel to the y-axis, it increases the y-coordinate of P by a factor a. So (y-coordinate of P′) = $a \times$ (y-coordinate of P).
Stretch by a factor $\frac{1}{a}$ parallel to the *x*-axis When a curve $y = f(x)$ is stretched one-way by a factor $\frac{1}{a}$ parallel to the x-axis, the equation of the stretched curve is $y = f(ax)$. When $a > 1$, the width of the curve is reduced. When $a < 1$, the width of the curve is increased.	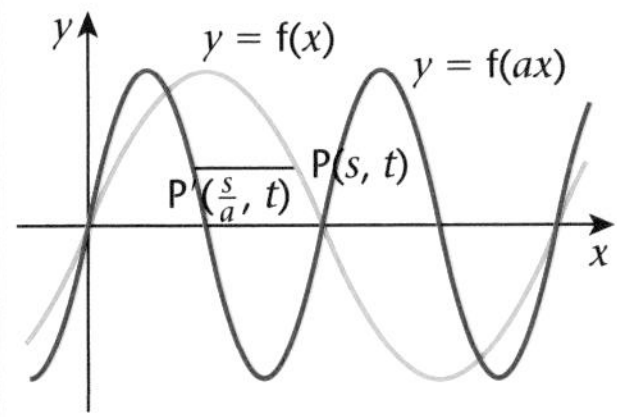	When the curve $y = f(x)$ is stretched by a factor $\frac{1}{a}$ parallel to the x-axis, the x-coordinate of P is scaled by a factor $\frac{1}{a}$. The y-coordinates of P and P′ are the same. To get the same value of y you need to multiply the x-coordinate of P′ by a.

You can use these relationships to sketch curves and to write down the equations of curves.

Example 7

This is the graph of $y = x^2$.

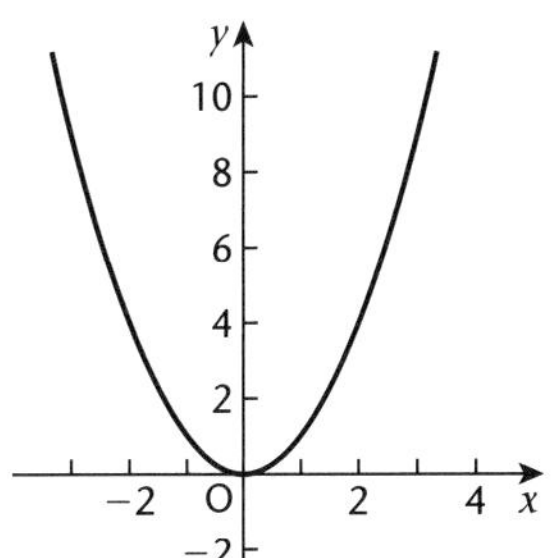

Use the graph to help you sketch each graph.

a $y = x^2 - 1$
b $y = 2x^2$
c $y = (x - 2)^2$

a

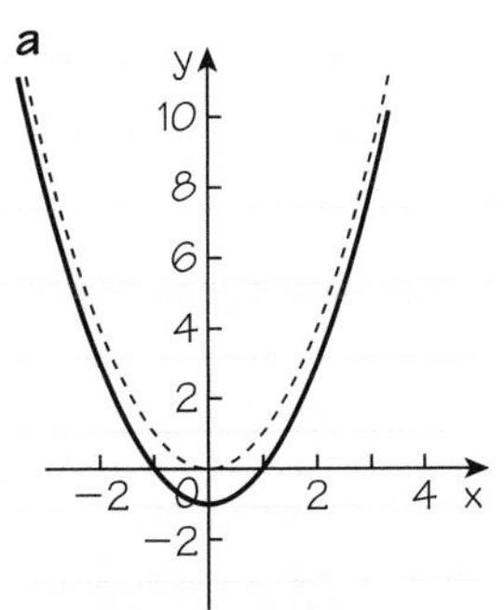

$y = x^2$ maps to $y = x^2 - 1$
$y = f(x)$ maps to $y = f(x) + a$ with $a = -1$.
So the curve translates 1 unit down the y-axis, i.e. there is a translation $\begin{pmatrix} 0 \\ -1 \end{pmatrix}$.

b

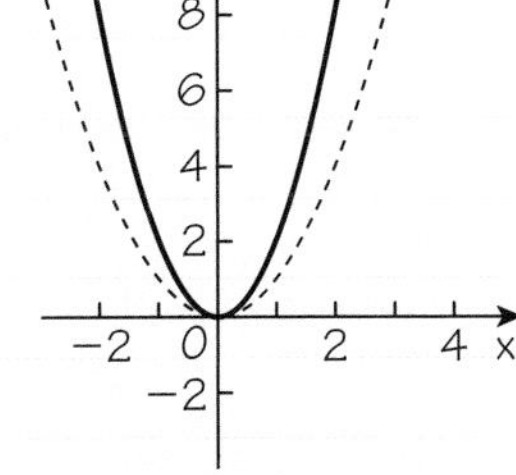

$y = x^2$ maps to $y = 2x^2$
$y = f(x)$ maps to $y = af(x)$ with $a = 2$.
So the curve is stretched by factor 2 parallel to the y-axis.

c

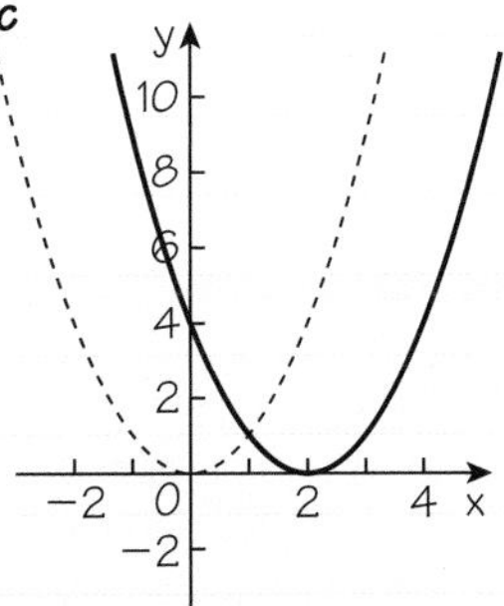

$y = x^2$ maps to $y = (x - 2)^2$
$y = f(x)$ maps to $y = f(x - a)$ with $a = 2$.
So the curve translates 2 units to the right, i.e. there is a translation $\begin{pmatrix} 2 \\ 0 \end{pmatrix}$.

Example 8

The diagrams show the graph $y = \cos x$ and a transformation of the graph.
Write down the equations of the transformed graphs.

a

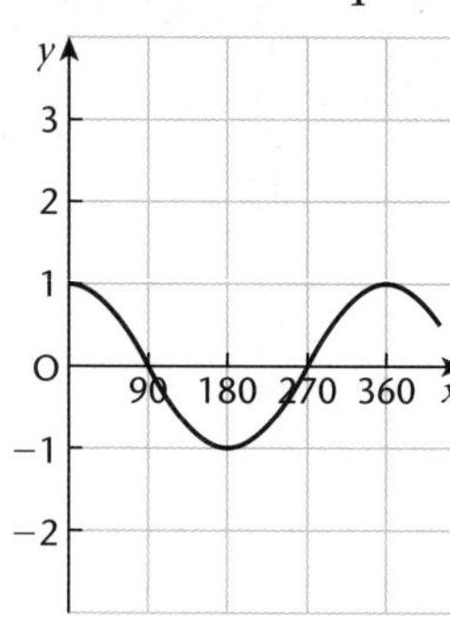

transforms to

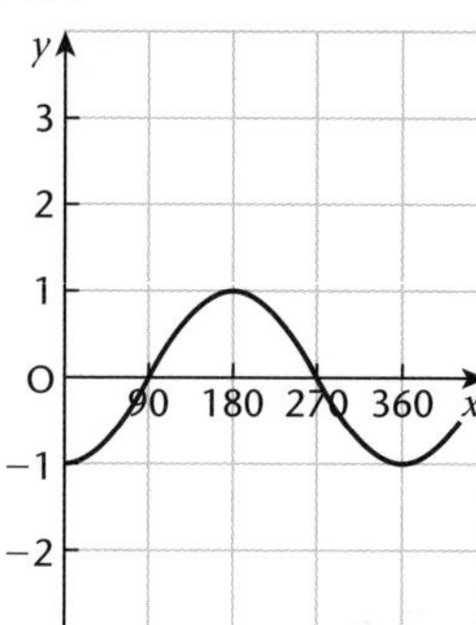

b

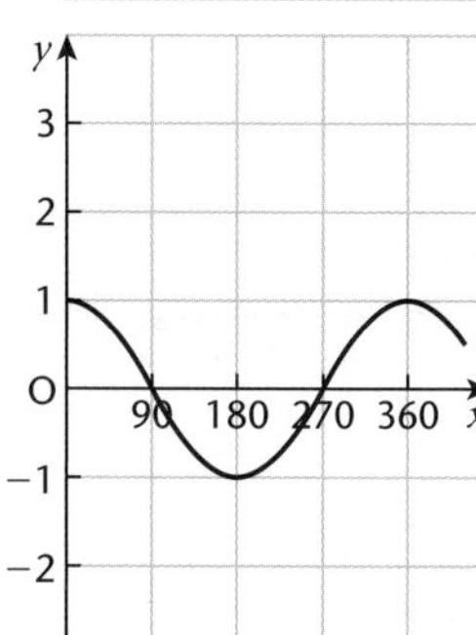

transforms to

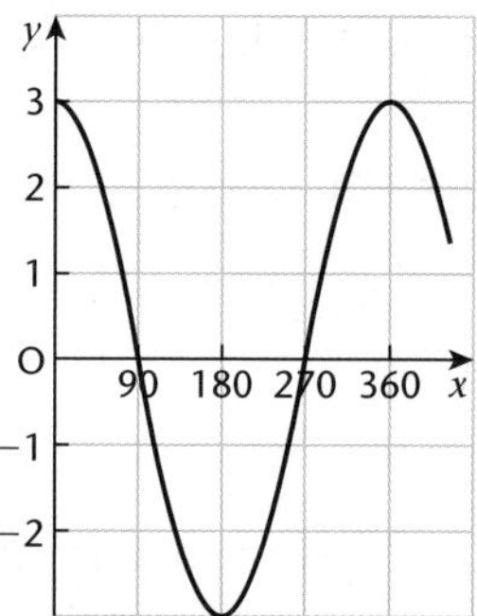

a $y = -\cos x$

The transformed curve is the reflection of $y = \cos x$ in the x-axis. The equation is $y = -f(x)$ where $f(x) = \cos x$.

b $y = 3 \cos x$

The transformed curve is a stretch by 3 units parallel to the y-axis. The equation is $y = af(x)$ where $f(x) = \cos x$ and $a = 3$.

Exam practice 17E

1 Describe the transformation that maps the curve $y = x^3$ to each of the following curves:

a $y = x^3 + 4$　　b $y = \frac{1}{2}x^3$　　c $y = (x + 2)^3$.

2 Describe the transformation that maps the line $y = 3x + 1$ to each of the following lines:

a $y = 3x - 2$　　b $y = 1 - 3x$　　c $y = 3(x - 2)$.

3 This is a graph of $y = \sin x$. Use transformations of this graph to help you sketch each of the following graphs:

a $y = \sin (x - 90)$

b $y = 3 \sin x$

c $y = \sin 2x$.

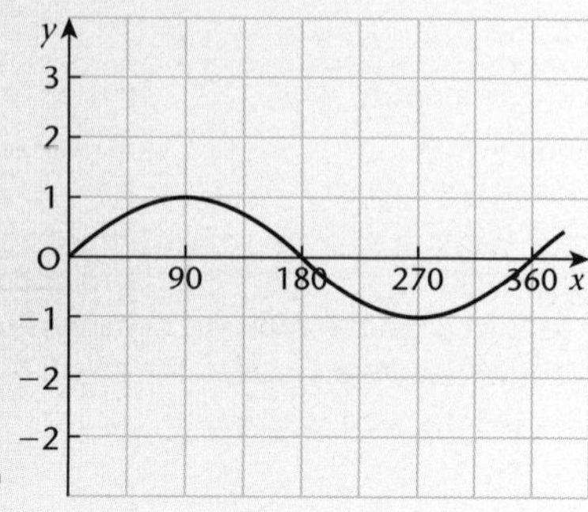

WWW

4 This graph shows the curve $y = 2^x$.
Use a copy of this graph to help you sketch each of the following graphs:

a $y = -2^x$ b $y = 2^{-x}$ c $y = 2^{x+2}$.

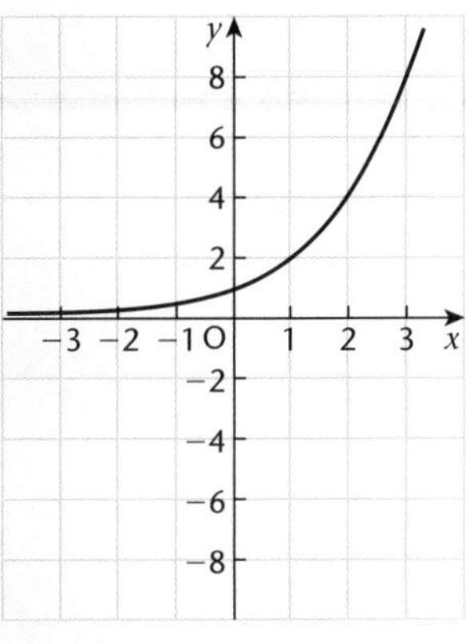

5 This is the graph of $y = \frac{1}{x}$.
Use a copy of this graph to sketch each of the following graphs:

a $y = 1 + \frac{1}{x}$ b $y = -\frac{1}{x}$.

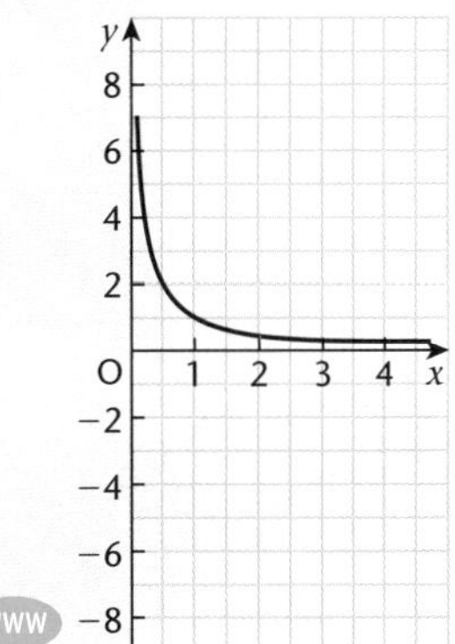

6 This is the graph of $y = x^2$.

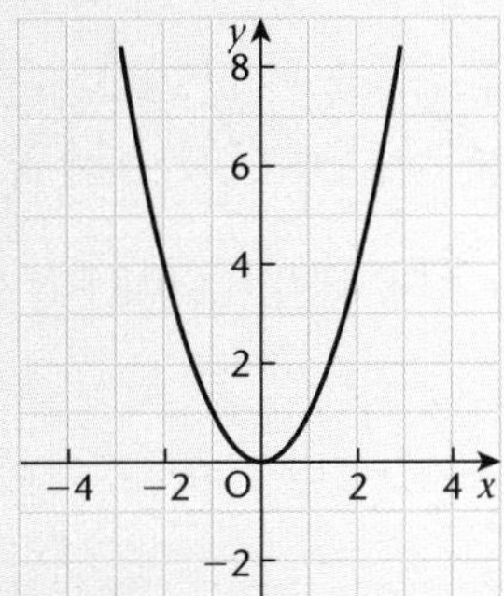

Write down the equation of the following transformations of the graph.

a

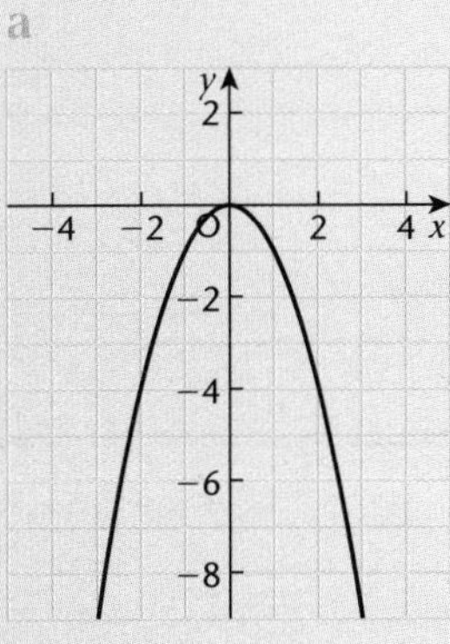

b

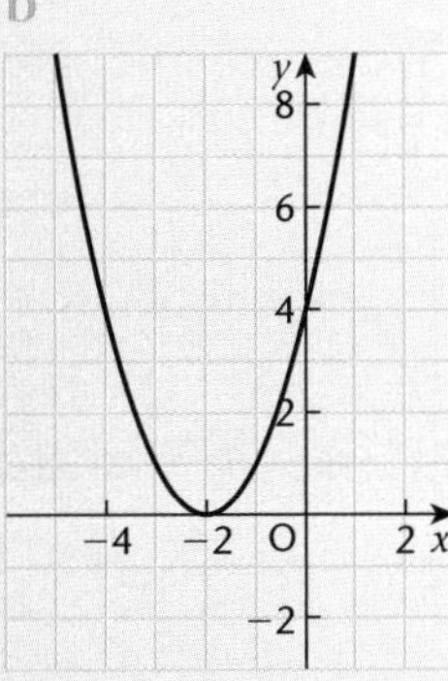

c

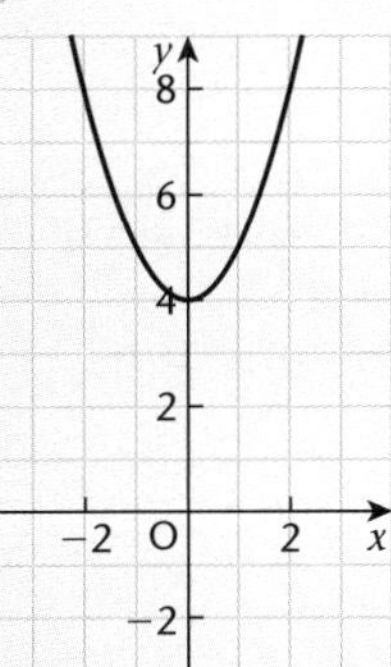

Enrichment task

This graph is a combination of transformations of $y = x^2$.
Find the equation of the graph.

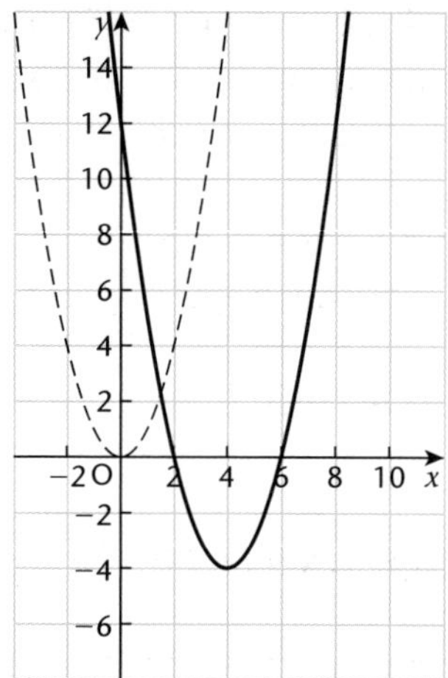

Summary of key points

- The equation $x^2 + y^2 = r^2$ gives a circle centre O and radius r.
- The shape of the graph of a quadratic equation is ∪ or ∩.

  The graph has a line of symmetry that goes through the greatest or least value of y.
- The graph of a cubic equation looks like

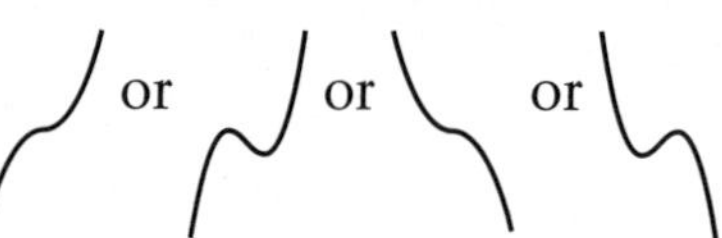

- The graph of $y = k^x$ looks like — The graph cuts the y-axis at $y = 1$.

  k^x is called an exponential function.

  1

- The graph of $y = \frac{1}{x}$ looks like

  $\frac{1}{x}$ is called a reciprocal function

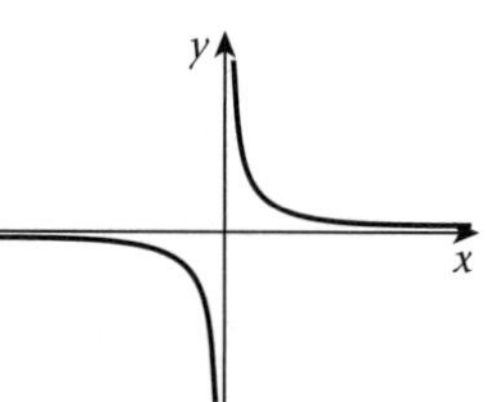

- The graph of $y = \sin x$ looks like

  $\sin x$ is called the sine function

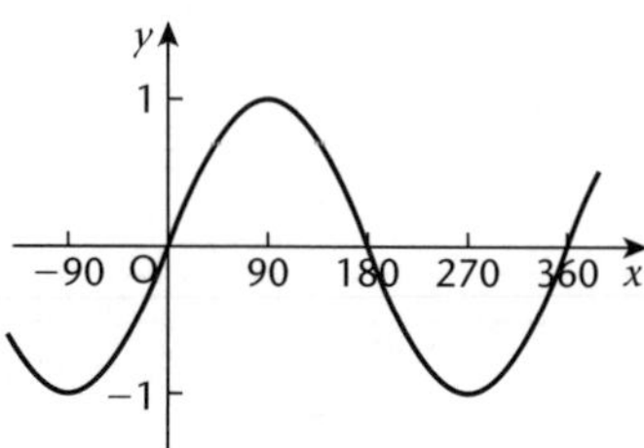

It has a repeating pattern and rotational symmetry.

- The graph of $y = \cos x$ looks like the graph of $y = \sin x$ translated 90° back along the horizontal axis.
- The graph of $y = -f(x)$ is the reflection of the graph of $y = f(x)$ in the x-axis.
- The graph of $y = f(-x)$ is the reflection of the graph of $y = f(x)$ in the y-axis.
- The graph of $y = f(x) + a$ is the translation of the graph of $y = f(x)$ by a units up the y-axis.
- For $y = f(x) - a$ the translation is a units down the y-axis.
- The graph of $y = f(x - a)$ is the translation of the graph of $y = f(x)$ by a units to the right.
- For $y = f(x + a)$ the translation is a units to the left.
- The graph of $y = af(x)$ is the graph of $y = f(x)$ stretched by a units parallel to the y-axis.
- The graph of $y = f(ax)$ is the graph of $y = f(x)$ stretched by $\frac{1}{a}$ units parallel to the x-axis.

Most candidates who get GRADE C or above can:

- plot the graph of a quadratic equation and use it to solve equations.

Most candidates who get GRADE A or above can also:

- sketch the graphs of $y = \sin x$ and $y = \cos x$.

Glossary

Cubic function an equation in the form $y = ax^3 + bx^2 + cx + d, a \neq 0$

Exponent power or index

Parabola the shape of the curve $y = ax^2 + bx + c$, with $a \neq 0$

Quadratic functions a function in the form $y = ax^2 + bx + c$, where a is not zero

Radians a type of angle measurement

Reciprocol the reciprocol of x is $\frac{1}{x}$

18 Vectors

This chapter will show you:
- ✓ what a vector is and how to represent it
- ✓ how to find the magnitude of a vector
- ✓ how to decide whether two vectors are equal in length and/or parallel
- ✓ what a negative vector is
- ✓ how to multiply a vector by a scalar quantity
- ✓ how to find the sum or difference of two vectors
- ✓ how to solve geometrical problems using vectors

Before you start you need to know:
- ✓ how to represent a line segment on a grid
- ✓ how to use Pythagoras' theorem
- ✓ how to use simple ratios
- ✓ the properties of special triangles, different types of quadrilaterals and regular hexagons

18.1 Basic vector information

A **scalar** quantity has only magnitude or size.

Temperature, distance and speed are scalar quantities.

A **vector** is a quantity that has both magnitude and direction.

Velocity and displacement are vectors. A ship is travelling due north at 15 nautical miles per hour. The ship has speed and direction. Taken together they are the **velocity** of the ship. Fay walks 100 m due east. Fay moves a distance in a given direction. This is a **displacement**.

A vector is represented by a **line segment**. A —a→— B

The vector is called **a** or **AB** or $\overrightarrow{AB}$.
The letters are in the order of the direction of the vector.

The magnitude of vector **a** is written |**a**| or a.

2**a** is a **scalar multiple** of **a**.
It is a vector in the same direction as **a** but twice as large. The line segment that represents 2**a** is twice as long.

The length of the line represents the **magnitude** of the vector.
The direction of the line represents the direction of the vector.
You can write **a** as $\underline{a}$ (underline the letter) and **AB** as $\overrightarrow{AB}$ (an arrow is drawn above it).

Example 1

In the diagram, each square is of side 1 unit.

a Find the magnitude of **a** and **b**:

b Draw line segments to represent

i 2**a**   ii $\frac{1}{2}$**a**   iii 2**b**.

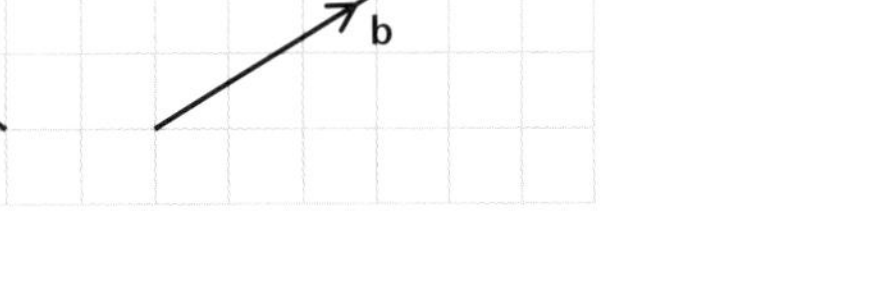

a $|\mathbf{a}| = \sqrt{9 + 16} = 5$

and $|\mathbf{b}| = \sqrt{9 + 25} = \sqrt{34}$

Using Pythagoras' theorem.

b

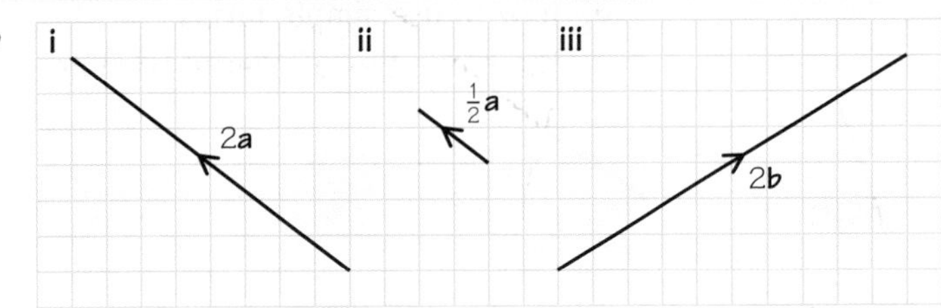

Two vectors that are in the same direction and have the same magnitude are equal.
If a vector **a** is equal in magnitude to a vector **b** but the vectors are opposite in direction then **a** = −**b** and **b** = −**a**.

Example 2

a Write down the vectors that are equal to **a** and **b**.

b Write down the vectors that are equal in magnitude and opposite in direction to **a**.

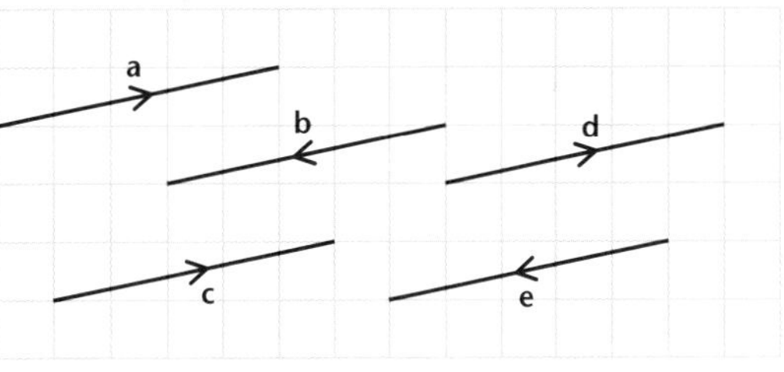

a **a** = **c** = **d**

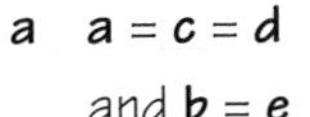

and **b** = **e**

a, **c** and **d** are the same size and in the same direction.

b **a** = −**b** and **a** = −**e**

so the vectors are **b** and **e**.

b and **e** are the same magnitude as **a** but are opposite in direction.

Exam practice 18A

Use squared paper for this exercise.

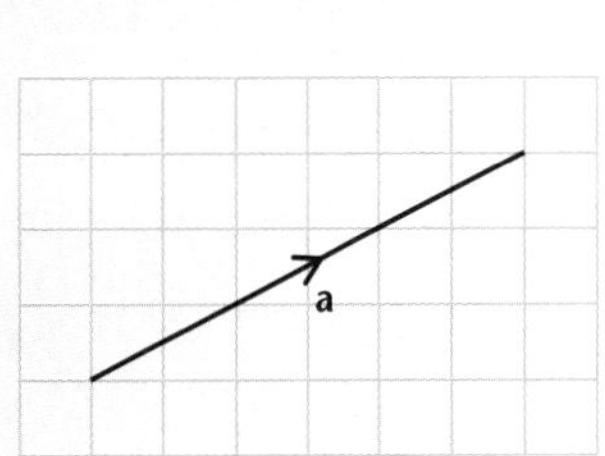

1 Draw line segments to represent:

a 2**a**   b −**a**   c −2**a**   d $\frac{2}{3}$**a**

2 Draw line segments to represent:

a $\frac{1}{2}\mathbf{b}$ b $-\mathbf{b}$ c $-2\mathbf{b}$ d $\frac{1}{3}\mathbf{b}$ e $\frac{3}{2}\mathbf{b}$

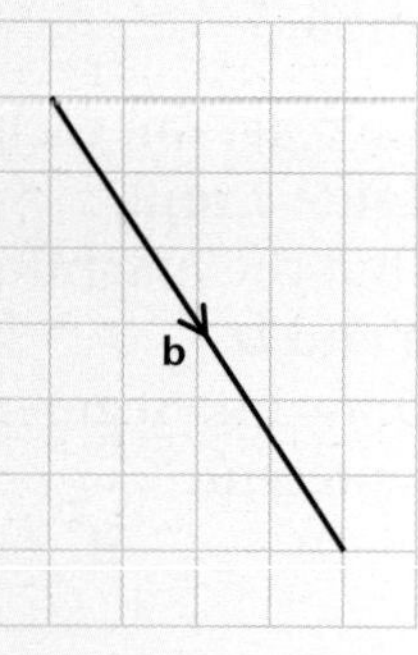

3 Draw line segments to represent:

a $-\mathbf{c}$ b $2\mathbf{c}$ c $-2\mathbf{c}$

d $\frac{3}{4}\mathbf{c}$ e $-\frac{1}{4}\mathbf{c}$

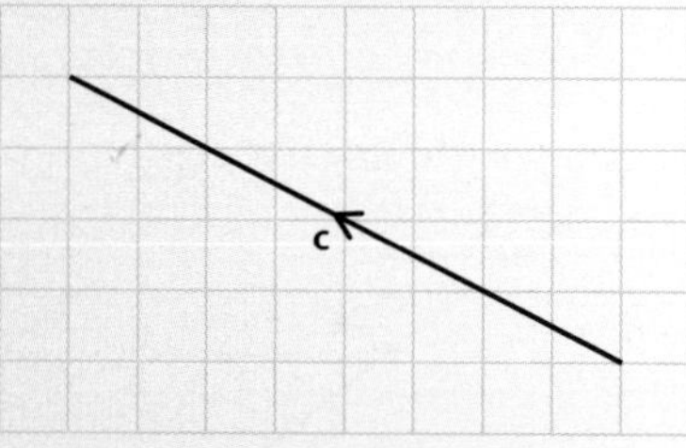

4 a Which two vectors are equal?

b Which two vectors have the same magnitude but are in opposite directions?

c Which vector is equivalent to $-\mathbf{f}$?

d Which vector is equal to $2\mathbf{b}$?

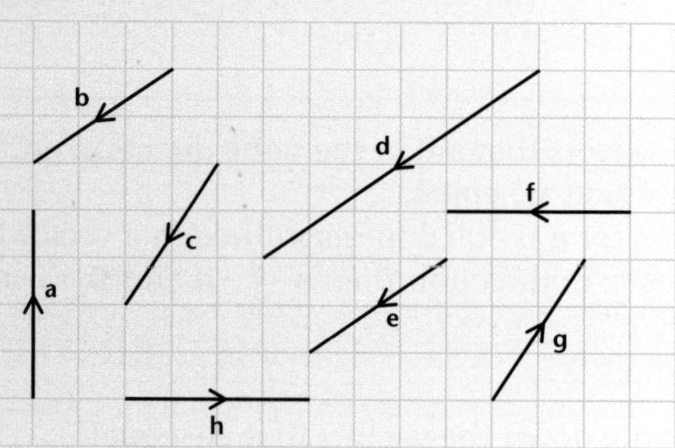

18.2 Vector addition and subtraction

Vector addition

In triangle ABC, $\overrightarrow{AB} = \mathbf{a}$ and $\overrightarrow{BC} = \mathbf{b}$.

$\overrightarrow{AC}$ is equivalent to **a** followed by **b**.
This is written as $\overrightarrow{AC} = \mathbf{a} + \mathbf{b}$.

So $\overrightarrow{AC}$ represents the vector sum of **a** and **b**.
This is the **triangle law** for the sum of two vectors.

The vector that represents the sum of two or more vectors is called the **resultant**. $\overrightarrow{AC}$ is the resultant of **a** and **b**.

The triangle law can be extended to add more than two vectors.

In this trapezium, $\overrightarrow{AD} = \mathbf{a} + \mathbf{b} + \mathbf{c}$.

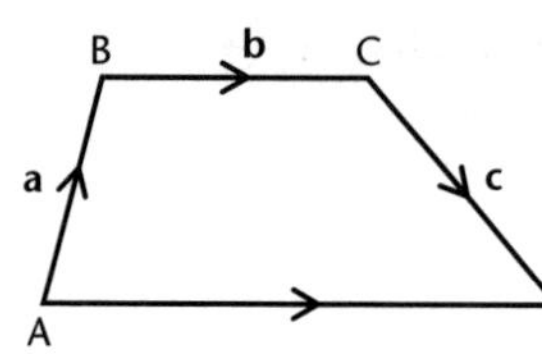

In this parallelogram AB and DC are opposite sides.
These sides are equal and parallel so $\overrightarrow{AB} = \overrightarrow{DC}$ and $\overrightarrow{DC} = \mathbf{a}$.
Also $\overrightarrow{AD} = \overrightarrow{BC}$, so $\overrightarrow{BC} = \mathbf{b}$.

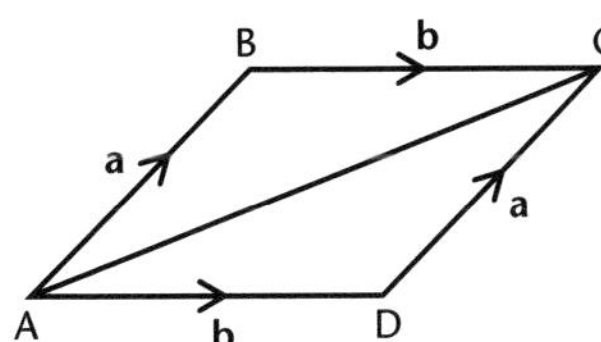

You know that $a + b = b + a$ for numbers. You can't assume it is also true for vectors. You need to prove it.

The triangle law gives:
$\overrightarrow{AB} + \overrightarrow{BC} = \mathbf{a} + \mathbf{b} = \overrightarrow{AC}$ and $\overrightarrow{AD} + \overrightarrow{DC} = \mathbf{b} + \mathbf{a} = \overrightarrow{AC}$.
So $\mathbf{a} + \mathbf{b} = \mathbf{b} + \mathbf{a}$.

Vector addition is **commutative**. This means that the order you do the addition in does not matter.

Example 3

Find the single vector equivalent to:

a $\overrightarrow{AC} + \overrightarrow{CB}$

b $\overrightarrow{CB} + \overrightarrow{BA} + \overrightarrow{AD}$

First put arrows on the diagram so that you can see the vectors. You can go from A to B via C or directly.

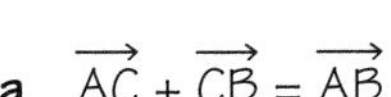

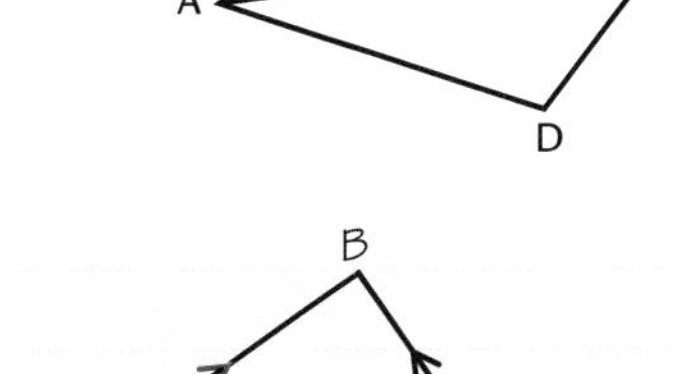

When you add vectors they must follow in the same sense, i.e. clockwise or anticlockwise, round the diagram.
The resultant is in the opposite sense.

b $\overrightarrow{CB} + \overrightarrow{BA} + \overrightarrow{AD} = \overrightarrow{CD}$

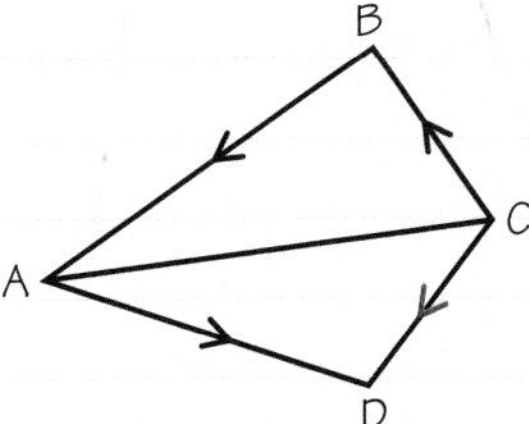

Vector addition is **associative**.
This means that when you add more than two vectors, it does not matter which two you add first.
For any vectors **a**, **b** and **c**, $(\mathbf{a} + \mathbf{b}) + \mathbf{c} = \mathbf{a} + (\mathbf{b} + \mathbf{c})$

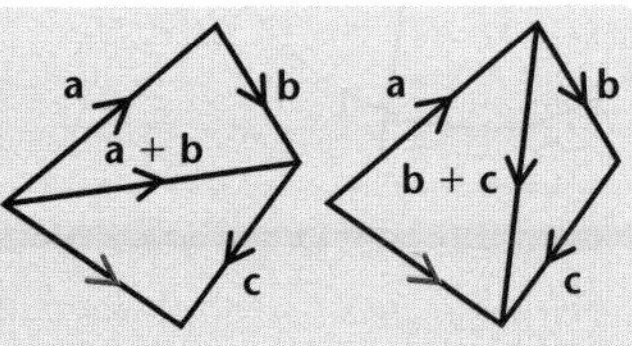

Example 4

a and **b** are vectors drawn on a grid with squares of side 1 unit.
Draw the line segment that represents each of the following resultants and calculate their magnitudes.

a $\mathbf{a} + \mathbf{b}$
b $\mathbf{a} + 2\mathbf{b}$
c $2\mathbf{a} + \mathbf{b}$

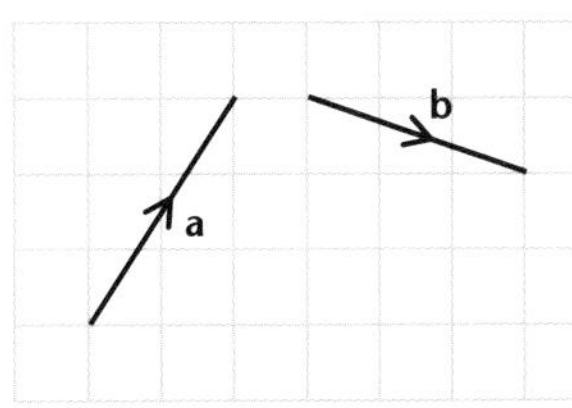

a

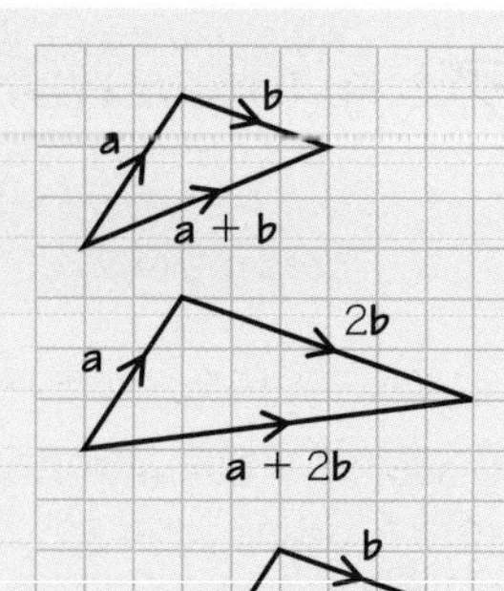

Magnitude of resultant = $\sqrt{25 + 4} = \sqrt{29}$

Draw **a** and **b** so that **b** follows on from **a**.

The resultant is 5 squares from left to right and 2 squares up so the magnitude of the resultant is the square root of $5^2 + 2^2$.

b

Magnitude of resultant = $\sqrt{64 + 1} = \sqrt{65}$

The resultant is 8 squares from left to right and 1 square up.

c

Magnitude of resultant = $\sqrt{49 + 25} = \sqrt{74}$

The resultant is 7 squares along and 5 squares up.

Vector subtraction

This diagram shows two vectors **a** and **b** and their sum.

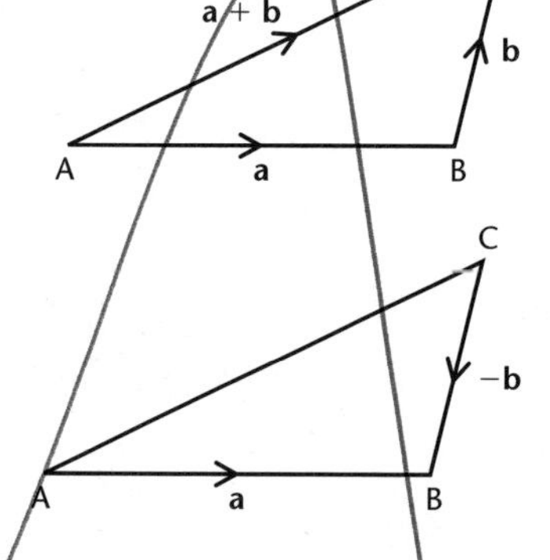

The vector −**b** can be shown on the diagram by changing the direction of the arrow.

You cannot use this diagram to find the sum of **a** and −**b** because the arrows representing the two vectors do not follow on from each other.

A vector is not changed if the line representing it is moved to a new position, provided its magnitude and direction remain unchanged.

This diagram shows the new position of −**b** so that **a** and −**b** follow on from each other.

Then $\overrightarrow{AD} = \mathbf{a} + (-\mathbf{b})$
$= \mathbf{a} - \mathbf{b}$

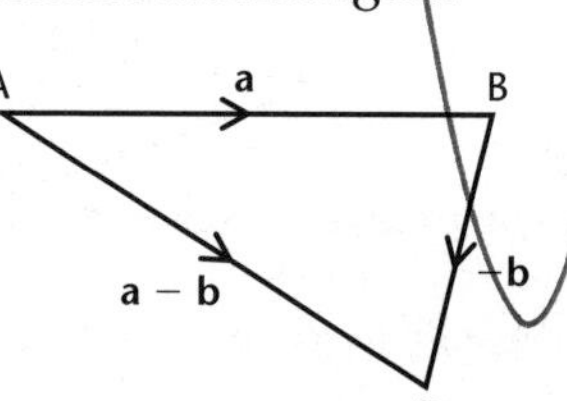

Example 5

Use the vectors **a** and **b** on this grid to draw the line segments that represent:

a **a** + **b** b **a** + 2**b**
c **a** − **b** d 2**a** − **b**

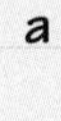

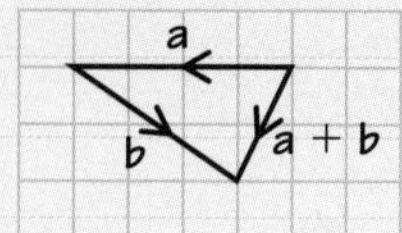

Redraw **b** so that it follows on from **a**.

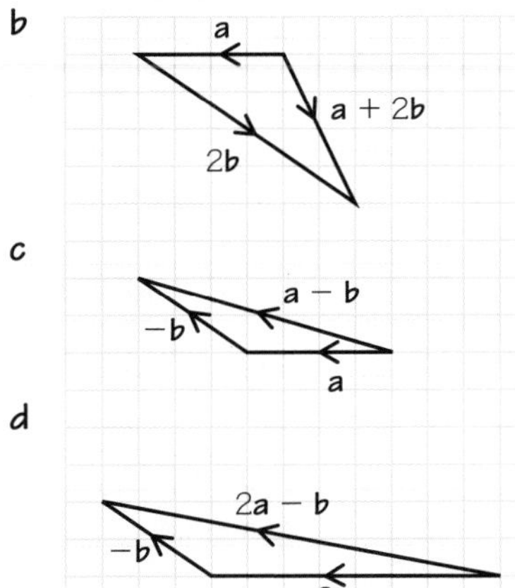

2b is a vector in the same direction as **b**, but twice as long.

−**b** is opposite to **b**. Draw −**b** so that it follows on from **a**.

Draw −**b** so that it follows on from 2**a**.

Example 6

Which single vector is equivalent to:

a $\overrightarrow{AB} - \overrightarrow{CB}$

b $\overrightarrow{CB} - \overrightarrow{EB}$

c $\overrightarrow{AD} - \overrightarrow{CD} + \overrightarrow{CB}$

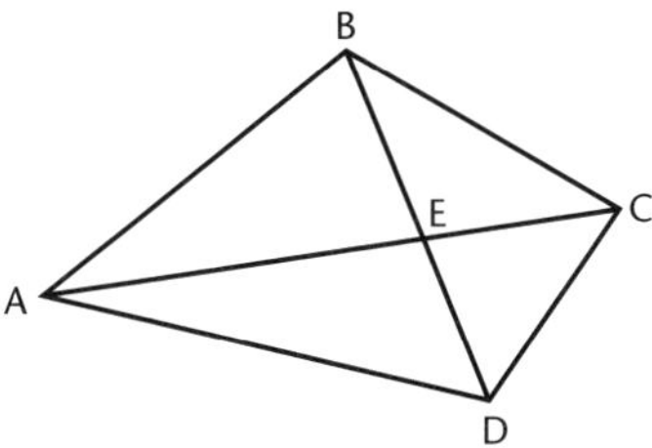

a $\overrightarrow{AB} - \overrightarrow{CB} = \overrightarrow{AB} + \overrightarrow{BC}$
$= \overrightarrow{AC}$

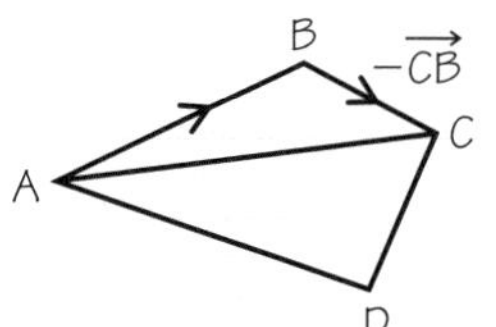

$-\overrightarrow{CB}$ is the direction from B to C, so $-\overrightarrow{CB} = \overrightarrow{BC}$.

b $\overrightarrow{CB} - \overrightarrow{EB} = \overrightarrow{CB} + \overrightarrow{BE}$
$= \overrightarrow{CE}$

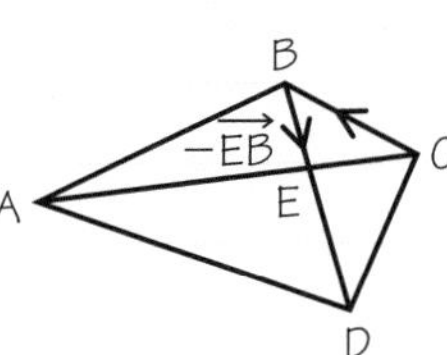

c $\overrightarrow{AD} - \overrightarrow{CD} + \overrightarrow{CB} = \overrightarrow{AD} + \overrightarrow{DC} + \overrightarrow{CB}$
$= \overrightarrow{AB}$

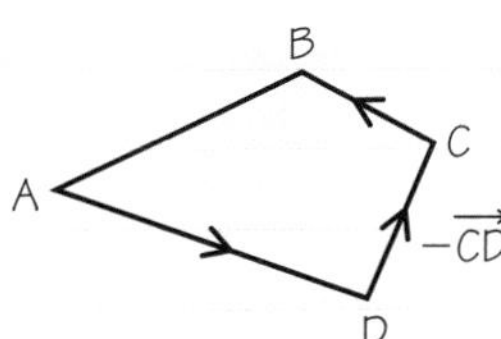

Exam practice 18B

1 What single vector is equivalent to:

a $\overrightarrow{DE} + \overrightarrow{EF}$ b $\overrightarrow{DF} + \overrightarrow{FE}$

c $\overrightarrow{EF} + \overrightarrow{FD}$ d $\overrightarrow{FE} + \overrightarrow{ED}$?

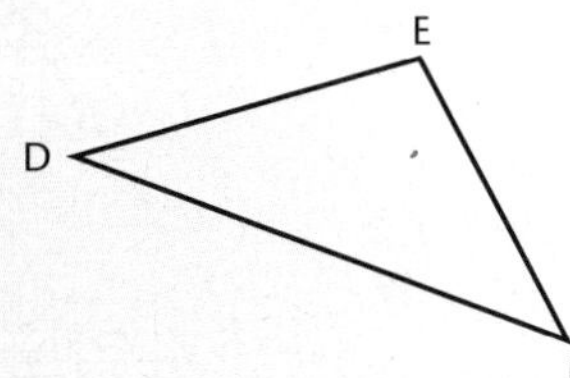

2 Give two vectors whose sum is equivalent to:
a $\overrightarrow{AC}$ b $\overrightarrow{AD}$ c $\overrightarrow{BA}$.

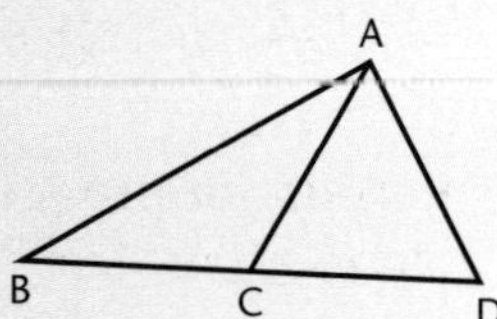

3 a Give two vectors whose sum is equivalent to $\overrightarrow{AC}$.
b Write down a single vector that equivalent to:
i $\overrightarrow{AB} + \overrightarrow{BD}$ ii $\overrightarrow{BC} + \overrightarrow{CD}$
iii $\overrightarrow{AD} + \overrightarrow{DB}$ iv $\overrightarrow{CD} + \overrightarrow{DB}$

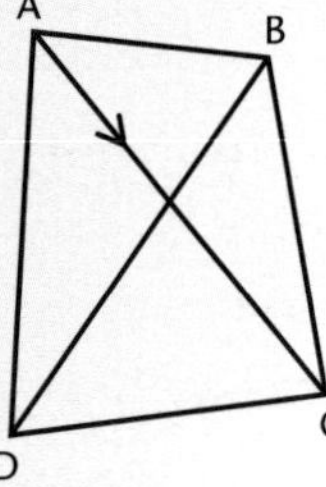

4 **a** and **b** are vectors drawn on a grid with squares of side 1 unit. On your own grid draw the line segment that represents each of the following resultants and calculate their magnitudes.
a $\mathbf{a} + \mathbf{b}$ b $\mathbf{a} + 2\mathbf{b}$
c $2\mathbf{a} - \mathbf{b}$ d $\mathbf{a} + \frac{1}{2}\mathbf{b}$

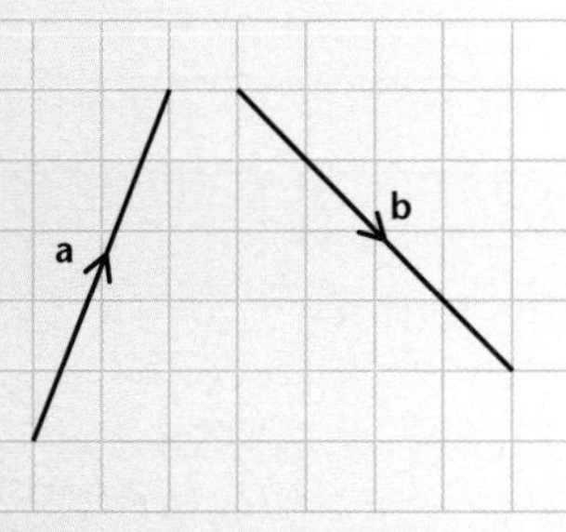

Remember that you can move the vectors to any position.

5 Which single vector is equivalent to:
a $\overrightarrow{PQ} - \overrightarrow{RQ}$
b $\overrightarrow{RP} - \overrightarrow{QP}$
c $\overrightarrow{RQ} - \overrightarrow{PQ}$?

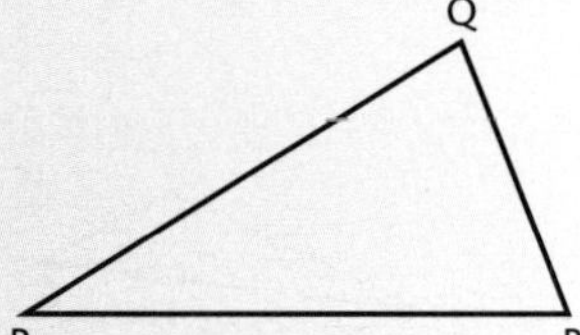

Remember that $-\overrightarrow{RQ} = \overrightarrow{QR}$.

6 Which single vector is equivalent to:
a $\overrightarrow{AX} - \overrightarrow{DX}$
b $\overrightarrow{XB} - \overrightarrow{AB}$
c $\overrightarrow{DC} - \overrightarrow{BC}$
d $\overrightarrow{BC} + \overrightarrow{CD} - \overrightarrow{AD}$
e $\overrightarrow{AB} - \overrightarrow{CB} - \overrightarrow{DC}$
f $\overrightarrow{CD} - \overrightarrow{XD} + \overrightarrow{XA}$?

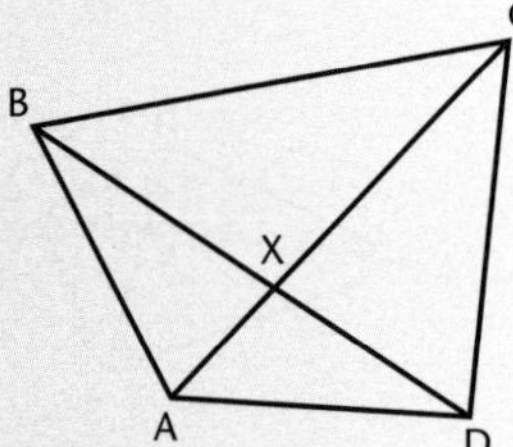

7 Copy the vectors **a** and **b** onto a grid. On this grid draw line segments to represent the vectors:
a $\mathbf{a} + \mathbf{b}$ b $\mathbf{a} + 2\mathbf{b}$ c $2\mathbf{a} - \mathbf{b}$
d $2\mathbf{a} - 3\mathbf{b}$ e $\mathbf{b} - 2\mathbf{a}$ f $3\mathbf{a} - 2\mathbf{b}$
g $\mathbf{a} - \frac{5}{2}\mathbf{b}$ h $2\mathbf{a} + \frac{3}{2}\mathbf{b}$

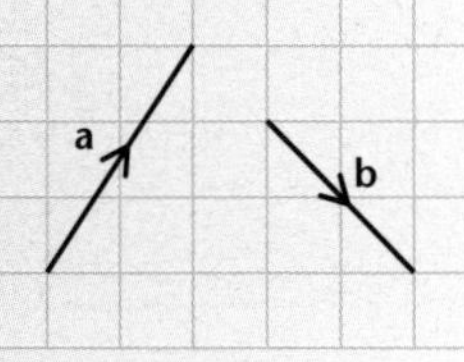

8 **a**, **b** and **c** are vectors drawn on a grid with squares of side 1 unit. Use your own grid to show that:
a $2\mathbf{a} + 2\mathbf{b} = 2(\mathbf{a} + \mathbf{b})$
b $(\mathbf{a} + \mathbf{b}) + \mathbf{c} = \mathbf{a} + (\mathbf{b} + \mathbf{c})$
c $(\mathbf{a} + \mathbf{b}) - \mathbf{c} = (\mathbf{a} - \mathbf{c}) + \mathbf{b}$
d $2(\mathbf{a} - \mathbf{c}) = 2\mathbf{a} - 2\mathbf{c}$

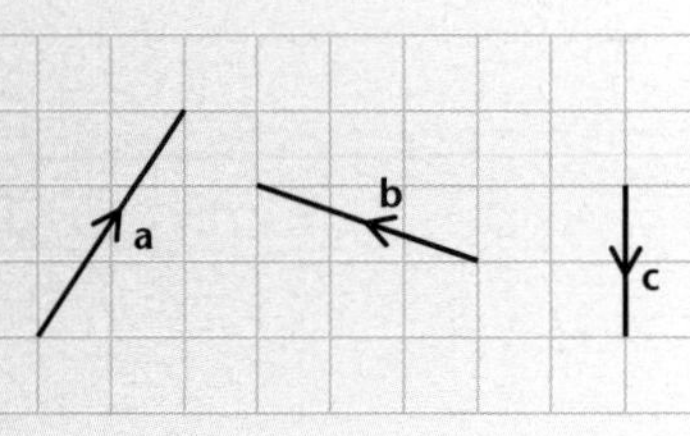

18.3 Using vectors for proofs

Vectors provide an algebraic method for proving geometrical results. You can use vectors to show relationships between lengths of lines and to show that lines are parallel.

Example 7

$\overrightarrow{OA} = \mathbf{a}$, $\overrightarrow{OB} = \mathbf{b}$ and M is the midpoint of AB.
Express, in terms of **a** and **b**,

a $\overrightarrow{AB}$ **b** $\overrightarrow{MB}$ **c** $\overrightarrow{OM}$

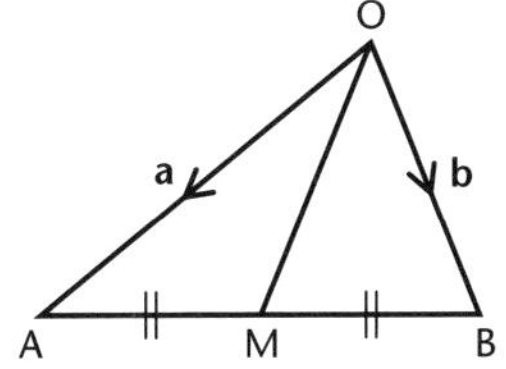

a $\overrightarrow{OA} + \overrightarrow{AB} = \overrightarrow{OB}$

$\mathbf{a} + \overrightarrow{AB} = \mathbf{b}$

$\overrightarrow{AB} = \mathbf{b} - \mathbf{a}$

b $\overrightarrow{MB} = \frac{1}{2}\overrightarrow{AB} = \frac{1}{2}(\mathbf{b} - \mathbf{a})$

c $\overrightarrow{OM} + \overrightarrow{MB} = \overrightarrow{OB}$

$\overrightarrow{OM} + \frac{1}{2}(\mathbf{b} - \mathbf{a}) = \mathbf{b}$

$\overrightarrow{OM} = \frac{1}{2}(\mathbf{a} + \mathbf{b})$

Example 8

In this parallelogram, $\overrightarrow{OA} = 2\mathbf{a}$, $\overrightarrow{OC} = 2\mathbf{c}$ and M is the midpoint of AC.

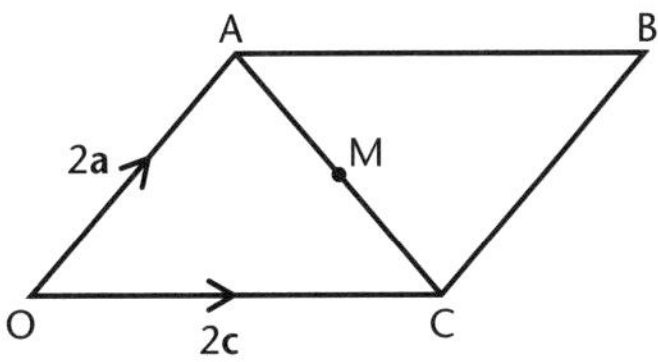

a Find $\overrightarrow{AM}$ in terms of **a** and **c**.

b Use vectors to show that M is the midpoint of $\overrightarrow{OB}$.

a $\overrightarrow{OA} + \overrightarrow{AC} = \overrightarrow{OC}$

$2\mathbf{a} + \overrightarrow{AC} = 2\mathbf{c}$

$\overrightarrow{AC} = 2(\mathbf{c} - \mathbf{a})$

But $\overrightarrow{AM} = \frac{1}{2}\overrightarrow{AC}$

so $\overrightarrow{AM} = \frac{1}{2} \times 2(\mathbf{c} - \mathbf{a}) = \mathbf{c} - \mathbf{a}$.

b $\overrightarrow{OM} = \overrightarrow{OA} + \overrightarrow{AM}$

$= 2\mathbf{a} + \mathbf{c} - \mathbf{a}$

$\overrightarrow{OM} = \mathbf{a} + \mathbf{c}$

$\overrightarrow{OA} + \overrightarrow{AB} = \overrightarrow{OB}$

But $\overrightarrow{AB} = \overrightarrow{OC} = 2\mathbf{c}$

so $2\mathbf{a} + 2\mathbf{c} = \overrightarrow{OB}$

$\overrightarrow{OB} = 2(\mathbf{a} + \mathbf{c})$

so $\overrightarrow{OB} = 2\overrightarrow{OM}$ and $\overrightarrow{OM} = \frac{1}{2}\overrightarrow{OB}$

M is the midpoint of OB.

You know the vectors $\overrightarrow{OA}$ and $\overrightarrow{AM}$ in terms of **a** and **c** so you can find the vector $\overrightarrow{OM}$ in terms of **a** and **c**.

Now find vector $\overrightarrow{OB}$. If it is a scalar multiple of $\overrightarrow{OM}$ then M lies on the line OB. If its magnitude is also twice that of OM then M is the midpoint of OB.

Exam practice 18C

1 $\overrightarrow{OA} = \mathbf{a}$, $\overrightarrow{OB} = \mathbf{b}$ and M is the midpoint of AB.
Express, in terms of **a** and **b**,
a $\overrightarrow{AB}$ b $\overrightarrow{MB}$ c $\overrightarrow{MO}$.

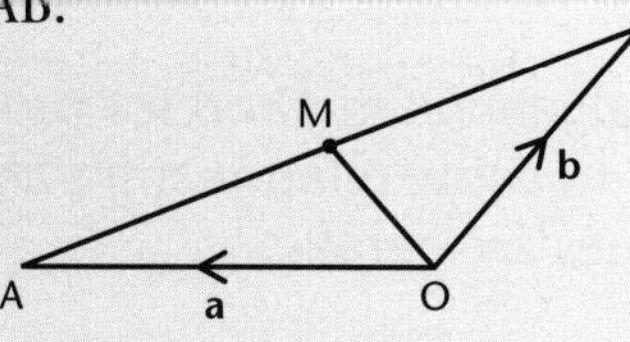

2 $\overrightarrow{OA} = \mathbf{a}$, $\overrightarrow{OB} = \mathbf{b}$ and $\overrightarrow{BC} = \mathbf{b}$.
Give, in terms of **a** and **b**,
a $\overrightarrow{AB}$ b $\overrightarrow{OC}$ c $\overrightarrow{AC}$.

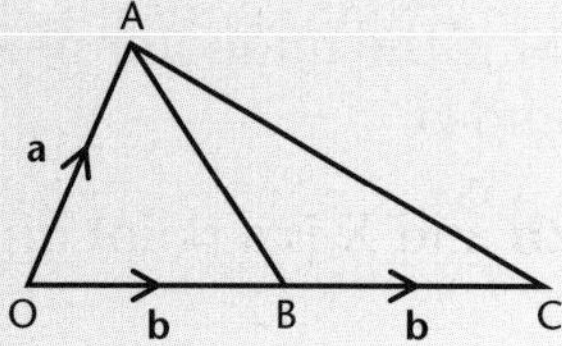

3 R is a point on PQ such that PR = 3RQ.
$\overrightarrow{OP} = 2\mathbf{p}$ and $\overrightarrow{OQ} = 2\mathbf{q}$.
Find, in terms of **p** and **q**,
a $\overrightarrow{PQ}$ b $\overrightarrow{RQ}$ c $\overrightarrow{OR}$.

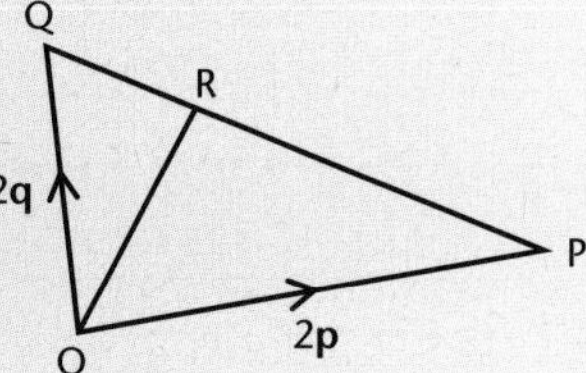

UAM 4 $\overrightarrow{OA} = 2\mathbf{a}$ and $\overrightarrow{OB} = 2\mathbf{b}$. M and N are the midpoints of OA and OB.

a Find, in terms of **a** and **b**,
i $\overrightarrow{OM}$ ii $\overrightarrow{ON}$
iii $\overrightarrow{AB}$ v $\overrightarrow{MN}$.

b Show that $\overrightarrow{MN}$ is parallel to $\overrightarrow{AB}$.

c What is the relationship between $\overrightarrow{MN}$ and $\overrightarrow{AB}$?

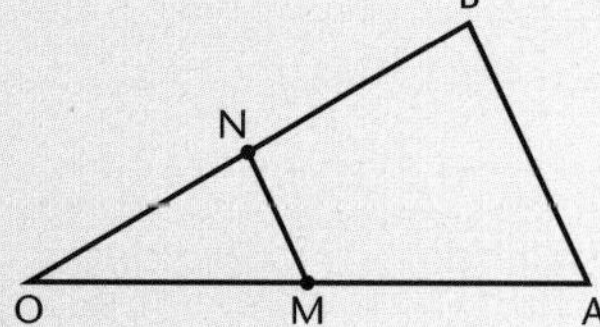

MN is parallel to AB if $\overrightarrow{MN}$ is a scalar multiple of $\overrightarrow{AB}$.

UAM 5 In the parallelogram, M is the midpoint of OC and N is the midpoint of AB.
$\overrightarrow{OA} = 2\mathbf{a}$ and $\overrightarrow{OB} = 2\mathbf{b}$.

a Find, in terms of **a** and **b**,
i $\overrightarrow{OC}$ ii $\overrightarrow{OM}$ iii $\overrightarrow{AB}$
iv $\overrightarrow{AN}$ v $\overrightarrow{ON}$.

b By comparing $\overrightarrow{OM}$ and $\overrightarrow{ON}$ what can you show about the points M and N?

6 In the square, D is a point on AB such that AD : DB = 2 : 1.
E is a point on OC such that OE:EC = 1 : 2.
F is the midpoint of OA and G is the midpoint of BC.
$\overrightarrow{OA} = \mathbf{a}$ and $\overrightarrow{OC} = \mathbf{c}$.

a Find, in terms of **a** and **c**.
i $\overrightarrow{AB}$ ii $\overrightarrow{AD}$ iii $\overrightarrow{FD}$
iv $\overrightarrow{OE}$ v $\overrightarrow{CG}$ vi $\overrightarrow{EG}$.

b i Show that FD is parallel to EG.
ii Give the relationship between the lengths of FD and EG.

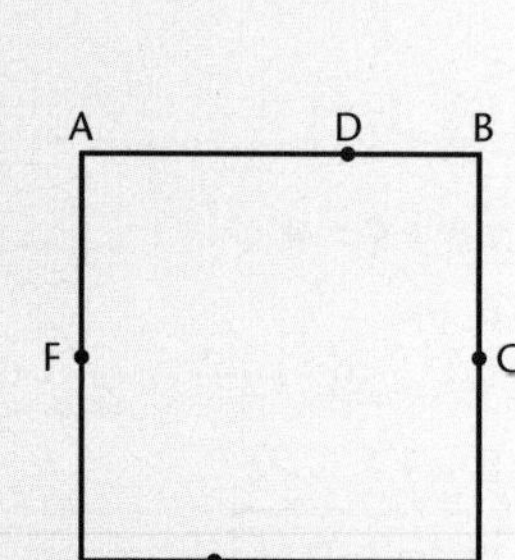

7 In the quadrilateral, $\overrightarrow{OP} = 2\mathbf{p}$, $\overrightarrow{PQ} = 2\mathbf{q}$, $\overrightarrow{OR} = 2\mathbf{r}$ and $\overrightarrow{RQ} = 2\mathbf{s}$.
X, Y, Z and W are the midpoints of the four sides.

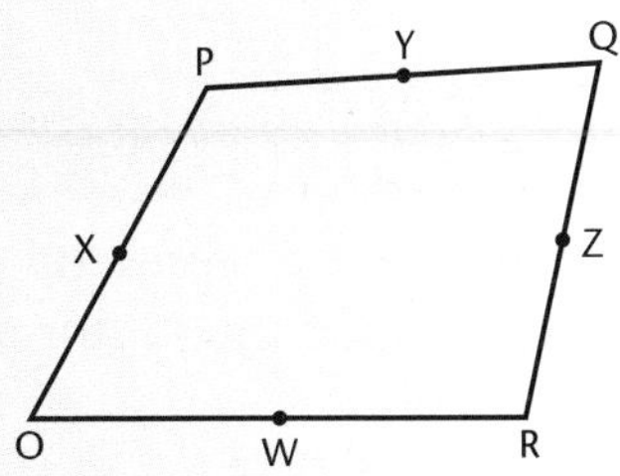

a Find $\overrightarrow{OQ}$ in terms of i $\mathbf{p}$ and $\mathbf{q}$ ii $\mathbf{r}$ and $\mathbf{s}$.
b Find $\overrightarrow{XY}$ in terms of $\mathbf{p}$ and $\mathbf{q}$.
c Find $\overrightarrow{WZ}$ in terms of $\mathbf{r}$ and $\mathbf{s}$.
d What can you conclude about the lines XY and WZ?

8 $\overrightarrow{OA} = 2\mathbf{a}$, $\overrightarrow{OB} = 2\mathbf{b}$ and X is a point on BM such that $BX = \frac{2}{3}BM$.
Find, in terms of $\mathbf{a}$ and $\mathbf{b}$,

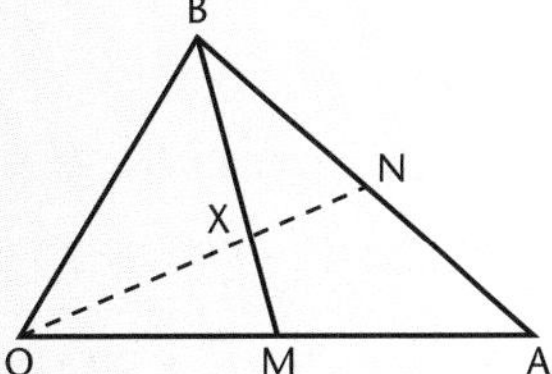

a i $\overrightarrow{BM}$ ii $\overrightarrow{BX}$ iii $\overrightarrow{OX}$
iv $\overrightarrow{BA}$ v $\overrightarrow{BN}$ vi $\overrightarrow{ON}$.
b Show that X lies on ON and that $OX = \frac{2}{3}ON$.

9 O is the centre of this regular hexagon.
AB = $\mathbf{a}$ and BC = $\mathbf{b}$.
Give each of the following vectors in terms of $\mathbf{a}$ and $\mathbf{b}$.

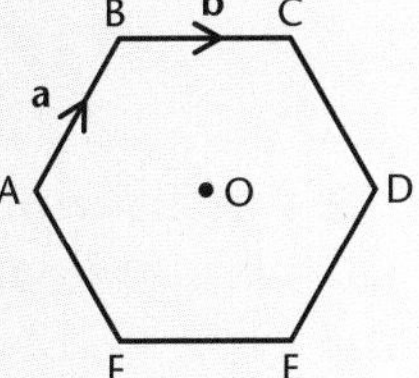

You need to know the properties of a regular hexagon for this question.

a $\overrightarrow{AC}$ b $\overrightarrow{AD}$ c $\overrightarrow{CD}$
d $\overrightarrow{FA}$ e $\overrightarrow{CE}$

10 In this parallelogram, $\overrightarrow{OA} = \mathbf{a}$ and $\overrightarrow{OB} = \mathbf{b}$.
OA is produced to D such that OA = AD.
P is the midpoint of AC.

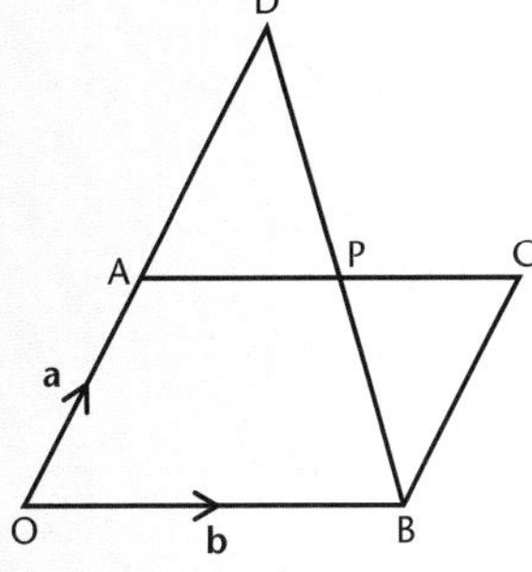

a Write down, in terms of $\mathbf{a}$ and $\mathbf{b}$, i $\overrightarrow{BD}$ ii $\overrightarrow{OC}$.
b Express in terms of $\mathbf{a}$ and $\mathbf{b}$, i $\overrightarrow{BP}$ ii $\overrightarrow{PD}$.
c How is P related to DB?
d X is on OC such that $OX = \frac{2}{3}OC$.
By expressing $\overrightarrow{BX}$ in terms of $\mathbf{a}$ and $\mathbf{b}$ show that X lies on BD and find the ratio of BX to XD.

Summary of key points

- Vectors can be represented by line segments. The length of the line segment gives the magnitude of the vector and its direction shows the direction in which the vector is acting.
- Two vectors that are in the same direction and have the same magnitude are equal.
- If a vector **a** is equal in magnitude to a vector **b** but the vectors are in opposite directions **a** = −**b** or **b** = −**a**.
- Vectors can be added using the triangle law
  a + **b** = **c**.

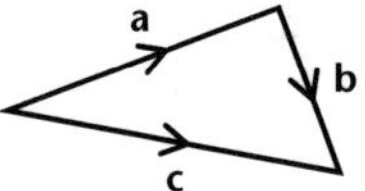

- Many simple geometrical properties can be proved using vectors.

Most candidates who get GRADE A or above can:

- use vectors to solve simple geometrical problems.

Glossary

Associative	the way in which numbers or quantities are grouped in a calculation does not matter: in vectors (**a** + **b**) + **c** = **a** + (**b** + **c**), in arithmetic (2 + 3) + 4 = 2 + (3 + 4)
Commutative	the order in which two numbers or quantities are combined does not matter: in vectors **a** + **b** = **b** + **a**. In arithmetic 3 + 4 = 4 + 3
Displacement	a change of position described by the distance moved and the direction of the move
Line segment	the straight line joining two points
Magnitude	the length of the line segment representing a vector
Resultant	the result of combining two or more vectors
Scalar	a quantity that has magnitude only
Scalar multiple	2**a** is a scalar multiple of **a**
Speed	the rate at which distance is covered
Triangle law	a description of how to add two vectors
Vector	a quantity that has both magnitude and direction
Velocity	the speed of an object in a particular direction

Examination practice papers

Paper 1

Time allowed: 1 hour 15 minutes

Calculators are not allowed

1 Which of these fractions is nearest to the value $\frac{1}{2}$?

$$\frac{2}{5} \quad \frac{23}{40} \quad \frac{9}{20}$$

You **must** show your working. *(3 marks)*

2

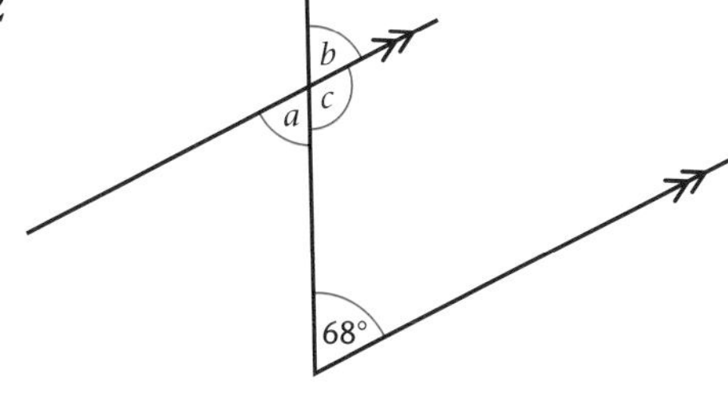

(a) Work out the value of *a*.
Give a reason for your answer. *(2 marks)*

(b) Work out the value of *b*.
Give a reason for your answer. *(2 marks)*

(c) Work out the value of *c*.
Give a reason for your answer. *(2 marks)*

3

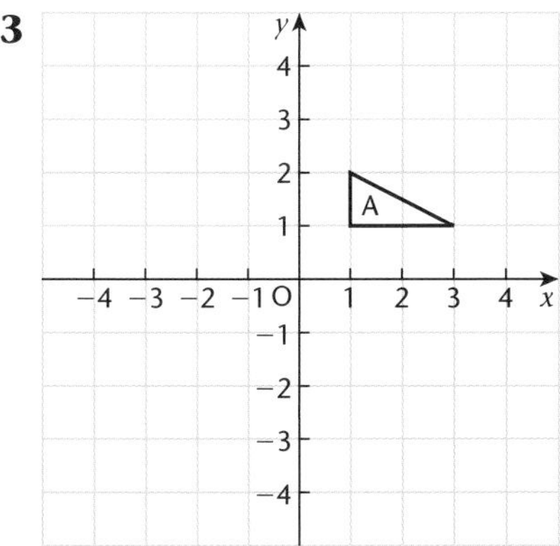

(a) (i) Translate triangle A 1 square to the right and 5 squares down. *(1 mark)*

(ii) Write down the translation vector for (i). *(1 mark)*

(b) Rotate triangle A through 180° about the origin. *(3 marks)*

4 Convert 5.6 cubic centimetres to cubic millimetres. *(2 marks)*

5 (a) Complete this table of values for the equation $y = x^2 - 5$.

x	-3	-2	-1	0	1	2	3	4
y	4	-1		-5	-4	-1		11

(2 marks)

(b) Draw the graph of $y = x^2 - 5$ on the axes below.

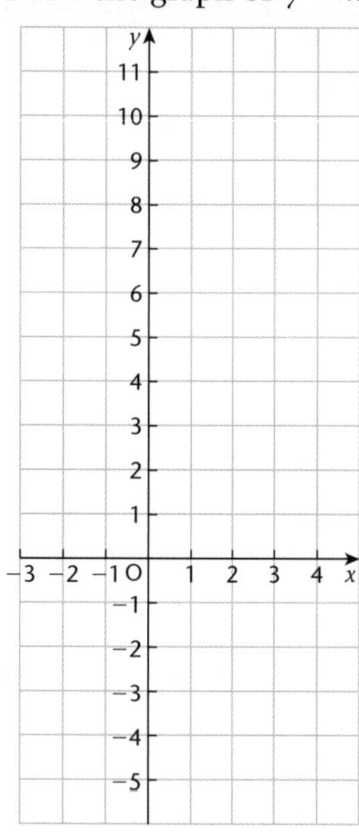

(2 marks)

(c) Write down the values of x where the line $y = 2$ crosses your graph. *(2 marks)*

6 (a) You are given that $-2 \leqslant 2n \leqslant 7$ and that n is an integer.

Work out all the possible values of n. *(3 marks)*

(b) Solve $4x - 5 > 5$. *(2 marks)*

7 Simplify

(a) $b^4 \times b$ *(1 mark)*

(b) $m^8 \div m^2$ *(1 mark)*

(c) $3(2p + 1) + 4(p - 2)$. *(2 marks)*

8 Use Pythagoras Theorem to explain why a triangle with sides 4 centimetres, 5 centimetres and 6 centimetres cannot be right angled. *(2 marks)*

9 (a) Expand $c\,(c^2 + 1)$. *(2 marks)*

(b) Expand and simplify

(i) $(x + 2)(x + 1)$ *(2 marks)*

(ii) $(2a + b)(3a - 4b)$. *(3 marks)*

10 Which three of these formulae represent areas?

a, b and c represent lengths.

π has no dimensions.

$3abc$	πb^2	$2(a+b)$	$3\pi ab$	$a^2 + 2b$	$\frac{b^3}{c}$

(3 marks)

11 Rearrange this formula to make w the subject.

$$2(w - x) = 10 - 3x$$ *(3 marks)*

12 (a) Work out the equation of the line that passes through the points $(1,-2)$ and $(4,-5)$. *(3 marks)*

(b) Line L has equation $y + 2x = 5$

Keira says that the line with equation $y = \frac{1}{2}x + 3$ is perpendicular to line L.

Is Keira correct?

You must explain your answer clearly. *(2 marks)*

13 (a) Factorise $x^2 - 7x + 12$. *(2 marks)*

(b) Write down the solutions to the equation $x^2 - 7x + 12 = 0$. *(1 mark)*

14 A cylinder has height 5 centimetres and volume 45π cubic centimetres.

A hemisphere has the same radius as the cylinder.

Work out the volume of the hemisphere.

Give your answer in terms of π. *(4 marks)*

15 ABCD is a rectangle.

AB = 2**a** and **AD** = 3**b**

M is the mid-point of DC.

X is a point such that **DX** = 3**a** + 6**b**

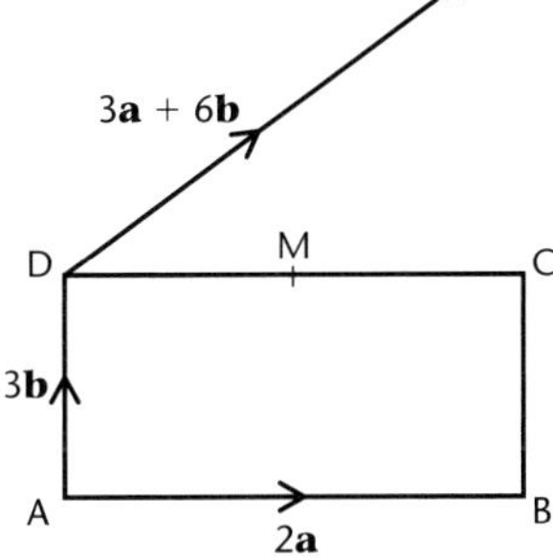

(a) Find, in terms of **a** and **b**, expressions for these vectors.

Give answers in their simplest forms.

(i) **AM** *(2 marks)*

(ii) **MX** *(2 marks)*

(b) Using part (a), write down a fact about

(i) the positions of A, M and X *(1 mark)*

(ii) the lengths AM and MX. *(1 mark)*

16 Solve $\frac{5}{2m-5} - \frac{3}{m+1} = \frac{1}{2}$. *(6 marks)*

Paper 2

Time allowed: 1 hour 15 minutes

Calculator allowed

1 A two-dimensional shape has equal sides.
Each side is x centimetres.
The perimeter of the shape is $4x$ centimetres.

Write down the two possible names of the shape. *(2 marks)*

2 Find the area of this shape made from rectangles.

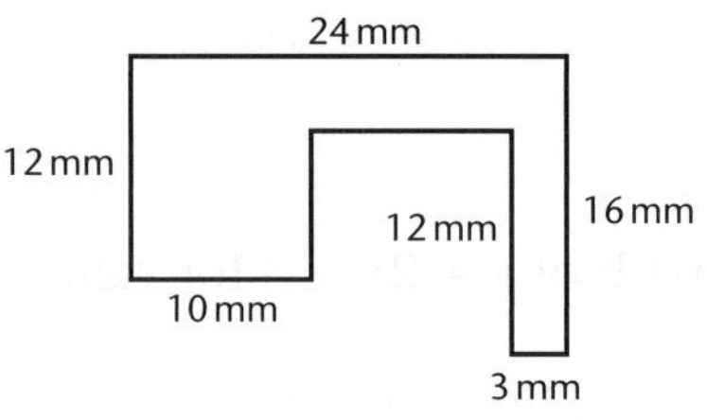

(4 marks)

3

N

A

(a) Measure and write down the bearing of B from A. *(1 mark)*

(b) Measure and write down the bearing of C from B. *(1 mark)*

(c) Measure and write down the bearing of A from C. *(1 mark)*

4 A train journey begins at 8.00am.
Details of the journey are shown.

8.00am to 8.30am – Travels a distance of 15 miles

8.30am to 9.00am – Stops at a station

9.00am to 10.00am – Travels a distance of 60 miles

Draw a distance–time graph on the axes provided.

Distance (miles)

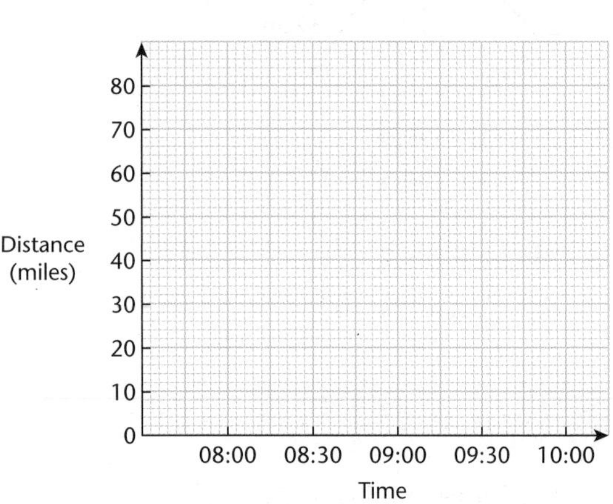

(3 marks)

5 Calculate the value of x.

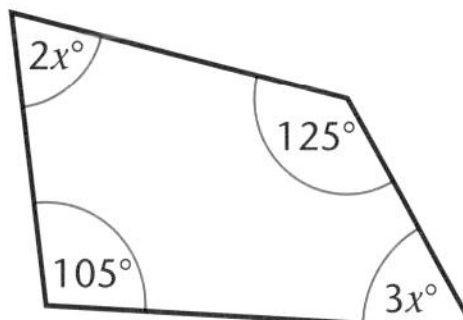

(4 marks)

6 Factorise

(a) $6p + 9$ *(1 mark)*

(b) $t^2 - 2t$. *(1 mark)*

7 Draw the graph of $y = 2x - 3$ for values of x between 0 and +5. *(3 marks)*

8 Calculate the area of these shapes.

(a)

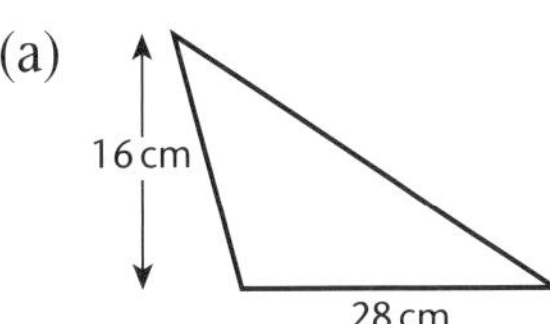

(2 marks)

(b)

7 m

(2 marks)

9 Explain clearly why the interior angle of a regular octagon is 135° *(2 marks)*

10 (a) Explain why a solution of the equation $x^3 - 2x = 40$ lies between $x = 3$ and $x = 4$. *(1 mark)*

(b) Use trial and improvement to find this solution.
Give your answer to one decimal place. *(3 marks)*

11

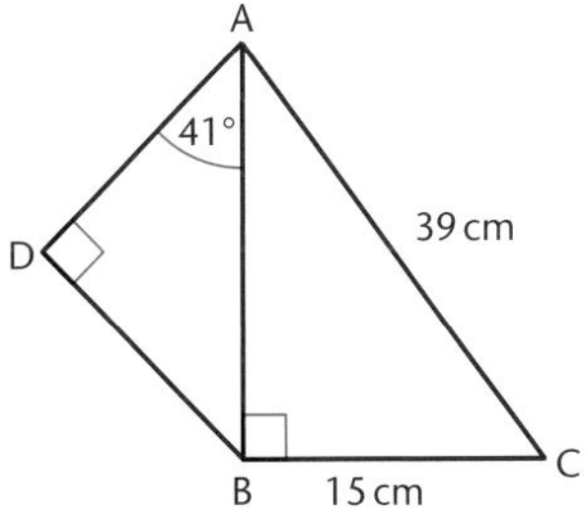

(a) Calculate AB. *(3 marks)*

(b) Calculate AD. *(3 marks)*

12 (a) Solve $\dfrac{3a + 18}{4} = 1 - a$. *(3 marks)*

(b) Simplify fully $(2p^3q^2)^3$. *(2 marks)*

(c) Factorise $9m^2 - n^2$. *(2 marks)*

13 (a) Solve these simultaneous equations.

$$3x - 4y = 8$$
$$2x - 6y = 7$$

(4 marks)

(b) The sketch below shows the graphs of $3x - 4y = 8$ and $2x - 6y = 7$.

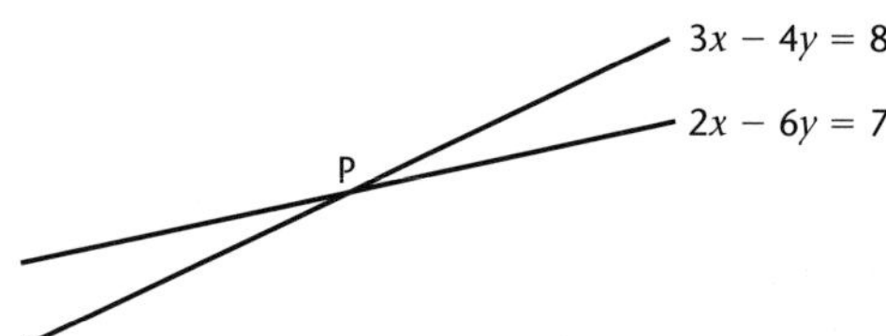

The graphs intersect at point P.
Write down the coordinates of P. *(1 mark)*

14

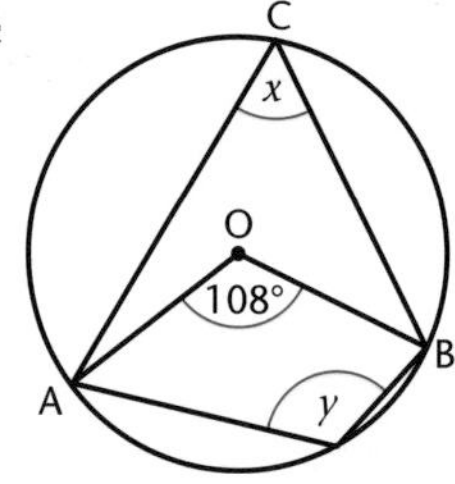

O is the centre of the circle.

Work out x and y. *(2 marks)*

15 (a) Here are a pair of similar pentagons.

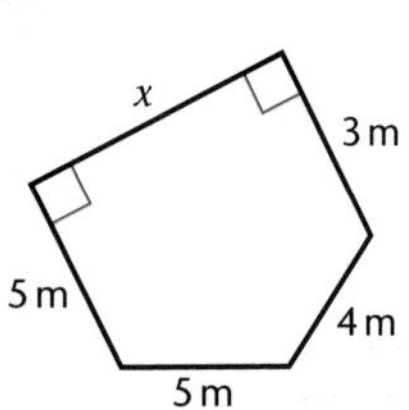

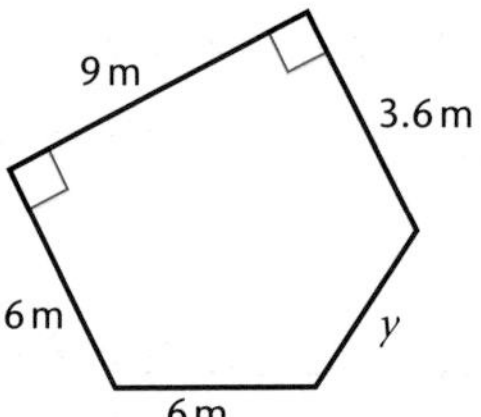

(i) Work out the value of y. *(3 marks)*

(ii) Work out the value of x. *(2 marks)*

(b) These two vases are similar.

The height of the larger vase is 1.5 times the height of the smaller vase.
The volume of the larger vase is 6750 cubic centimetres.

Work out the volume of the smaller vase. *(3 marks)*

16 (a) The graph of $y = f(x)$ is shown.

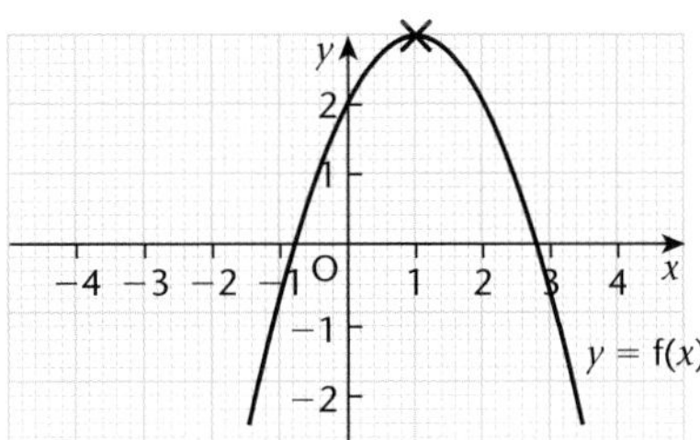

The maximum point A has coordinates (1, 3).

(i) Sketch on the same axes, the graph of $y = f(x + 2)$ *(1 mark)*

(ii) State the coordinates of the maximum point on the graph of $y = f(x + 2)$. *(1 mark)*

(b) The graph of $y = 2x(2x - 3)$ can be transformed to the graph of $y = x(x - 3)$.
Describe fully the transformation required. *(3 marks)*

17 A sketch graph of $y = \sin x$ is shown.

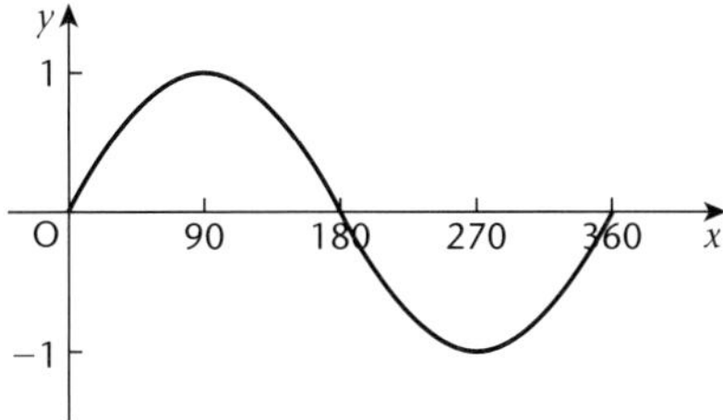

(a) Solve $2 \sin x = -1$ for values of x between 0° and 360° *(2 marks)*

(b) State the number of solutions of $\sin x = 0.8$ for values of x between 0° and 720°. *(1 mark)*

18 A firework is a cone of height 20 centimetres and radius 8 centimetres. The cone is filled with powder to a height of 10 centimetres as shown in the diagram.

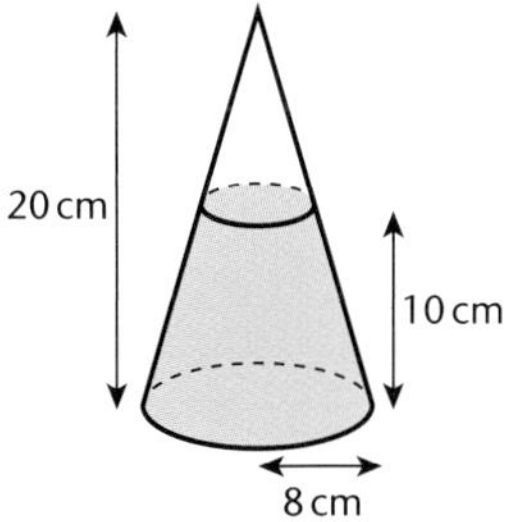

Work out the volume of the powder. *(3 marks)*

Answers

Exam practice 1A

1 26
2 a always true b always false, $5 + 3 = 8$
c always true
3 a false, $3 + 5 = 8$
b true, $2 + 3 = 5$
4 a could be true or false
b could be true or false
c always true
d always true
e always false
5 $2 \times 3 = 6$
6 $3 - 4 = -1$
7 a could be true or false e.g $q = 4$ gives an odd number, $q = 2$ gives an even number
b always false, $2n + 1$ is odd
c could be true or false; only true when $q = 3n$, where n is a whole number
8 a always true b always false
c always truc

Exam practice 1B

1 a i $2 \times 3 \times 3 \times 5$ ii $2 \times 2 \times 3 \times 5 \times 5$
b 30
2 a 54
b No, 36 does not divide into 54 exactly.
3 a i $2 \times 3 \times 7$ ii $2 \times 3 \times 3 \times 7$
b 42
c i 42 ii 84
4 a 30
b i 30, all the factors already present in 30.
ii 60, need to multiply 30 by 2 because 2×2 is a factor of 12.
5 a 2
b i 6 has just one factor of 2, so the extra 2 in 16 does not affect the HCF.
ii 24 and 36 both have a factor of 3, as does 6, so $2 \times 3 = 6$ is the HCF.

Exam practice 1C

1 a i $\frac{4}{16}$ ii $\frac{6}{16}$ iii $\frac{12}{16}$
b $\frac{1}{4}$
2 a $\frac{8}{30}$ b $\frac{25}{30}$ c $\frac{28}{30}$ d $\frac{24}{30}$
3 a $\frac{1}{4}$ b $\frac{3}{4}$ c $\frac{11}{24}$ d $\frac{4}{15}$ e $\frac{1}{4}$
4 a $\frac{2}{3}$ b $\frac{3}{8}$ c $\frac{2}{3}$
5 a $\frac{2}{9}, \frac{5}{12}, \frac{2}{3}$ b $\frac{5}{8}, \frac{7}{16}, \frac{9}{32}$
6 a $\frac{5}{9}$ or $\frac{4}{9}$: $\frac{5}{9} - \frac{1}{2} = \frac{1}{18}$ and $\frac{1}{2} - \frac{4}{9} = \frac{1}{18}$
b $\frac{3}{4}$ or $\frac{7}{12}$: $\frac{3}{4} - \frac{2}{3} = \frac{1}{12}$ and $\frac{7}{12} - \frac{2}{3} = -\frac{1}{12}$
c $\frac{5}{9}$ and $\frac{7}{12}$
7 a e.g. $\frac{12}{34}$ b e.g. $\frac{12}{24}$ c $\frac{25}{51}$

Exam practice 1D

1 a 0.75 b 0.075
2 a 0.875 b 0.02625
3 a 0.28 b 0.375 c 0.18
d 0.0875 e 0.0175
4 b, c and f
5 a $0.\dot{3}$ b $0.\dot{6}$ c $0.\dot{7}$ d $0.8\dot{3}$
6 a $\frac{9}{20}$ b $\frac{19}{8}$
7 $\frac{4}{3} = 1.333...$
8 a $\frac{6}{25}, \frac{3}{16}, \frac{2}{13}$, 0.105, 0.05 b $\frac{6}{25}$

Exam practice 1E

1 a 0.75 b 0.125 c 1.6 d 0.0518
2 a $\frac{3}{20}$ b $\frac{9}{10}$ c $\frac{7}{8}$ d $\frac{2}{3}$
3 a 86% b 2% c 157% d 26.5%
e 0.5% f 25% g 80% h 30%
i 12.5% j 450%
4 80%
5 $\frac{5}{9}$ ($55\frac{5}{9}$%)
6 a 155%, 1.72, $1\frac{3}{4}$ b $\frac{1}{3}$, 35%, $\frac{2}{5}$, 0.5

Exam practice 1F

1 a £50 b 12p c £7
d £200 e £15 f 30 kg
2 a £7.50 b £157.50
3 6500
4 36 cm^2
5 a £7122.50 b £162.25 c £1622.50
6 28.5%
7 76.5% (3 s.f.)
8 a 14.0625% b i 14.0625% ii 14.0625%

Exam practice 2A

1 a $6x^2$ b $6p^2$ c $10ab$ d $8y$
e $20x$ f $9x^3$ g $12a^4$ h $4p$
i $-4x^2$ j $6xy$ k $25b^2$ l $-12xy$
m $16x^2$ n $18y^2$ p $20b^2$
2 a $12a^3b^3$ b $15ab^2$ c $6p^2q^3$ d $8x^3y^3$
e $10s^3t$ f $4x^3y^6$ g $8x^4yz$ h $16p^3q^5$
i $14x^8y^2$ j $4x^7$ k $8a^3b^9$ l $64x^{15}y^6$
3 a $6x$ b $4x$ c $10x$
d $5 - 2y$ e $11x + 6$ f $7x$
g $12p$ h $-4b$ i $3 - 5y$

4 a $2x^2 + 10x$ b $a^2 + 6a - 5$
c $2x^2 + 3x - 9$ d $3x^2 + xy - 1$
e $p^2 + 6$ f $7 - y - y^2$
g $7x^2 - 5x - 2$ h $a^2 + 4$
i $4x^2 + 8$

5 He multiplied the powers instead of adding them.

6 a $\frac{a}{6}$ b $\frac{x}{15}$ c $\frac{23y}{20}$
d $\frac{3a}{10}$ e $\frac{2y}{9}$ f $\frac{23b}{42}$

Exam practice 2B

1 a $25 - 10x$ b $6y - 9y^2$
c $6x^2y - 8xy^2$ d $6x^3 - 10x^2$
e $x^3y - 2x^3y^2$ f $2p^3q^2 - 2pq^4$
g $3a^2b^3 - 3ab^3c$ h $4x^3y - 8xy^3$
i $5x^2yz - 5xy^2z^2$

2 a $5x^2 + 12x$ b $21 - x$
c $2x^2 + 12x$ d $4 - 9a + 2a^2$
e $4b^2 - 10b - 10$ f $5x - 16y$
g $x^2 + 4xy - 9y^2$ h $x - 11y$
i $-5x^2 + 5x - 2$

3 a $x^2 + 3x + 2$ b $x^2 + 8x + 15$
c $a^2 + 8a + 7$ d $2x^2 + 3x + 1$
e $3x^2 + 10x + 8$ f $2x^2 + 26x + 72$
g $6x^2 + 7x + 2$ h $10x^2 + 19x + 6$
i $42x^2 + 47x + 10$

4 a $x^2 - 5x + 6$ b $x^2 - 5x + 4$
c $x^2 - 8x + 15$ d $3x^2 - 14x + 8$
e $4x^2 - 23x + 15$ f $5a^2 - 21a + 4$
g $6x^2 - 13x + 6$ h $10b^2 - 17b + 3$
i $12s^2 - 41s + 35$

5 a $x^2 - 3x - 10$ b $x^2 - x - 6$
c $x^2 + x - 6$ d $2x^2 - x - 6$
e $x^2 + x - 12$ f $x^2 + 4x - 12$
g $6x^2 + x - 1$ h $10x^2 + x - 3$
i $6a^2 + 11a - 10$

6 a $x^2 + 4x + 4$ b $x^2 + 12x + 36$
c $x^2 + 10x + 25$ d $x^2 + 2x + 1$
e $9x^2 + 30x + 25$ f $x^2 + 2xy + y^2$
g $x^2 - 4x + 4$ h $x^2 - 6x + 9$
i $x^2 - 20x + 100$ j $9x^2 - 6x + 1$
k $x^2 - 2xy + y^2$ l $25x^2 - 20x + 4$
m $x^2 - 9$ n $4x^2 - 1$
p $a^2 - b^2$ q $9x^2 - 4$
r $16x^2 - 9$ s $25y^2 - 4$

7 a $6x^2 - 5x - 6$ b $7x^2 + 23x + 6$
c $6x^2 + 13x - 28$ d $4a^2 - b^2$
e $9s^2 - 24st + 16t^2$ f $x^4 + 4x^2 + 3$
g $x^2y^2 - 16$ h $x^2y^2 + 3xyz + 2z^2$
i $y^4 - y^2 - 6$ j $x^3 - 8x^2 + 15x$
k $3x^4 + 23x^3 + 30x^2$ l $3x^3 - 4x^2 - 6x + 8$

8 $(4x - 3)^2 = 16x^2 - 24x + 9$

Exam practice 2C

1 a 2 b 3 c x d x^2 e y
f $2t$ g $2x$ h xy i $4ab$

2 a $3(x + 2)$ b $3(x - 4)$ c $4(2x + 1)$
d $2(x + 3)$ e $5(x + 1)$ f $x(x + 3)$
g $a(a - 2)$ h $t(t - 6)$ i $v(v + 2)$
j $x(2 - x)$ k $a(2a + 5)$ l $2x(3 - x)$
m $2(x + y)$ n $x(x - y)$ p $5(a + 2b)$
q $a(b + c)$ r $x(2x + y)$ s $y(x + y)$
t $2(x^2 + 2y^2)$ u $x(x^2 - 2)$

3 a $y^2(y - 1)$ b $x^2(x - 3)$
c $2b(a - 3b)$ d $xy(x + y)$
e $5x(x - 2y)$ f $2y(2y + x)$
g $3pq(1 - 3pq)$ h $4ab(3 + a)$
i $2x^2(3x^2 + 1)$ j $3a^2b(1 - 2ab)$
k $3xy(4x^2 + 3y)$ l $4pq(4q^2 - 5p)$

4 a $2(x + y + 2)$ b $2(a + 2b - c)$
c $2(2a^2 + a - 4b)$ d $3(xy + 2x + 4)$
e $3(x + 2x^2 + 3)$ f $a(b + c + d)$
g $xy(x - 2y + 4)$ h $2p(4q + p - 2q^2)$
i $3xy(1 + 2x + 3y^2)$

Exam practice 2D

1 a $(x + 3)^2$
b No, last term needs to be 81.
c $(x + 5)^2$ d $(x + 4)^2$
e $(x - 2)^2$ f $(x - 1)^2$
g No, middle term needs to be $10x$.
h $(2x + 5)^2$
i No, last term needs to be +1.
j $(3x - 1)^2$ k $(6x + 4)^2$
l No, last term needs to be +4.
m $(a - 3b)^2$ n $(2x - 7)^2$ p $(2x + y)^2$

2 a $(x + 2)(x - 2)$ b $(x + 6)(x - 6)$
c $(x + 9)(x - 9)$ d $(x + y)(x - y)$
e $(2x + 3)(2x - 3)$ f $(5a + 3)(5a - 3)$
g $(3a + 4)(3a - 4)$ h $(1 + s)(1 - s)$
i $(2 + 5x)(2 - 5x)$ j $(2x + 5y)(2x - 5y)$
k $(6a + 7b)(6a - 7b)$ l $(xy + 1)(xy - 1)$

3 $a^2 - b^2 = (a + b)(a - b)$ which is not $(a - b)^2$.

Exam practice 2E

1 a $(x + 4)(x + 1)$ b $(x + 4)(x + 3)$
c $(x + 12)(x + 1)$ d $(x + 2)(x + 9)$
e $(x + 2)(x + 3)$ f $(x + 2)(x + 5)$
g $(2x + 3)(x + 2)$ h $(2x + 3)(x + 1)$
i $(3x + 2)(x + 1)$ j $(2x + 9)(2x + 1)$
k $(3x + 5)(2x + 3)$ l $(3x + 4)(2x + 3)$

2 a $(x - 6)(x - 2)$ b $(x + 8)(x - 2)$
c $(x - 5)(x + 3)$ d $(x - 1)(x - 6)$
e $(x - 4)(x - 1)$ f $(x - 6)(x - 2)$
g $(3x - 1)(x - 1)$ h $(3x - 4)(x - 3)$
i $(2x - 3)(3x - 2)$ j $(2x - 5y)(3x - 2y)$
k $(3x - 4)(x - 1)$ l $(4x - 3)(x - 2)$

3 a $(x + 4)(x - 3)$ b $(x - 4)(x + 1)$
c $(x + 6)(x - 2)$ d $(x - 4)(x + 2)$
e $(x + 3)(x - 2)$ f $(x + 9)(x - 1)$
g $(3x + 1)(2x - 1)$ h $(4x - 1)(2x + 1)$
i $(5x + 3)(x - 1)$ j $(2x + 3)(2x - 5)$
k $(7x + 3)(x - 1)$ l $(9a - 4b)(a + b)$

4 a $(x - 9)(x + 1)$
b $(y + 3)(y - 3)(y^2 + 1)$

5 a $2(x + 3)^2$ b $5(3x + 1)(3x - 1)$
c $(7 - 4x)(1 + x)$ d $(x + 4)(x - 1)$
e $2(2x + 3)(2x - 3)$ f $3(x - 2)(x + 1)$
g $(9 - x)(1 + x)$ h $(2x - 3)(x + 1)$
i $4(x + 2)^2$ j $\left(\frac{x}{2} - \frac{1}{3}\right)\left(\frac{x}{2} + \frac{1}{3}\right)$
k $(2s + 1)(s + 8)$ l $(2a + b)(a + 3b)$
m $(5x - 2)(x + 2)$
n $(x - 2 + y)(x - 2 - y)$
p $(2 - x)^2$
q $(3 + x)(2 - x)$
r $(x - 9)(x - 1)$
s $(a - b + c)(a - b - c)$
t $(x^2 + 2)(x + 2)(x - 2)$
u $(2y - 1)(2y + 1)(y + 1)(y - 1)$
v $(a + 2b)(a - 2b)(a^2 + 4b^2)$

6 a No combination of $2x$, x and ±3, ±1 gives $-7x$.
b No combination of x and 9, 1 or 3, 3 gives $12x$.
c No combination of $15x$, x or $5x$, $3x$ and ±14, ±1 or ±2, ±7 gives $-39x$.

Exam practice 2F

1 a $\frac{x}{2y}$ b $\frac{x}{2}$ c $\frac{x}{y}$ d $\frac{a}{b}$
e $\frac{1}{3x}$ f $\frac{2y}{3}$ g $\frac{s}{5}$ h $\frac{\pi r}{2}$
i $\frac{x}{2}$ j $\frac{b^2}{2}$ k $\frac{3x}{2y}$ l $\frac{b}{c}$
m $\frac{4}{x^2}$ n $\frac{3x}{4y}$ p $\frac{1}{2r^3}$ q $\frac{x}{3y^3}$

2 a $\frac{x - y}{2x}$ b $\frac{2a}{a - 3b}$ c $\frac{y - x}{3}$
d $\frac{1}{x - 3}$ e $\frac{2}{5}$ f $\frac{x + 3}{2}$
g $\frac{3 - b}{a}$ h $\frac{6y}{3x - 1}$ i $\frac{s - t}{7t}$
j $\frac{1}{x}$ k $\frac{3a}{a - 5}$ l $\frac{s - 3t}{2t^2 + s}$

3 LHS $= \frac{a(2 - b)}{4ab} = \frac{2 - b}{4b}$

4 a $\frac{1}{x - 1}$ b $\frac{1}{p - 3}$ c $x + 1$
d $\frac{1}{x + 1}$ e $x - 5$ f $3x - 2$
g $\frac{2}{a - 3}$ h $\frac{2}{t - 4}$ i $\frac{x + 3}{2(x - 2)}$
j $\frac{1}{2(x + 3)}$ k $\frac{1}{a - b}$ l $\frac{2(x - 2)}{3}$
m $\frac{x}{(x + 1)(x - 2)}$ n $\frac{x - 2}{x}$ p $\frac{x}{2x - 1}$
q $\frac{x + 4}{x - 2}$ r $\frac{x - 3}{x + 5}$ s $\frac{x - 3}{3x + 1}$
t $\frac{a}{a + 2}$ u $\frac{x + 5}{2x - 3}$ v $\frac{2x - 5}{x - 3}$

Exam practice 2G

1 False, $1 + 2 + 3 + 4 = 10$ which is not a multiple of 4.
2 False, $1 + 2 + 3 + 4 = 10$ which is not a multiple of 4.
3 True, if a and b are any whole numbers, $2a$ and $2b$ are even whole numbers and their product is $4ab$ which is a multiple of 4.
4 If a is any whole number, $2a$ is even and $4a^2$ is even.
5 No, $\frac{2}{3} + \frac{3}{4} = 1\frac{5}{12}$.
6 No, $5 + 7 = 12$ which is even.
7 True, $10a + b - (10b + a) = 9a - 9b = 9(a - b)$. The result is a multiple of 9.
8 True, for any three consecutive natural numbers one is a multiple of 3 and at least one of the three is even i.e. the product is a multiple of 6.

Exam practice 3A

1 a $x = 7$ b $x = 23$ c $x = -1$ d $x = -9$
e $x = 12$ f $x = 2$ g $x = 2$ h $x = 11$
i $x = 7$ j $x = -1$ k $x = -2$ l $x = -3$

2 a $x = 2$ b $x = 1$ c $x = 3$ d $x = 2$
e $x = 2\frac{1}{4}$ f $x = 3$ g $x = 4$ h $x = 1\frac{1}{8}$
i $x = \frac{1}{2}$ j $x = 3$ k $x = -1$ l $x = -2$
m $x = 1\frac{1}{3}$ n $x = 1$ p $x = \frac{1}{6}$ q $x = -\frac{1}{7}$
r $x = 2\frac{2}{5}$ s $x = -2\frac{1}{4}$

3 a $x = 10$ b $x = 2$ c $x = 2\frac{1}{3}$
d $x = 30$ e $x = 10$ f $x = 72$

4 $2x = 10$, $x = 5$

5 a $x = 4$ b $x = -2$ c $x = 6$ d $x = -5$
e $x = 11$ f $x = 3$ g $x = \frac{1}{2}$ h $x = -\frac{1}{7}$
i $x = \frac{3}{4}$ j $x = -4$ k $x = 1$ l $x = 1$

6 a $x = 2$ b $x = \frac{1}{2}$ c $x = 2\frac{5}{7}$
d $x = 2$ e $x = 0$ f $x = -2\frac{1}{2}$
g $x = 4\frac{1}{2}$ h $x = 1\frac{1}{2}$ i $x = 1$

7 a $x = 5$ b $x = 9$ c $x = -4\frac{1}{2}$
d $x = \frac{1}{2}$ e $x = -5\frac{1}{2}$ f $x = 1\frac{2}{3}$
g $x = -\frac{2}{5}$ h $x = 4$ i $x = 22$
j $x = 1\frac{3}{10}$ k $x = -13$ l $x = 13$
m $x = \frac{5}{11}$ n $x = -1\frac{1}{8}$

Exam practice 3B

1 a 10 b 20 c 40 d 28
e $4\frac{4}{5}$ f 30 g 5 h $\frac{9}{10}$
i 10 j 30 k 5 l 21
m 3 n $-\frac{6}{7}$ p $-7\frac{1}{2}$ q $\frac{2}{5}$

2 a 4 b 7 c -5 d -2
e $12\frac{1}{2}$ f $\frac{2}{3}$ g 22 h $-6\frac{3}{5}$
i 3 j 22 k $2\frac{1}{4}$ l $\frac{1}{2}$

3 a $1\frac{1}{2}$ b $1\frac{5}{9}$ c $\frac{1}{2}$ d 2 e -8
f 2 g $-4\frac{2}{3}$ h -14 i $1\frac{2}{7}$ j $\frac{5}{13}$
k 5 l $-\frac{1}{3}$ m 2 n 2 p -16

Exam practice 3C

1 a $5cp$ b $30np$ c $(x - 3)$ cm
2 a £$(C + 5)$ b £$(2p + 4)$ c $(5a + 4b)$p
3 a $(2x + 6)$ cm b $(4x + 3y)$ cm
4 x in one box, $x - 10$ in the other; total number is $x + x - 10 = 2x - 10 = 2(x - 5)$
5 Perimeter is $(x^2 + 2x + 1)$ cm $= (x + 1)^2$ cm.
6 $(2x + 5)$p where xp is the cost of a plain muffin.

Exam practice 3D

1 $5 + x = 8.5$, $x = 3.5$
2 a $(200 - 3c)$p b $200 - 3c = 80$ c 40p
3 6 cm
4 a 13 b 8 c 6 d 2
5 50°
6 a 4 b 12 m
7 120p
8 6
9 $4 - 2x + 6 = 1$; $4 - 6 = -2$, not 2

Exam practice 3E

1 a $P = 2(l + w)$ b i 70 cm ii 5 cm
2 a $T = 30n + c$ b $2\frac{1}{2}$ hours
3 a $A = 2a(b + c)$ b 5 mm
4 6.6 cm^2
5 a 1 b -25
6 a 10 b 2500
7 a 4 b 1 c 20
8 a 52 b 29
c Yes, $2^2 + 3^2 = (-2)^2 + (-3)^2$.
9 a 24π b $\frac{9}{\pi}$
10 $\sqrt{2}$ or $-\sqrt{2}$ 11 $\pm\frac{3\sqrt{3}}{2}$

Exam practice 3F

1 a $n = T - 6$ b $b = N + 3$ c $r = \frac{d}{2}$
d $b = \frac{A}{l}$ e $d = \frac{C}{\pi}$ f $s = \frac{d}{t}$
g $y = 2x$ h $x = \frac{y-2}{3}$ i $p = \frac{t}{5} + 8$
j $y = \frac{c-x}{2}$ k $x = \frac{y-c}{m}$ l $A = \frac{3V}{h}$
m $b = \frac{a}{2} + 4$ n $a = \frac{w}{3} + 2b$
p $h = (G + s)t$ q $x = \frac{2w}{y} - b$
2 a $b = \frac{2A}{h} - c$ b 6
3 a $h = \frac{P - ar}{a}$ b $y = \frac{x}{1-c}$
c $x = \pm\sqrt{y-k}$ d $r = \pm\sqrt{\frac{V}{\pi h}}$
e $c = \frac{2A}{a+b}$ f $l = \frac{T^2 g}{4\pi^2}$
g $x = \frac{a(2b-y)}{b}$ h $P = \frac{100A}{100 + RT}$
i $y = \frac{2x}{x-2}$ j $x = -3c - 2k$
k $x = \frac{k^2}{1-k}$ l $a = \frac{2A - b - c}{2}$
m $x = \frac{(r^2 + 2y - 6)}{(y-3)}$ n $b = -\frac{2a}{3}$
p $a = \frac{3(2A - bh)}{h}$ q $a = \frac{2S - nk - nl}{2n}$
r $r = \sqrt[3]{\frac{3V}{4\pi}}$ s $y = \pm\sqrt{A - x^2}$
4 No, $\sqrt{(b^2 + x^2)}$ is not $b + x$.

Exam practice 4A

1 a $x = 5, y = 3$ b $x = 3, y = -1$
c $x = 6, y = 4$ d $x = 2, y = 7$
e $x = 5, y = 2$ f $x = 2, y = 1$
2 a $x = 1, y = 2$ b $x = 4, y = -2$
c $x = -1, y = 2$ d $x = 7, y = 10$
e $x = 6, y = -5$ f $a = 3, b = -2$
3 a $x = 1, y = 1$ b $x = -1, y = 3$
c $x = \frac{1}{2}, y = \frac{1}{2}$ d $x = 9, y = 8$
e $x = -3, y = 4$ f $s = -2, t = -3$
4 a $x = 3, y = 2$ b $a = 4, b = -2$
c $x = -1, y = -1$ d $x = -1, y = 4$
e $x = 6, y = -2$ f $p = 2, q = \frac{3}{2}$
5 a Length = 2 × width so $x = 2(y - 1)$
i.e. $2y - x = 2$.
b Perimeter $= 2x + 2y - 2$, $\therefore x + y = 10$.
c 6 cm
6 $x = 18, y = 72$
7 6 or 14

Exam practice 4B

1 a 2, 3 b 6, 7 c $-4, -9$
d $-5, -7$ e $5, -6$ f $-12, 4$
g $-\frac{3}{2}, -5$ h $\frac{5}{3}, 2$ i $\frac{1}{5}, -6$
j $-\frac{3}{2}, -\frac{4}{3}$ k $\frac{3}{4}, -\frac{5}{2}$ l $\frac{8}{3}, 6$
2 a $-4, 3$ b $-5, 8$ c $-2, 4$
d $-3, 2$ e $-\frac{1}{2}, 3$ f $-3, 8$
g $1, \frac{9}{4}$ h 0, 3 i 2, 3
j $-2, 5$
3 a $-1, 4$ b $-5, 3$ c $-4, 3$
d $-\frac{5}{2}, \frac{3}{2}$ e $-1, 8$ f $-\frac{3}{4}, 2$
g $-1, 4$ h $5, -6$ i $-\frac{2}{3}, 3$
j 2 k $\frac{5}{3}$ l 0, 1
4 11
5 4 cm
6 21 and 23

Exam practice 4C

1 a 4 b 36 c $\frac{25}{4}$
2 a $a = -4, b = -12$
b $a = 9, b = 3$
3 a i $(x - 2)^2 - 2$ ii $(x + 5)^2 - 27$
iii $(x + \frac{7}{2})^2 - \frac{61}{4}$
b i $2 \pm \sqrt{2}$ ii $-5 \pm 3\sqrt{3}$
iii $-\frac{7}{2} \pm \sqrt{\frac{61}{4}}$

Exam practice 4D

1 a $-3.41, -0.59$ b $-4.30, -0.70$
c 0.44, 4.56 d 0.59, 8.41
e $-0.77, 7.77$ f $-6.74, 0.74$
2 a $-1.43, -0.23$ b $-2.78, -0.72$
c $-1.74, 0.34$ d $-0.53, 2.53$
e $-0.65, 1.15$ f 0.07, 1.60
3 a 0.21, 4.79 b $-0.56, 3.56$
c $-3.73, -0.27$ d $-0.81, 2.47$
e $-1.19, 1.69$ f $-0.21, 1.21$

4 a $\frac{7 \pm \sqrt{41}}{2}$ b $\frac{5 \pm \sqrt{41}}{2}$ c $\frac{-4 \pm \sqrt{6}}{5}$
d $-3 \pm \sqrt{11}$ e $-2 + \frac{\sqrt{22}}{2}$ f $\frac{-5 \pm \sqrt{5}}{4}$
5 $1 + \frac{\sqrt{89}}{4}$ cm

Exam practice 4E

1 a $x = 4, y = 3$ or $x = -3, y = -4$
b $x = -1, y = 2$ or $x = 2, y = -1$
c $x = 5, y = 3$ or $x = -\frac{9}{2}, y = -\frac{10}{3}$
d $x = 2, y = 4$ or $x = \frac{50}{9}, y = -\frac{20}{3}$
e $x = 3, y = 5$ or $x = -1, y = -3$
f $x = 4, y = 5$ or $x = -\frac{32}{9}, y = -\frac{19}{3}$
2 a $x = 2, y = 2$
b $x = 3, y = -1$ or $x = \frac{13}{5}, y = -\frac{9}{5}$
c $x = 5, y = 12$ or $x = \frac{33}{5}, y = \frac{56}{5}$
3 15 cm
4 14 and 17

Exam practice 4F

1 3.6 2 1.4 3 3.1 4 2.3 5 2.7

Exam practice 5A

1 a 14, 16 b 64, 81
c 128, 256 d 13, 16
e 1, 0 f 10 000, 100 000
g 19, 23 h 10, 5
2 a $a = 16, b = 64$ b $a = 18, b = 30$
c $a = 49, b = 16$ d $a = 1, b = -8$
e $a = 6, b = 18$ f $a = -1, b = 14$
3 a $x + 10, x + 12$ b always 2
4 a $x + 1 = 0, x + 0 = -1$
b $x = -1$ in every equation.
5 a 16
b Number of squares must be a square number. 30 is not.
6 a 1, 4, 9, 16, 25 b 13
c 81, (pattern number)^2
7 a $9x, 11x$
b $x + 16, x + 25$
c $4x + 17, 5x + 16$
d $16x = 32, 32x = 64$
e $5(x - 1), 6(x - 3)$
f $x - 2 = 2, x - 3 = 1$
g (6, 13), (7, 15)

Exam practice 5B

1 a 7, 15, 31 b 8, 18, 38
c 10, 101, 10 202
2 a 30, 84, 246
b 200 is not equal to $3 \times (84 - 2)$, other terms > 200
3 a 2, 5, 8 b 9, 13, 17 c 0, 1, 3
d 1, −2, −5 e 2, 6, 12 f 0, 3, 8
4 a 6, 11 b 51
c No, if $5n + 1 = 37$ n is not a whole number.
5 a 2, 5, 10 b 145
c $n^2 + 1 = 100$ does not give a whole number value for n.

6 a 420
b If $n = 7$, $n(n+1) = 56$, so 56 is the 7th term.
c No two consecutive whole numbers have a product of 60.
7 a $12 - 2n$
b $T_n - T_{n-1}$ is $10 - 2n - (12 - 2n) = -2$ i.e. the difference is 2.
8 a $\frac{1}{2}(n+1)(n+2)$
b $\frac{1}{2}(n+1)(n+2) + \frac{1}{2}n(n+1) = (n+1)^2$ which is a square number.

Exam practice 5C

1 $2n + 5$
2 a $3n - 2$ b $17 - 2n$ c 2^{7-n}
d 10^{3-n} e $6(n+1)$ f $10(11 - n)$
3 $2n + 1$
4 $3n + 1$
5 $2n + 2$
6 a $2n + 4$ b 18
7 a $3n$ b i 33 ii Yes, 1.
8 a $6n + 2$ b 13 c 2
9 a $N = 4w + 4$ b 19 feet
10 a

$n - 7$		$n - 5$
	n	
$n + 5$		$n + 7$

b $7n - 6$

11 a

$n - 1$	n	$n + 1$
	$n + 5$	

b If numbers are $n - 1$, n and $n + 1$, $T_n^2 = n$ and $T_{n-1} \times T_{n+1} = (n - 1)(n + 1) = n^2 - 1$.

Exam practice 6A

1 a y^o b y^o c x^o
2 $a = 70$ (corresponding angles)
3 $b = 105$ (vert. opp angles)
4 $c = 120$ (vert. opp angles), $d = 60$ ($c + d = 180$)
5 $e = 50$ ($e + 130 = 180$)
6 $a = 125$ (vert. opp angles, corresponding angles)
7 $b = 84$ (vert. opp. angles, $96 + b = 180$)
8 $x = 75$ (alt. angles), $y = 25$ (angles on str. line)
9 $p = 65$ (corres. angles), $q = 55$ (corres. angles, angles on a str. line)
10 $z = 43$ (alt. angles twice)
11 $a = 25$ (alt. angles), $b = 95$ (corres. angles)
12 $p = 30$ (alt. angles), $q = 45$ (alt. angles), $r = 285$ (angles at a point)
13 $x = 110$ (alt. angles, twice)

Exam practice 6B

1 $a = 60$ 2 $b = 52$
3 $c = 55$ 4 $b = 79$
5 $r = 106, s = 40$ 6 $j = 70, k = 50$
7 $m = 126, n = 54$ 8 $r = 106$
9 $x = 25, y = 65$ 10 $q = 138, r = 62$

11 $x = 30$; 30°, 60°, 90°
12 $x = 22.5$; 22.5°, 67.5°, 90°

Exam practice 6C

1 a isosceles b right-angled
c equilateral d isosceles
e equiangular (equilateral)
2 Third angle is 60°, so all are 60°.
3 Yes, third angle is 65° so two angles are 65° and the triangle is isosceles.
4 $g = 84$ (isos. △)
5 $h = 36$ (isos. △), $i = 144$ (angles on str. line)
6 $h = 65$ (isos. △), $i = 115$ (angles on str. line)
7 $j = 50$ (str. line, isos. △), $k = 80$ (angles of △)
8 $k = 25$ (isos. △, vert. opp. angles)
9 $m = 60$ (equilateral △, alternate angles)
10 $a = 40$ (str. line, isos. △),
$b = 70$ (str. line, corresponding angles)

Exam practice 6D

1 83 2 115 3 68 4 78
5 32 6 57 7 71 8 89

Exam practice 6E

1 $a = 36$, $b = 36$
2 $c = 74$, $d = 68$
3 $f = 74$, $g = 44$, $h = 118$
4 $c = 42$, $d = 18$, $e = 18$
5 $p = 38$, $q = 35$, $r = 73$
6 $i = 127$, $j = 59$
7 a $a = 57$, $b = 114$ b 68
8 a b  c 
9 a No, e.g. an isosceles trapezium.
b Yes, adj. ∠s total 180°.
10 a parallelogram b rectangle
c rectangle d square
e rhombus

Exam practice 6F

1 a 85 b 114
2 a 100 b 82
3 a 60° b 45° c 30° d 20°
4 a 108° b 135° c 150° d 162°
5 a 12 b 9 c 10
6 a i yes ii no iii no
b i no ii yes iii yes.
Every exterior angle must be a factor of 360°.
7 105
8 a 60 b 135
9 a regular hexagon b 60 c 120
10 a 72 b 36
11 a i 108 ii 36
b 72°, 72°, 36°
c i isosceles △ ii isosceles △
12 a i 120 ii 30 b 90°
c i isosceles triangle ii rectangle
13 a 120°, 60°, 60°, 120° b trapezium

Exam practice 7A

1 a 100 mm b 7.6 km c 7 cm
d 4.5 m e 8 m f 2000 mm
g 17.8 cm h 3500 m
2 a 3 ft b 3 yd
c 64 km d 40 miles
3 a 30 cm b 24 in c 75 cm
4 a 120 cm, 1 m, 30 in, 2 ft
b No, 80 miles ≈ 128 km.
5 a 120 mm^2 b 4.5 cm^2 c 500 000 m^2
d 0.0056 km^2 e 400 000 m^2 f 5.64 cm^2
g 247 acres h 10 ha

Exam practice 7B

1 a i 36 cm^2 ii 8100 mm^2 (81 cm^2)
iii 0.16 km^2
b i 60 cm^2 ii 1750 m^2 iii 33.5 cm^2
c 40.5 cm^2
2 a 192 cm^2 b 65 cm^2 c 37 cm^2
d 376 cm^2 e 384 cm^2 f 54 cm^2
3 a 1440 m b i 128 000 m^2 ii 12.8 ha
4 a 360 cm^2 b 120 cm^2 c 240 cm^2
5 a 3500 cm^2 b 2.82 m^2
6 a $2x^2 = 32$, $x^2 = 16$, $x = 4$
b 24 cm
7 5 m × 8 m
8 12 cm

Exam practice 7C

1 a 40 cm^2 b 28.5 cm^2 c 160 cm^2
d 22.5 cm^2 e 60 cm^2 f 84 cm^2
2 a 6 cm^2 b 12 cm^2 c 9 cm^2
d 12 cm^2 e 12 cm^2
3 a 72 cm^2 b 32 cm^2 c 40.5 cm^2
d 135 cm^2 e 145 cm^2
4 a 60 cm^2 b 25.5 cm^2
5 a 104 cm^2 b 312 cm^2
c 84 cm^2 d 170 cm^2
6 a 126 cm^2 b 252 cm^2
7 34 m^2
8 138 cm^2
9 a 60 cm × 40 cm b 2400 cm^2
c 1836 cm^2 d 564 cm^2
10 98 cm^2
11 a 35.2 cm^2 b 52.8 cm^2
12 7.5 cm
13 17 cm^2

Exam practice 7D

1 a 60 cm b 48 m c 180 mm
2 225 cm
3 a 24 cm b 72 cm
4 a 60 cm b 2.5 m c 32 mm
5 a 8π cm b 9π m^2 c $\frac{60}{\pi}$ cm
6 a 188 cm b 53.1
7 a 283 cm b 6360 cm^2
8 50.3 cm, 66.0 cm, 84.8 cm
9 a 25.7 cm b 39.3 cm^2

10 a $1520\,m^2$
 b $1130\,mm^2$ ($11.3\,cm^2$) both to 3 s.f.
11 a $227\,cm^2$
 b Yes, area of second plate is $491\,cm^2$.
12 $3.13\,m^2$
13 $11.1\,cm^2$
14 a $400\,cm^2$ b $154\,cm^2$ c $246\,cm^2$
15 a $81.1\,m$ b $146\,m^2$
16 a $4590\,cm^2$ b $4090\,cm^2$ c $12\,800\,cm^2$

Exam practice 7E

1 a i $18.8\,cm$ ii $141\,cm^2$
 b i $17.3\,cm$ ii $72.7\,cm^2$
 c i $17.1\,cm$ ii $40.1\,cm^2$
 d i $1.90\,cm$ ii $3.23\,cm^2$
2 a $76.4°$ b $43.0°$ c $229.2°$
3 a $4.58\,cm$ b $11.5\,cm$ c $6.25\,cm$
4 a $60°$ b $\frac{3\pi}{2}\,cm^2$
5 a $110\,cm$ b $157\,cm^2$
6 a arc length $= 2 \times \pi \times 12 \times \frac{120}{360}\,cm = 8\pi\,cm$
 b $48\pi\,cm^2$ c $4\,cm$ d $64\pi\,cm^2$
7 a i $7\pi\,m$ ii $22.0\,m$
 b i $12.25\pi\,m^2$ ii $38.5\,m^2$
8 $18.3\,cm^2$
9 a $\pi - 2\,m^2$ or $1.14\,m$
 b student's proof
10 $123\,mm^2$

Exam practice 8A

1 a 6 b 3 c 1
 d 4 e Yes, $4(5 + 6 + 3) = 56$.
2 a cuboid b cylinder
 c triangular prism d cuboid
 e triangular prism
3 a i 6 ii 12 iii 8 b 1
4 a 8 b 18 c 12

Exam practice 8B

Questions 1 to 7 drawn on 1 cm squares.

1 a b
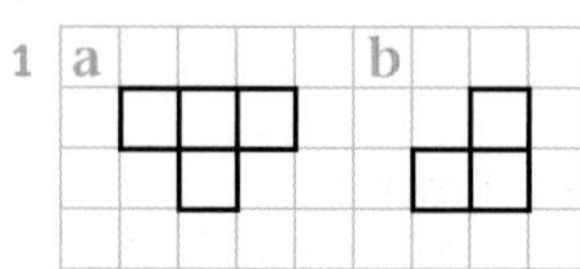

2 a b
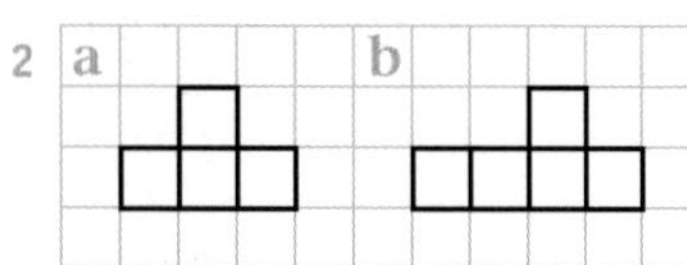

3 a b
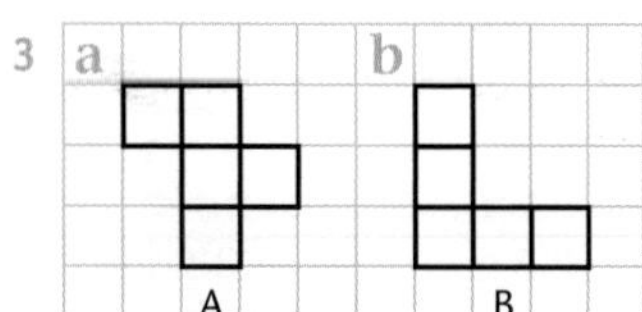

4 a i ii
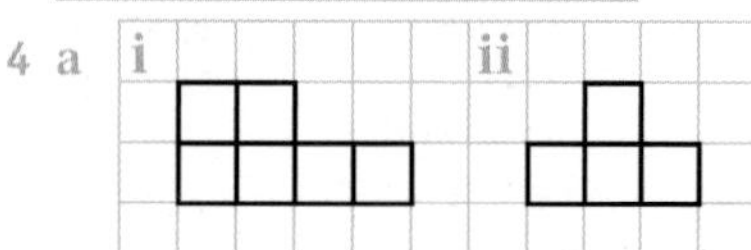

b
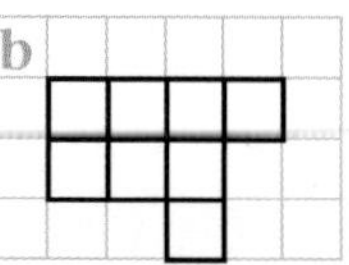

5 a i ii

b
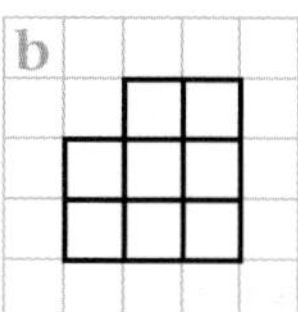

6 a
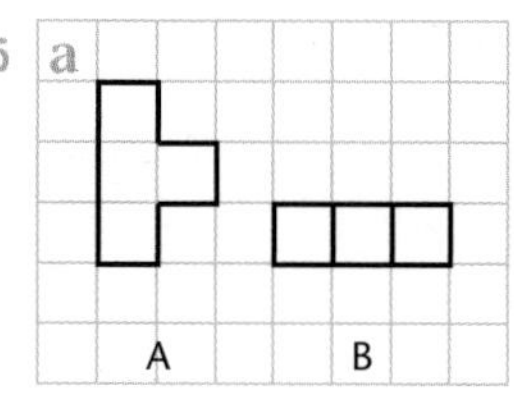

b
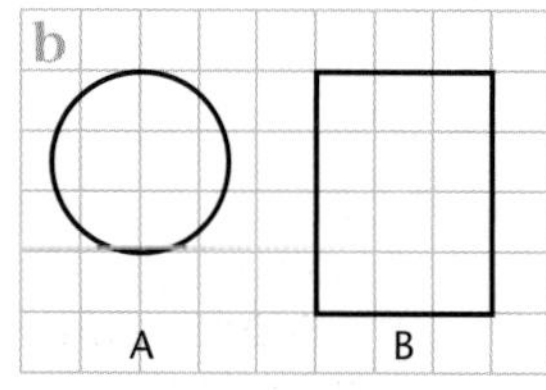

c
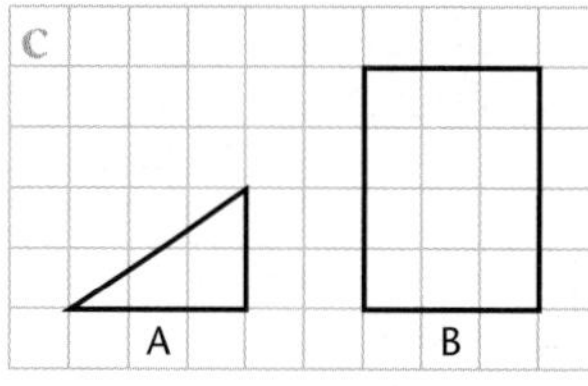

d
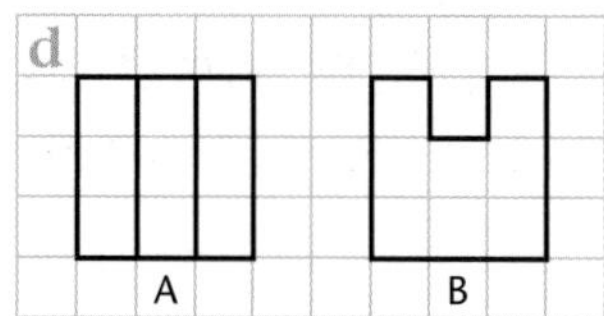

7 a
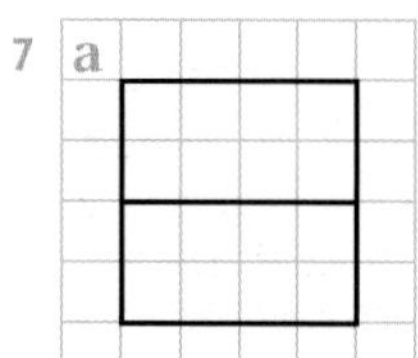

b
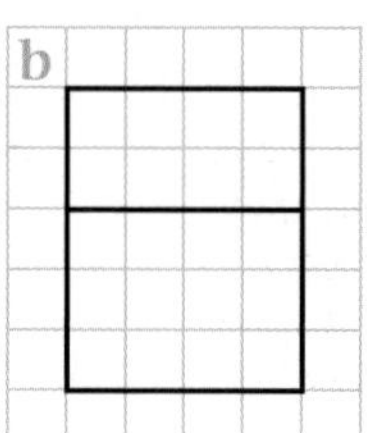

c
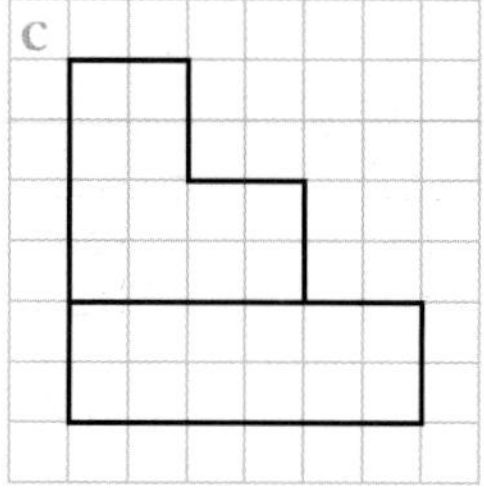

8 a b

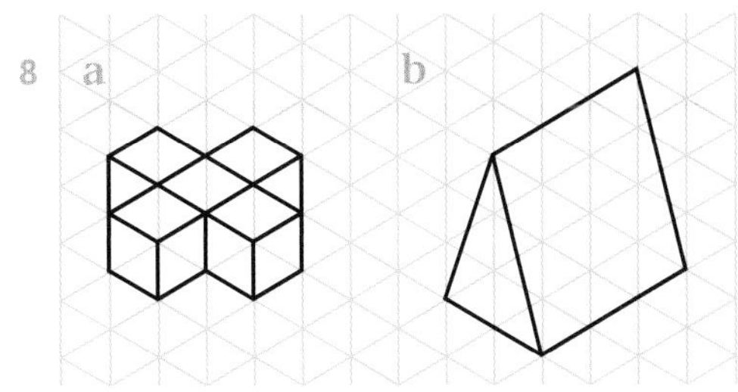

Exam practice 8C

1 $1800\,cm^2$
2 $390\,cm^2$
3 $95.5\,m^2$
4 $113.2\,cm^2$
5 No, one can will paint 73 completely.
6 a $234\,cm^2$ b $348\,cm^2$
7 a $960\,cm^2$ b $18\,320\,cm^2$
8 a 23.2 cm b $232\,cm^2$
9 a $50.3\,cm^2$ b $301.6\,cm^2$ c 75.0%
10 $11.0\,cm^2$ ($1100\,mm^2$)
11 a i $1.32\,m^2$ ii $132\,m^2$
b 606
12 a C ($271\,cm^2$) b A ($236\,cm^2$) c A ($324\,cm^2$)

Exam practice 8D

1 a $36\,cm^3$ b $9\,cm^3$ c $13\,cm^3$
2 a $2\,500\,000\,cm^3$ b $6000\,mm^3$
c $5\,000\,000\,000\,cm^3$ d $7\,500\,000\,mm^3$
e $79\,mm^3$ f $8.5\,cm^3$
3 a $24\,cm^3$ b $4500\,cm^3$ c $56.25\,cm^3$
4 a $144\,cm^3$ b $540\,cm^3$ c $140.4\,cm^3$
5 a 27 b i $8\,cm^3$ ii $216\,cm^3$
6 $60\,000\,cm^3$
7 No, volume $= 0.15 \times 1.5 \times 2\,m^3 = 0.45\,m^3$.
8 a No b Depth is $\frac{360}{12 \times 6} = 5$ cm.
9 a No b Depth is $\frac{5}{5 \times 3}\,m = \frac{1}{3}\,m$ (33.3 cm).
10 a $6000\,cm^3$ b $2080\,cm^2$ c 143 cm
11 $96\,cm^2$

Exam practice 8E

1 a $70\,cm^3$ b $84\,cm^3$ c $93\,cm^3$
2 a $202.5\,cm^3$ b $36\,m^3$ c $504\,cm^3$
3 a $386\,cm^3$ b $2.30\,cm^3$ c $50.4\,cm^3$
4 a $6283.2\,cm^3$ b $6283.2\,cm^3$
5 a $3.71\,cm^3$ b 21.5%
6 a $34\,cm^2$ b $408\,cm^3$

Exam practice 8F

1 a $38\,cm^3$ b $20\,cm^3$ c $7.8\,cm^3$ d $25\,cm^3$
2 a i $462\,cm^3$ ii $251\,cm^2$ iii $405\,cm^2$
b i $102\,cm^3$ ii $94.1\,cm^2$ iii $135\,cm^2$
c i $29.9\,cm^3$ ii $42.4\,cm^2$ iii $59.0\,cm^2$
3 5.97 cm
4 a $942\,cm^3$ b $314\,cm^3$ c 66.7%
5 $586\,cm^3$
6 a i $1260\,cm^2$ ii $4190\,cm^3$
b i $452\,cm^2$ ii $905\,cm^3$
c i $8.04\,m^2$ ii $2.14\,m^3$
7 a $16\,800\,mm^3$ b $3770\,mm^2$
8 $38.9\,cm^3$
9 a 18.6 cm × 12.4 cm × 12.4 cm
b $1500\,cm^3$ (3 s.f.)
c 52.4%
10 $120\,cm^3$
11 a $24\,cm^2$ b $56\,cm^3$
12 10 cm

Exam practice 8G

1 a 4000 ml b $2500\,cm^3$
c $\frac{1}{4}$ d 1500 ml
2 a 2 b 20 000 c $\frac{3}{4}$ d 5000
3 a 4 b 10
4 a i yes ii 40 litres ≈ 8.8 gall
b i yes ii 2 litres ≈ 3.5 pints
5 a $0.225\,m^3$ b 225 litres
6 a $314\,000\,cm^3$ b 314 litres
7 $6.25\,m^2$
8 31.5 litres
9 a $30\,000\,cm^3$, 30 litres b 20 min
10 a 6 cm × 4 cm × 4 cm
b 50.3 ml (16π ml)

Exam practice 8H

1 a 2000 g b 3200 kg c 7.46 kg d 2.45 t
e $\frac{1}{2}$ kg f 0.583 t g 50 g h 1.4 kg
i 3 g j 60 mg k 8 g l 7.5 g
2 a 7.5 t b 200
3 a 588 g b 476 g
4 a 3547.5 g
b i yes ii mass of 2 litres ≈ 1.96 kg
5 $0.9\,g/cm^3$
6 a $2572\,cm^3$ b $908\,cm^2$ (3 s.f.)
c 20.1 kg
7 a $1000\,cm^3$ b $0.8\,g/cm^3$
8 a $30\,cm^3$ b $7.5\,g/cm^3$

Exam practice 8I

1 a, c and d are true, the others false.
2 a area b length c volume d length
e area f volume g area h length
3 a cm^2 b cm c cm^2 d cm^3
e cm^3 f cm g cm^2 h cm^2
4 b and c
5 a length b none c volume
d area e none
6 Yes, terms inside bracket have dimensions of a volume and an area.

Exam practice 9A

1 5 cm 2 13 cm 3 65 mm
4 4 cm 5 10 cm 6 12.0 cm
7 11.1 cm 8 20.0 cm
9 a $x = 6.71$ b 6.71 cm and 13.4 cm
10 4.04 cm and 8.04 cm

Exam practice 9B

1 10.5 cm 2 4.5 cm 3 3.3 cm
4 5.5 cm 5 72 mm 6 12.1 cm
7 a 12.7 cm b 18 cm, 24 cm
8 a 12 cm b 25 cm

Exam practice 9C

1 a yes, ∠Q b no c yes, ∠Y
d yes, ∠C e no f no

Exam practice 9D

1 5 km
2 5.83 km
3 73.3 m
4 4.85 m
5 a 90° b 136 m
6 14.8 cm
7 2.28 m
8 66.7 cm
9 a Rhombus, diagonal bisects at right angles and all the sides are equal.
b i 3.75 cm ii 15 cm
10 BC = 7.63 m, CD = 4.03 m
11 589 m
12 a 8.01 m b 7.61 m
13 a trapezium
b 0.7 m
c i 1.10 m ii 2.74 m^2
d 4.38 m^3
14 37.3 cm

Exam practice 9E

1 a 50 cm b 53.9 cm
2 a 8.49 cm b 10.4 cm
3 a 11.3 cm b 13.9 cm
4 a 6.40 cm b 7.07 cm
5 a 8.60 cm b 11.2 cm c 13.2 cm
6 a 4 cm b 8.54 cm c 9.43 cm
7 a 4.25 cm b 8.19 cm
8 a 8.49 cm b 4.24 cm c 5.57 cm
9 a 3 cm b 9.11 cm

Exam practice 10A

1 a isosceles
b i 4 units ii $\sqrt{29}$ units
c i (1, 3) ii $(2, \frac{1}{2})$
2 a kite
b
c
d (2, 1)
3 a i $(\frac{1}{2}, 5)$ ii (0, 1)
b x-coordinates of the midpoints are different.

4 a parallelogram
b i 3 units ii $\sqrt{17}$ units
c $(3\frac{1}{2}, 3)$, $(\frac{1}{2}, 3)$
d They have the same y-coordinates.

Exam practice 10B

1 a and b

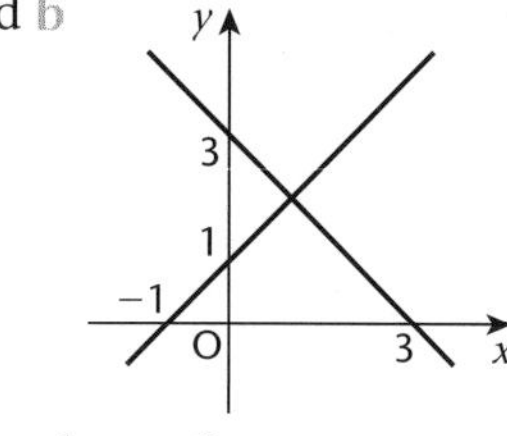

c $x = 1, y = 2$
2 a

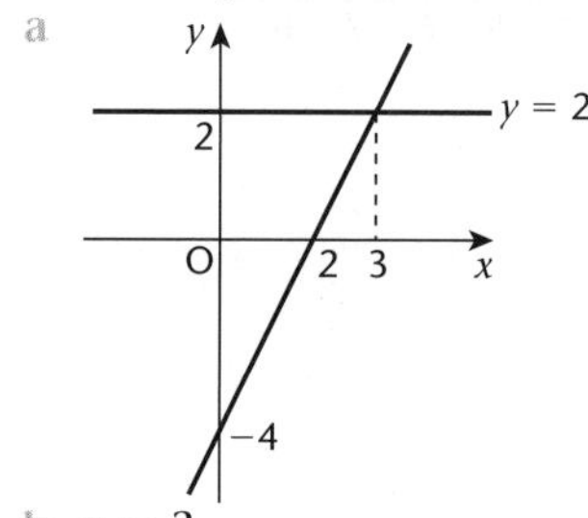

b $x = 3$
c $y = 2x - 4$ and $y = 2$ then $2 = 2x - 4$, so value of x that satisfies $2 = 2x - 4$ is the value of x on the line $y = 2x - 4$ when $y = 2$.
3 a and c

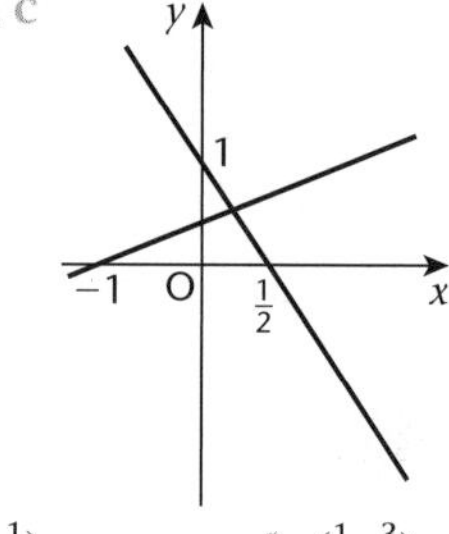

b $(\frac{1}{3}, \frac{1}{3})$ d $(\frac{1}{5}, \frac{3}{5})$
e Values of x and y at the point of intersection satisfy both equations.
4 a

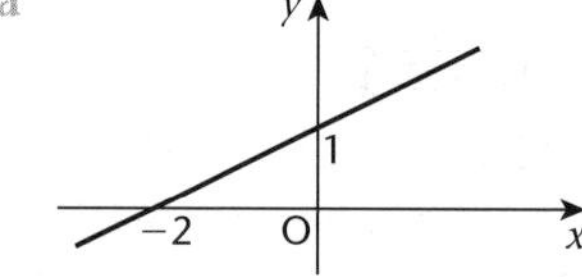

b (4, 3)
c When $x = 2$, $y = 2$ not 4, so the point (2, 4) does not lie on the line.
5 (8, 8)
6 $x = 1, y = 1$

Exam practice 10C

1 a 3 b 2 c −1 d −2 e $-\frac{1}{2}$ f $-\frac{2}{3}$
2 b and e
3 $y = 3x - 1$ and $y = 4 + 3x$
4 No, their gradients are different.
5 a 1 b $-\frac{10}{7}$
6 a −1 b $\frac{7}{10}$

Exam practice 10D

1 a $y = -2$ b $x = 2$ c $y = -x$

2 a A(1, 2), B(5, 6)

b 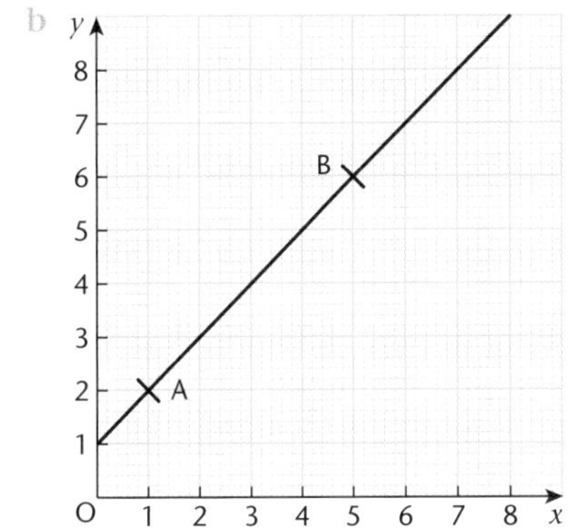

c 1 d $y = x + 1$

3 a $\frac{1}{3}$ b $3y - x = 2$

4 a -2 b $2x + y = 7$

5 a $2y - x = 4$ b $2y - x = 9$

6 a $2y - x + 2 = 0$ b $2x + y = 5$

7 a $4x + y = 8$ b $y + 4x + 8 = 0$

c $4y - x = 3$

8 a $P = 16t + 30$ b £30 c £16

9 $C = 50 + 10t$

10 a 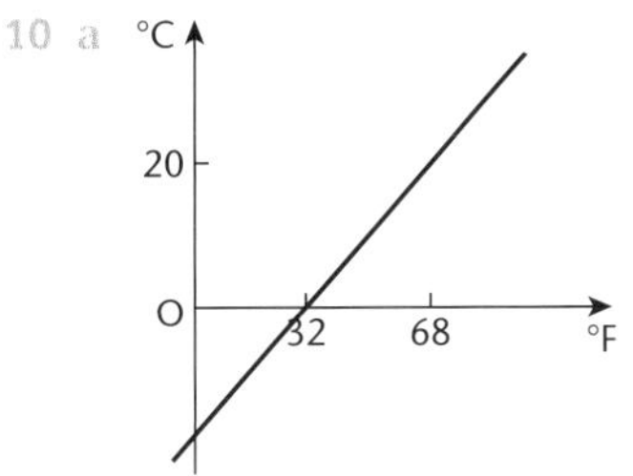

b 5°C c $C = \frac{5}{9}(F - 32)$

11 a

b i $14.40 ii £25 c $P = \frac{5}{9}D$

12 a −360 (360 million litres runs out each day)

b A = 7400 − 360t

c Water runs out at the same rate.

Exam practice 10E

1 16 km/h

2 a 72 km/h b 14 m/s

3 $43\frac{3}{4}$ mph

4 a 2160 n.m. b 20.7 mph

Exam practice 10F

1 a 17 miles b 30 c 5.5 miles d 34 mph

2 a 78 miles b 42 miles

c 36 minutes d 51.4 mph

3 a 8.45 b 2.7 km

c 12 km/h d 7.0 km/h

4 a 2.4 miles b 48 minutes

c 30 minutes d 0.48 miles

e Back, 2.4 miles in 30 minutes compared with 2.4 miles in 48 minutes.

5 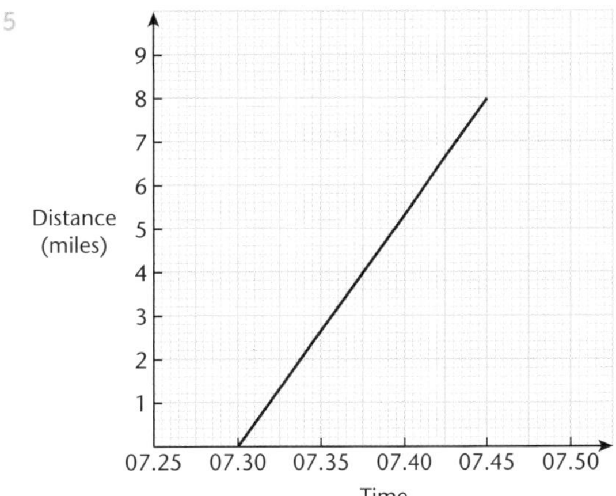

6 a 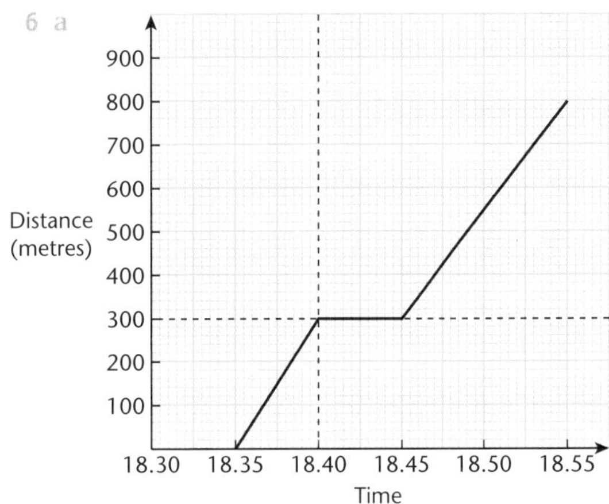

b 500 m

7 a 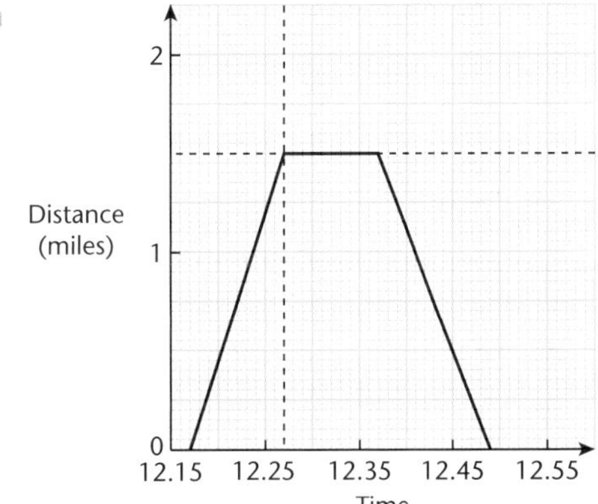

b 7.5 mph c 1.25 miles

Exam practice 10G

1 a (5, 4, 3), 7.07, $(2\frac{1}{2}, 2, 1\frac{1}{2})$

b (2, 4, 4), 6, (1, 2, 2)

c (2, 6, 3), 7, $(1, 3, 1\frac{1}{2})$

d (−3, 4, 3), 5.83, $(-1\frac{1}{2}, 2, 1\frac{1}{2})$

2 a 1.73 b 4.12

3 a $(3\frac{1}{2}, 5\frac{1}{2}, 2\frac{1}{2})$ b $(6\frac{1}{2}, 8, 1)$

Exam practice 11A

1 a $x \leqslant -1$ b $x > -1$
c $0 < x \leqslant 5$ d $-1 \leqslant x < 6$

2 a −3 −2 −1 b 5 6 7
c 3 4 5

3 a $x < 4$ b $x < 5$ c $x > 3$
d $x < 6$ e $x > -3$ f $x > 2.5$
g $x \geqslant 5$ h $x \geqslant 3$ i $x \leqslant 14$
j $p < -3$ k $x > 2$ l $s \geqslant -2$

4 a $x < 3$ b $x > 2$ c $x < 2$
d $x \leqslant 8$ e $x < 2$ f $y > 2$
g $a \geqslant 3$ h $x \leqslant 5$ i $x > 1\frac{2}{3}$
j $t < 4\frac{2}{3}$ k $k \geqslant 7$ l $y \leqslant 2$
m $s \leqslant -1$ n $x > 1$ p $p \leqslant -0.5$

5 a 7, 8, 9 b −2, −1, 0, 1 c 4, 5, 6
d 3, 4 e 0, 1, 2, 3 f 0, 1, 2
g 2, 3
h −3, −2, −1, 0, 1
i 1

6 a and b $-3 < x$ means $x > -3$

Exam practice 11B

1 a
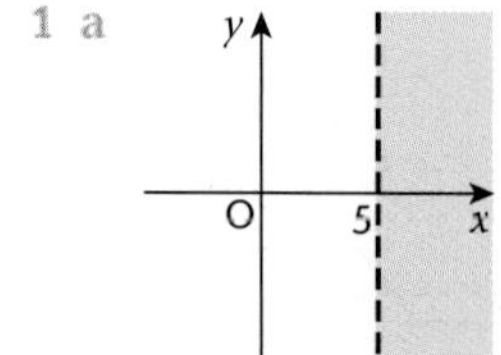

b
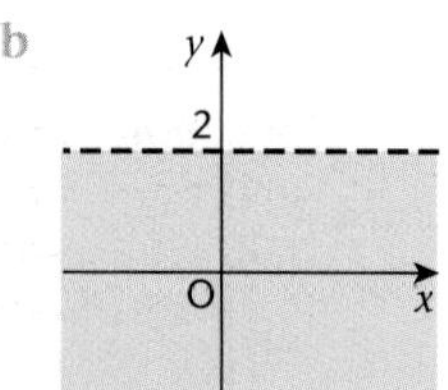

c
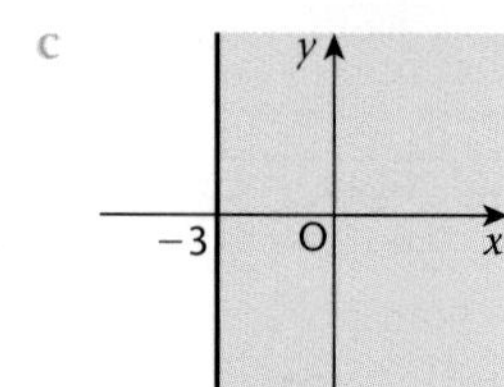

d
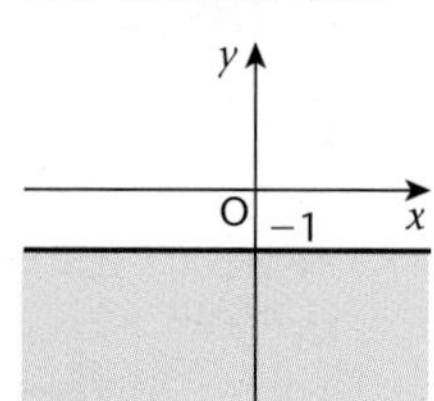

2 a
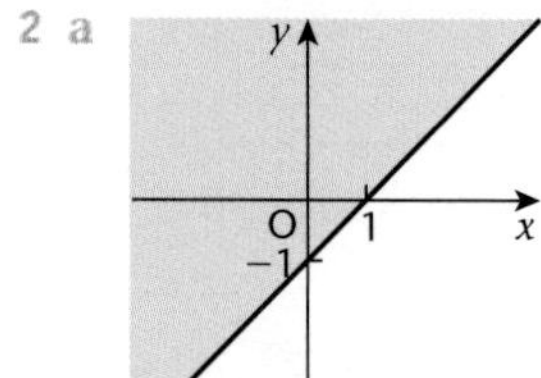

b
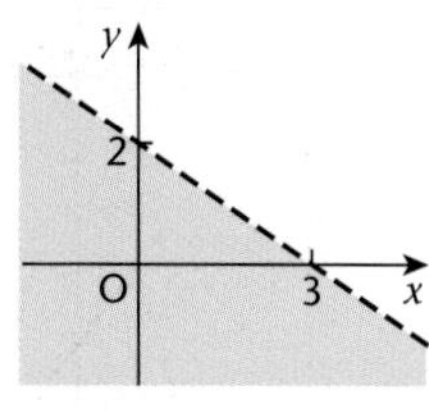

c
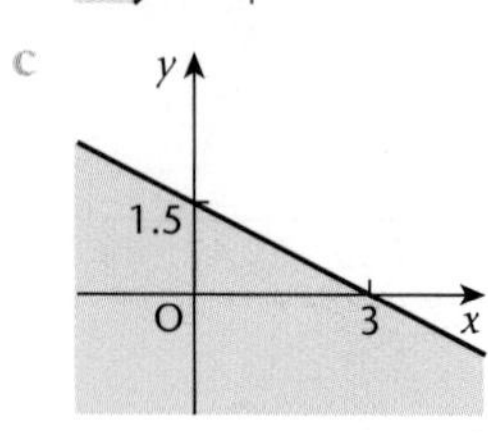

d
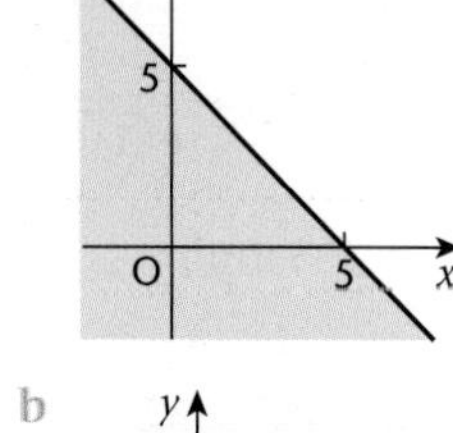

3 a
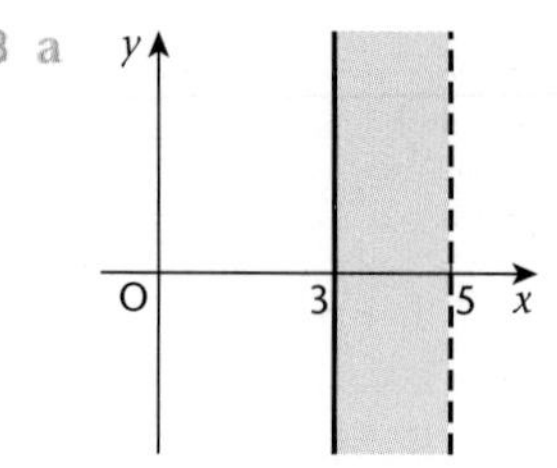

b
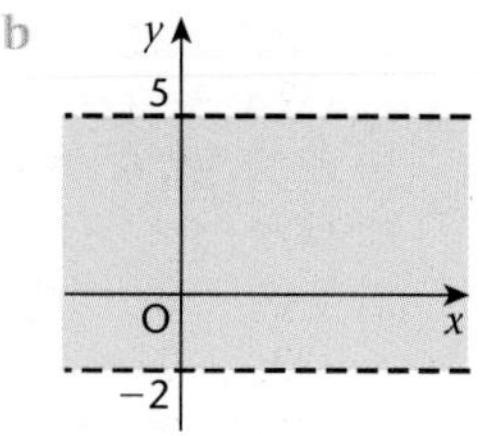

c
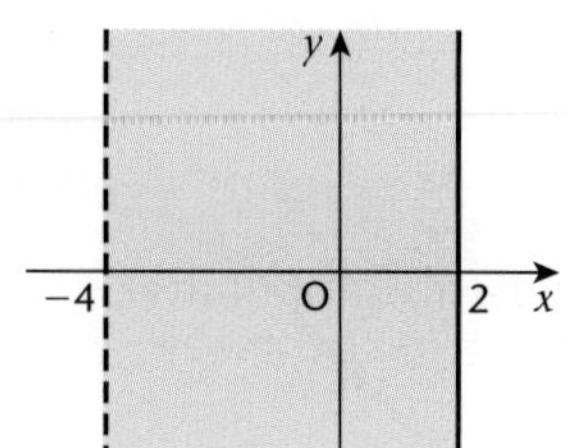

4 a $x + y \leqslant 0$
b $y \leqslant x$
c $-3 \leqslant x < 1$
d $-4 < y \leqslant 2$
e $x \geqslant -3, y \leqslant 3, y > \frac{3x}{4}$
f $x \leqslant 5, y \geqslant -3, y \leqslant x$
g $x < 3, y > 2, y < \frac{1}{3}x + 3$
h $y \leqslant 4, y \geqslant x, x + y \geqslant 0$

5 a
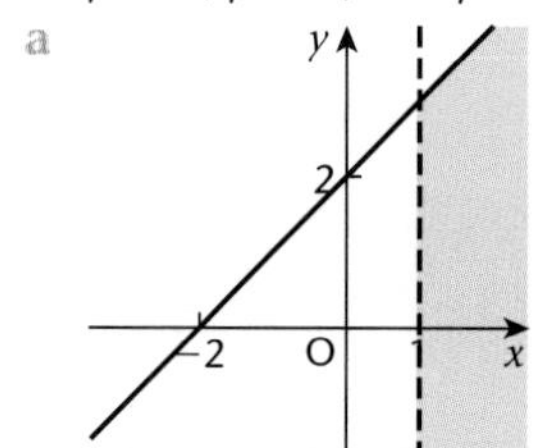

b
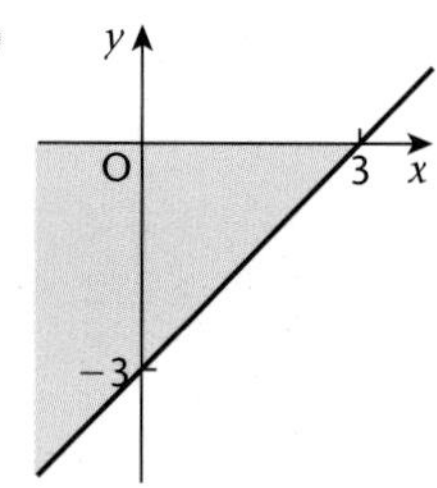

c d
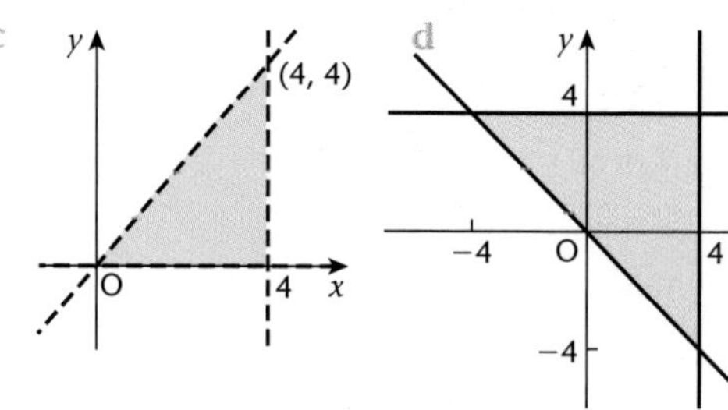

6 a
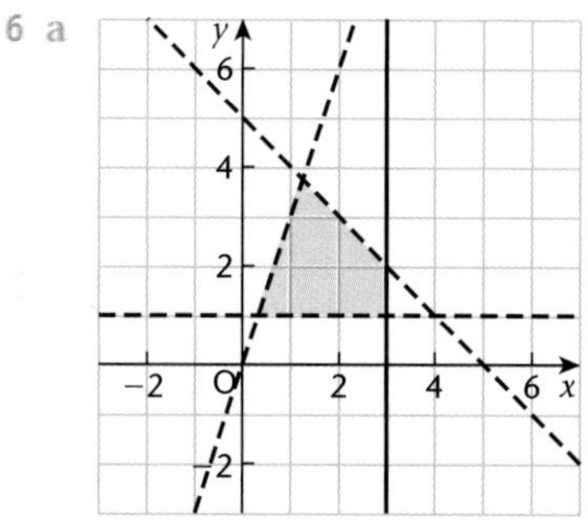

b (1, 2), (2, 2)

Exam practice 12A

1 B, C, D, F
2 a 37° b 5 cm
3 a 110° b 4 cm
4 a 20 cm b 110°

Exam practice 12B

1 a yes, SSS b yes, AAS c yes, SAS
d no e yes, RHS f yes, SAS
g yes, AAS h yes, SSS

5 b Yes, △s ABC and ADC are congruent so CB = CD.

6 b angles RPQ and SPQ, and angles RQP and SQP.

Exam practice 12C

1 a 72° b 6.6 cm c 5.6 cm
d 5.2 cm e 61° f 6.9 cm
g 33°
h i Yes, ∠C can be acute or obtuse.
ii No, as∠C would be a right angle
3 b 9.3 cm
4 c 11.5 cm

Exam practice 12D

1 b 3.8 cm
2 b 7.1 cm
3 b 3.6 cm

Exam practice 12E

1 d 30°
2 d 45°
3 b 6.9 cm
4 b 8.5 cm
5 b 6.1 cm
6 b 7.3 cm
7 a 90°
8 c It divides the triangle into two congruent (AAS) triangles.
10 b 90°
12 b 12.9 cm
13 b i 3.6 cm ii 7.6 cm

Exam practice 13A

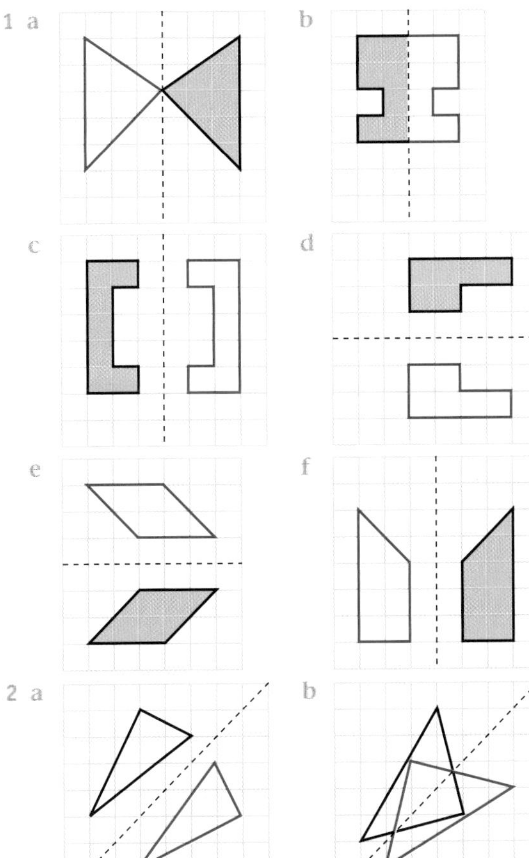

3 a parallelogram
b

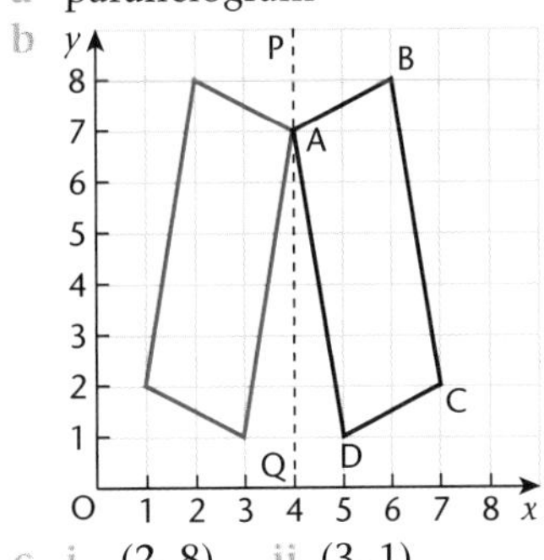

c i (2, 8) ii (3, 1)

4 a

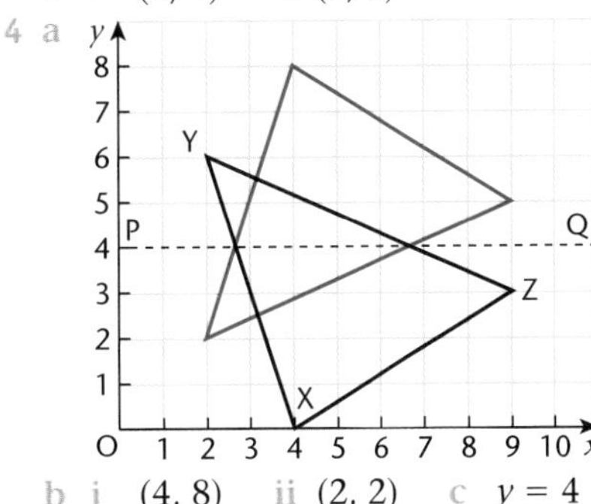

b i (4, 8) ii (2, 2) c $y = 4$

Exam practice 13B

1 a Reflection in the line $y = 4$.
b Reflection in the line $x = 5$.
2 a Reflection in the line $y = x$.
b Reflection in the line $y = x$.

3

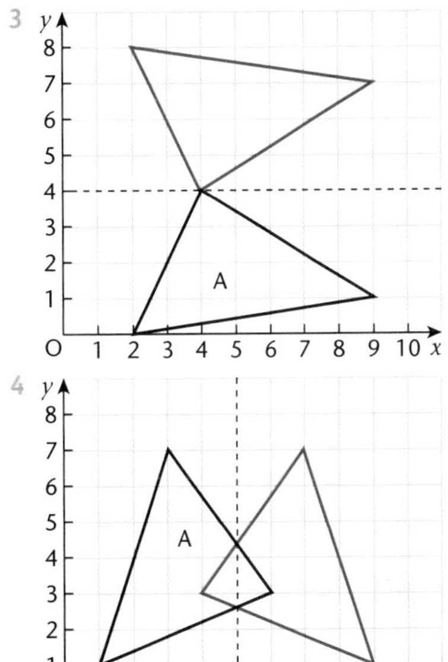

Exam practice 13C

1 a i 2 ii 2 b i 2 ii 0 c i 3 ii 0
2 a i 2 ii 2 b i 4 ii 4 c i 0 ii 2
3 a Yes, Kay chooses one of:

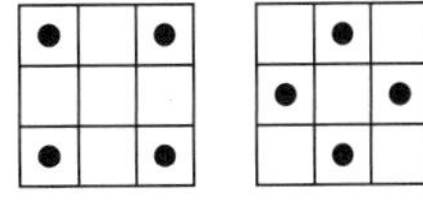

b Jim chooses both.

Exam practice 13D

1 a i 90° anticlockwise. ii A
b i 45° clockwise. ii B
c i 90° clockwise. ii C

2 a b c

3 a 90° clockwise about (1, 1).
b 90° anticlockwise about (−3, 0).
c 180° about (2, 0).
d 90° clockwise about (3, 3).

4 a

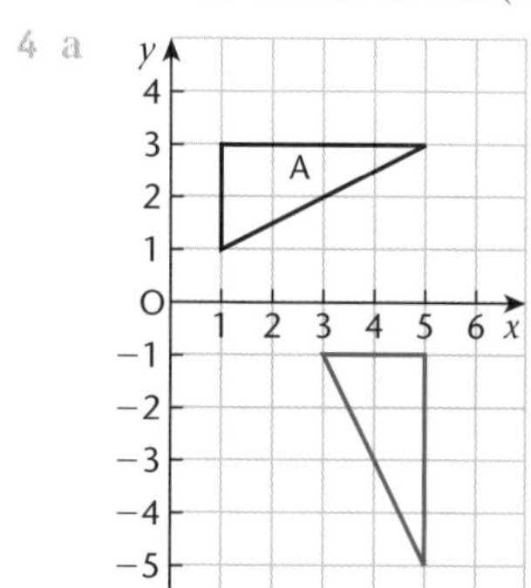

b

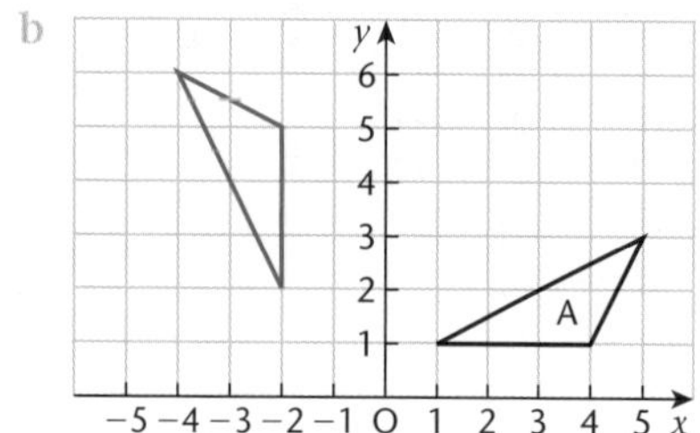

5 a

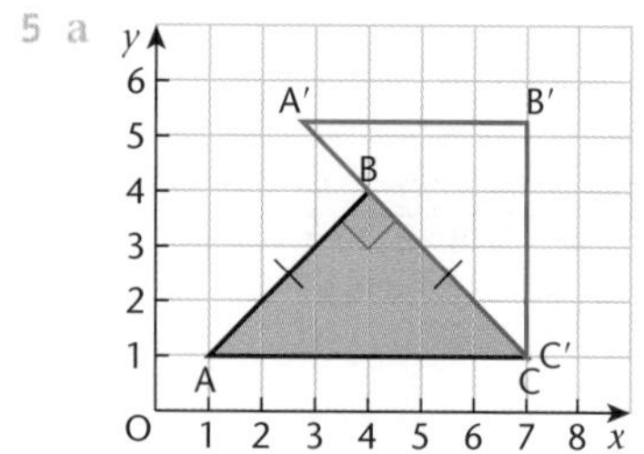

b

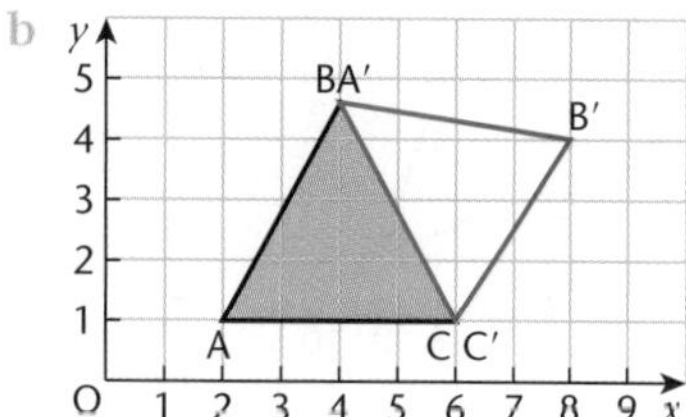

Exam practice 13E

1 Translations described by the vector:

a $\begin{pmatrix}4\\1\end{pmatrix}$ b $\begin{pmatrix}-4\\3\end{pmatrix}$ c $\begin{pmatrix}-5\\0\end{pmatrix}$ d $\begin{pmatrix}-2\\3\end{pmatrix}$

e $\begin{pmatrix}0\\6\end{pmatrix}$ f $\begin{pmatrix}6\\2\end{pmatrix}$ g $\begin{pmatrix}0\\-3\end{pmatrix}$ h $\begin{pmatrix}2\\-3\end{pmatrix}$

2

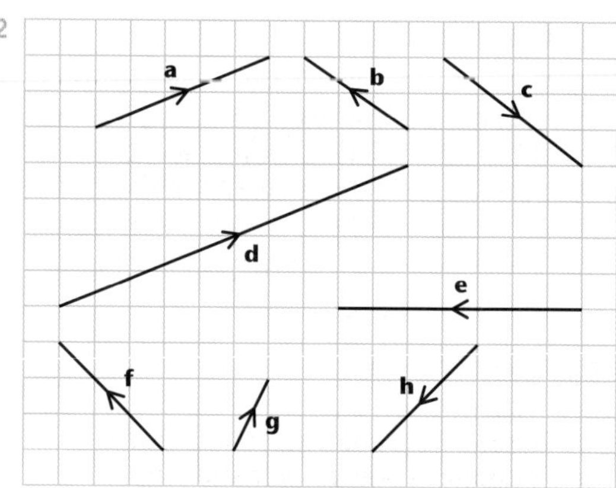

3 i parallel ii perpendicular

4

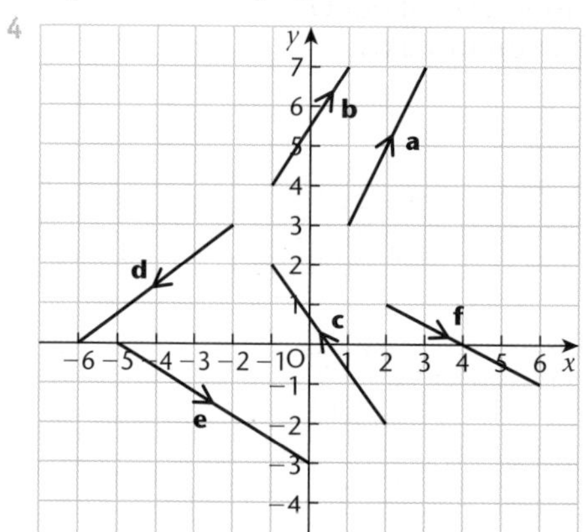

Exam practice 13F

1 a $\begin{pmatrix}3\\0\end{pmatrix}$ b $\begin{pmatrix}3\\-3\end{pmatrix}$ c $\begin{pmatrix}-3\\-1\end{pmatrix}$ d $\begin{pmatrix}0\\3\end{pmatrix}$

2 a

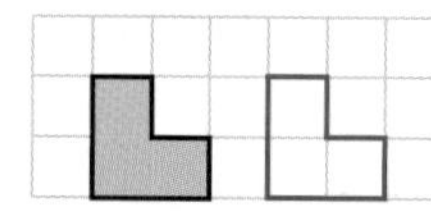

b

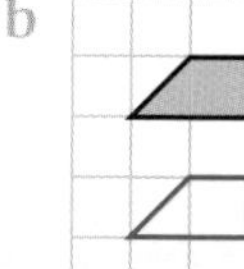

c

3 a rectangle b i (1, 5) ii (3, 1)
c $\begin{pmatrix}4\\1\end{pmatrix}$ d i (5, 6) ii (7, 2)
e Yes, same vector as in part c but with opposite signs.

4 a $\begin{pmatrix}4\\1\end{pmatrix}$

b

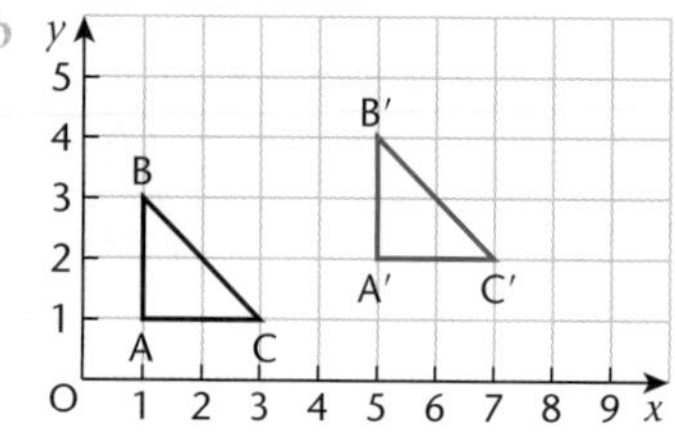

c i (5, 4) ii (7, 2)

5 a $\begin{pmatrix} 4 \\ -1 \end{pmatrix}$ b

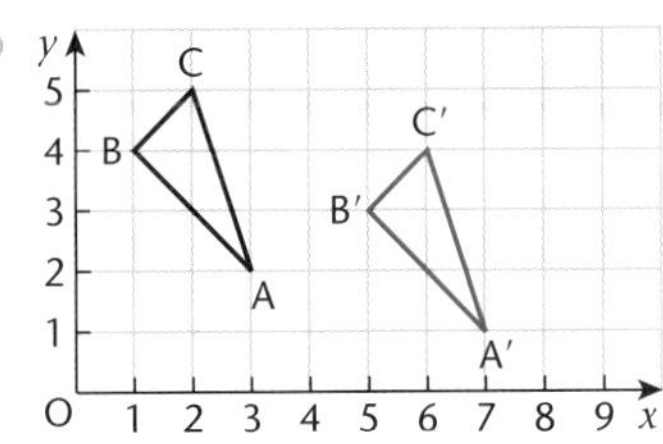

c i (5, 3) ii (6, 4)

Exam practice 13G

1 a E b A c B d D e E

2 a Translates 1 square left and 5 down.
b Translates 2 squares left and 3 up.
c Rotation 90° anticlockwise about O.
d Rotation 180° about O.
e Reflection in y-axis.

3

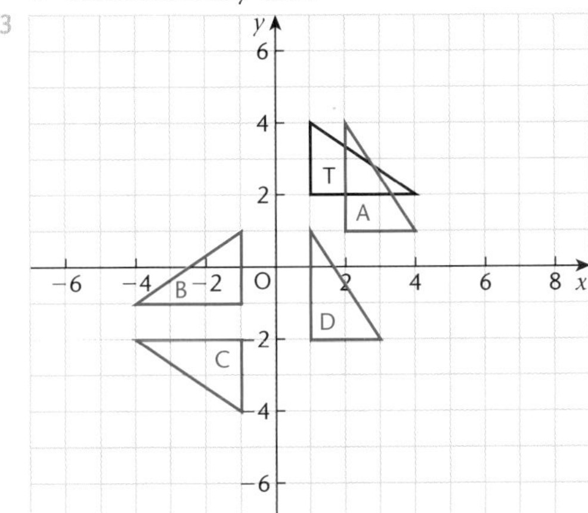

4 Rotation 180° about O.

5

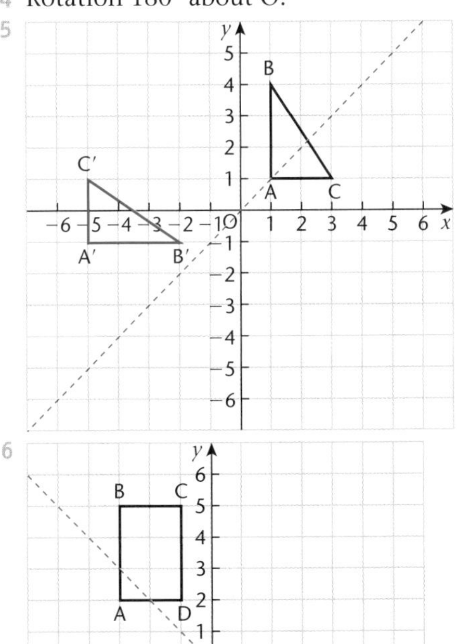

6

7 a Reflection in the line $y = x$.

b

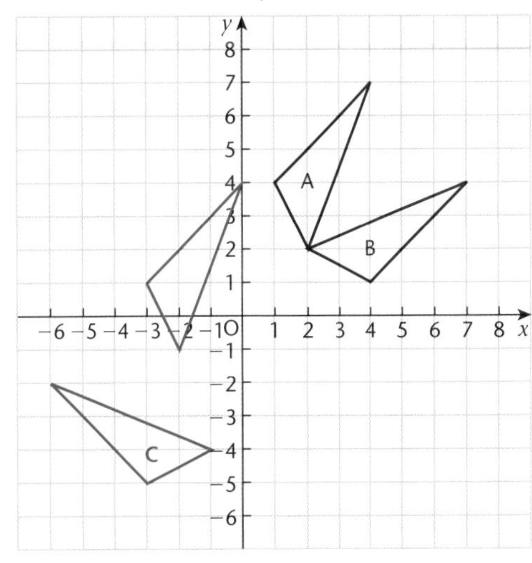

8 a, b and c

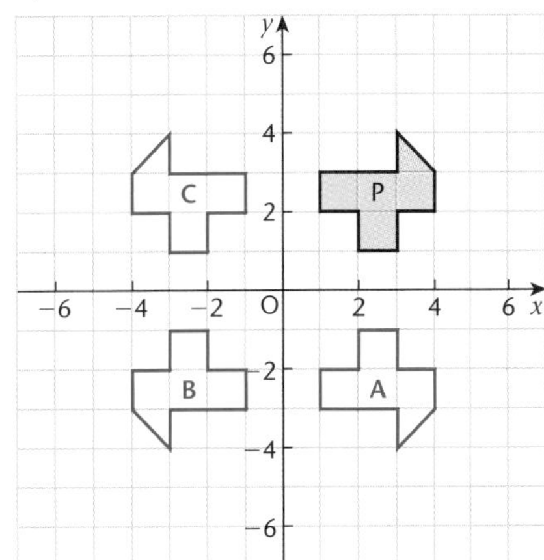

d Reflection in the x-axis.

9 a i, ii and iii

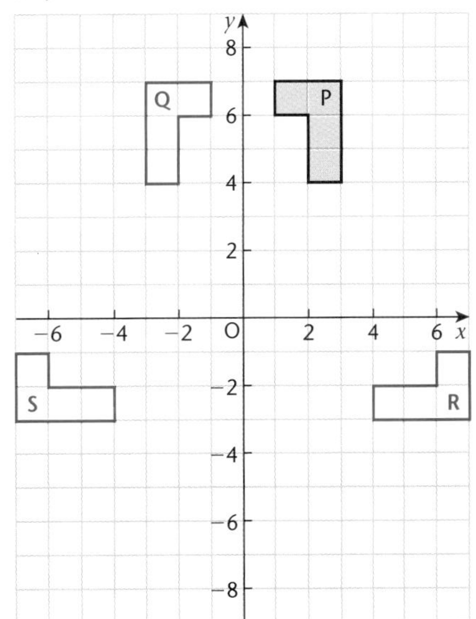

b i Reflection in the y-axis.
ii Rotation 90° clockwise about O.
iii Rotation 90° anticlockwise about O.

10 a 90° anticlockwise. b $\begin{pmatrix} -2 \\ -7 \end{pmatrix}$

11 Reflection in BD, rotation 90° clockwise about D.

12 Reflection in y-axis, translation by the vector $\begin{pmatrix} 4 \\ 0 \end{pmatrix}$, or rotation 180° about the point $(0, \frac{1}{2})$.

Exam practice 14A

1 a 2

b $\frac{1}{3}$

c 4

d $\frac{1}{2}$

2 a 2 b $\frac{1}{2}$

3 a

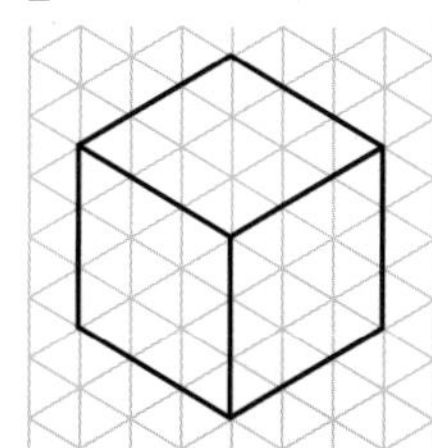

b

4 Width increases by 100% but length by only 50%.

Exam practice 14B

1 a

b

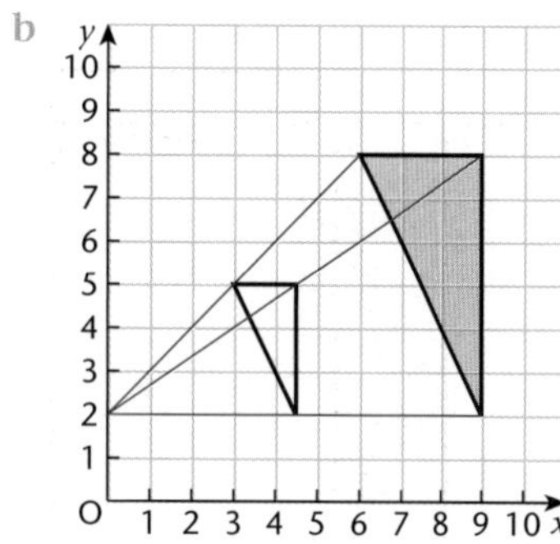

c

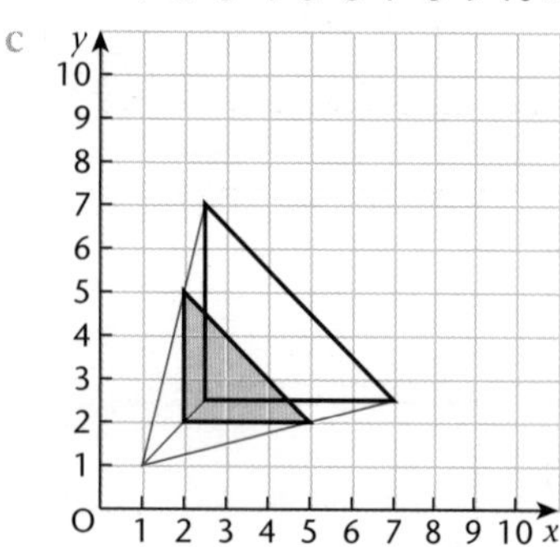

2 a Centre (1, 3), scale factor 2.

b Centre (1, 9), scale factor 3.

c Centre (9, 9), scale factor $\frac{1}{2}$.

Exam practice 14C

1 a

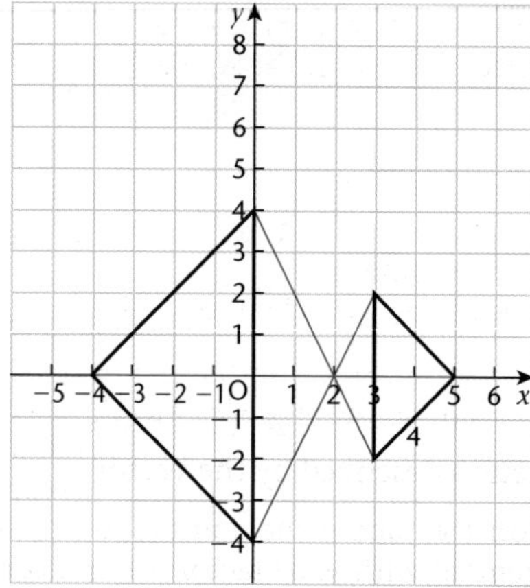

b

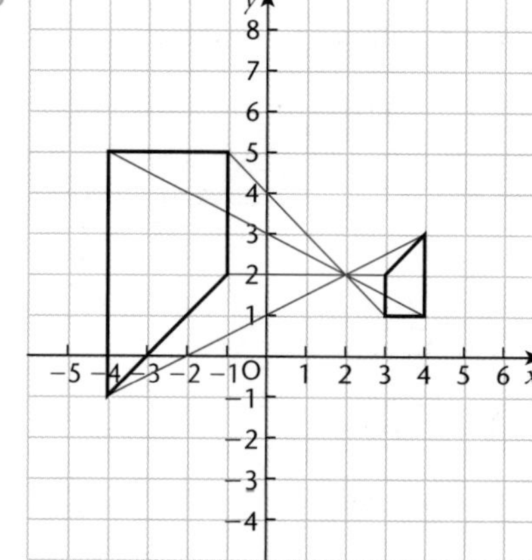

c

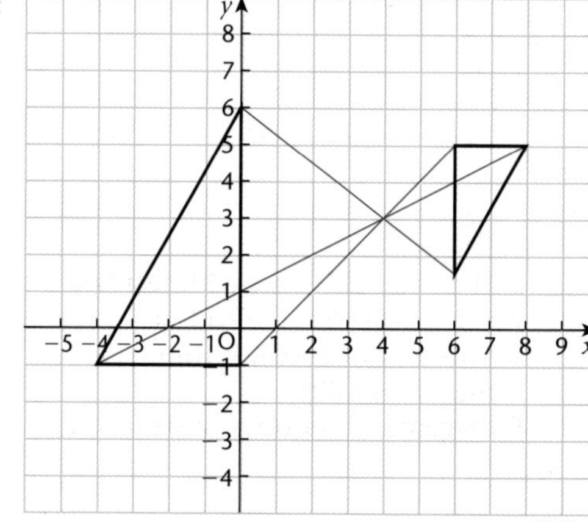

d

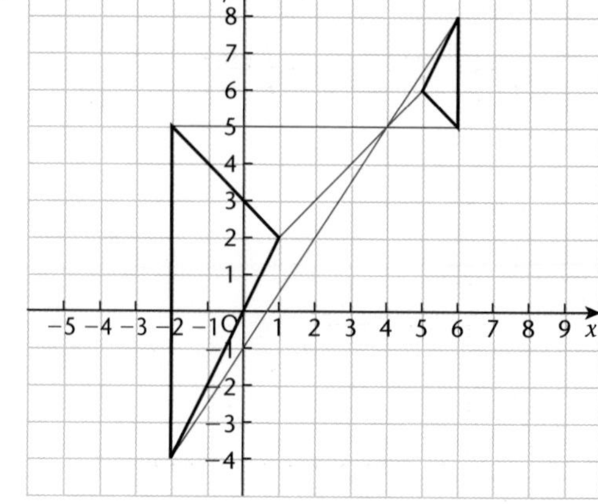

2 a Centre the origin, scale factor -2.
  b Centre (3, 4), scale factor $-\frac{1}{2}$.
  c Centre (2, 1), scale factor -3.
  d Centre (0, 2), scale factor -2.

Exam practice 14D

1 Reflection in line $y = 4$.
2 Reflection in line $x = 5$.
3 Translation described by the vector $\begin{pmatrix} 2 \\ -3 \end{pmatrix}$.
4 Rotation about the point (2, 4), 90° clockwise.
5 Enlargement centre $(6\frac{1}{3}, 5\frac{1}{3})$, scale factor $-\frac{1}{2}$.
6 Translation described by the vector $\begin{pmatrix} -5 \\ -2 \end{pmatrix}$.
7 Rotation 180° about the point (5, 6), or an enlargement with scale factor -1 and centre (5, 6).
8 Enlargement, centre (1, 8), scale factor 2.

Exam practice 14E

1 a D and F   b A and E
2 a T   b F
  c T   d T
  e F   f T
  g F
3 a F   b T   c T   d F   e T
4 a 2   b 12 cm²
5 a 2   b i $\frac{1}{2}$ ii $\frac{1}{4}$
6 a 2   b 24 cm³
7 12.5 cm²   8 8.79 cm³
9 1562.5 litres   10 12 cm
11 a $16\frac{2}{3}$ cm
  b △s are similar so ∠ADE = ∠ABC.
12 a 9 cm
  b ∠ABC
13 5 cm
14 a ∠ADE = ∠ABC (parallel lines) and
  ∠AED = ∠ACB (parallel lines)
  so three ∠s of △ADE = three ∠s of △ABC
  ∴ they are similar.
  b Enlargement, centre A, scale factor $\frac{4}{3}$.
15 $37\frac{1}{3}$ cm²

Exam practice 14F

1 a 2.5 m   b 4.75 m²
2 a 7 cm   b 3.5 km   c 2 km
3 600 m
4 2.5 km
5 a 6 m by 8 m
  b 10 m²
6 a 5 cm
  b

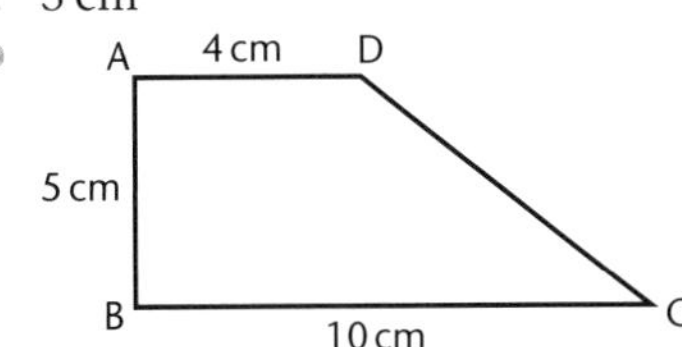

7 a

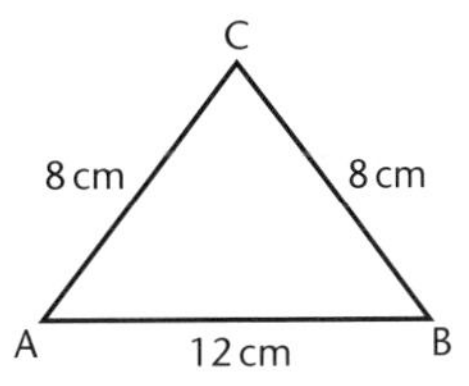

  c isosceles triangle

8 construction

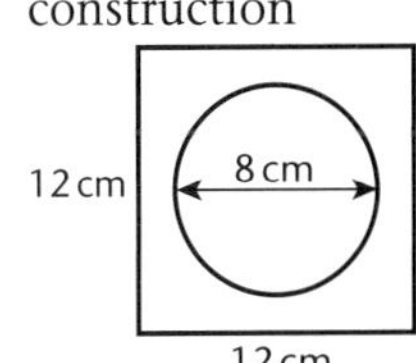

Exam practice 14G

1

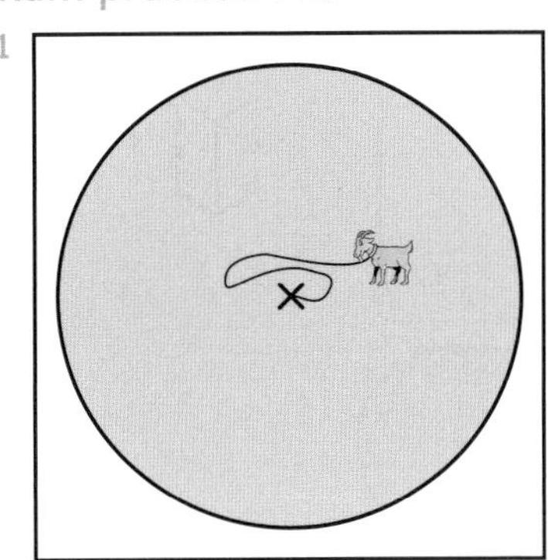

2 a 7 km
  b

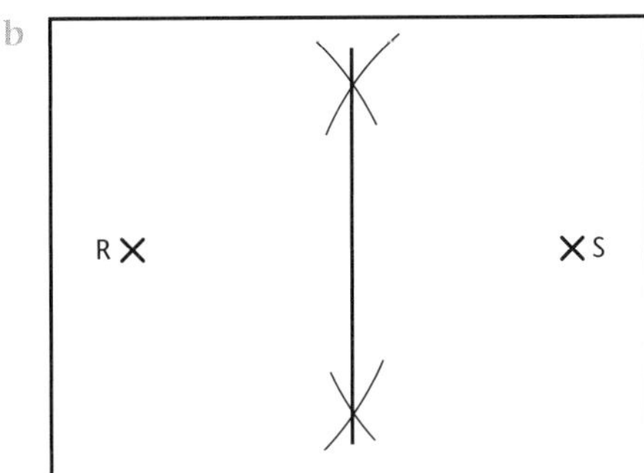

  c

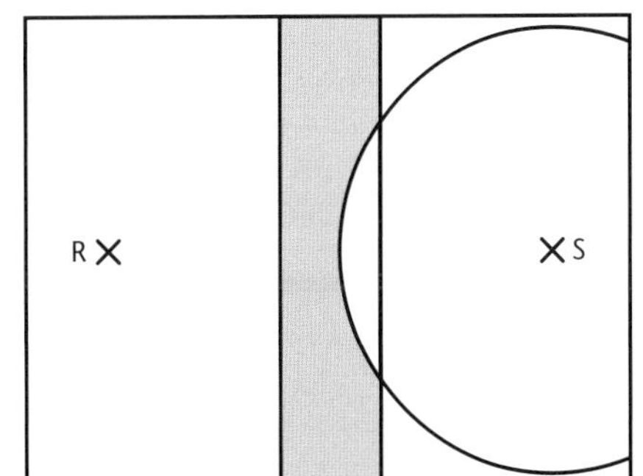

3

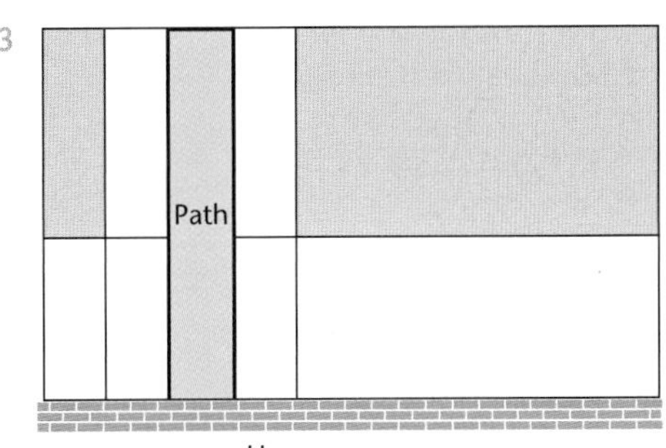

4

5

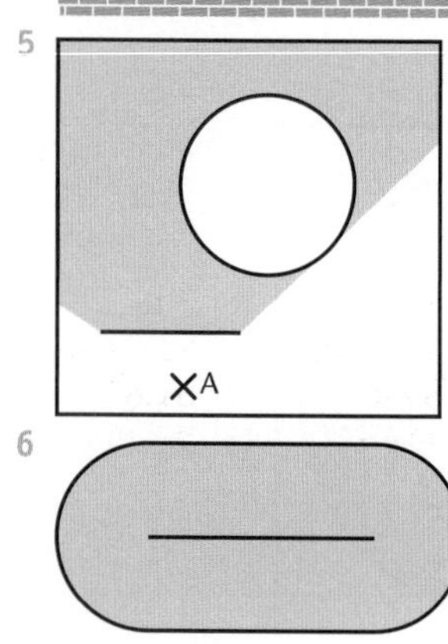

6

Exam practice 15A

1 6 cm
2 24 cm
3 12.8 cm
4 12 cm
5 AB, the nearer the chord to the centre of the circle the longer it is.

Exam practice 15B

1 a i AD ii BC
b i ∠ABD or ∠ACD ii ∠ABC or ∠ADC
c i C ii A d i BC ii AB
e ∠BAC and ∠BDC
2 90°
3 56°
4 a $a = 144°$ (∠ at centre result)
b $i = 126°, j = 63°$ (∠ at centre result)
c $x = 129°$ (∠ at centre result)
d $m = n = 73°$ (∠ at centre result)
e $q = 43°$ (∠ at centre result)
f $c = d = 90°$ (∠ in semicircle)
g $a = 48°$ (∠ in semicircle, ∠s of a triangle)
h $a = 40°, b = 35°$ (isos △), $c = 150°$ (∠ at centre result)
i $p = 37°$ (isos △), $q = 74°$ (∠ at centre result), $r = 53°$ ($p + r = 90°$)
j $a = 30°$ (isos △), $b = 60°$ (∠ in semicircle), $c = 60°$ (∠ at centre result)
k $p = 196°$ (∠ at centre result)
l $b = 45°$ (isos △, base ∠s sum to 90°)
5 a $x = 53°$ b $y = 45°$

Exam practice 15C

1 $a = b = 48°$
2 $c = 38°$, $d = 42°$
3 $c = 110°$
4 $d = e = 33°, f = 66°$
5 $j = 34°, k = 65°$
6 $x = 132°, y = 42°$
7 $x = 96°, y = 33°$
8 $m = 104°, n = 76°$
9 $p = 35°, q = 58°$
10 28° ($p + 90° + 62° = 180°$)

Exam practice 15D

1 $p = 92°, q = 76°$
2 $r = 100°, s = 104°$
3 $a = b = 110°, c = 70°$
4 $m = 104°, n = 70°$
5 $a = 120°, b = 50°$
6 $p = 80°, q = 74°$
7 $b = 148°$
8 $x = 117°, y = 63°$
9 $p = 68°, q = 112°, r = 112°, s = 68°$

Exam practice 15E

1 $x = y = 55°$
2 $p = 106°, q = 53°$
3 $b = 90°$
4 $a = 76°$
5 $x = y = 61°$

Exam practice 15F

1 a $y = 47°$ (alt. segment theorem)
b $z = 66°$ (∠s in a △)
2 a $x = 45°, y = 45°, z – 90°$
b ∠ABC = ∠BCE
3 a 54° b 90° c 36°
4 a $a = 40°$
b $x = 34°, y = 56°, z = 56°$
c $x = 62°, y = 62°$
d $a = 62°, b = 62°, c = 56°, d = 56°$
e $p = 61°, q = 61°, r = 58°$
f $p = 73°, q = 34°, r = 73°$
5 a i 42° ii 104° iii 28° b isosceles
6 $p = 106°, q = 67°, r = 106°$
7 $a = 110°, b = 35°, c = 70°$
8 a 73° b 17° c 17°
9 a 43° b 86° c 78° d 51°

Exam practice 16A

1 a i 0.9004 ii 3.4874
iii 0.1317 iv 0.4599
b i 26.6° ii 59.1°
iii 4.6° iv 34.1°
2 a 33.7° b 52.5° c 62.1° d 55.3°
3 a 34.9° b 34.4°
4 a 66.3° b 70.3°
5 a 11.2 cm b 7.52 cm c 131 mm
6 a 10.3 cm b 9.75 cm c 9.73 cm
7 a 16.1 cm b 34.6 cm
8 a 13.7 cm b 68.7 cm²
9 a AB = 5, BC = 4, AC = 6.40
b AB is parallel to the x-axis and BC to the y-axis so ∠ABC = 90°.
c 38.7°
10 a 36.9° b 5 cm
11 159 m

Exam Practice 16B

1 a i 0.7780 ii 0.9744
iii 0.1650 iv 0.8854
b i 30° ii 42.1°
iii 10.4° iv 50.7°
2 a i 0.7071 ii 0.5592
iii 0.8434 iv 0.4258
b i 36.9° ii 39.6°
iii 83.1° iv 66.7°
3 a i $\frac{3}{5}$ ii $\frac{4}{5}$ iii $\frac{3}{4}$
b i $\frac{8}{17}$ ii $\frac{15}{17}$ iii $\frac{8}{15}$
4 a i cosine ii cosine iii sine
b i 42.8° ii 48.2° iii 27.5°
5 a 32.0° b 29.9° c 52.3°
6 a 10.9 cm b 10.0 cm c 5.07 cm
d 10.0 cm e 13.3 cm f 5.32 cm
7 a $\frac{1}{2}, \frac{\sqrt{3}}{2}, \frac{1}{\sqrt{3}}$ b $\frac{\sqrt{3}}{2}, \frac{1}{2}, \sqrt{3}$
8 a 68.0° b 3.71 m
9 51.3°
10 57.1°

Exam Practice 16C

1 a i 155° ii 215° iii 315°
b i 220° ii 320° iii 140°
2 a 295° b 115° c 236°
3 a N P 123° A b N S 80° F
c N T 56° L d N V 175° T
4 a 8 km, 075° b 4 km, 113°
c 8 km, 255° d 7 km, 245°
e 4 km, 293°

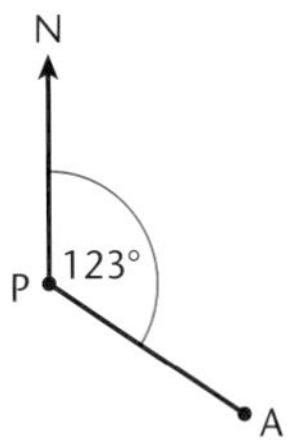

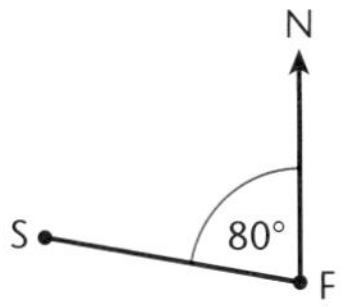

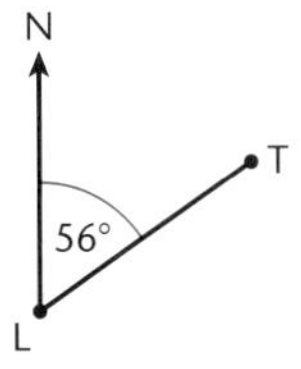

Exam practice 16D

1 a −0.5592 b 0.2250 c −5.6713
d −0.1132 e 0.2198
2 a 0.5 b −0.5
c 0.9135 d −0.6820
3 a 120° b 143.1° c 154.1°
4 a 45.6° b 126.9° c 140.4°
d 131.1° e 55.3°

Exam practice 16E

1 18.8 cm
2 9.85 cm
3 a 9.67 cm b 6.98 cm
4 ∠B = 38.1°, ∠C = 87.9°
5 a DE = 6.35 cm, DF = 4.57 cm
b PR = 13.8 cm, QR = 9.72 cm
6 a 70.5° or 109.5°
b 5.51 cm or 9.51 cm
7 68.8 m
8 BC = 4.84 km, AC = 2.72 km

Exam practice 16F

1 a 4.85 cm b 10.6 cm c 8.86 cm
2 a 5.21 cm b 12.5 cm c 21.1 cm
3 a 29.8° b 59.4° c 81.8°
4 a 25.2° b 118.8° c 98.1°

Exam practice 16G

1 a i 5.84 cm ii 63.9°
b i 24.8 cm ii 23.7°
2 a i 28.0 cm ii 21.8 cm
b i 62.3° ii 6.56 cm
3 a i 7.08 cm ii 76.4°
b i 10.1 cm ii 76.9°
4 a 27.1 cm b 37.7°
5 a ∠X = 58.8°, ∠Y = 71.8°, ∠Z = 49.4°
b ∠A = 29.0°, ∠B = 46.6°, ∠C = 104.4°
6 a i 082° ii 313°
b 11.8 n.m.
7 5.79 n.m. on a bearing of 347.2°
8 165°, 13.9 cm
9 250 m, 336.6°
10 24.9 km
11 100.0°

Exam Practice 16H

1 a 15.9 cm² b 111 cm² c 115 cm²
d 37.4 cm² e 13.7 cm² f 18.8 cm²
2 a i 8.36 cm ii 5.43 cm
b 22.5 cm²
3 a 11.0 cm b 75.8° c 72.8 cm²
4 a 11.0 cm b 25.7° c 13.3 cm²
5 a 6.99 cm b 23.6 cm²

Exam practice 16I

1 a i 9.43 cm ii 9.90 cm
b 17.6°
2 18.9°
3 a 8.66 cm b 35.3°
4 a 28.3 cm b 26.5 cm c 61.9°
5 56.1°
6 a 10.9 cm b 74.7°

Exam practice 17A

1 $x^2 + y^2 = 16$ b $x^2 + y^2 = 36$

2 $x = -1.4, y = -6.8$, or $x = 4.6, y = 5.2$

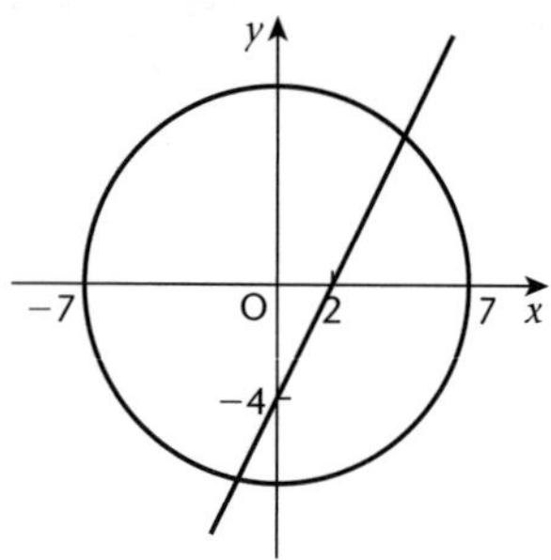

3 $x = 0, y = -5$ or $x = 3, y = 4$

Exam practice 17B

1 a Missing values are −9 and −6.

b

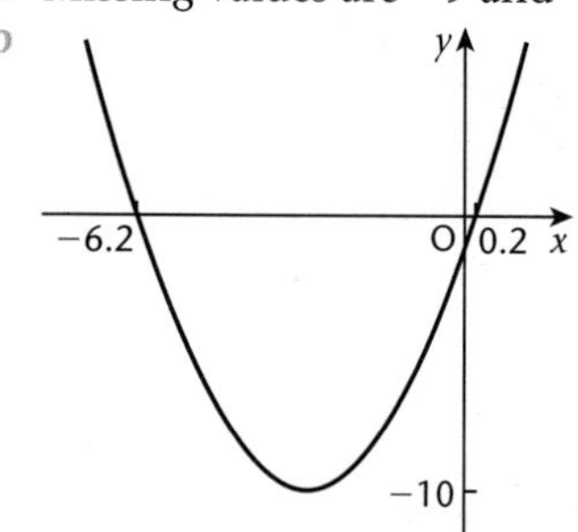

c i −6.2 and 0.2 ii $x^2 + 6x - 1 = 0$

d −10

2 a Missing values are −12, 2 and 0.

b

c −1.7 and 1.2 d $3\frac{1}{8}$

3 a

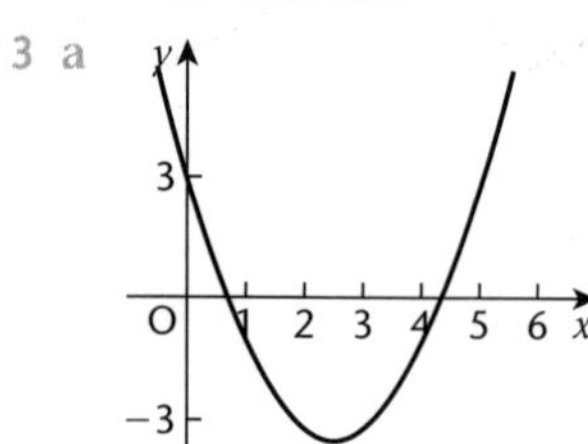

b $-3\frac{1}{4}$

4 a

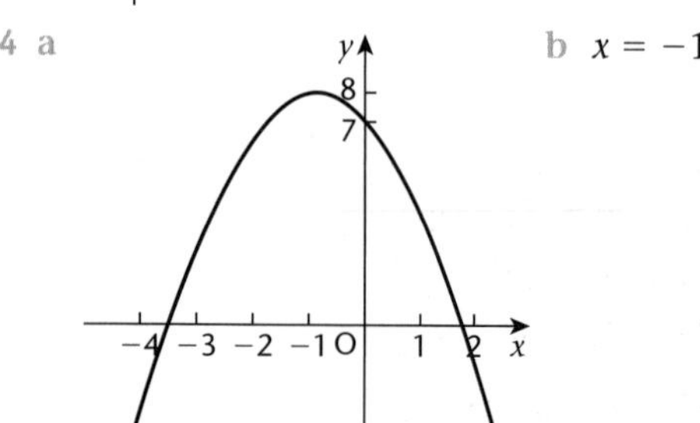

b $x = -1$

5 a $(x - 9)(x + 4)$

b $x = 2\frac{1}{2}$ c $-42\frac{1}{4}$

6 a $(3 + x)(2 - x)$

b $x = -\frac{1}{2}$

7 a $a = 2, b = 1$

b 1

8 a $a = \frac{3}{2}, b = -4\frac{1}{4}$

b $-4\frac{1}{4}$

9 a $a = 2, b = 7$

b 7

Exam practice 17C

1 a Missing values are −2 and −0.875.

b

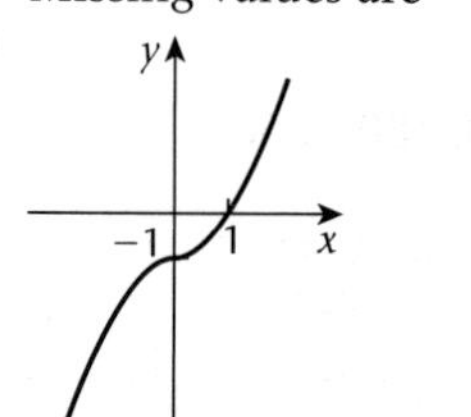

c i 1 ii $x^3 = 1$

d 1.3

2 a Missing values are −1 and 1.

b

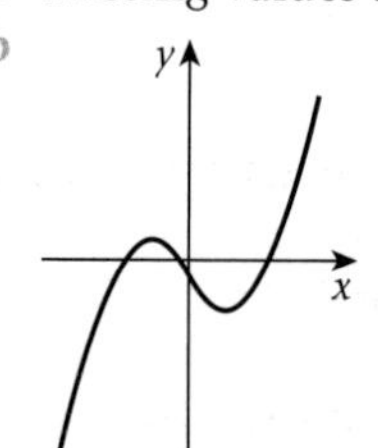

c i −1.5, −0.3, 1.9 ii $x^3 - 3x - 1 = 0$

d −2 and 1 (twice)

e $y = -x - 6$

3 a Missing values are 0.25, 0.5, 8.

b

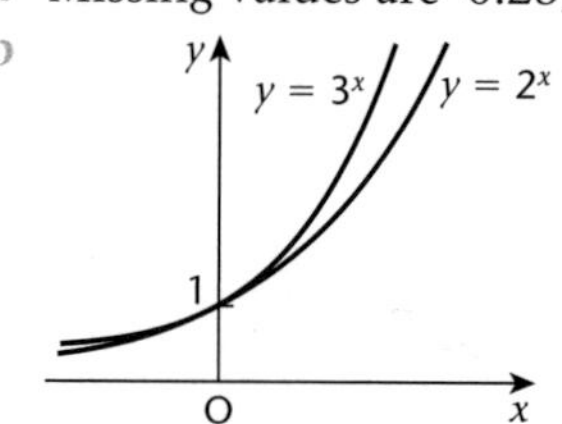

c 1.6

d

x	−3	−2	−1	0	1	2	3
y	0.04	0.11	0.33	1	3	9	27

4 a Missing values are −0.5, −2, 0.33.

b and d

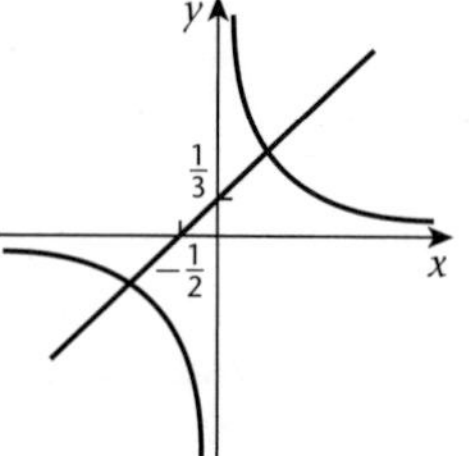

e $x = 1, y = 1; x = -1\frac{1}{2}, y = -\frac{2}{3}$

5 a $y = x^3$ b $y = \frac{1}{x}$

c $y = x$ d $y = 4^x$

6 B

Exam practice 17D

1 a
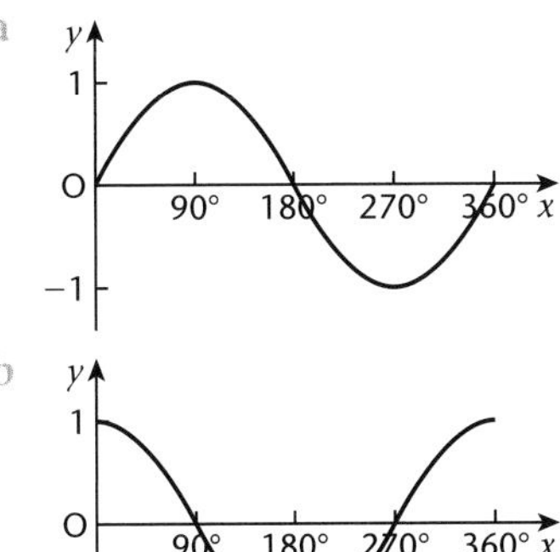

b

2 a 180°   b 0, 180°, 360°
c 0, 360°

3 a 60°, 300°   b 120°, 240°   c 46°, 314°
d 41°, 319°   e 66°, 294°   f 71°, 289°

4 a 14°, 166°   b 224°, 316°   c 19°, 161°

Exam practice 17E

1 a 4 units up the y-axis.
b Stretched by a factor of $\frac{1}{2}$ parallel to the y-axis.
c Moves 2 units to the left.

2 a Moves down 3 units parallel to the y-axis.
b Reflection in the y-axis.
c Moves down 7 units parallel to the y-axis.

3 a
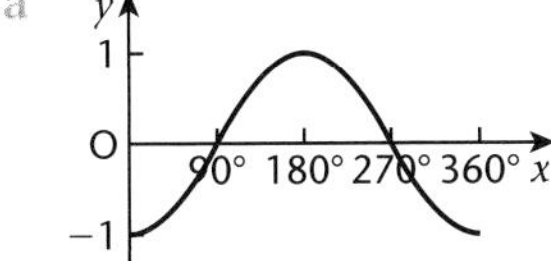

b
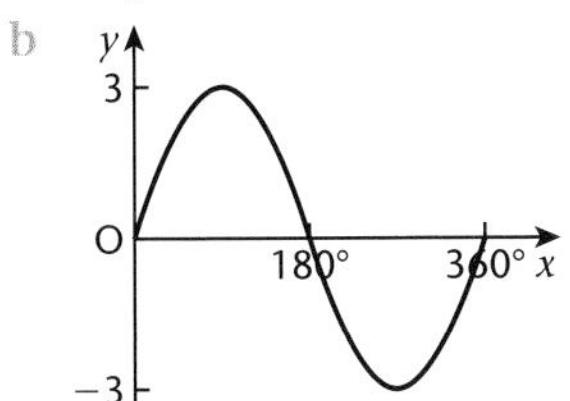

c
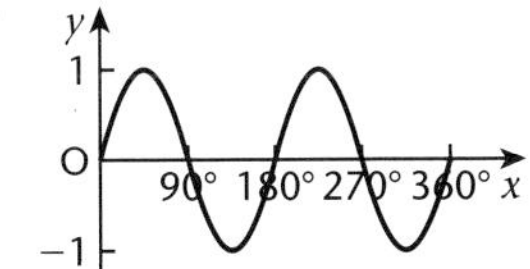

4 a
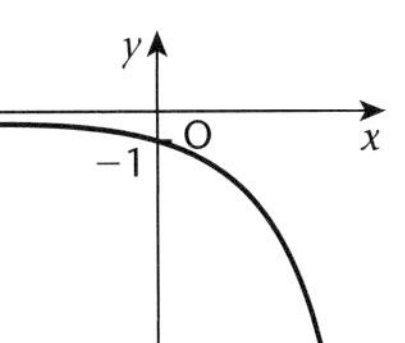

b
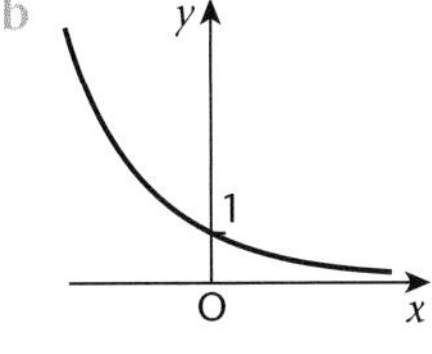

c
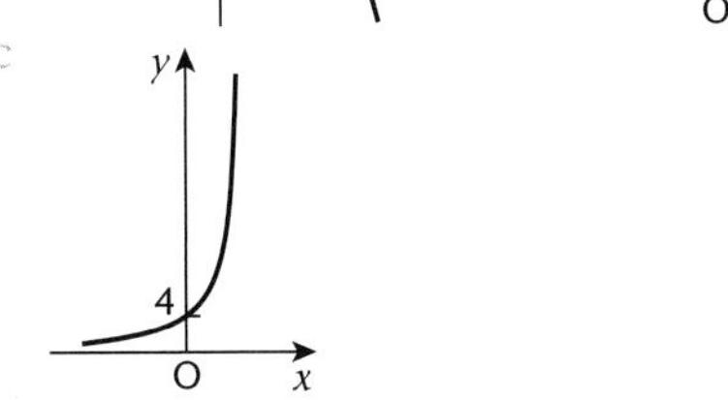

5 a
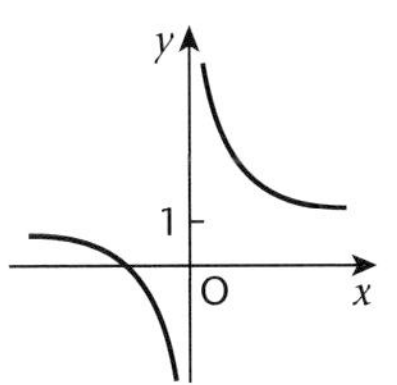

b
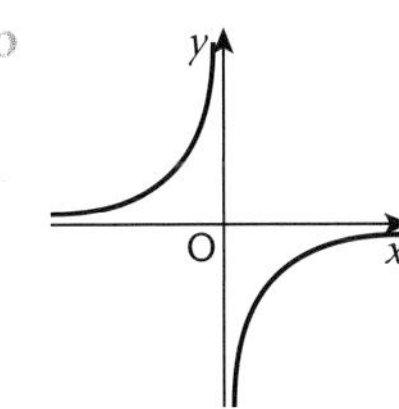

6 a $y = -x^2$
b $y = (x + 2)^2$
c $y = x^2 + 4$

Exam practice 18A

1
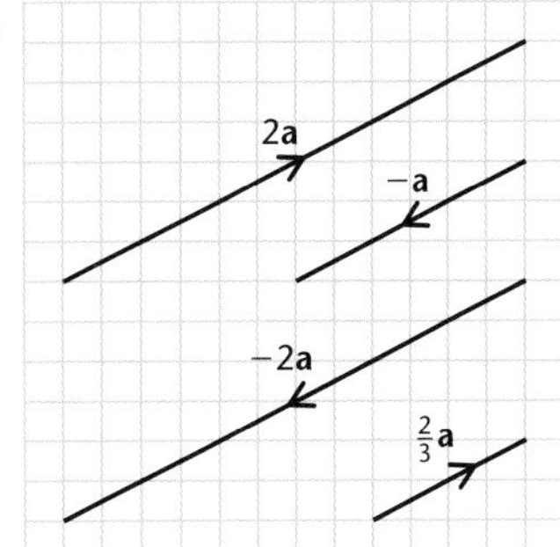

2
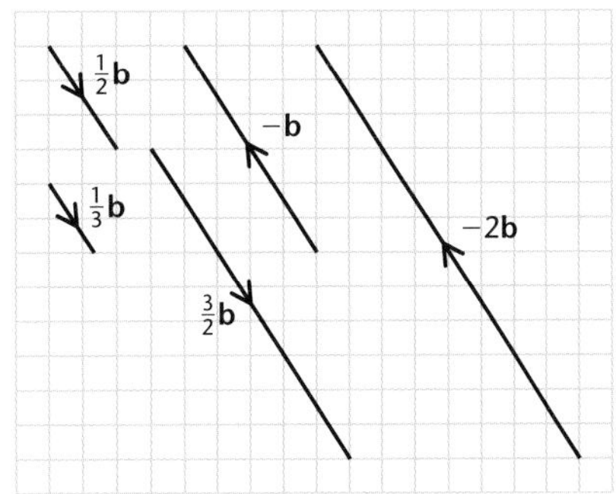

3
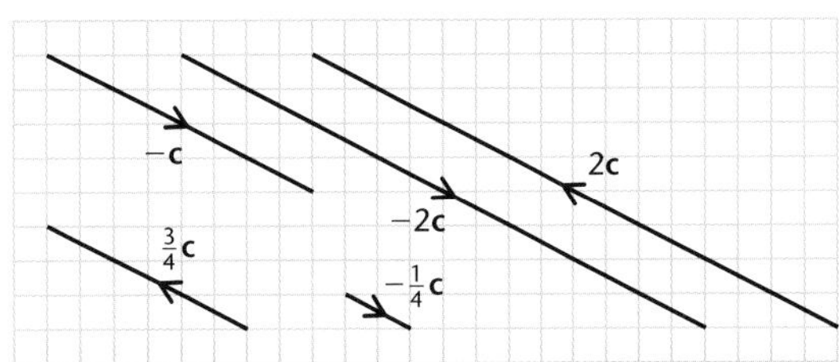

4 a **b** and **e**
b **c** and **g** or **f** and **h**
c **h**
d **d**

Exam practice 18B

1 a $\overrightarrow{DF}$ b $\overrightarrow{DE}$ c $\overrightarrow{ED}$ d $\overrightarrow{FD}$

2 a $\overrightarrow{AD} + \overrightarrow{DC}$, $\overrightarrow{AB} + \overrightarrow{BC}$
b $\overrightarrow{AB} + \overrightarrow{BD}$, $\overrightarrow{AC} + \overrightarrow{CD}$
c $\overrightarrow{BD} + \overrightarrow{DA}$, $\overrightarrow{BC} + \overrightarrow{CA}$

3 a $\overrightarrow{AB} + \overrightarrow{BC}$ or $\overrightarrow{AD} + \overrightarrow{DC}$
b i $\overrightarrow{AD}$ ii $\overrightarrow{BD}$ iii $\overrightarrow{AB}$ iv $\overrightarrow{CB}$

4

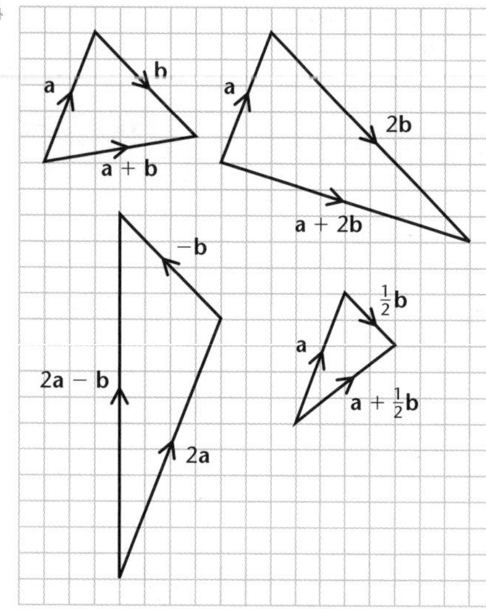

Magnitudes of resultants are

a $\sqrt{37}$ b $\sqrt{109}$ c 14 d 5.

5 a $\overrightarrow{PR}$ b $\overrightarrow{RQ}$ c $\overrightarrow{RP}$

6 a $\overrightarrow{AD}$ b $\overrightarrow{XA}$ c $\overrightarrow{DB}$

d $\overrightarrow{BA}$ e $\overrightarrow{AD}$ f $\overrightarrow{CA}$

7

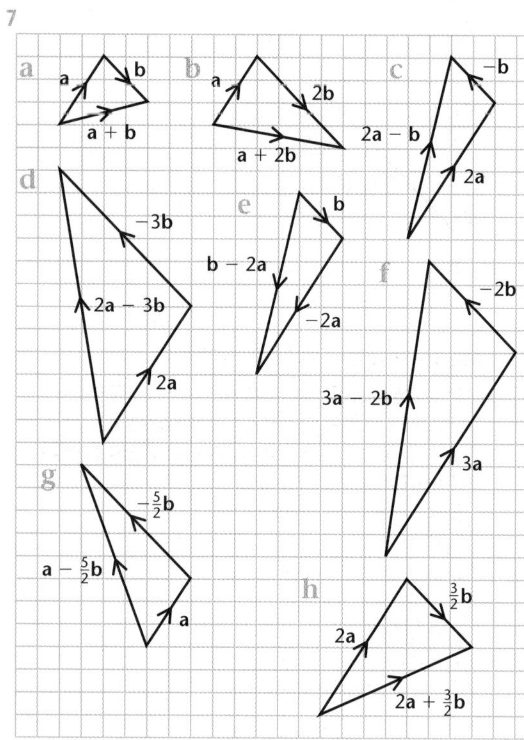

8 a

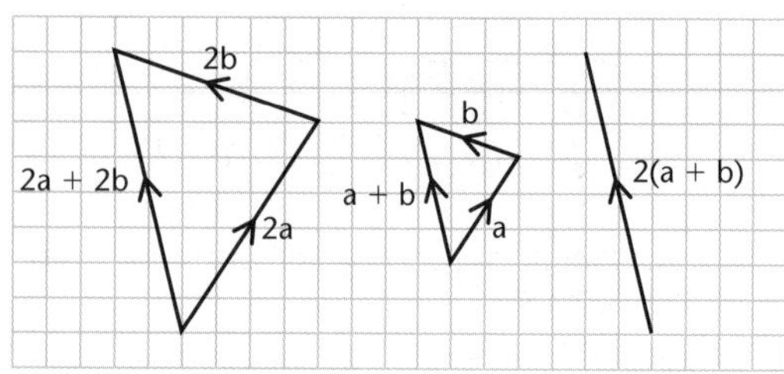

b

c

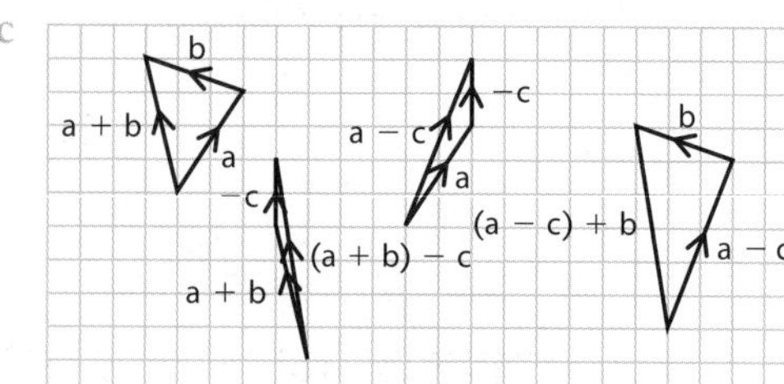

d

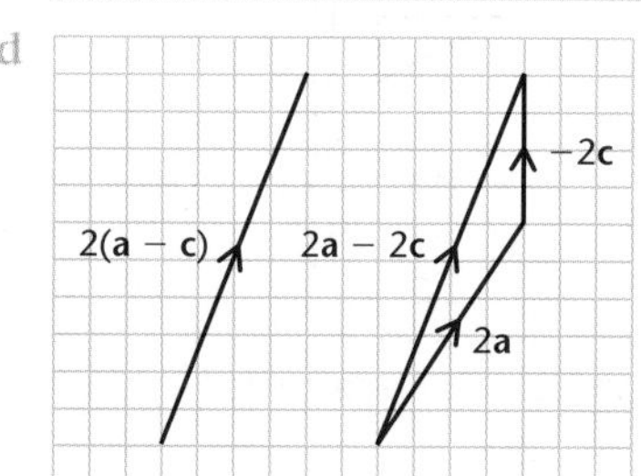

Exam practice 18C

1 a $\mathbf{b} - \mathbf{a}$ b $\frac{1}{2}(\mathbf{b} - \mathbf{a})$ c $-\frac{1}{2}(\mathbf{a} + \mathbf{b})$

2 a $\mathbf{b} - \mathbf{a}$ b $2\mathbf{b}$ c $2\mathbf{b} - \mathbf{a}$

3 a $2(\mathbf{q} - \mathbf{p})$ b $\frac{1}{2}(\mathbf{q} - \mathbf{p})$ c $\frac{1}{2}(\mathbf{p} + 3\mathbf{q})$

4 a i $\mathbf{a}$ ii $\mathbf{b}$

iii $2(\mathbf{b} - \mathbf{a})$ iv $(\mathbf{b} - \mathbf{a})$

b $\overrightarrow{AB} = 2(\mathbf{b} - \mathbf{a}) = 2\overrightarrow{MN}$, so $\overrightarrow{AB}$ and $\overrightarrow{MN}$ are parallel.

c $MN = \frac{1}{2}AB$

5 a i $2(\mathbf{a} + \mathbf{b})$ ii $\mathbf{a} + \mathbf{b}$ iii $2(\mathbf{b} - \mathbf{a})$

iv $\mathbf{b} - \mathbf{a}$ v $\mathbf{a} + \mathbf{b}$

b $\overrightarrow{OM} = \mathbf{a} + \mathbf{b} = \overrightarrow{ON}$, so M and N are the same point.

6 a i $\mathbf{c}$ ii $\frac{2}{3}\mathbf{c}$ iii $\frac{1}{2}\mathbf{a} + \frac{2}{3}\mathbf{c}$

iv $\frac{1}{3}\mathbf{c}$ v $\frac{1}{2}\mathbf{a}$ vi $\frac{1}{2}\mathbf{a} + \frac{2}{3}\mathbf{c}$

b i and ii $\overrightarrow{FD} = \frac{1}{2}\mathbf{a} + \frac{2}{3}\mathbf{c} = \overrightarrow{EG}$, so FD is parallel to EG and FD = EG.

7 a i $2\mathbf{p} + 2\mathbf{q}$ ii $2\mathbf{r} + 2\mathbf{s}$

b $\mathbf{p} + \mathbf{q}$ c $\mathbf{r} + \mathbf{s}$.

d They are parallel and equal since $\mathbf{p} + \mathbf{q} = \mathbf{r} + \mathbf{s}$.

8 a i $\mathbf{a} - 2\mathbf{b}$ ii $\frac{2}{3}(\mathbf{a} - 2\mathbf{b})$ iii $\frac{2}{3}(\mathbf{a} + \mathbf{b})$

iv $2(\mathbf{a} - \mathbf{b})$ v $\mathbf{a} - \mathbf{b}$ vi $\mathbf{a} + \mathbf{b}$

b $\overrightarrow{OX} = \frac{2}{3}(\mathbf{a} + \mathbf{b}) = \frac{2}{3}\overrightarrow{ON}$, so X lies on ON and $OX = \frac{2}{3}ON$.

9 a $\mathbf{a} + \mathbf{b}$ b $2\mathbf{b}$ c $\mathbf{b} - \mathbf{a}$

d $\mathbf{a} - \mathbf{b}$ e $\mathbf{b} - 2\mathbf{a}$

10 a i $2\mathbf{a} - \mathbf{b}$ ii $\mathbf{a} + \mathbf{b}$

b i $\mathbf{a} - \frac{1}{2}\mathbf{b}$ ii $\mathbf{a} - \frac{1}{2}\mathbf{b}$

c P is the midpoint of DB.

d $\overrightarrow{BX} = \frac{1}{3}(2\mathbf{a} - \mathbf{b}) = \frac{1}{3}\overrightarrow{BD}$, 1 : 2

Examination practice papers

Paper 1

1 $\frac{9}{20}$

2 a 68° (alternate angles)

b 68° (vert. opp. angles)

c 112° (angles on straight line)

3 a i and b

a ii $\begin{pmatrix}1\\-5\end{pmatrix}$

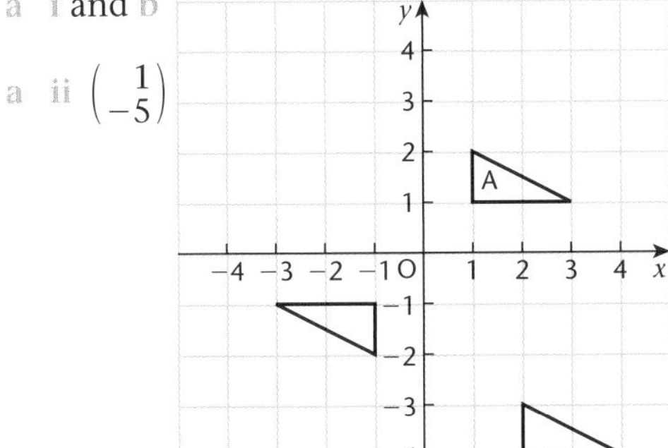

4 $5600\,mm^3$

5 a missing values are −4 and 4

b

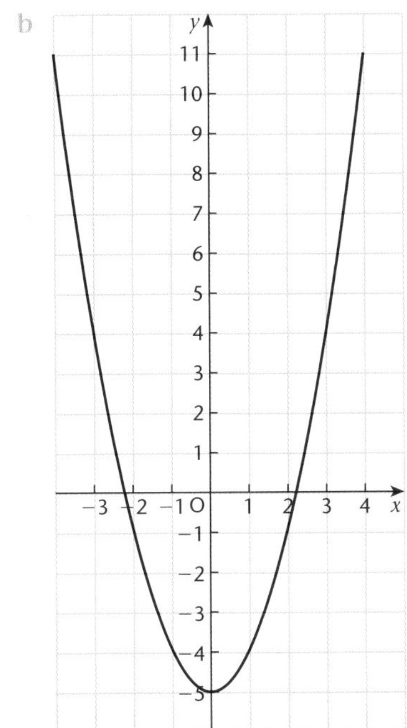

c ±2.6

6 a −1, 0, 1, 2, 3   b $x > 2.5$

7 a b^5 b m^6 c $10p - 5$

8 Square of longest side is 36. Sum of squares of the other two sides is 41. There is a right angle only if these two values are equal.

9 a $c^3 + c$

b i $x^2 + 3x + 2$ ii $6a^2 - 5ab - 4b^2$

10 $\pi b^2, 3\pi ab, \frac{b^3}{c}$

11 $w = 5 - \frac{1}{2}x$

12 a $y = -x - 1$

b Yes, grad of $y = -2x + 5$ is −2, grad of $y = \frac{1}{2}x + 3$ is $\frac{1}{2}$. Product of gradients is −1 so the lines are perpendicular.

13 a $(x - 4)(x - 3)$ b $x = 3$ or 4

14 18π cubic centimetres

15 a i $\mathbf{a} + 3\mathbf{b}$ ii $2\mathbf{a} + 6\mathbf{b}$

b i They lie on a straight line   ii MX = 2AM

16 −4.5 and 5

Paper 2

1 square, rhombus

2 $212\,mm^2$

3 a 062°   b 140°   c 279°

4

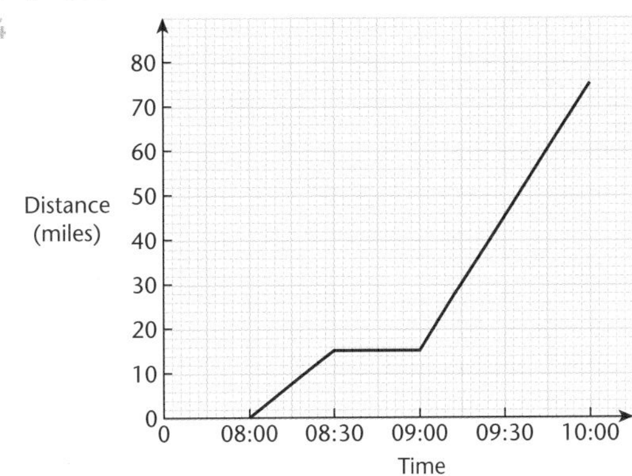

5 26

6 a $3(2p + 3)$ b $t(t - 2)$

7

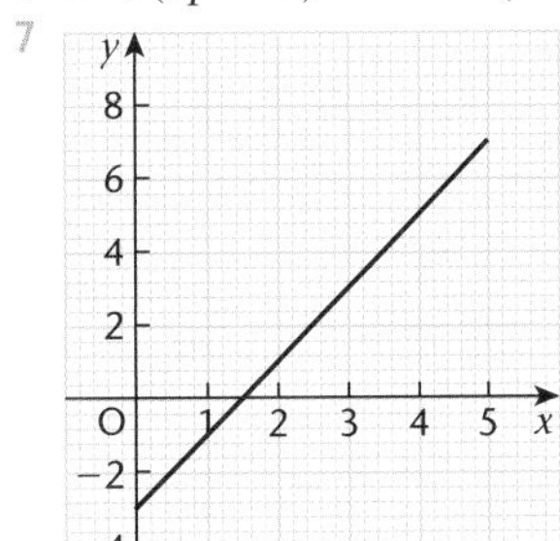

8 a $224\,cm^2$ b $19.2\,m^2$ (3 s.f.)

9 exterior angle $= \frac{360°}{8} = 45°$

so interior angle $= 180° - 45° = 135°$

10 a if $x = 3$, $x^3 - 2x = 21 < 40$ and if $x = 4$, $x^3 - 2x = 56 > 40$ so x lies between 3 and 4

b 3.6

11 a 36 cm   b 27.2 (3 s.f.)

12 a $a = -2$ b $8p^9q^6$ c $(3m + n)(3m - n)$

13 a $x = 2, y = -\frac{1}{2}$ b $(2, -\frac{1}{2})$

14 $x = 54°, y = 126°$

15 a i 4.8 m   ii 7.5 m

b 2000 cubic centimetres

16 a i

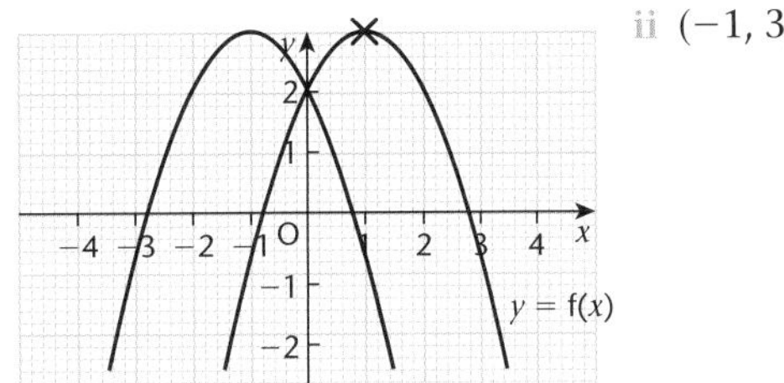

ii (−1, 3)

b stretched by $\frac{1}{2}$ units parallel to the x-axis.

17 a 210°, 330°   b 4

18 $373\frac{1}{3}\pi$ cubic units

Index